PREFACE

This solutions manual contains solutions to all the end-of-chapter-problems in the text book *Fundamentals of Physics,* 4*th* Edition, by David Halliday, Robert Resnick, and Jearl Walker.

About one third of the solutions here can also be found in the student solutions manual by J. Richard Christman and Edward Derringh. Several graduate students at the physics department in the Johns Hopkins University prepared initial solutions to many of the problems. The authors are grateful to all of them for their contribution to this manual.

Two of our student assistants, Henry Y. Kuo and Edward X. Zhang, were responsible for typesetting the manual using AMS TeX. Their unwavering dedication and ever-improving skill is invaluable to the project.

We would also like to acknowledge the good people of Wiley, including Cliff Mills, Joan Kalkut, Catherine Faduska, and especially Catherine Donovan, for their help, support, and great patience.

Jerry J. Shi and Jenny J. Quan
Pasadena City College
Pasadena, California
March 1994

CONTENTS

CHAPTER 23

1E
(a)

$$F = \frac{q_1 q_2}{4\pi\epsilon_0 r^2} = \frac{(1.00\,\text{C})^2(8.99 \times 10^9\,\text{N} \cdot \text{m}^2/\text{C}^2)}{(1.00\,\text{m})^2} = 8.99 \times 10^9\,\text{N}.$$

(b)

$$F = \frac{q_1 q_2}{4\pi\epsilon_0 r^2} = \frac{(1.00\,\text{C})^2(8.99 \times 10^9\,\text{N} \cdot \text{m}^2/\text{C}^2)}{(1.00 \times 10^3\,\text{m})^2} = 8.99 \times 10^3\,\text{N}.$$

2E
The magnitude of the force is given by

$$F = \frac{1}{4\pi\epsilon_0}\frac{q_1 q_2}{r^2},$$

where q_1 and q_2 are the magnitudes of the charges and r is the distance between them. Thus

$$F = \frac{(8.99 \times 10^9\,\text{N} \cdot \text{m}^2/\text{C}^2)(3.00 \times 10^{-6}\,\text{C})(1.50 \times 10^{-6}\,\text{C})}{(12.0 \times 10^{-2}\,\text{m})^2} = 2.81\,\text{N}.$$

3E
The magnitude of the force that either charge exerts on the other is given by

$$F = \frac{1}{4\pi\epsilon_0}\frac{q_1 q_2}{r^2},$$

where r is the distance between them. Thus

$$r = \sqrt{\frac{q_1 q_2}{4\pi\epsilon_0 F}}$$

$$= \sqrt{\frac{(8.99 \times 10^9\,\text{N} \cdot \text{m}^2/\text{C}^2)(26.0 \times 10^{-6}\,\text{C})(47.0 \times 10^{-6}\,\text{C})}{5.70\,\text{N}}} = 1.38\,\text{m}.$$

4E
The charge transferred is

$$Q = it = (2.5 \times 10^4\,\text{A})(20 \times 10^{-6}\,\text{s}) = 0.50\,\text{C}.$$

5E

(a) From Newtons's third law $m_1a_1 = m_2a_2$, so

$$m_2 = \frac{m_1a_1}{a_2} = \frac{(6.3 \times 10^{-7}\,\text{kg})(7.0\,\text{m/s}^2)}{9.0\,\text{m/s}^2} = 4.9 \times 10^{-7}\,\text{kg}.$$

(b) Since $F = q^2/4\pi\epsilon_0 r^2 = m_1a_1$,

$$q = r\sqrt{4\pi\epsilon_0 m_1 a_1}$$

$$= (3.2 \times 10^{-3}\,\text{m})\sqrt{\frac{(6.3 \times 10^{-7}\,\text{kg})(7.0\,\text{m/s}^2)}{8.99 \times 10^9\,\text{N}\cdot\text{m}^2/\text{C}^2}} = 7.1 \times 10^{-11}\,\text{C}.$$

6E

(a) The magnitude of the force is

$$F_{12} = \frac{1}{4\pi\epsilon_0}\frac{q_1 q_2}{d^2} = 8.99 \times 10^9\,\text{N}\cdot\text{m}^2/\text{C}^2\frac{(20.0 \times 10^{-6}\,\text{C})^2}{(1.50\,\text{m})^2} = 1.60\,\text{N}.$$

(b) The magnitude of the force on q_1 now becomes

$$F_1 = \sqrt{F_{12}^2 + F_{13}^2 + 2F_{12}F_{13}\cos\theta}$$
$$= F_{12}\sqrt{2 + 2\cos\theta}$$
$$= (1.60\,\text{N})\sqrt{2 + 2\cos 60°} = 2.77\,\text{N},$$

where we have used $F_{12} = F_{13} = kq_1q_2/d^2 = kq_1q_3/d^2$.

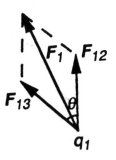

7E

Let the initial charge on either spheres 1 and 2 be q. After being touched by sphere 3, sphere q retains only half of q. After being touched by sphere 3, sphere 2 has $(q + q/2)/2 = 3q/4$ left. So $\mathbf{F}' = \text{const.}\,(q/2)(3q/4) = (3/8)\text{const.}\,q^2 = (3/8)\mathbf{F}$.

8P

Since q_3 is in equilibrium $F_{31} + F_{32} = 0$, i.e.

$$\frac{1}{4\pi\epsilon_0}\frac{q_1 q_3}{(2d)^2} + \frac{1}{4\pi\epsilon_0}\frac{q_2 q_3}{d^2} = 0,$$

which gives $q_1 = -4q_2$.

9P

(a) Let the force F on Q be

$$F = \frac{1}{4\pi\epsilon_0}\left[\frac{q_1 Q}{(-a - a/2)^2} + \frac{q_2 Q}{(a - a/2)^2}\right] = 0,$$

and solve for q_1: $q_1 = 9q_2$.

(b) Now

$$F = \frac{1}{4\pi\epsilon_0}\left[\frac{q_1 Q}{(-a - 3a/2)^2} + \frac{q_2 Q}{(a - 3a/2)^2}\right] = 0,$$

which gives $q_1 = -25q_2$.

10P

Place the origin of a coordinate system at the lower left corner of the squre. Take the y axis to be vertically upward and the x axis to be horizontal. The force exerted by the charge $+q$ on the charge $+2q$ is

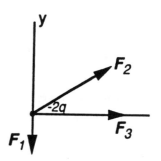

$$\mathbf{F}_1 = \frac{1}{4\pi\epsilon_0}\frac{q(2q)}{a^2}(-\mathbf{j}),$$

the force by the charge $-q$ to $2q$ is

$$\mathbf{F}_2 = \frac{1}{4\pi\epsilon_0}\frac{(2q)(-q)}{(\sqrt{2}a)^2}\left(-\frac{\mathbf{i}+\mathbf{j}}{\sqrt{2}}\right) = \frac{1}{4\pi\epsilon_0}\frac{q^2}{a^2}\left(\frac{\mathbf{i}}{\sqrt{2}} + \frac{\mathbf{j}}{\sqrt{2}}\right),$$

and the force by the charge $-2q$ to $+2q$ is

$$\mathbf{F}_3 = \frac{1}{4\pi\epsilon_0}\frac{(2q)(-2q)}{a^2}(-\mathbf{i}) = \frac{1}{4\pi\epsilon_0}\frac{4q^2}{a^2}\mathbf{i}.$$

Thus the horizontal (x) component of the resultant force on the charge $-2q$ is

$$F_x = F_{1x} + F_{2x} + F_{3x} = \frac{1}{4\pi\epsilon_0}\frac{q^2}{a^2}\left(\frac{1}{\sqrt{2}} + 4\right)$$

$$= (8.99 \times 10^9 \, \text{N} \cdot \text{m}^2/\text{C}^2)\frac{(1.0 \times 10^{-7} \, \text{C})^2}{5.0 \times 10^{-2} \, \text{m})^2}\left(\frac{1}{\sqrt{2}} + 4\right) = 0.17\,\text{N},$$

while the vertical (y) component is

$$F_y = F_{1y} + F_{2y} + F_{3y} = \cdot\frac{1}{4\pi\epsilon_0}\frac{q^2}{a^2}\left(-2 + \frac{1}{\sqrt{2}}\right) = -0.046\,\text{N}.$$

11P

Let the two charges be q_1 and q_2. Then $q_1 + q_2 = 5.0 \times 10^{-5}$ C. Also $F_{12} = q_1 q_2 / 4\pi\epsilon_0 r^2$, i.e.

$$1.0\,\text{N} = \frac{q_1 q_2 (8.99 \times 10^9\,\text{N} \cdot \text{m}^2/\text{C}^2)}{(2.0\,\text{m})^2}.$$

Solve for q_1 and q_2: $q_1, q_2 = 1.2 \times 10^{-5}$ C and 3.8×10^{-5} C.

12P

Assume the charge distributions are spherically symmetric so Coulomb's law can be used. Let q_1 and q_2 be the original charges and choose the coordinate system so the force on q_2 is positive if it is repelled by q_1. Take the distance between the charges to be r. Then the force on q_2 is

$$F_a = -\frac{1}{4\pi\epsilon_0} \frac{q_1 q_2}{r^2}.$$

The negative sign indicates that the spheres attract each other.

After the wire is connected the spheres, being identical, have the same charge. Since charge is conserved the total charge is the same as it was originally. This means the charge on each sphere is $(q_1 + q_2)/2$. The force is now one of repulsion and is given by

$$F_b = \frac{1}{4\pi\epsilon_0} \frac{(q_1 + q_2)^2}{4r^2}.$$

Solve the two force equations simultaneously for q_1 and q_2. The first gives

$$q_1 q_2 = -4\pi\epsilon_0 r^2 F_a = \frac{(0.500\,\text{m})^2 (0.108\,\text{N})}{8.99 \times 10^9\,\text{N} \cdot \text{m}^2/\text{C}^2} = -3.00 \times 10^{-12}\,\text{C}^2$$

and the second gives

$$q_1 + q_2 = r\sqrt{4 \times 4\pi\epsilon_0 F_b} = (0.500\,\text{m})\sqrt{\frac{4(0.0360\,\text{N})}{8.99 \times 10^9\,\text{N} \cdot \text{m}^2/\text{C}^2}} = 2.00 \times 10^{-6}\,\text{C}.$$

Thus

$$q_2 = \frac{-(3.00 \times 10^{-12}\,\text{C}^2)}{q_1}$$

and

$$q_1 - \frac{3.00 \times 10^{-12}\,\text{C}^2}{q_1} = 2.00 \times 10^{-6}\,\text{C}.$$

Multiply by q_1 to obtain the quadratic equation

$$q_1^2 - (2.00 \times 10^{-6}\,\text{C})q_1 - 3.00 \times 10^{-12}\,\text{C}^2 = 0.$$

The solutions are

$$q_1 = \frac{-2.00 \times 10^{-6}\,\text{C} \pm \sqrt{(2.00 \times 10^{-6}\,\text{C})^2 + 4(3.00 \times 10^{-12}\,\text{C}^2)}}{2}.$$

If the plus sign is used $q_1 = 1.00 \times 10^{-6}$ C and if the minus sign is used $q_1 = -3.00 \times 10^{-6}$ C. Use $q_2 = (-3.00 \times 10^{-12})/q_1$ to calculate q_2. If $q_1 = 1.00 \times 10^{-6}$ C then $q_2 = -3.00 \times 10^{-6}$ C and if $q_1 = -3.00 \times 10^{-6}$ C then $q_2 = 1.00 \times 10^{-6}$ C. Since the spheres are identical the solutions are essentially the same: one sphere originally had charge 1.00×10^{-6} C and the other had charge -3.00×10^{-6} C.

Another solution exists. If the signs of the charges are reversed the forces remain the same, so a charge of -1.00×10^{-6} C on one sphere and a charge of 3.00×10^{-6} C on the other also satisfies the conditions of the problem.

13P
Let the third charge q_3 be located on the line joining the two charges, a distance x from $q_1 = 1.0\mu$ C. Then the net force exerted on q_3 is

$$F_3 = \frac{q_3}{4\pi\epsilon_0}\left[\frac{q_1}{x^2} + \frac{q_2}{(r-x)^2}\right] = 0.$$

Substitute $q_1 = +1.0\mu$ C, $q_2 = -3.0\mu$ C and $r = 10$ cm into the above equation and solve for x: $x = 14$ cm.

14P
(a)

$$F_{21} = \frac{1}{4\pi\epsilon_0}\frac{|q_1 q_2|}{r_{12}^2} = \frac{1}{4\pi\epsilon_0}\frac{q_1 q_2}{(x_2 - x_1)^2 + (y_2 - y_1)^2}$$

$$= \frac{(8.99 \times 10^9\,\text{N}\cdot\text{m}^2/\text{C}^2)|(3.0 \times 10^{-6}\,\text{C})(-4.0 \times 10^{-6}\,\text{C})|}{[(-2.0 - 3.5)^2 + (1.5 - 0.5)^2](10^{-4}\,\text{m}^2)}$$

$$= 36\,\text{N}.$$

The direction of $\mathbf{F}_{21}$ is such that it makes an angle θ with $+x$ axis, where

$$\theta = \tan^{-1}\left(\frac{y_2 - y_1}{x_2 - x_1}\right) = \tan^{-1}\left(\frac{1.5\,\text{cm} - 0.5\,\text{cm}}{-2.0\,\text{cm} - 3.5\,\text{cm}}\right) = -10°.$$

(b) Let the third charge be located at (x_3, y_3), a distance r from q_2. Since q_1, q_2 and q_3 must be on the same line, we have $x_3 = x_2 - r\cos\theta$ and $y_3 = y_2 - r\sin\theta$. The force on q_2 exerted by q_3 is $F_{23} = q_2 q_3/4\pi\epsilon_0 r^2$, which must cancel with the force exerted by q_1 on q_2:

$$F_{23} = \frac{|q_2 q_3|}{4\pi\epsilon_0 r^2} = F_{21},$$

which gives

$$r = \sqrt{\frac{|q_2 q_3|}{4\pi\epsilon_0 F_{12}}} = \sqrt{\frac{(4.0 \times 10^{-6}\,\text{C})(4.0 \times 10^{-6}\,\text{C})(8.99 \times 10^9\,\text{N} \cdot \text{m}^2/\text{C}^2)}{36\,\text{N}}} = 6.3\,\text{cm}.$$

So $x_3 = x_2 - r\cos\theta = -2.0\,\text{cm} - (6.3\,\text{cm})\cos(-10°) = -8.3\,\text{cm}$ and $y_3 = y_2 - r\sin\theta = 1.5\,\text{cm} - (6.3\,\text{cm})\sin(-10°) = 2.6\,\text{cm}$.

15P

(a) If the system of three charges is to be in equilibrium the force on each charge must be zero. Let the third charge be q_0. It must lie between the other two or else the forces acting on it due to the other charges would be in the same direction and q_0 could not be in equilibrium. Suppose q_0 is a distance x from q, as shown on the diagram to the right. The force acting on q_0 is then given by

$$F_0 = \frac{1}{4\pi\epsilon_0}\left[\frac{qq_0}{x^2} - \frac{4qq_0}{(L-x)^2}\right] = 0,$$

where the positive direction was taken to be toward the right. Solve this equation for x. Canceling common factors yields $1/x^2 = 4/(L-x)^2$ and taking the square root yields $1/x = 2/(L-x)$. The solution is $x = L/3$.

The force on q is

$$F_q = \frac{1}{4\pi\epsilon_0}\left[\frac{qq_0}{x^2} + \frac{4q^2}{L^2}\right] = 0.$$

Solve for q_0: $q_0 = -4qx^2/L^2 = -(4/9)q$, where $x = L/3$ was used.

The force on $4q$ is

$$F_{4q} = \frac{1}{4\pi\epsilon_0}\left[\frac{4q^2}{L^2} + \frac{4qq_0}{(L-x)^2}\right] = \frac{1}{4\pi\epsilon_0}\left[\frac{4q^2}{L^2} + \frac{4(-4/9)q^2}{(4/9)L^2}\right]$$

$$= \frac{1}{4\pi\epsilon_0}\left[\frac{4q^2}{L^2} - \frac{4q^2}{L^2}\right] = 0.$$

With $q_0 = -(4/9)q$ and $x = L/3$ all three charges are in equilibrium.

(b) If q_0 moves toward q the force of attraction exerted by q is greater in magnitude than the force of attraction exerted by $4q$ and q_0 continues to move toward q and away from its initial position. The equilibrium is unstable.

16P

(a) The magnitudes of the gravitational and electrical forces must be the same:

$$\frac{1}{4\pi\epsilon_0} \frac{q^2}{r^2} = G\frac{mM}{r^2},$$

where q is the charge on either body, r is the center-to-center separation of the Earth and moon, G is the universal gravitational constant, M is the mass of the Earth, and m is the mass of the moon. Solve for q:

$$q = \sqrt{4\pi\epsilon_0 GmM}.$$

According to Appendix C of the text, $M = 5.98 \times 10^{24}$ kg, and $m = 7.36 \times 10^{22}$ kg, so

$$q = \sqrt{\frac{(6.67 \times 10^{-11}\,\text{N} \cdot \text{m}^2/\text{kg}^2)(7.36 \times 10^{22}\,\text{kg})(5.98 \times 10^{24}\,\text{kg})}{8.99 \times 10^9\,\text{N} \cdot \text{m}^2/\text{C}^2}}$$
$$= 5.7 \times 10^{13}\,\text{C}.$$

Notice that the distance r cancels because both the electric and gravitational forces are proportional to $1/r^2$.

(b) The charge on a hydrogen ion is $e = 1.60 \times 10^{-19}$ C so there must be

$$\frac{q}{e} = \frac{5.7 \times 10^{13}\,\text{C}}{1.6 \times 10^{-19}\,\text{C}} = 3.6 \times 10^{32}\,\text{ions}.$$

Each ion has a mass of 1.67×10^{-27} kg so the total mass needed is

$$(3.6 \times 10^{32})(1.67 \times 10^{-27}\,\text{kg}) = 6.0 \times 10^5\,\text{kg}.$$

17P

(a) Let the side length of the square be a. Then the magnitude of the force on each Q is

$$F_Q = \frac{1}{4\pi\epsilon_0}\left[\frac{\sqrt{2}Qq}{a^2} + \frac{Q^2}{(\sqrt{2}a)^2}\right].$$

Let $F_Q = 0$, we get $Q = -2\sqrt{2}q$.

(b) For both F_Q and $F_q = 0$ we would require $Q = -2\sqrt{2}q$ and $q = -2\sqrt{2}Q$. These two equation cannot be simultaneously valid unless $Q = q = 0$. So this is impossible.

18P

The magnitude of the force of either of the charges on the other is given by

$$F = \frac{1}{4\pi\epsilon_0}\frac{q(Q-q)}{r^2},$$

where r is the distance between the charges. You want the value of q that maximizes the function $f(q) = q(Q - q)$. Set the derivative df/dq equal to zero. This yields $2q - Q = 0$, or $q = Q/2$.

19P

(a) A force diagram for one of the balls is shown to the right. The force of gravity mg acts downward, the electrical force F_e of the other ball acts to the left, and the tension in the thread acts along the thread, at the angle θ to the vertical. The ball is in equilibrium, so its acceleration is zero. The y component of Newtons second law yields $T \cos \theta - mg = 0$ and the x component yields $T \sin \theta - F_e = 0$. Solve the first equation for T ($T = mg/\cos \theta$) and substitute the result into the second to obtain $mg \tan \theta - F_e = 0$. Now

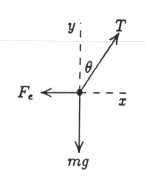

$$\tan \theta = \frac{x/2}{\sqrt{L^2 - (x/2)^2}} \, .$$

If L is much larger than x we may neglect $x/2$ in the denominator and write $\tan \theta \approx x/2L$. This is equivalent to approximating $\tan \theta$ by $\sin \theta$. The magnitude of the electrical force of one ball on the other is

$$F_e = \frac{q^2}{4\pi\epsilon_0 x^2} \, .$$

When these two substitutions are made in the equation $mg \tan \theta = F_e$, it becomes

$$\frac{mgx}{2L} = \frac{1}{4\pi\epsilon_0} \frac{q^2}{x^2} \, ,$$

so

$$x^3 = \frac{1}{4\pi\epsilon_0} \frac{2q^2 L}{mg} \, ,$$

and

$$x = \left(\frac{q^2 L}{2\pi\epsilon_0 mg} \right)^{1/3} \, .$$

(b) Solve $x^3 = (1/4\pi\epsilon_0)(2q^2 L/mg)$ for q:

$$q = \pm \sqrt{\frac{4\pi\epsilon_0 mgx^3}{2L}} = \pm \sqrt{\frac{(0.010 \, \text{kg})(9.8 \, \text{m/s}^2)(0.050 \, \text{m})^3}{2(8.99 \times 10^9 \, \text{N} \cdot \text{m}^2/\text{C}^2)(1.20 \, \text{m})}} = \pm 2.4 \times 10^{-8} \, \text{C} \, .$$

20P

If one of them is discharged, there would no electrostatic repulsion between the two balls and they would both come to the position $\theta = 0$, making contact with each other. A redistribution of charges would then occur, with each of the balls getting $q/2$. They would then again be separated due to electrostatic repulsion, which results in the new separation

$$x' = \left[\frac{(q/2)^2 L}{2\pi\epsilon_0 mg}\right]^{1/3} = \left(\frac{1}{4}\right)^{1/3} x = \left(\frac{1}{4}\right)^{1/3} (5.0\,\text{cm}) = 3.1\,\text{cm}.$$

21P

(a) Since the rod is in equilibrium the net force acting on it is zero and the net torque about any point is also zero. Write an expression for the net torque about the bearing, equate it to zero, and solve for x. The charge Q on the left exerts an upward force of magnitude $(1/4\pi\epsilon_0)(qQ/h^2)$, at a distance $L/2$ from the bearing. Take the torque to be positive. The attached weight exerts a downward force of magnitude W, at a distance $L/2 - x$ from the bearing. This torque is positive. The charge Q on the right exerts an upward force of magnitude $(1/4\pi\epsilon_0)(2qQ/h^2)$, at a distance $L/2$ from the bearing. This torque is negative. The equation for rotational equilibrium is

$$\frac{1}{4\pi\epsilon_0}\frac{qQ}{h^2}\frac{L}{2} + W\left(\frac{L}{2} - x\right) - \frac{1}{4\pi\epsilon_0}\frac{2qQ}{h^2}\frac{L}{2} = 0.$$

The solution for x is

$$x = \frac{L}{2}\left(1 + \frac{1}{4\pi\epsilon_0}\frac{qQ}{h^2 W}\right).$$

(b) The net force on the rod vanishes. If N is the magnitude of the upward force exerted by the bearing then

$$W - \frac{1}{4\pi\epsilon_0}\frac{qQ}{h^2} - \frac{1}{4\pi\epsilon_0}\frac{2qQ}{h^2} - N = 0.$$

Solve for h so that $N = 0$. The result is

$$h = \sqrt{\frac{1}{4\pi\epsilon_0}\frac{3qQ}{W}}.$$

22E

The magnitude of the force is

$$F = \frac{1}{4\pi\epsilon_0}\frac{e^2}{r^2} = (8.99 \times 10^9\,\text{N} \cdot \text{m}^2/\text{C}^2)\frac{(1.60 \times 10^{-19}\,\text{C})^2}{(2.82 \times 10^{-10}\,\text{m})^2} = 2.89 \times 10^{-9}\,\text{N}.$$

23E

$$F = \frac{q^2}{4\pi\varepsilon_0 r^2} = \frac{(-e/3)^2}{4\pi\varepsilon_0 r^2} = \frac{(8.99 \times 10^9\,\text{N} \cdot \text{m}^2/\text{C}^2)(1.60 \times 10^{-19}\,\text{C})^2}{9(2.6 \times 10^{-15}\,\text{m})^2} = 3.8\,\text{N}.$$

24E

The mass of an electron is $m = 9.11 \times 10^{-31}$ kg so the number of electrons in a collection with total mass $M = 75.0$ kg is

$$N = \frac{M}{m} = \frac{75.0\,\text{kg}}{9.11 \times 10^{-31}\,\text{kg}} = 8.23 \times 10^{31} \text{ electrons}.$$

The total charge of the collection is $q = -Ne = -(8.23 \times 10^{31})(1.60 \times 10^{-19}\,\text{C}) = -1.32 \times 10^{13}$ C.

25E

$$Q = N_A q = (6.02 \times 10^{23})(2)(1.60 \times 10^{-19}\,\text{C}) = 1.9 \times 10^6 \text{ C} = 1.9\,\text{MC}.$$

26E

(a) The magnitude of the force between the ions is given by

$$F = \frac{q^2}{4\pi\epsilon_0 r^2},$$

where q is the charge on either of them and r is the distance between them. Solve for the charge:

$$q = r\sqrt{4\pi\epsilon_0 F} = (5.0 \times 10^{-10})\sqrt{\frac{3.7 \times 10^{-9}\,\text{N}}{8.99 \times 10^9\,\text{N} \cdot \text{m}^2/\text{C}^2}} = 3.2 \times 10^{-19}\,\text{C}.$$

(b) Let N be the number of electrons missing from each ion. Then $Ne = q$, or

$$N = \frac{q}{e} = \frac{3.2 \times 10^{-19}\,\text{C}}{1.60 \times 10^{-19}\,\text{C}} = 2.$$

27E

(a) The magnitude of the force is given by

$$F = \frac{q^2}{4\pi\epsilon_0 r^2},$$

where q is the magnitude of the charge on each drop and r is the center-to-center separation of the drops. Thus

$$F = \frac{(8.99 \times 10^9\,\text{N} \cdot \text{m}^2/\text{C}^2)(1.00 \times 10^{-16}\,\text{C})^2}{(1.00 \times 10^{-2}\,\text{m})^2} = 8.99 \times 10^{-19}\,\text{N}.$$

(b) If N is the number of excess electrons (of charge $-e$ each) on each drop then

$$N = -\frac{q}{e} = -\frac{-1.00 \times 10^{-16}\,\mathrm{C}}{1.60 \times 10^{-19}\,\mathrm{C}} = 625\,.$$

28E

(a) the number of electrons to be removed is

$$n = \frac{q}{e} = \frac{1.0 \times 10^{-7}\,\mathrm{C}}{1.60 \times 10^{-19}\,\mathrm{C}} = 6.3 \times 10^{11}.$$

(b) The fraction is

$$\mathrm{frac} = \frac{n}{NZ} = \frac{6.3 \times 10^{11}}{(2.95 \times 10^{22})(29)} = 7.4 \times 10^{-13}.$$

29E

Let $q^2/4\pi\epsilon_0 r^2 = mg$, we get

$$r = q\sqrt{\frac{1}{4\pi\epsilon_0 mg}} = (1.6 \times 10^{-19}\,\mathrm{C})\sqrt{\frac{8.99 \times 10^9\,\mathrm{N}\cdot\mathrm{m}^2/\,\mathrm{C}^2}{(1.67 \times 10^{-27}\,\mathrm{kg})(9.8\,\mathrm{m/s}^2)}} = 0.119\,\mathrm{m}.$$

30E

The second electron must be placed a distance d under the first one to produce an upward force that balances the weight of the first one. So

$$W = mg = \frac{1}{4\pi\epsilon_0}\frac{e^2}{d^2},$$

which gives

$$d = e\sqrt{\frac{1}{4\pi\epsilon_0}\frac{1}{mg}}$$

$$= (1.6 \times 10^{-19}\,\mathrm{C})\sqrt{\frac{8.99 \times 10^9\,\mathrm{N}\cdot\mathrm{m}^2/\,\mathrm{C}^2}{(9.11 \times 10^{-31}\,\mathrm{kg})(9.8\,\mathrm{m/s}^2)}} = 5.1\,\mathrm{m}.$$

31P

If charge of magnitude q passes through the lamp in time t the current is $i = q/t$. The charge is the total charge on one mole of electrons, or $q = N_A e$, where N_A is the Avogadro constant. Thus $i = N_A e/t$, or

$$t = \frac{N_A e}{i} = \frac{(6.02 \times 10^{23})(1.60 \times 10^{-19}\,\text{C})}{0.83\,\text{A}} = 1.2 \times 10^5\,\text{s}.$$

This is equivalent to 1.3 d.

32P

The current intercepted would be

$$I = (4\pi R^2)\left(\frac{\Delta q}{\Delta t}\right)$$
$$= 4\pi (6.37 \times 10^6\,\text{m})^2 (1500/\text{s})(1.6 \times 10^{-19}\,\text{C}) = 0.122\,\text{A}.$$

33P

The numer of moles of H_2O molecules in a glass of water (of volume V) is $n = \rho V/M$, where ρ is the density of water and M is its molar mass. Each H_2O molecule has 10 protons. Thus

$$Q = 18\,en N_A = \frac{18\,e\rho V N_A}{M}$$
$$= \frac{10(1.6 \times 10^{-19}\,\text{C})(1.00 \times 10^3\,\text{kg/m}^3)(250 \times 10^{-6}\,\text{m}^3)(6.02 \times 10^{23}/\text{mole})}{1.8 \times 10^{-2}\,\text{kg/mole}}$$
$$= 1.3 \times 10^7\,\text{C}.$$

34P

(a) Every cesium ion at a corner of the cube exerts a force of the same magnitude on the chlorine ion at the cube center. Each force is a force of attraction and is directed toward the cesium ion that exerts it, along the body diagonal of the cube. We can pair every cesium ion with another, diametrically positioned at the opposite corner of the cube. Since the two ions in such a pair exerts forces that have the same magnitude but are oppositely directed, the two forces sum to zero and, since every cesium ion can be paired in this way, the total force on the chlorine ion is zero.

(b) Rather than remove a cesium ion, superpose charge $-e$ at the position of one cesium ion. This neutralizes the ion and, as far as the electrical force on the chlorine ion is concerned, it is equivalent to removing the ion. The forces of the 8 cesium ions at the cube corners sum to zero, so the only force on the chlorine ion is the force of the added charge.

The length of a body diagonal of a cube is $\sqrt{3}a$, where a is the length of a cube edge. Thus the distance from the center of the cube to a corner is $d = (\sqrt{3}/2)a$. The force has magnitude

$$F = \frac{1}{4\pi\epsilon_0}\frac{e^2}{d^2} = \frac{1}{4\pi\epsilon_0}\frac{e^2}{(3/4)a^2}$$

$$= \frac{(8.99 \times 10^9\,\text{N} \cdot \text{m}^2/\text{C}^2)(1.60 \times 10^{-19}\,\text{C})^2}{(3/4)(0.40 \times 10^{-9}\,\text{m})^2} = 1.9 \times 10^{-9}\,\text{N}.$$

Since both the added charge and the chlorine ion are negative the force is one of repulsion. The chlorine ion is pushed away from the site of the missing cesium ion.

35P
In this case the net charge on each penny would be $q_{\text{net}} = \eta q$, where $q = 137000\,\text{C}$ and $\eta = 0.00010\%$. The force is then

$$F = \frac{q_{\text{net}}^2}{4\pi\epsilon_0 r^2} = \frac{[(0.00010\%)(137000\,\text{C})]^2(8.99 \times 10^9\,\text{N} \cdot \text{m}^2/\text{C}^2)}{(1.0\,\text{m})^2} = 1.7 \times 10^8\,\text{N}.$$

Therefore the magnitudes of the positive charge on the proton and negative charge on the electron cannot possibly differ by as much as 0.00010%.

36P
The net charge carried by John whose mass is m is roughly,

$$q = (0.01\%)\frac{mN_A Z_e}{M}$$

$$= (0.01\%)\frac{(200\,\text{lb})(0.4536\,\text{kg/lb})(6.02 \times 10^{23}/\text{mol})(18)(1.6 \times 10^{-19}\,\text{C})}{0.018\,\text{kg/mol}}$$

$$= 8.7 \times 10^5\,\text{C},$$

and the net charge carried by Mary is half of that. So the electrostatic force between them is estimated to be

$$F \approx \frac{1}{4\pi\epsilon_0}\frac{q(q/2)}{d^2} = (8.99 \times 10^9\,\text{N} \cdot \text{m}^2/\text{C}^2)\frac{(8.7 \times 10^5\,\text{C})^2}{2(30\,\text{m})^2} = 4 \times 10^{18}\,\text{N}.$$

37E
Apply the principle of charge conservation.
(a) An electron.
(b) A proton.

None of the reactions given include a beta decay, so the number of protons, the number of neutrons, and the number of electrons are each conserved. Atomic numbers (numbers of protons and numbers of electrons) and molar masses (combined numbers of protons and neutrons) can be found in Appendix D of the text.

(a) ^{1}H has 1 proton, 1 electron, and 0 neutrons and ^{9}Be has 4 protons, 4 electrons, and $9 - 4 = 5$ neutrons, so X has $1 + 4 = 5$ protons, $1 + 4 = 5$ electrons, and $0 + 5 - 1 = 4$ neutrons. One of the neutrons is freed in the reaction. X must be boron with a molar mass of $5 + 4 = 9$ g/ mol: ^{9}B.

(b) ^{12}C has 6 protons, 6 electrons, and $12 - 6 = 6$ neutrons and ^{1}H has 1 proton, 1 electron, and 0 neutrons, so X has $6 + 1 = 7$ protons, $6 + 1 = 7$ electrons, and $6 + 0 = 6$ neutrons. It must be nitrogen with a molar mass of $7 + 6 = 13$ g/ mol: ^{13}N.

(c) ^{15}N has 7 protons, 7 electrons, and $15 - 7 = 8$ neutrons; ^{1}H has 1 proton, 1 electron, and 0 neutrons; and ^{4}He has 2 protons, 2 electrons, and $4 - 2 = 2$ neutrons; so X has $7 + 1 - 2 = 6$ protons, 6 electrons, and $8 + 0 - 2 = 6$ neutrons. It must be carbon with a molar mass of $6 + 6 = 12$: ^{12}C.

39E
(a)
$$F = \frac{1}{4\pi\epsilon_0} \frac{q^2}{r^2} = \frac{(8.99 \times 10^9 \, \text{N} \cdot \text{m}^2/\text{C}^2)[2(1.60 \times 10^{-19} \, \text{C})]^2}{(9.0 \times 10^{-15} \, \text{m})^2} = 11 \, \text{N}.$$

(b)
$$a = \frac{F}{m} = \frac{11 \, \text{N}}{4(1.60 \times 10^{-27} \, \text{kg})} = 1.7 \times 10^{27} \, \text{m/s}^2.$$

40E
The fine structure constant is
$$\alpha = \frac{e^2}{2\epsilon_0 hc} = \frac{(1.60 \times 10^{-19} \, \text{C})^2}{2(8.85 \times 10^{-12} \, \text{C}^2/\text{N} \cdot \text{m}^2)(6.63 \times 10^{-34} \, \text{N} \cdot \text{m} \cdot \text{s})(3.0 \times 10^8 \, \text{m/s})}$$
$$\approx \frac{1}{137}.$$

41E
(a) The Planck time is
$$T_P = \sqrt{\frac{hG}{2\pi c^5}} \, .$$

The product of a speed and a time is a length, so we may take the Planck length to be
$$L_P = T_P c = \sqrt{\frac{hG}{2\pi c^5}} c^2 = \sqrt{\frac{hG}{2\pi c^3}} \, .$$

(*b*) Substitute values:

$$L_P = \sqrt{\frac{(6.63 \times 10^{-34}\,\text{J}\cdot\text{s})(6.67 \times 10^{-11}\,\text{N}\cdot\text{m}^2/\text{kg}^2)}{2\pi(3.00 \times 10^8\,\text{m/s})^3}} = 1.61 \times 10^{-35}\,\text{m}.$$

42 P

(*a*) Suppose the Planck mass is the combination $h^n G^m c^p$, where n, m, p are exponents. Since the units of h are $\text{kg}\cdot\text{m}^2/s$, the units of G are $\text{m}^3/\text{kg}\cdot\text{s}^2$, and the units of c are m/s, the units of $h^n G^m c^p$ are

$$\left(\frac{\text{kg}^n \text{m}^{2m}}{\text{s}^n}\right)\left(\frac{\text{m}^{3m}}{\text{kg}^m \text{s}^{2m}}\right)\left(\frac{\text{m}^p}{\text{s}^p}\right) = \text{kg}^{(n-m)}\text{m}^{(2n+3m+p)}\text{s}^{(-n-2m-p)}.$$

For this combination of units to be kg, we want $n - m = 1$, $2n + 3m + p = 0$, and $-n - 2m - p = 0$. Solve these equations simultaneously for n, m, and p. Add the last two to get $n + m = 0$. This means $n = -m$ and the first two equations become $-2m = 1$ and $m + p = 0$. The first gives $m = -1/2$ and the second gives $p = -m = +1/2$. Finally $n = -m$ gives $n = +1/2$. Thus the Planck mass is

$$M_P = h^{1/2}G^{-1/2}c^{1/2} = \sqrt{hc/G}.$$

(*b*) Substitute the values:

$$M_P = \sqrt{\frac{(6.63 \times 10^{-34}\,\text{J}\cdot\text{s})(3.00 \times 10^8\,\text{m/s})}{6.67 \times 10^{-11}\,\text{N}\cdot\text{m}^2/\text{kg}^2}} = 5.46 \times 10^{-8}\,\text{kg}.$$

CHAPTER 24

1E

(a) $F_A = eE_A = (1.60 \times 10^{-19}\,\text{C})(40\,\text{N/C}) = 6.4 \times 10^{-18}\,\text{C}$.

(b) $E_B = E_A/2 = 20\,\text{N/C}$.

2E

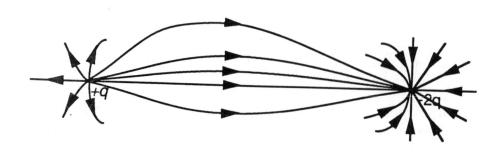

3E

The lines of forces due to $+Q$ and $-Q$ are similar to those in Fig. 24-5. Just turn the book by 90° so that the line joining the two charges in Fig. 24-5 becomes horizontal. Obviously the force on $+q$ is to the right.

4E

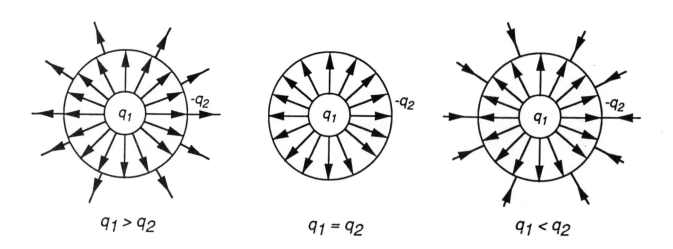

5E

The diagram to the right is an edge view of the disk and shows the field lines above it. Near the disk the lines are perpendicular to the surface and since the disk is uniformly charged the lines are uniformly distributed over the surface. Far away from the disk the lines are like those of a single point charge (the charge on the disk). Extended back to the disk (along the dotted lines of the diagram) they intersect at the center of the disk.

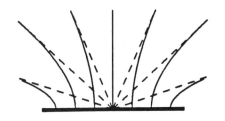

If the disk is positively charged the lines are directed outward from the disk. If the disk is negatively charged they are directed inward toward the disk. Lines below the disk are exactly like those above.

6E

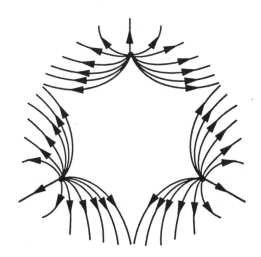

7E

Solve q from $E = q/4\pi\epsilon_0 r^2$:

$$q = 4\pi\epsilon_0 E r^2 = \frac{(1.00\,\text{N/C})(1.00\,\text{m})^2}{8.99 \times 10^9\,\text{N} \cdot \text{m}^2/\,\text{C}^2} = 1.11 \times 10^{-10}\,\text{C}.$$

9E

Since the magnitude of the electric field produced by a point charge q is given by $E = q/4\pi\epsilon_0 r^2$, where r is the distance from the charge to the point where the field has magnitude E, the charge is

$$q = 4\pi\epsilon_0 r^2 E = \frac{(0.50\,\text{m})^2(2.0\,\text{N/C})}{8.99 \times 10^9\,\text{N} \cdot \text{m}^2/C^2} = 5.6 \times 10^{-11}\,\text{C}.$$

10E

(a) The field Q_1 produces at Q_2 is

$$E_1 = \frac{Q_1}{4\pi\epsilon_0 r^2} = \frac{(2.0 \times 10^{-7}\,\text{C})(8.99 \times 10^9\,\text{N}\cdot\text{m}^2/\text{C}^2)}{(0.12\,\text{m})^2} = 1.3 \times 10^5\,\text{N/C};$$

the field Q_2 produces at Q_1 is

$$E_2 = \frac{Q_2}{4\pi\epsilon_0 r^2} = \frac{(8.5 \times 10^{-8}\,\text{C})(8.99 \times 10^9\,\text{N}\cdot\text{m}^2/\text{C}^2)}{(0.12\,\text{m})^2} = 5.3 \times 10^4\,\text{N/C}.$$

(b) $F = E_1 Q_2 = E_2 Q_1 = (1.3 \times 10^5\,\text{N/C})(8.5 \times 10^{-8}\,\text{C}) = 1.1 \times 10^{-2}\,\text{N}.$

11E

(a)

$$E = \frac{2Q}{4\pi\epsilon_0 (r/2)^2} = \frac{8Q}{4\pi\epsilon_0 r^2} = \frac{(8(2.0 \times 10^{-7}\,\text{C})(8.99 \times 10^9\,\text{N}\cdot\text{m}^2/\text{C}^2)}{(0.15\,\text{m})^2} = 6.4 \times 10^5\,\text{N/C}.$$

E points toward the negative charge.

(b) $F = eE = (1.60 \times 10^{-19}\,\text{C})(6.4 \times 10^5\,\text{N/C}) = 1.0 \times 10^{-13}\,\text{N}.$ **F** points toward the positive charge.

12E

Since the charge is uniformly distributed throughout a sphere the electric field at the surface is exactly the same as it would be if the charge were all at the center. That is, the magnitude of the field is

$$E = \frac{q}{4\pi\epsilon_0 R^2},$$

where q is the magnitude of the total charge and R is the sphere radius. The magnitude of the total charge is ze, so

$$E = \frac{ze}{4\pi\epsilon_0 R^2} = \frac{(8.99 \times 10^9\,\text{N}\cdot\text{m}^2/\text{C}^2)(94)(1.60 \times 10^{-19}\,\text{C})}{(6.64 \times 10^{-15}\,\text{m})^2} = 3.07 \times 10^{21}\,\text{N/C}.$$

The field is normal to the surface and since the charge is positive it points outward from the surface.

13E

From symmetry, the only pair of charges which produces a non-vanishing field **E** is the one in the middle of the two vertical sides of the squre. So

$$E = \frac{1}{4\pi\epsilon_0}\left(\frac{q}{d^2} + \frac{2q}{d^2}\right) = \frac{3q}{4\pi\epsilon_0 d^2},$$

E points to the right.

14P

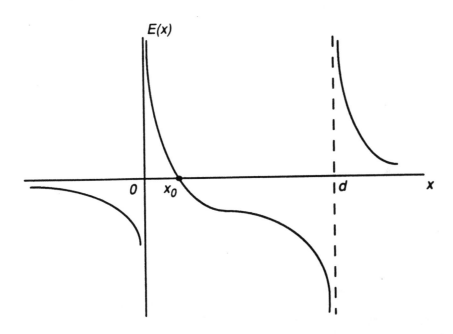

The $E(x)$ vs. x curve is plotted above. Here $x_0 = d/(\sqrt{3}+1)$, where $E = 0$.

15P
(a) Convince yourself that a point where $E = 0$ can only be located to the right of the positive charge. Denote the separation between the point and the positive charge by x, then

$$E = \frac{1}{4\pi\epsilon_0}\left[\frac{2.0q}{x^2} - \frac{5.0q}{(x+a)^2}\right] = 0.$$

Solve for x: $x = 1.7a$.
(b)

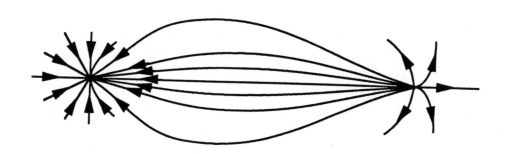

(a)

$$E_A = \frac{1}{4\pi\epsilon_0}\left[\frac{1.0q}{d^2} - \frac{2.0q}{(2d)^2}\right] = \frac{q}{8\pi\epsilon_0 d^2}.$$

$\mathbf{E}_A$ points to the left.

$$E_B = \frac{1}{4\pi\epsilon_0}\left[\frac{1.0q}{(d/2)^2} + \frac{2.0q}{(d/2)^2}\right] = \frac{3q}{\pi\epsilon_0 d^2}.$$

$\mathbf{E}_B$ points to the right.

$$E_C = \frac{1}{4\pi\epsilon_0}\left[\frac{2.0q}{d^2} - \frac{1.0q}{(2d)^2}\right] = \frac{7q}{16\pi\epsilon_0 d^2}.$$

$\mathbf{E}_C$ points to the left.

(b)

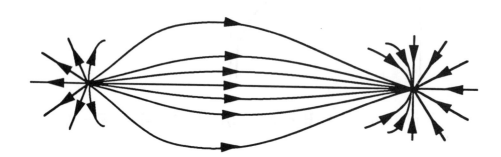

17P

At points between the charges the individual electric fields are in the same direction and do not cancel. Charge q_2 has a greater magnitude than charge q_1 so a point of zero field must be closer to q_1 than to q_2. It must be to the right of q_1 on the diagram. Put the origin at q_2 and let x be the coordinate of P, the point where the field vanishes. Then the total electric field at P is given by

$$E = \frac{1}{4\pi\epsilon_0}\left[\frac{q_2}{x^2} - \frac{q_1}{(x-d)^2}\right],$$

where q_1 and q_2 are the magnitudes of the charges. If the field is to vanish,

$$\frac{q_2}{x^2} = \frac{q_1}{(x-d)^2}.$$

Take the square root of both sides to obtain $\sqrt{q_1}/x = \sqrt{q_2}/(x-d)$. The solution for x is

$$x = \left(\frac{\sqrt{q_2}}{\sqrt{q_2} - \sqrt{q_1}}\right)d = \left(\frac{\sqrt{4.0q_1}}{\sqrt{4.0q_1} - \sqrt{q_1}}\right)d$$

$$= \left(\frac{2.0}{2.0 - 1.0}\right)d = 2.0d = (2.0)(50\,\text{cm}) = 100\,\text{cm}\,.$$

The point is 50 cm to the right of q_1.

18P

(a) The fields from the two charges of $5.0q$ each cancel out. So

$$E_p = \frac{1}{4\pi\epsilon_0}\left[\frac{3.0q}{d^2} - \frac{12q}{(2d)^2}\right] = 0.$$

19P

In the figure to the right, each of the six arrows represents the net electric field of a pair of diametrically opposite charges (e.g. the one which points vertically upward represents the field of the $-12q$ and the $-6q$ charges). Since each of the six E-fields has a magnitude of $E = 6q/4\pi\epsilon_0 r^2$, where r is roughly the radius of the clock, by symmetry the net E-field should point at A, i.e. the 9:30 mark.

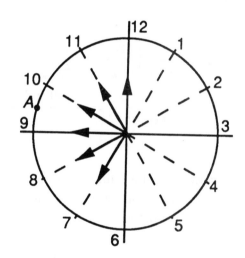

20P

(a) By symmetry the fields due to the two electrons placed in line with the midpoint of a side cancel out. So

$$E = \frac{1}{4\pi\epsilon_0}\frac{e}{(\sqrt{3}a/2)^2} = \frac{e}{3\pi\epsilon_0 a^2}$$

$$= \frac{4(1.60 \times 10^{-19}\,\text{C})(8.99 \times 10^9\,\text{N}\cdot\text{m}^2/\text{C}^2)}{3(0.20\,\text{m})^2} = 4.8 \times 10^{-8}\,\text{N/C}.$$

E is perpendicular to the side line and points toward the corner of the triangle opposite to the side.

(b) $F = eE = (1.60 \times 10^{-19}\,\text{C})(4.8 \times 10^{-8}\,\text{N/C}) = 7.7 \times 10^{-27}\,\text{N}$. F points in the direction opposite to E.

21P

By symmetry the fields due to the two charges of magnitude q each cancel out. So

$$\mathbf{E}_p = \frac{1}{4\pi\epsilon_0} \frac{2.0q\mathbf{i}}{(a/\sqrt{2})^2} = \frac{q\mathbf{i}}{\pi\epsilon_0 a^2},$$

where $\mathbf{i}$ is unit vector from the $+2.0q$ charge to P.

22P

Choose the coordinate axes as shown on the diagram to the right. At the center of the square the electric fields produced by the charges at the lower left and upper right corners are both along the x axis and each points away from the center and toward the charge that produces it. Since each charge is a distance $d = \sqrt{2}a/2 = a/\sqrt{2}$ away from the center the net field due to these two charges is

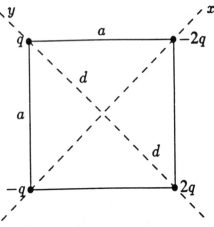

$$E_x = \frac{1}{4\pi\epsilon_0}\left[\frac{2q}{a^2/2} - \frac{q}{a^2/2}\right]$$

$$= \frac{1}{4\pi\epsilon_0}\frac{q}{a^2/2} = \frac{(8.99\times 10^9\,\text{N}\cdot\text{m}^2/\text{C}^2)(1.0\times 10^{-8}\,\text{C})}{(0.050\,\text{m})^2/2} = 7.19\times 10^4\,\text{N/C}.$$

At the center of the square the field produced by the charges at the upper left and lower right corners are both along the y axis and each points toward the center, away from the charge that produces it. The net field produced at the center by these charges is

$$E_y = \frac{1}{4\pi\epsilon_0}\left[\frac{2q}{a^2/2} - \frac{q}{a^2/2}\right] = \frac{1}{4\pi\epsilon_0}\frac{q}{a^2/2} = 7.19\times 10^4\,\text{N/C}.$$

The magnitude of the field is

$$E = \sqrt{E_x^2 + E_y^2} = \sqrt{2}(7.19\times 10^4\,\text{N/C}) = 1.02\times 10^5\,\text{N/C}$$

and the angle it makes with the x axis is

$$\theta = \tan^{-1}\frac{E_y}{E_x} = \tan^{-1}(1) = 45°.$$

It is upward in the diagram, from the center of the square toward the center of the upper side.

23E

The magnitude of the dipole moment is given by $p = qd$, where q is the positive charge in the dipole and d is the separation of the charges. For the dipole described in the problem $p = (1.60 \times 10^{-19} \text{ C})(4.30 \times 10^{-9} \text{ m}) = 6.88 \times 10^{-28} \text{ C} \cdot \text{m}$. The dipole moment is a vector that points from the negative toward the positive charge.

24E

Use Eq. 24-12:

$$F = qE = \frac{ep}{2\pi\epsilon_0 z^3} = \frac{2(1.60 \times 10^{-19} \text{ C})(3.6 \times 10^{-29} \text{ C} \cdot \text{m})(8.99 \times 10^9 \text{ N} \cdot \text{m}^2/\text{C}^2)}{(25 \times 10^{-9} \text{ m})^3}$$

$$= 6.6 \times 10^{-15} \text{ N}.$$

25E

$$E = \frac{1}{4\pi\epsilon_0}\left[\frac{q}{(z - d/2)^2} + \frac{q}{(z + d/2)^2}\right].$$

For $z \gg d$, we have $(z \pm d/2)^{-2} \approx z^2$, so

$$E \approx \frac{1}{4\pi\epsilon_0}\left(\frac{q}{z^2} + \frac{q}{z^2}\right) = \frac{2q}{4\pi\epsilon_0 z^2}.$$

27P

Think of the quadrupole as composed of two dipoles, each with dipole moment of magnitude $p = qd$. The moments point in opposite directions and produce fields in opposite directions at points on the dipole axis. Consider a point on the axis a distance z above the center of the quadrupole and take an upward pointing field to be positive. Then the field produced by the upper dipole of the pair is $qd/2\pi\epsilon_0(z - d/2)^3$ and the field produced by the lower is $-qd/2\pi\epsilon_0(z + d/2)^3$. Use the binomial expansions $(z - d/2)^{-3} \approx z^{-3} - 3z^{-4}(-d/2)$ and $(z + d/2)^{-3} \approx z^{-3} - 3z^{-4}(d/2)$ to obtain

$$E = \frac{qd}{2\pi\epsilon_0}\left[\frac{1}{z^3} + \frac{3d}{2z^4} - \frac{1}{z^3} + \frac{3d}{2z^4}\right] = \frac{6qd^2}{4\pi\epsilon_0 z^4}.$$

Let $Q = 2qd^2$. Then

$$E = \frac{3Q}{4\pi\epsilon_0 z^4}.$$

28E

Use Eq. 24-19. Take $E > 0$ for **E** pointing in the $+z$ direction.

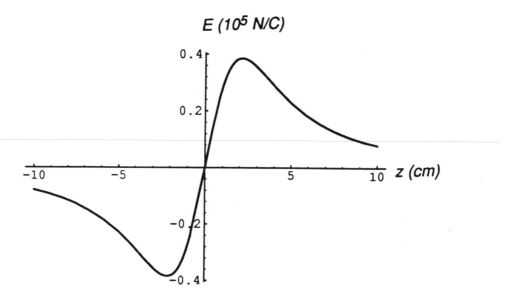

E (10^5 N/C)

29P

From Eq. 24-19, Let $dE/dz = 0$ we get

$$\frac{dE}{dz} = \frac{d}{dz}\left[\frac{qz}{4\pi\epsilon_0(z^2 + R^2)^{3/2}}\right] = \frac{q(z^2 + R^2)^{3/2} - 3qz(z^2 + R^2)^{1/2}}{4\pi\epsilon_0(z^2 + R^2)^3} = 0,$$

i.e. $(z^2 + R^2)^{1/2} - 3z = 0$. Solve for z: $z = \pm R/\sqrt{2}$.

30P

The electric field at a point on the axis of a uniformly charged ring, a distance z from the ring center, is given by

$$E = \frac{qz}{4\pi\epsilon_0(z^2 + R^2)^{3/2}},$$

where q is the charge on the ring and R is the radius of the ring (see Eq. 24–19). For q positive the field points upward at points above the ring and downward at points below the ring. Take the positive direction to be upward. Then the force acting on an electron on the axis is

$$F = -\frac{eqz}{4\pi\epsilon_0(z^2 + R^2)^{3/2}}.$$

For small amplitude oscillations $z \ll R$ and z can be neglected in the denominator. Thus

$$F = -\frac{eqz}{4\pi\epsilon_0 R^3}.$$

The force is a restoring force: it pulls the electron toward the equilibrium point $z = 0$. Furthermore, the magnitude of the force is proportional to z, just as if the electron were

652

attached to a spring with spring constant $k = eq/4\pi\epsilon_0 R^3$. The electron moves in simple harmonic motion with an angular frequency given by

$$\omega = \sqrt{\frac{k}{m}} = \sqrt{\frac{eq}{4\pi\epsilon_0 m R^3}},$$

where m is the mass of the electron.

31P
By symmetry, each of the two rods produces the same electric field $\mathbf{E}_0$ pointing in the $+y$ axis at the center of the circle. So the net field is

$$\mathbf{E} = 2E_0\mathbf{j} = 2\mathbf{j}\int \frac{\cos\theta dq}{4\pi\epsilon_0 R^2} = 2\mathbf{j}\int_{-\pi/2}^{+\pi/2} \frac{\cos\theta \cdot qRd\theta}{4\pi\epsilon_0 R^2 \cdot \pi R}$$

$$= \left(\frac{1}{4\pi\epsilon_0}\frac{4q}{4\pi^2}\right)\mathbf{j}.$$

32P
By symmetry, both $+Q$ and $-Q$ produce an equal value of electric field, $\mathbf{E}_0$, pointing vertically downward. The magnitude of $\mathbf{E}_P$ is thus

$$E_P = 2E_0 = 2\int_0 \frac{\sin\theta dQ}{4\pi\epsilon_0 r^2} = 2\int_0^{\pi/2} \frac{\sin\theta Qrd\theta}{4\pi\epsilon_0 r^2(\pi r/2)} = \frac{Q}{\pi^2\epsilon_0 r^2},$$

and $\mathbf{E}_P$ points vertically downward.

33P
From symmetry we only need to consider the y-component of $\mathbf{E}_P$. Consider an infinitesimal segment of length dx in the rod. We have

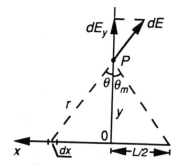

$$dE_y = \cos\theta dE = \frac{y}{r} \cdot \frac{qdx/L}{4\pi\epsilon_0 r^2} = \frac{q\cos\theta d\theta}{4\pi\epsilon_0 Ly},$$

where we used $x = y\tan\theta$ and $r = y/\cos\theta$. Thus

$$E = 2\int_0^{\theta_m} \frac{q\cos\theta d\theta}{4\pi\epsilon_0 Ly} = \frac{2q}{4\pi\epsilon_0 Ly}\sin\theta_m = \frac{qL/2}{2\pi\epsilon_0 Ly\sqrt{y^2 + (L/2)^2}}$$

$$= \frac{q}{2\pi\epsilon_0 y\sqrt{4y^2 + L^2}}.$$

Note that the factor of 2 in the first step above is due to the fact that each half of the rod contributes equally to E.

34P

(a) $\lambda = -q/L$.

(b)

$$\mathbf{E}_P = \frac{\mathbf{i}}{4\pi\epsilon_0} \int_0^L \frac{\lambda\, dx}{(a+L-x)^2} = -\frac{q\mathbf{i}}{4\pi\epsilon_0 L} \int_0^L \frac{dx}{(a+L-x)^2}$$

$$= \frac{q(-\mathbf{i})}{4\pi\epsilon_0 a(L+a)}.$$

(c) If $a \gg L$ then $a(L+a) \simeq a^2$, and

$$\mathbf{E}_P \approx \frac{q(-\mathbf{i})}{4\pi\epsilon_0 a^2},$$

indeed the electric field of a point charge.

35P

Consider an infinitesimal section of the rod of length dx, a distance x from the left end, as shown in the diagram to the right. It contains charge $dq = \lambda\, dx$ and is a distance r from P. The magnitude of the field it produces at P is given by

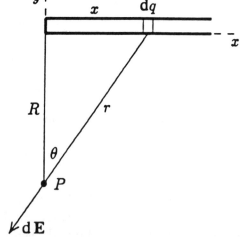

$$dE = \frac{1}{4\pi\epsilon_0}\frac{\lambda\, dx}{r^2}.$$

The x component is

$$dE_x = -\frac{1}{4\pi\epsilon_0}\frac{\lambda\, dx}{r^2}\sin\theta$$

and the y component is

$$dE_y = -\frac{1}{4\pi\epsilon_0}\frac{\lambda\, dx}{r^2}\cos\theta.$$

Use θ as the variable of integration. Substitute $r = R/\cos\theta$, $x = R\tan\theta$, and $dx = (R/\cos^2\theta)\, d\theta$. The limits of integration are 0 and $\pi/2\,\mathrm{rad}$. Thus

$$E_x = -\frac{\lambda}{4\pi\epsilon_0}\int_0^{\pi/2}\sin\theta\, d\theta = \frac{\lambda}{4\pi\epsilon_0}\cos\theta\Big|_0^{\pi/2} = -\frac{\lambda}{4\pi\epsilon_0 R}.$$

and

$$E_y = -\frac{\lambda}{4\pi\epsilon_0}\int_0^{\pi/2}\cos\theta\, d\theta = -\frac{\lambda}{4\pi\epsilon_0}\sin\theta\Big|_0^{\pi/2} = -\frac{\lambda}{4\pi\epsilon_0 R}.$$

654

Notice that $E_x = E_y$ no matter what the value of R. Thus $\mathbf{E}$ makes an angle of 45° with the negative x axis for all values of R.

36E
Use $(1+x)^n \approx 1 + nx$ for $|x| \ll 1$. Thus for $z \gg R$

$$
\begin{aligned}
E(z) &= \frac{\sigma}{2\epsilon_0}\left(1 - \frac{z}{\sqrt{z^2 + R^2}}\right) = \frac{\sigma}{2\epsilon_0}\left[1 - \left(1 + \frac{R^2}{z^2}\right)^{-1/2}\right] \\
&\approx \frac{\sigma}{2\epsilon_0}\left[1 - \left(1 - \frac{R^2}{2z^2}\right)\right] = \frac{\sigma R^2}{4\epsilon_0 z^2} = \frac{\sigma(\pi R^2)}{4\pi\epsilon_0 z^2} \\
&= \frac{Q}{4\pi\epsilon_0 z^2}.
\end{aligned}
$$

37P
(a) Let $E = \sigma/2\epsilon_0 = E_0 = 3 \times 10^6$ N/C. Thus

$$
q = \pi R^2 \sigma = 2\pi\epsilon_0 R^2 E_0 = \frac{(2.5 \times 10^{-2}\,\text{m})^2(3.0 \times 10^6\,\text{N/C})}{2(8.99 \times 10^9\,\text{N} \cdot \text{m}^2/\text{C}^2)} = 1.0 \times 10^{-7}\,\text{C}.
$$

(b)

$$
N = \frac{\pi(2.5 \times 10^{-2}\,\text{m})^2}{0.015 \times 10^{-18}\,\text{m}^2} = 1.3 \times 10^{17}.
$$

(c) The fraction is

$$
\text{frac} = \frac{q}{Ne} = \frac{1.0 \times 10^{-7}\,\text{C}}{(1.3 \times 10^{17})(1.6 \times 10^{-19}\,\text{C})} = 5.0 \times 10^{-6}.
$$

38P
At a point on the axis of a uniformly charged disk a distance z above the center of the disk the magnitude of the electric field is

$$
E = \frac{\sigma}{2\epsilon_0}\left[1 - \frac{z}{\sqrt{z^2 + R^2}}\right],
$$

where R is the radius of the disk and σ is the surface charge density on the disk. See Eq. 24–27. The magnitude of the field at the center of the disk ($z = 0$) is $E_c = \sigma/2\epsilon_0$. You want to solve for the value of z such that $E/E_c = 1/2$. This means

$$
1 - \frac{z}{\sqrt{z^2 + R^2}} = \frac{1}{2}
$$

or

$$\frac{z}{\sqrt{z^2 + R^2}} = \frac{1}{2}.$$

Square both sides, then multiply them by $z^2 + R^2$ to obtain $z^2 = (z^2/4) + (R^2/4)$. Thus $z^2 = R^2/3$ and $z = R/\sqrt{3}$.

39E

The magnitude of the force acting on the electron is $F = eE$, where E is the magnitude of the electric field at its location. The acceleration of the electron is given by Newton's second law:

$$a = \frac{F}{m} = \frac{eE}{m} = \frac{(1.60 \times 10^{-19}\,\text{C})(2.00 \times 10^4\,\text{N/C})}{9.11 \times 10^{-31}\,\text{kg}} = 3.51 \times 10^{15}\,\text{m/s}^2\,.$$

40E

$$E = \frac{F}{e} = \frac{ma}{e} = \frac{(9.11 \times 10^{-31}\,\text{kg})(1.80 \times 10^9\,\text{m/s}^2)}{1.60 \times 10^{-19}\,\text{C}} = 1.02 \times 10^{-2}\,\text{N/C},$$

$\mathbf{E}$ points westward.

41E

(a) $F_e = Ee = (3.0 \times 10^6\,\text{N/C})(1.6 \times .10^{-19}\,\text{C}) = 4.8 \times 10^{-13}\,\text{N}.$
(b) $F_i = Eq_{\text{net}} = Ee = 4.8 \times 10^{-13}\,\text{N}.$

42E

Let $mg = qE = 2eE$. Thus

$$E = \frac{mg}{2e} = \frac{(6.64 \times 10^{-27}\,\text{kg})(9.8\,\text{m/s}^2)}{2(1.6 \times 10^{-19}\,\text{C})} = 2.03 \times 10^{-7}\,\text{N/C}.$$

$\mathbf{E}$ should point upward.

43E

(a) The magnitude of the force on the particle is given by $F = qE$, where q is the magnitude of the charge carried by the particle and E is the magnitude of the electric field at the location of the particle. Thus

$$E = \frac{F}{q} = \frac{3.0 \times 10^{-6}\,\text{N}}{2.0 \times 10^{-9}\,\text{C}} = 1.5 \times 10^3\,\text{N/C}\,.$$

The force points downward and the charge is negative, so the field points upward.

(b) The magnitude of the electrostatic force on a proton is

$$F_e = eE = (1.60 \times 10^{-19}\,\text{C})(1.5 \times 10^3\,\text{N/C}) = 2.4 \times 10^{-16}\,\text{N}.$$

A proton is positively charged, so the force is in the same direction as the field, upward.

(c) The magnitude of the gravitational force on the proton is

$$F_g = mg = (1.67 \times 10^{-27}\,\text{kg})(9.8\,\text{m/s}^2) = 1.6 \times 10^{-26}\,\text{N}.$$

The force is downward.

(d) The ratio of the forces is

$$\frac{F_e}{F_g} = \frac{2.4 \times 10^{-16}\,\text{N}}{1.64 \times 10^{-26}\,\text{N}} = 1.5 \times 10^{10}.$$

44E
Let $mg = |q|E$ and solve for $|q|$:

$$|q| = \frac{mg}{E} = \frac{4.4\,\text{N}}{150\,\text{N/C}} = 2.9 \times 10^{-2}\,\text{C}.$$

Since $q\mathbf{E}$ must be upward while $\mathbf{E}$ is downward, q is negative.

45E
(a)

$$a = \frac{F}{m} = \frac{eE}{m} = \frac{(1.60 \times 10^{-19}\,\text{C})(1.40 \times 10^6\,\text{N/C})}{9.11 \times 10^{-31}\,\text{kg}} = 2.46 \times 10^{17}\,\text{m/s}^2.$$

(b)

$$t = \frac{v}{a} = \frac{3.00 \times 10^7\,\text{m/s}}{2.46 \times 10^{17}\,\text{m/s}^2} = 1.22 \times 10^{-10}\,\text{s}.$$

(c)

$$s = \frac{1}{2}at^2 = \frac{1}{2}(2.46 \times 10^{17}\,\text{m/s}^2)(1.22 \times 10^{-10}\,\text{s})^2 = 1.83 \times 10^{-3}\,\text{m}.$$

46E
(a) The magnitude of the force acting on the proton is $F = eE$, where E is the magnitude of the electric field. According to Newton's second law the acceleration of the proton is $a = F/m = eE/m$, where m is the mass of the proton. Thus

$$a = \frac{(1.60 \times 10^{-19}\,\text{C})(2.00 \times 10^4\,\text{N/C})}{1.67 \times 10^{-27}\,\text{kg}} = 1.92 \times 10^{12}\,\text{m/s}^2.$$

(*b*) Assume the proton starts from rest and use the kinematic equations $x = \frac{1}{2}at^2$ and $v = at$ to show that $v = \sqrt{2ax} = \sqrt{2(1.92 \times 10^{12}\,\text{m/s}^2)(0.0100\,\text{m})} = 1.96 \times 10^5\,\text{m/s}$.

47E
(a) Use $v_f^2 - v_i^2 = -v_i^2 = 2as$ and $a = F/m = -eE/m$ to solve for s:

$$s = \frac{-v_i^2}{2a} = \frac{-mv_i^2}{-2eE} = \frac{-(9.11 \times 10^{-31}\,\text{kg})(5.00 \times 10^6\,\text{m/s})^2}{-2(1.60 \times 10^{-19}\,\text{C})(1.00 \times 10^3\,\text{N/C})} = 7.12 \times 10^{-2}\,\text{m}.$$

(b)

$$t = \frac{s}{\bar{v}} = \frac{2s}{v_i} = \frac{2(7.12 \times 10^{-2}\,\text{m})}{5.00 \times 10^6\,\text{m/s}} = 2.85 \times 10^{-8}\,\text{s}.$$

(c) from $\Delta v^2 = 2a\Delta s$

$$\frac{\Delta K}{K_i} = \frac{\Delta(\frac{1}{2}mv^2)}{\frac{1}{2}mv_i^2} = \frac{\Delta v^2}{v_i^2} = \frac{2a\Delta s}{v_i^2} = \frac{-2eE\Delta s}{mv_i^2}$$

$$= \frac{-2(1.60 \times 10^{-19}\,\text{C})(1.00 \times 10^3\,\text{N/C})(8.00 \times 10^{-3}\,\text{m})}{(9.11 \times 10^{-31}\,\text{kg})(5.00 \times 10^6\,\text{m/s})^2} = -11.2\%.$$

48E
(a)

$$W = \rho V = \frac{\pi D^3 \rho}{6} = \frac{\pi(1.2 \times 10^{-6}\,\text{m})^3(1.00 \times 10^3\,\text{kg/m}^3)}{6} = 8.87 \times 10^{-15}\,\text{N}.$$

(b) From $W = F = qE = NeE$ we solve for N, the number of excessive electrons:

$$N = \frac{W}{eE} = \frac{8.87 \times 10^{-15}\,\text{N}}{(1.60 \times 10^{-19}\,\text{C})(462\,\text{N/C})} = 120.$$

49E
When the drop is in equilibrium the force of gravity is balanced by the force of the electric field: $mg = qE$, where m is the mass of the drop, q is the charge on the drop, and E is the magnitude of the electric field. The mass of the drop is given by $m = (4\pi/3)r^3\rho$, where r is its radius and ρ is its mass density. Thus

$$q = \frac{mg}{E} = \frac{4\pi r^3 \rho g}{3E}$$

$$= \frac{4\pi(1.64 \times 10^{-6}\,\text{m})^3(851\,\text{kg/m}^3)(9.8\,\text{m/s}^2)}{3(1.92 \times 10^5\,\text{N/C})} = 8.0 \times 10^{-19}\,\text{C}$$

and $q/e = (8.0 \times 10^{-19}\,\text{C})/(1.60 \times 10^{-19}\,\text{C}) = 5$.

50P
You need to find the largest common denominator of the group of numbers listed in the problem. One way to start this is to find the closest separation between any pair of the numbers. For example, take $13.13 \times 10^{-19}\,\text{C} - 11.50 \times 10^{-19}\,\text{C} = 1.63 \times 10^{-19}\,\text{C}$. You can easily verify that this value is a common denominator. So this is the value of e that can be deduced.

51P
(a)

$$\begin{aligned} \mathbf{F} &= q\mathbf{E} = qE_x\mathbf{i} + qE_y\mathbf{j} \\ &= (8.00 \times 10^{-5}\,\text{C})(3.00 \times 10^3\,\text{N/C})\mathbf{i} + (8.00 \times 10^{-5}\,\text{C})(-600\,\text{N/C})\mathbf{j} \\ &= (0.240\,\text{N})\mathbf{i} - (0.0480\,\text{N})\mathbf{j}. \end{aligned}$$

So the magnitude of $\mathbf{F}$ is $F = \sqrt{(0.240\,\text{N})^2 + (0.0480\,\text{N})^2} = 0.245\,\text{N}$, and $\mathbf{F}$ makes an angle θ with the $+x$ direction, where

$$\theta = \tan^{-1}\left(\frac{F_y}{F_x}\right) = \tan^{-1}\left(\frac{-0.0480\,\text{N}}{0.240\,\text{N}}\right) = -11.3^\circ.$$

(b) The coordinates (x, y) at $t = 3.00\,\text{s}$ are

$$\begin{cases} x = \dfrac{1}{2}a_x t^2 = \dfrac{F_x t^2}{2m} = \dfrac{(0.240\,\text{N})(3.00\,\text{s})^2}{2(1.0 \times 10^{-2}\,\text{kg})} = 108\,\text{m}, \\[2mm] y = \dfrac{1}{2}a_y t^2 = \dfrac{xa_y}{a_x} = \dfrac{xF_y}{F_x} = \dfrac{(108\,\text{m})(-0.0480\,\text{N})}{0.240\,\text{N}} = -21.6\,\text{m}. \end{cases}$$

52P
(a) Use $s = \bar{v}t = vt/2$:

$$v = \frac{2s}{t} = \frac{2(2.0 \times 10^{-2}\,\text{m})}{1.5 \times 10^{-8}\,\text{s}} = 2.7 \times 10^6\,\text{m/s}.$$

(b) Use $s = \frac{1}{2}at^2$ and $E = F/e = ma/e$:

$$E = \frac{ma}{e} = \frac{2sm}{et^2} = \frac{2(2.0 \times 10^{-2}\,\text{m})(9.11 \times 10^{-31}\,\text{kg})}{(1.60 \times 10^{-19}\,\text{C})(1.5 \times 10^{-8}\,\text{s})^2} = 1.0 \times 10^3\,\text{N/C}.$$

53P

(a)

$$\mathbf{a} = \frac{\mathbf{F}}{m} = \frac{-e\mathbf{E}}{m} = \frac{(-1.6 \times 10^{-19}\,\text{C})(120\,\text{N/C})\mathbf{j}}{9.11 \times 10^{-31}\,\text{kg}} = -2.11 \times 10^{13}\mathbf{j}(\,\text{m/s}^2).$$

(b) Since $a_x = 0$, the time t it takes for the x coordinate of the electron to change by 2.0 cm is $t = 2.0\,\text{cm}/(1.5 \times 10^5\,\text{m/s}) = 1.3 \times 10^{-7}\,\text{s}$. So v_x remains at $1.5 \times 10^5\,\text{m/s}$, which v_y becomes

$$v_y = 3.0 \times 10^3\,\text{m/s} - (2.11 \times 10^{13}\,\text{m/s}^2)(1.3 \times 10^{-7}\,\text{s}) = -2.7 \times 10^6\,\text{m/s}.$$

Thus $\bar{\mathbf{v}}$ becomes $(1.5 \times 10^5\mathbf{i} - 2.7 \times 10^6\mathbf{j})\,\text{m/s}$.

54P

Take the positive direction to be to the right in the diagram. The acceleration of the proton is $a_p = eE/m_p$ and the acceleration of the electron is $a_e = -eE/m_e$, where E is the magnitude of the electric field, m_p is the mass of the proton, and m_e is the mass of the electron. Take the origin to be at the initial position of the proton. Then the coordinate of the proton at time t is $x = \frac{1}{2}a_pt^2$ and the coordinate of the electron is $x = L + \frac{1}{2}a_et^2$. They pass each other when their coordinates are the same, or $\frac{1}{2}a_pt^2 = L + \frac{1}{2}a_et^2$. This means $t^2 = 2L/(a_p - a_e)$ and

$$x = \frac{a_p}{a_p - a_e}L = \frac{eE/m_p}{(eE/m_p) + (eE/m_e)}L = \frac{m_e}{m_e + m_p}L$$
$$= \frac{9.11 \times 10^{-31}\,\text{kg}}{9.11 \times 10^{-31}\,\text{kg} + 1\!:\!67 \times 10^{-27}\,\text{kg}}(0.050\,\text{m}) = 2.7 \times 10^{-5}\,\text{m}\,.$$

55P

(a) Suppose the pendulum is at the angle θ with the vertical. The force diagram is shown to the right. T is the tension in the thread, mg is the force of gravity, and qE is the force of the electric field. The field points upward and the charge is positive, so the force is upward. Take the angle shown to be positive. Then the torque on the sphere about the point where the thread is attached to the upper plate is $\tau = -(mg - qE)\ell\sin\theta$. If $mg > qE$ then the torque is a restoring torque; it tends to pull the pendulum back to its equilibrium position.

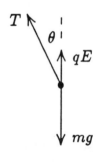

If the amplitude of the oscillation is small, $\sin\theta$ can be replaced by θ in radians and the torque is $\tau = -(mg - qE)\ell\theta$. The torque is proportional to the angular displacement and the pendulum moves in simple harmonic motion. Its angular frequency is $\omega = \sqrt{(mg - qE)\ell/I}$, where I is the rotational inertia of the pendulum. Since $I = m\ell^2$ for a simple pendulum,

$$\omega = \sqrt{\frac{(mg - qE)\ell}{m\ell^2}} = \sqrt{\frac{g - qE/m}{\ell}}$$

and the period is

$$T = \frac{2\pi}{\omega} = 2\pi\sqrt{\frac{\ell}{g - qE/m}} \; .$$

If $qE > mg$ the torque is not a restoring torque and the pendulum does not oscillate.

(b) The force of the electric field is now downward and the torque on the pendulum is $\tau = -(mg + qE)\ell\theta$ if the angular displacement is small. The period of oscillation is

$$T = 2\pi\sqrt{\frac{\ell}{g + qE/m}} \; .$$

56P

The electric field is upward in the diagram and the charge is negative, so the force of the field on it is downward. The magnitude of the acceleration is $a = eE/m$, where E is the magnitude of the field and m is the mass of the electron. Its numerical value is

$$a = \frac{(1.60 \times 10^{-19}\,\text{C})(2.00 \times 10^3\,\text{N/C})}{9.11 \times 10^{-31}\,\text{kg}} = 3.51 \times 10^{14}\,\text{m/s}^2 \; .$$

Put the origin of a coordinate system at the initial position of the electron. Take the x axis to be horizontal and positive to the right; take the y axis to be vertical and positive toward the top of the page. The kinematic equations are $x = v_0 t \cos\theta$, $y = v_0 t \sin\theta - \frac{1}{2}at^2$, and $v_y = v_0 \sin\theta - at$.

First find the greatest y coordinate attained by the electron. If it is less than d the electron does not hit the upper plate. If it is greater than d it will hit the upper plate if the corresponding x coordinate is less than L. The greatest y coordinate occurs when $v_y = 0$. This means $v_0 \sin\theta - at = 0$ or $t = (v_0/a)\sin\theta$ and

$$\begin{aligned}
y_{\text{max}} &= \frac{v_0^2 \sin^2\theta}{a} - \frac{1}{2}a\frac{v_0^2 \sin^2\theta}{a^2} = \frac{1}{2}\frac{v_0^2 \sin^2\theta}{a} \\
&= \frac{(6.00 \times 10^6\,\text{m/s})^2 \sin^2 45°}{2(3.51 \times 10^{14}\,\text{m/s}^2)} = 2.56 \times 10^{-2}\,\text{m} \; .
\end{aligned}$$

Since this is greater than $d\,(= 2.00\,\text{cm})$ the electron might hit the upper plate.

Now find the x coordinate of the position of the electron when $y = d$. Since

$$v_0 \sin\theta = (6.00 \times 10^6\,\text{m/s})\sin 45° = 4.24 \times 10^6\,\text{m/s}$$

and

$$2ad = 2(3.51 \times 10^{14}\,\text{m/s}^2)(0.0200\,\text{m}) = 1.40 \times 10^{13}\,\text{m}^2/\text{s}^2 \; ,$$

the solution to $d = v_0 t \sin \theta - \frac{1}{2} a t^2$ is

$$t = \frac{v_0 \sin \theta - \sqrt{v_0^2 \sin^2 \theta - 2ad}}{a}$$

$$= \frac{4.24 \times 10^6 \text{ m/s} - \sqrt{(4.24 \times 10^6 \text{ m/s})^2 - 1.40 \times 10^{13} \text{ m}^2/\text{s}^2}}{3.51 \times 10^{14} \text{ m/s}^2} = 6.43 \times 10^{-9} \text{ s} .$$

The negative root was used because we want the *earliest* time for which $y = d$.
The x coordinate is

$$x = v_0 t \cos \theta$$

$$= (6.00 \times 10^6 \text{ m/s})(6.43 \times 10^{-9} \text{ s}) \cos 45° = 2.72 \times 10^{-2} \text{ m} .$$

This is less than L so the electron hits the upper plate at $x = 2.72 \text{ cm}$.

57E
(a) $p = (1.5 \times 10^{-9} \text{ C})(6.20 \times 10^{-6} \text{ m}) = 9.30 \times 10^{-15} \text{ C} \cdot \text{m}$.
(b) $\Delta U = pE - (-pE) = 2pE = 2(9.30 \times 10^{-15} \text{ C} \cdot \text{m})(1100 \text{ N/C}) = 2.05 \times 10^{-11} \text{ J}$.

58E
Use $\vec{\tau} = \vec{p} \times \vec{E}$.
(a) Now $\vec{\tau} = 0$ as $\vec{p} \parallel \vec{E}$.
(b) Now $\tau = pE \sin 90° = 2(1.6 \times 10^{-19} \text{ C})(0.78 \times 10^{-9} \text{ m})(3.4 \times 10^6 \text{ N/C}) = 8.5 \times 10^{-22} \text{ N} \cdot \text{m}$.
(c) Now $\vec{\tau} = o$ again, since $\vec{p} \parallel (-\vec{E})$.

59P
$W = \Delta U = -\vec{p}_f \cdot \vec{E} - (-\vec{p}_i \cdot \vec{E}) = (\vec{p}_i - \vec{p}_f) \cdot \vec{E} = pE \cos \theta_0 - pE \cos(\theta_0 + \pi) = 2pE \cos \theta_0$.

60P
The magnitude of the torque acting on the dipole is given by $\tau = pE \sin \theta$, where p is the magnitude of the dipole moment, E is the magnitude of the electric field, and θ is the angle between the dipole moment and the field. It is a restoring torque: it always tends to rotate the dipole moment toward the direction of the electric field. If θ is positive the torque is negative and vice-versa. Write $\tau = -pE \sin \theta$. If the amplitude of the motion is small we may replace $\sin \theta$ with θ in radians. Thus $\tau = -pE\theta$. Since the magnitude of the torque is proportional to the angle of rotation, the dipole oscillates in simple harmonic motion, just like a torsional pendulum with torsion constant $\kappa = pE$. The angular frequency ω is given by

$$\omega^2 = \frac{\kappa}{I} = \frac{pE}{I},$$

where I is the rotational inertia of the dipole. The frequency of oscillation is

$$f = \frac{\omega}{2\pi} = \frac{1}{2\pi} \sqrt{\frac{pE}{I}} .$$

CHAPTER 25

1E
(a) The mass flux is $wd\rho v = (3.22\,\text{m})(1.04\,\text{m})(1000\,\text{kg/m}^3)(0.207\,\text{m/s}) = 693\,\text{kg/s}$.
(b) Since water flows only through an area wd, the flux through a larger area is still $693\,\text{kg/s}$.
(c) Now the mass flux is $(wd/2)v = (693\,\text{kg/s})/2 = 347\,\text{kg/s}$.
(d) In this case the water flows through an area $(wd/2)$, so the flux is $347\,\text{kg/s}$.
(e) Now the flux is $(wd\cos\theta)v = (693\,\text{kg/s})(\cos 34°) = 575\,\text{kg/s}$.

2E
The vector area $\mathbf{A}$ and the electric field $\mathbf{E}$ are shown on the diagram to the right. The angle θ between them is $180° - 35° = 145°$ so the electric flux through the area is $\Phi = \mathbf{E} \cdot \mathbf{A} = EA\cos\theta = (1800\,\text{N/C})(3.2 \times 10^{-3}\,\text{m})^2 \cos 145° = -1.5 \times 10^{-2}\,\text{N} \cdot \text{m}^2/\text{C}$.

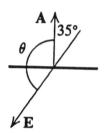

3E
Use $\Phi = \mathbf{E} \cdot \mathbf{A}$ where $\mathbf{A} = A\mathbf{j} = (1.40\,\text{m})^2\mathbf{j}$.
(a) $\Phi = (6.00\,\text{N/C}\mathbf{i}) \cdot (1.40\,\text{m})^2\mathbf{j} = 0$.
(b) $\Phi = (-2.00\,\text{N/C}\mathbf{j}) \cdot (1.40\,\text{m})^2\mathbf{j} = -3.92\,\text{N} \cdot \text{m}^2/\text{C}$.
(c) $\Phi = (-3.00\mathbf{i} + 4.00\mathbf{k})(\,\text{N/C}) \cdot (1.40\,\text{m})^2\mathbf{j} = 0$.
(d) The tototal flux of a uniform field through an enclosed surface is always zero.

4P
Choose a coordinate system originated at the center of the flat base, such that the base is in the xy plane and the rest of the hemisphere is in the $Z > 0$ half space.
(a) $\Phi = \pi R^2(-\mathbf{k}) \cdot E\mathbf{k} = -\pi R^2 E$.
(b) Since the flux through the entire hemisphere is zero, the flux through teh curved surface is $\Phi_c = -\Phi_{\text{base}} = \pi R^2 E$.

5E
Use $\Phi = q_{\text{enclosed}}/\epsilon_0$.
(a) A surface which encloses the charges $2q$ and $-2q$.
(b) A surface which encloses the charges $2q$ and q.
(c) The maximum amount of negative charge you can enclose by any surface which encloses the charge $2q$ is $-q$, so it is impossible to get a flux of $-2q/\epsilon_0$.

6E

Use $\Phi = q_{\text{enclosed}}/\epsilon_0$ and the fact that the amount of positive (negative) charges on the left (right) side of the conductor is $q(-q)$. Thus: $\Phi_1 = q/\epsilon_0$, $\Phi_2 = -q/\epsilon_0$, $\Phi_3 = q/\epsilon_0$, $\Phi_4 = (q - q)/\epsilon_0 = 0$, and $\Phi_5 = (q + q - q)/\epsilon_0 = q/\epsilon_0$.

7E

Use Gauss' law: $\epsilon_0 \Phi = q$, where Φ is the total flux through the cube surface and q is the net charge inside the cube. Thus

$$\Phi = \frac{q}{\epsilon_0} = \frac{1.8 \times 10^{-6}\,\text{C}}{8.85 \times 10^{-12}\,\text{C}^2/\text{N}\cdot\text{m}^2} = 2.0 \times 10^5\,\text{N}\cdot\text{m}^2/\text{C}\,.$$

8E

Let $\Phi_0 = 10^3\,\text{N}\cdot\text{m}^2/\text{C}$. The net flux through the entire surface of the dice is given by

$$\Phi = \sum_{i=1}^{6} \Phi_i = \sum_{i=1}^{6} (-1)^i i \Phi_0 = \Phi_0(-1 + 2 - 3 + 4 - 5 + 6) = 3\Phi_0.$$

Thus the net charge enclosed is

$$q = \epsilon_0 \Phi = 3\epsilon_0 \Phi_0 = 3(8.85 \times 10^{-12}\,\text{C}^2/\text{N}\cdot\text{m}^2)(10^3\,\text{N}\cdot\text{m}^2/\text{C})$$
$$= 2.66 \times 10^{-8}\,\text{C}.$$

9E

Imagine if we place the charge q at the center of a cube of side length d. Then the surface in question is just the bottom side of that cube. Now, by symmetry the flux through all the six surfaces of the cube should be the same, so the flux through the bottom side is

$$\Phi = \frac{1}{6}\Phi_{\text{total}} = \frac{q}{6\epsilon_0}.$$

10E

The flux through the flat surface encircled by the rim is given by $\Phi = \pi a^2 E$. Thus the flux through the netting is $\Phi' = -\Phi = -\pi a^2 E$.

11P

Let A be the area of one face of the cube, E_u be the magnitude of the electric field at the upper face, and E_ℓ be the magnitude of the field at the lower face. Since the field is downward the flux through the upper face is negative and the flux through the lower face is positive. The flux through the other faces is zero, so the total flux through the cube surface is $\Phi = A(E_\ell - E_u)$. The net charge inside the cube is given by Gauss' law:

$$q = \epsilon_0 \Phi = \epsilon_0 A(E_\ell - E_u) = (8.85 \times 10^{-12}\,\mathrm{C^2/N \cdot m^2})(100\,\mathrm{m})^2(100\,\mathrm{N/C} - 60.0\,\mathrm{N/C})$$
$$= 3.54 \times 10^{-6}\,\mathrm{C} = 3.54\,\mu\mathrm{C}$$

12P
Let $A = (1.40\mathrm{m})^2$. Then
(a)

$$\Phi = (3.00y\mathbf{j}) \cdot (-A\mathbf{j})|_{y=0} + (3.00y\mathbf{j}) \cdot (A\mathbf{j})|_{y=1.40\mathrm{m}}$$
$$= (3.00)(1.40\mathrm{N/C})(1.40\mathrm{m})^2 = 8.23\mathrm{N \cdot m^2/C}.$$

(b) The electric field can be rewritten as $\mathbf{E} = 3.00y\mathbf{j} + \mathbf{E}_0$, where $\mathbf{E}_0 = -4.00\mathbf{i} + 6.00\mathbf{j}$ is a constant field which does not contribute to the net flux through the cube. Thus Φ is still $8.23\mathrm{N \cdot m^2/C}$.
(c) The charge is $q = \epsilon_0\Phi = (8.85 \times 10^{-12}\,\mathrm{C^2/N \cdot m^2})(8.23\mathrm{N \cdot m^2/C}) = 7.29 \times 10^{-11}\mathrm{C}$ in each case.

13P
The total flux through any surface that completely surrounds the point charge is q/ϵ_0. If you stack identical cubes side by side and directly on top of each other, you will find that 8 cubes meet at any corner. Thus one-eighth of the field lines emanating from the point charge pass through a cube with a corner at the charge and the total flux through the surface of such a cube is $q/8\epsilon_0$. Now the field lines are radial, so at each of the 3 cube faces that meet at the charge the lines are parallel to the face and the flux through the face is zero. The fluxes through each of the other 3 faces are the same so the flux through each of them is one-third the total. That is, the flux through each of these faces is $(1/3)(q/8\epsilon_0) = q/24\epsilon_0$.

14P
Consider a spherical surface of radius r centered at the location of a point mass m. Then by symmetry the gravitational flux through the surface is

$$\oint \mathbf{g} \cdot d\mathbf{A} = 4\pi r^2 g.$$

Thus

$$\mathbf{g} = \frac{\mathbf{e}_r}{4\pi r^2} \oint \mathbf{g} \cdot d\mathbf{A} = \frac{\mathbf{e}_r}{4\pi r^2}(-4\pi m G)$$
$$= -\frac{Gm}{r^2}\mathbf{e}_r,$$

where $\mathbf{e}_r$ is the umit vector along $\mathbf{r}$. This is the Newton's law of gravitation. Here the minus sign indicates that the gravitational force is attractive.

15E

The surface charge density is $\sigma = E\epsilon_o = (2.3 \times 10^5 \mathrm{N/C})(8.85 \times 10^{-12}\, \mathrm{C^2/N \cdot m^2}) = 2.0 \times 10^{-6}\mathrm{C/m^2}$.

16E

(a) The charge on the surface of the sphere is the product of the surface charge density σ and the surface area of the sphere ($4\pi r^2$, where r is the radius). Thus

$$q = 4\pi r^2 \sigma = 4\pi \left(\frac{1.2\,\mathrm{m}}{2}\right)^2 (8.1 \times 10^{-6}\, \mathrm{C/m^2}) = 3.66 \times 10^{-5}\, \mathrm{C}\,.$$

(b) Choose a Gaussian surface in the form a sphere, concentric with the conducting sphere and with a slightly larger radius. The flux is given by Gauss' law:

$$\Phi = \frac{q}{\epsilon_0} = \frac{3.66 \times 10^{-5}\, \mathrm{C}}{8.85 \times 10^{-12}\, \mathrm{C^2/N \cdot m^2}} = 4.1 \times 10^6\, \mathrm{N \cdot m^2/C}\,.$$

17E

(a)

$$\sigma = \frac{q}{\pi D^2} = \frac{2.4 \times 10^{-6}\mathrm{C}}{\pi(1.3\mathrm{m})^2} = 4.5 \times 10^{-7}\mathrm{C/m^2}.$$

(b)

$$E = \frac{\sigma}{\epsilon_o} = \frac{4.5 \times 10^{-7}\mathrm{C/m^2}}{8.85 \times 10^{-12}\, \mathrm{C^2/N \cdot m^2}} = 5.1 \times 10^4\mathrm{N/C}.$$

18E

(a) Draw a Gaussian surface A which is just outside the inner surface of the spherical shell. Then $\mathbf{E}$ is zero everywhere on surface A. Thus

$$\oint_A \mathbf{E} \cdot d\mathbf{A} = \frac{(Q' + Q)}{\epsilon_0} = 0,$$

where Q' is the charge on the inner surface of the shell. This gives $Q' = -Q$.
(b) Since $\mathbf{E}$ remains zero on surface A the result is unchanged.
(c) Now

$$\oint_A \mathbf{E} \cdot d\mathbf{A} = \frac{(Q' + q + Q)}{\epsilon_0} = 0,$$

so $Q' = -(Q+q)$.

(d) Yes, since **E** remains zero on surface A regardless of where you place the sphere inside the shell.

19P

(a) Consider a Gaussian surface that is completely within the conductor and surrounds the cavity. Since the electric field is zero everywhere on the surface, the net charge it encloses is zero. The net charge is the sum of the charge q in the cavity and the charge q_w on the cavity wall, so $q + q_w = 0$ and $q_w = -q = -3.0 \times 10^{-6}$ C.

(b) The net charge Q of the conductor is the sum of the charge on the cavity wall and the charge q_s on the outer surface of the conductor, so $Q = q_w + q_s$ and $q_s = Q - q_w = (10 \times 10^{-6}$ C$) - (-3.0 \times 10^{-6}$ C$) = +1.3 \times 10^{-5}$ C.

20P

Draw a Gaussian surface entirely inside the conductor, enclosing its cavity wall. Then **E** $= 0$ everywhere on the surface. Let the net charge on the cavity wall be q, then

$$\oint_A \mathbf{E} \cdot d\mathbf{A} = \frac{q}{\epsilon_0} = 0,$$

i.e. $q = 0$.

21E

The magnitude of the electric field produced by a uniformly charged infinite line is $E = \lambda/2\pi\epsilon_0 r$, where λ is the linear charge density and r is the distance from the line to the point where the field is measured. See Eq. 24–14. Thus

$$\lambda = 2\pi\epsilon_0 E r = 2\pi(8.85 \times 10^{12}\,\text{C}^2/\text{N} \cdot \text{m}^2)(4.5 \times 10^4\,\text{N/C})(2.0\,\text{m}) = 5.0 \times 10^{-6}\,\text{C/m}.$$

22E

(a) The total charge on the drum of diameter D is

$$q = \sigma(\pi D^2) = \pi\epsilon_0 E D^2$$
$$= \pi(8.85 \times 10^{-12}\,\text{C}^2/\text{N} \cdot \text{m}^2)(2.3 \times 10^5\text{N/C})(0.12\text{m})^2 = 9.2 \times 10^{-8}\text{C}.$$

(b) The new charge is
$q' = q(D'/D)^2 = (9.2 \times 10^{-8}\text{C})(8.0\text{cm}/12\text{cm})^2 = 4.1 \times 10^{-8}\text{C}.$

23P

Draw a cylindrical Gaussian A surface of radius r and unit length concentric with the metal tube. Then by symmetry

$$\oint_A \mathbf{E} \cdot d\mathbf{A} = 2\pi r E = \frac{q_{enclosed}}{\epsilon_0}.$$

(a) For $r > R$, $q_{enclosed} = \lambda$, so $E(r) = \lambda/2\pi r \epsilon_0$.
(b) For $r < R$, $q_{enclosed} = 0$, so $E = 0$.
The plot of E vs r is shown below. Here

$$E_0 = \frac{\lambda}{2\pi r \epsilon_0} = \frac{(2.0 \times 10^{-8} \mathrm{C/m})}{2\pi (0.030 \mathrm{m})(8.85 \times 10^{-12}\, \mathrm{C^2/N \cdot m^2})} = 1.2 \times 10^4 \mathrm{N/C}.$$

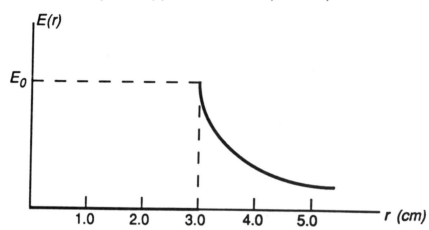

24P

Consider a cylindrical Gaussian surface A of radius r and unit length, concentric with both the cylinders. Then from

$$\oint_A \mathbf{E} \cdot d\mathbf{A} = 2\pi r E = \frac{q_{enclosed}}{\epsilon_0}.$$

we have $E = q_{enclosed}/2\pi \epsilon_0 r$.
(a) For $r < a$ $q_{enclosed} = 0$, so $E = 0$
(b) For $a < r < b$ $q_{enclosed} = -\lambda$, so $|E| = \lambda/2\pi \epsilon_0 r$.

25P

The net electric field within the cyinder is always given by $E = \lambda/2\pi \epsilon_0 r$, where $\lambda = 3.6 \mathrm{nC/m}$ and $0 < r < R = 1.5 \mathrm{cm}$ is the distance measured from the wire. It will not vanish regardless of σ. The $\mathbf{E}$ field outside the cylinder can indeed be zero, provided that $2\pi R\sigma = \lambda$, or

$$\sigma = \frac{\lambda}{2\pi R} = \frac{3.6 \times 10^{-9} \mathrm{C/m}}{(2\pi)(1.5 \times 10^{-2} \mathrm{m})} = 3.8 \times 10^{-8} \mathrm{C/m^2}.$$

26P The electric field is radially outward from the central wire. You want to find its magnitude in the region between the wire and the cylinder as a function of the distance r

from the wire. Use a Gaussian surface in the form of a cylinder with radius r and length ℓ, concentric with the wire. The radius is greater than the radius of the wire and less than in the radius of the inner cylinder wall. Only the charge on the wire is enclosed by the Gaussian surface; denote it by q. The area of the rounded surface of the Gaussian cylinder is $2\pi r\ell$ and the flux through it is $\Phi = 2\pi r\ell E$. If we neglect fringing there is no flux through the ends of the cylinder, so Φ is the total flux. Gauss' law yields $q = 2\pi\epsilon_0 r\ell E$. Since the magnitude of the field at the cylinder wall is known take the Gaussian surface to coincide with the wall. Then r is the radius of the wall and

$$
\begin{aligned}
q &= 2\pi(8.85 \times 10^{-12}\,\mathrm{C^2/N \cdot m^2})(0.014\,\mathrm{m})(0.16\,\mathrm{m})(2.9 \times 10^4\,\mathrm{N/C}) \\
&= 3.6 \times 10^{-9}\,\mathrm{C}.
\end{aligned}
$$

27P
Use $E(r) = \lambda_{\text{enclosed}}/2\pi\epsilon_0 r$ (see Problem 24).
(a) $E(r) = \dfrac{(q - 2q)}{2\pi\epsilon_0 Lr} = -\dfrac{q}{2\pi\epsilon_0 Lr}$.
(b) The inner surface of the shell is charged to $-q$ while the out shell is charged to $-2q - (-q) = -q$.
(c) Now $\lambda_{\text{enclosed}} = q/L$ so

$$
E(r) = \frac{q}{2\pi\epsilon_0 Lr}.
$$

$\mathbf{E}(r)$ points radially outward by symmetry.

28P
Denote the inner (outer) cylinders with subscripts i and o, respectimvely. Then
(a) Since $r_i < r = 4.0\text{cm} < r_o$,

$$
E(r) = \frac{\lambda_i}{2\pi\epsilon_0 r} = \frac{5.0 \times 10^{-6}\,\mathrm{C/m}}{2\pi(8.85 \times 10^{-12}\,\mathrm{C^2/N \cdot m^2})(4.0 \times 10^{-2}\mathrm{m})} = 2.3 \times 10^6\,\mathrm{N/C}.
$$

$\mathbf{E}(r)$ points radially outward.
(b) Since $r > r_o$, we have

$$
E(r) = \frac{\lambda_i + \lambda_o}{2\pi\epsilon_0 r} = \frac{5.0 \times 10^{-6}\,\mathrm{C/m} - 7.0 \times 10^{-6}\,\mathrm{C/m}}{2\pi(8.85 \times 10^{-12}\,\mathrm{C^2/N \cdot m^2})(8.0 \times 10^{-2}\mathrm{m})} = -4.5 \times 10^5\,\mathrm{N/C},
$$

where the minus sign indicates that $\mathbf{E}(r)$ points radially inward.

29P

Use $mv^2/r = F_c = |e|E$. Thus

$$K = \frac{1}{2}mv^2 = \frac{|e|Er}{2} = \frac{|e|\lambda r}{4\pi\epsilon_0 r}$$

$$= \frac{|e|(30 \times 10^{-9}\,\text{C/m})}{4\pi(8.85 \times 10^{-12}\,\text{C}^2/\text{N}\cdot\text{m}^2)} = 270\,|e|\,V = 270\text{eV}.$$

30P

(a) The diagram to the right shows a cross section of the charged cylinder (solid circle). Consider a Gaussian surface in the form of a cylinder with radius r and length ℓ, concentric with the cylinder of charge The cross section is shown as a dotted circle. Use Gauss' law to find an expression for the magnitude of the electric field at the Gaussian surface.

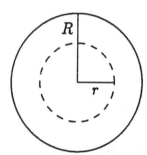

The charge within the Gaussian cylinder is $q = \rho V = \pi r^2 \ell \rho$, where $V\,(= \pi r^2 \ell)$ is the volume of the cylinder.

If ρ is positive the electric field lines are radially outward and are therefore normal to the rounded portion of the Gaussian cylinder and are distributed uniformly over it. None pass through the ends of the cylinder. Thus the total flux through the Gaussian cylinder is $\Phi = EA = 2\pi r\ell E$, where $A\,(= 2\pi r\ell)$ is the area of rounded portion of the cylinder.

Gauss' law ($\epsilon_0\Phi = q$) yields $2\pi\epsilon_0 r\ell E = \pi r^2\ell\rho$, so

$$E = \frac{\rho r}{2\epsilon_0}.$$

(b) Take the Gaussian surface to be a cylinder with length ℓ and radius r (greater than R). The flux is again $\Phi = 2\pi r\ell E$. The charge enclosed is the total charge in a section of the charged cylinder with length ℓ. That is, $q = \pi R^2\ell\rho$. Gauss' law yields $2\pi\epsilon_0 r\ell E = \pi R^2\ell\rho$, so

$$E = \frac{R^2\rho}{2\epsilon_0 r}.$$

31E

According to Eq. 25-15 the electric field due to either sheet of charge with surface charge density σ is perpendicular to the plane of the sheet and has magnitude $E = \sigma/2\epsilon_0$. Thus by the superpostion principle:
(a) $E = \sigma/\epsilon_0$, pointing to the left,
(b) $E = 0$,
(c) $E = \sigma/\epsilon_0$, pointing to the right.

32E

(a) To calculate the electric field at a point very close to the center of a large, uniformly charged, conducting plate, we may replace the finite plate with an infinite plate with the same area charge density and take the magnitude of the field to be $E = \sigma/\epsilon_0$, where σ is the area charge density for the surface just under the point. The charge is distributed uniformly over both sides of the original plate, with half being on the side near the field point. Thus

$$\sigma = \frac{q}{2A} = \frac{6.0 \times 10^{-6}\,\text{C}}{2(0.080\,\text{m})^2} = 4.69 \times 10^{-4}\,\text{C/m}^2\,.$$

The magnitude of the field is

$$E = \frac{4.69 \times 10^{-4}\,\text{C/m}^2}{8.85 \times 10^{-12}\,\text{C}^2/\text{N}\cdot\text{m}^2} = 5.3 \times 10^7\,\text{N/C}\,.$$

The field is normal to the plate and since the charge on the plate is positive it points away from the plate.

(b) At a point far away from the plate the electric field is nearly that of a point particle with charge equal to the total charge on the plate. The magnitude of the field is $E = q/4\pi\epsilon_0 r^2$, where r is the distance from the plate. Thus

$$E = \frac{(8.99 \times 10^9\,\text{N}\cdot\text{m}^2/\text{C}^2)(6.0 \times 1o^{-6}\,\text{C})}{(30\,\text{m})^2} = 60\,\text{N/C}\,.$$

33E

The charge distribution in this problem is equivalent to that of an infinite sheet of charge with charge density σ plus a small circular pad of radius R located at the middle of the sheet with charge density $-\sigma$. Denote the electric fields produced by the sheet and the pad with subscripts 1 and 2, respectively. The net electric field $\mathbf{E}$ is then

$$\mathbf{E} = \mathbf{E}_1 + \mathbf{E}_2 = \frac{\sigma}{2\epsilon_0}\mathbf{k} + \frac{(-\sigma)}{2\epsilon_0}\left(1 - \frac{Z}{\sqrt{Z^2 + R^2}}\right)\mathbf{k}$$

$$= \frac{\sigma Z}{2\epsilon_0\sqrt{Z^2 + R^2}}\mathbf{k},$$

where Eq. 24-27 was used for $\mathbf{E}_2$.

34P

The forces acting on the ball are shown in the diagram next page. The gravitational force has magnitude mg, where m is the mass of the ball; the electrical force has magnitude qE, where q is the charge on the ball and E is the electric field at the position of the ball; and the tension in the thread is denoted by T. The electric field produced by the plate is normal to the plate and points to the right. Since the ball is positively charged the electric force on it also points to the right. The tension in the thread makes the angle θ (= 30°) with the vertical.

Since the ball is in equilibrium the net force on it vanishes. The sum of the horizontal components yields $qE - T\sin\theta = 0$ and the sum of the vertical components yields $T\cos\theta - mg = 0$. The expression $T = qE/\sin\theta$, from the first equation, is substituted into the second to obtain $qE = mg\tan\theta$.

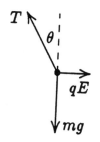

The electric field produced by a large uniform plane of charge is given by $E = \sigma/2\epsilon_0$, where σ is the surface charge density. Thus

$$\frac{q\sigma}{2\epsilon_0} = mg\tan\theta$$

and

$$\sigma = \frac{2\epsilon_0 mg\tan\theta}{q}$$
$$= \frac{2(8.85 \times 10^{-12}\,\text{C}^2/\text{N}\cdot\text{m}^2)(1.0 \times 10^{-6}\,\text{kg})(9.8\,\text{m/s}^2)\tan 30°}{2.0 \times 10^{-8}\,\text{C}}$$
$$= 5.0 \times 10^{-9}\,\text{C/m}^2.$$

35P

The charge on the metal plate, which is negative, exerts a force of repulsion on the electron and stops it. First find an expression for the acceleration of the electron, then use kinematics to find the stopping distance. Take the initial direction of motion of the electron to be positive. Then the electric field is given by $E = \sigma/\epsilon_0$, where σ is the surface charge density on the plate. The force on the electron is $F = -eE = -e\sigma/\epsilon_0$ and the acceleration is

$$a = \frac{F}{m} = -\frac{e\sigma}{\epsilon_0 m},$$

where m is the mass of the electron.

The force is constant, so we use constant acceleration kinematics. If v_0 is the initial velocity of the electron, v is the final velocity, and x is the distance traveled between the initial and final positions, then $v^2 - v_0^2 = 2ax$. Set $v = 0$ and replace a with $-e\sigma/\epsilon_0 m$, then solve for x. You should get

$$x = -\frac{v_0^2}{2a} = \frac{\epsilon_0 m v_0^2}{2e\sigma}.$$

Now $\frac{1}{2}mv_0^2$ is the initial kinetic energy K_0, so

$$x = \frac{\epsilon_0 K_0}{e\sigma}.$$

You must convert the given value of K_0 to joules. Since $1.00\,\text{eV} = 1.60 \times 10^{-19}\,\text{J}$, $100\,\text{eV} = 1.60 \times 10^{-17}\,\text{J}$. Thus

$$x = \frac{(8.85 \times 10^{-12}\,\text{C}^2/\text{N}\cdot\text{m}^2)(1.60 \times 10^{-17}\,\text{J})}{(1.60 \times 10^{-19}\,\text{C})(2.0 \times 10^{-6}\,\text{C/m}^2)} = 4.4 \times 10^{-4}\,\text{m}.$$

672

36P

Let **i** be a unit vector pointing to the left. Then

(a) To the left of the plates: $\mathbf{E} = (\sigma/2\epsilon_0)\mathbf{i}$(from the right plate)$+(-\sigma/2\epsilon_0)\mathbf{i}$(from the left one)$= 0$.

(b) To the right of the plates: $\mathbf{E} = (\sigma/2\epsilon_0)(-\mathbf{i})$(from the right plate)$+(-\sigma/2\epsilon_0)(-\mathbf{i})$(from the left one)$= 0$.

(c) Between the plates: $\mathbf{E} = (\sigma/2\epsilon_0)\mathbf{i}$(from the right plate)$+(-\sigma/2\epsilon_0)(-\mathbf{i})$(from the left one)$= (\sigma/\epsilon_0)\mathbf{i}$.

37P

Use the result of part (c) of the previous problem to obtain σ: $E = \sigma/\epsilon_0$, or $\sigma = \pm\epsilon_0 E = \pm(8.85 \times 10^{-12}\,\mathrm{C}^2/\mathrm{N} \cdot \mathrm{m}^2)(55\mathrm{N/C}) = \pm4.9 \times 10^{-10}\mathrm{C/m}^2$.

38P

(a) Use $mg = eE = e\sigma/\epsilon_0$ to obtain σ:

$$\sigma = \frac{mg\epsilon_0}{e} = \frac{(9.11 \times 10^{-31}\mathrm{kg})(9.8\,\mathrm{m/s}^2)(8.85 \times 10^{-12}\,\mathrm{C}^2/\mathrm{N} \cdot \mathrm{m}^2)}{1.60 \times 10^{-19}\mathrm{C}} = 4.9 \times 10^{-22}\mathrm{C/m}^2.$$

(b) Downward (since the electric force exerted on the electron must be upward.)

39P

(a) Use a Gaussian surface in the form of a box with rectangular sides. The cross section is shown with dotted lines in the diagram to the right. It is centered at the central plane of the slab so the left and right faces are each a distance x from the central plane. Take the thickness of the rectangular solid to be a, the same as its length, so the left and right faces are squares.

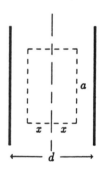

The electric field is normal to the left and right faces and is uniform over them. If ρ is positive it points outward at both faces: toward the left at the left face and toward the right at the right face. Furthermore, the magnitude is the same at both faces. The electric flux through each of these faces is Ea^2. The field is parallel to the other faces of the Gaussian surface and the flux through them is zero. The total flux through the Gaussian surface is $\Phi = 2Ea^2$.

The volume enclosed by the Gaussian surface is $2a^2x$ and the charge contained within it is $q = 2a^2x\rho$. Gauss' law yields $2\epsilon_0 Ea^2 = 2a^2x\rho$. Solve for E:

$$E = \frac{\rho x}{\epsilon_0}.$$

673

(b) Take a Gaussian surface of the same shape and orientation, but with $x > d/2$, so the left and right faces are outside the slab. The total flux through the surface is again $\Phi = 2Ea^2$ but the charge enclosed is now $q = a^2 d\rho$. Gauss's law yields $2\epsilon_0 Ea^2 = a^2 d\rho$, so

$$E = \frac{\rho d}{2\epsilon_0}.$$

40E

Charge is distributed uniformly over the surface of the sphere and the electric field it produces at points outside the sphere is like the field of a point particle with charge equal to the net charge on the sphere. That is, the magnitude of the field is given by $E = q/4\pi\epsilon_0 r^2$, where q is the magnitude of the charge on the sphere and r is the distance from the center of the sphere to the point where the field is measured. Thus

$$q = 4\pi\epsilon_0 r^2 E = \frac{(0.15\,\text{m})^2(3.0 \times 10^3\,\text{N/C})}{8.99 \times 10^9\,\text{N}\cdot\text{m}^2/\text{C}^2} = 7.5 \times 10^{-9}\,\text{C}.$$

The field points inward, toward the sphere center, so the charge is negative: -7.5×10^{-9} C.

41E

(a) The flux is still $-750\,\text{N}\cdot\text{m}^2/\text{C}$, since it depends only on the amount of charge enclosed.
(b) Use $\Phi = 4\pi r^2(d\Phi/dA) = q/\epsilon_0$ to obtain q:

$$q = 4\pi\epsilon_0 r^2\left(\frac{d\Phi}{dA}\right) = 4\pi(8.85 \times 10^{-12}\,\text{C}^2/\text{N}\cdot\text{m}^2)(0.100\text{m})^2(-750\text{N}\cdot\text{m}^2/\text{C})$$

$$= -8.34 \times 10^{-10}\text{C}.$$

42E

(a) For $r < R$, $E = 0$ (see Eq. 25-18).
(b) For $r \gtrsim R$,

$$E = \frac{1}{4\pi\epsilon_0}\frac{q}{r^2} = \frac{q}{4\pi\epsilon_0 R^2} = \frac{(8.99 \times 10^9\text{N}\cdot\text{m}^2/\text{C}^2)(2.0 \times 10^{-7}\text{C})}{(0.25\text{m})^2}$$

$$= 2.9 \times 10^4\text{N/C}.$$

(c) For $r > R$,

$$E = \frac{1}{4\pi\epsilon_0}\frac{q}{r^2} = (2.9 \times 10^4\text{N/C})\left(\frac{0.25\text{m}}{3.0\text{m}}\right)^2 = 200\text{N/C}.$$

43E

(a) Since $r_1 = 10.0$cm $< r = 12.0$cm $< r_2 = 15.0$cm,

$$E(r) = \frac{1}{4\pi\epsilon_0}\frac{q_1}{r^2} = \frac{(8.99 \times 10^9\,\mathrm{N \cdot m^2/C^2})(4.00 \times 10^{-8}\,\mathrm{C})}{(0.120\mathrm{m})^2}$$
$$= 2.50 \times 10^4\,\mathrm{N/C}.$$

(b) Since $r_1 < r_2 < r = 20.0$cm,

$$E(r) = \frac{1}{4\pi\epsilon_0}\frac{q_1 + q_2}{r^2} = \frac{(8.99 \times 10^9\,\mathrm{N \cdot m^2/C^2})(4.00 + 2.00)(10^{-8}\,\mathrm{C})}{(0.200\mathrm{m})^2}$$
$$= 1.35 \times 10^4\,\mathrm{N/C}.$$

44E

Use Eqs. 25-17, 25-18 and the superposition principle.
(a) $E = 0$.
(b) $E = (1/4\pi\epsilon_0)(q_a/r^2)$.
(c) $E = (1/4\pi\epsilon_0)(q_a + q_b)/r^2$.
(d) Comparing the results of (b) and (c) above, you can see that if E remains the same on the outer shell then $q_b = 0$, otherwise $q_b \neq 0$.

45E

Use Gauss' law to find an expression for the magnitude of the electric field a distance r from the center of the atom. The field is radially outward and is uniform over any sphere centered at the atom's center. Take the Gaussian surface to be a sphere of radius r with its center at the center of the atom. If E is the magnitude of the field then the total flux through the Gaussian sphere is $\Phi = 4\pi r^2 E$. The charge enclosed by the Gaussian surface is the positive charge at the center of the atom and that portion of the negative charge within the surface. Since the negative charge is uniformly distributed throughout a sphere of radius R we can compute the charge inside the Gaussian sphere using a ratio of volumes. That is, the negative charge inside is $-Zer^3/R^3$. Thus the total charge enclosed is $Ze - Zer^3/R^3$. Gauss' law yields

$$4\pi\epsilon_0 r^2 E = Ze\left(1 - \frac{r^3}{R^3}\right).$$

Solve for E:

$$E = \frac{Ze}{4\pi\epsilon_0}\left(\frac{1}{r^2} - \frac{r}{R^3}\right).$$

46E

Since $\sigma = q/4\pi r^2$,

$$E = \frac{\sigma}{\epsilon_0} = \frac{1}{\epsilon_0}\left(\frac{q}{4\pi r^2}\right) = \frac{1}{4\pi\epsilon_0}\frac{q}{r^2}.$$

47P

Put the origin of a spherical coordinate at the location of the point charge. Draw a spherical Gaussian surface A of radius r centered at the origin and note the spherical symmetry of the charge distribution:

$$\Phi = \oint_A \mathbf{E} \cdot d\mathbf{A} = 4\pi r^2 E(r) = \frac{q_{encl}}{\epsilon_0},$$

or

$$E(r) = \frac{1}{4\pi\epsilon_0}\frac{q_{encl}}{r^2}.$$

(a) Now $q_{encl} = q$ so $E(r) = q/4\pi\epsilon_0 r^2$.
(b) Now q_{encl} is still q so $E(r) = q/4\pi\epsilon_0 r^2$.
(c) No.
(d) Yes. In fact the inner surface of the shell is charged to $-q$ while the outer shell is charged to q.
(e) Yes, since the electroc field due to the first point charge plus the shell is not zer0.
(f) No, because of the electrostatic shielding of the shell.
(g) No. In fact $\mathbf{f}_1 = \mathbf{f}_{shell\ to\ 1} + \mathbf{f}_{2\ to\ 1}$ and $\mathbf{f}_2 = \mathbf{f}_{shell\ to\ 2} + \mathbf{f}_{1\ to\ 2} = \mathbf{f}_{shell\ to\ 2} - \mathbf{f}_{2\ to\ 1}$. Since $\mathbf{f}_{shell\ to\ 1} \neq -\mathbf{f}_{shell\ to\ 2}$, we have $\mathbf{f}_1 \neq -\mathbf{f}_2$.

48P

At all points where there is an electric field it is radially outward. For each part of the problem use a Gaussian surface in the form of a sphere that is concentric with the sphere of charge and passes through the point where the electric field is to be found. The field is uniform on the surface, so

$$\oint \mathbf{E} \cdot d\mathbf{A} = 4\pi r^2 E,$$

where r is the radius of the Gaussian surface.

(a) Here r is less than a and the charge enclosed by the Gaussian surface is $q(r/a)^3$. Gauss' law yields

$$4\pi r^2 E = \left(\frac{q}{\epsilon_0}\right)\left(\frac{r}{a}\right)^3,$$

so

$$E = \frac{qr}{4\pi\epsilon_0 a^3}.$$

676

(b) Here r is greater than a but less than b. The charge enclosed by the Gaussian surface is q, so Gauss' law becomes

$$4\pi r^2 E = \frac{q}{\epsilon_0}$$

and

$$E = \frac{q}{4\pi\epsilon_0 r^2}\,.$$

(c) The shell is conducting so the electric field inside it is zero.

(d) For $r > c$ the charge enclosed by the Gaussian surface is zero (charge q is inside the shell cavity and charge $-q$ is on the shell). Gauss' law yields

$$4\pi r^2 E = 0\,,$$

so $E = 0$.

(e) Consider a Gaussian surface that lies completely within the conducting shell. Since the electric field is everywhere zero on the surface $\oint \mathbf{E} \cdot d\mathbf{A} = 0$ and, according to Gauss' law, the net charge enclosed by the surface is zero. If Q_i is the charge on the inner surface of the shell, then $q + Q_i = 0$ and $Q_i = -q$. Let Q_0 be the charge on the outer surface of the shell. Since the net charge on the shell is $-q$, $Q_i + Q_0 = -q$. This means $Q_0 = -q - Q_i = -q - (-q) = 0$.

49P
For $r < a$, $E = 0$. For $a < r < b$,

$$E = \frac{1}{4\pi\epsilon_0}\frac{q_{encl}}{r^2} = \frac{\rho}{4\pi\epsilon_0 r^2}\cdot\frac{4\pi}{3}(r^3 - a^3)$$

For $r > b$,

$$E = \frac{1}{4\pi\epsilon_0}\frac{q_{encl}}{r^2} = \frac{\rho}{4\pi\epsilon_0 r^3}\cdot\frac{4\pi}{3}(b^3 - a^3)$$

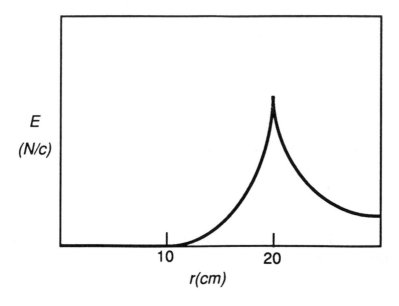

677

50P

(a)

$$E = \frac{q}{4\pi\epsilon_0 r_1^2} = \frac{(8.99 \times 10^9 \text{N} \cdot \text{m}^2/\text{C}^2)(1.0 \times 10^{-7}\text{C})}{(0.015\text{m})^2} = 4.0 \times 10^6 \text{N/C}.$$

E points from q_1 to P.

(b) **E** $= 0$, since P_2 is inside the metal.

51P

The proton is in uniform circular motion, with the electrical force of the charge on the sphere providing the centripetal force. According to Newton's second law $F = mv^2/r$, where F is the magnitude of the force, v is the speed of the proton, and r is the radius of its orbit, essentially the same as the radius of the sphere.

The magnitude of the force on the proton is $F = eq/4\pi\epsilon_0 r^2$, where q is the magnitude of the charge on the sphere. Thus

$$\frac{1}{4\pi\epsilon_0}\frac{eq}{r^2} = \frac{mv^2}{r},$$

so

$$q = \frac{4\pi\epsilon_0 mv^2 r}{e} = \frac{(1.67 \times 10^{-27}\,\text{kg})(3.00 \times 10^5\,\text{m/s})^2(0.0100\,\text{m})}{(8.99 \times 10^9\,\text{N} \cdot \text{m}^2/\text{C}^2)(1.60 \times 10^{-19}\,\text{C})}$$

$$= 1.04 \times 10^{-9}\,\text{C}.$$

The force must be inward, toward the center of the sphere, and since the proton is positively charged the electric field must also be inward. The charge on the sphere is negative: $q = -1.04 \times 10^{-9}$ C.

52P

(a)

$$Q = \int \rho dV = 4\pi \int_0^R \rho(r)r^2 dr = 4\pi \int_0^R \left(\frac{\rho_s r}{R}\right)r^2 dr$$

$$= \pi\rho_s R^3.$$

(b) Since the distribution of charge is spherically symmetrical so must be the electric field. Thus

$$E(r) = \frac{1}{4\pi\epsilon_0}\frac{q_{encl}}{r^2} = \frac{1}{4\pi\epsilon_0 r^2}\int_0^r \frac{4\pi\rho_s r^3}{R}dr$$

$$= \frac{\rho_s r^2}{4\epsilon_0 R} = \frac{(\pi\rho_s R^3)r^2}{4\pi\epsilon_0 R^4} = \frac{1}{4\pi\epsilon_0}\frac{Q}{R^4}r^2.$$

53P

You wish to find an expression for the electric field inside the shell in terms of A and the distance from the center of the shell, then select A so the field does not depend on the distance.

Use a Gaussian surface in the form of a sphere with radius r_g, concentric with the spherical shell and within it ($a < r_g < b$). Gauss' law will be used to find the magnitude of the electric field a distance r_g from the shell center.

The charge that is both in the shell and within the Gaussian sphere is given by the integral $q_s = \int \rho \, dV$ over the portion of the shell within the Gaussian surface. Since the charge distribution has spherical symmetry, we may take dV to be the volume of a spherical shell with radius r and infinitesimal thickness dr: $dV = 4\pi r^2 \, dr$. Thus

$$q_s = 4\pi \int_a^{r_g} \rho r^2 \, dr = 4\pi \int_a^{r_g} \frac{A}{r} r^2 \, dr = 4\pi A \int_a^{r_g} r \, dr = 2\pi A(r_g^2 - a^2).$$

The total charge inside the Gaussian surface is $q + q_s = q + 2\pi A(r_g^2 - a^2)$.

The electric field is radial, so the flux through the Gaussian surface is $\Phi = 4\pi r_g^2 E$, where E is the magnitude of the field. Gauss' law yields

$$4\pi\epsilon_0 E r_g^2 = q + 2\pi A(r_g^2 - a^2).$$

Solve for E:

$$E = \frac{1}{4\pi\epsilon_0}\left[\frac{q}{r_g^2} + 2\pi A - \frac{2\pi A a^2}{r_g^2}\right].$$

For the field to be uniform the first and last terms in the brackets must cancel. They do if $q - 2\pi A a^2 = 0$ or $A = q/2\pi a^2$.

54P*
(a) From Gauss's law

$$\mathbf{E}(\mathbf{r}) = \frac{1}{4\pi\epsilon_0}\frac{q_{encl}\mathbf{r}}{r^3}$$

$$= \frac{1}{4\pi\epsilon_0}\frac{(4\pi\rho r^3/3)\mathbf{r}}{r^3}$$

$$= \frac{\rho\mathbf{r}}{3\epsilon_0}.$$

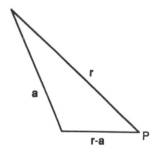

(b) The charge distribution in this case is equivalent to that of a whole sphere of charge density ρ plus a smaller sphere of charge density $-\rho$ which fills the void. By superposition

$$\mathbf{E}(\mathbf{r}) = \frac{\rho\mathbf{r}}{3\epsilon_0} + \frac{(-\rho)(\mathbf{r} - \mathbf{a})}{3\epsilon_0}$$

$$= \frac{\rho\mathbf{a}}{3\epsilon_0}.$$

55P
Suppose there is no charge in the immediate vicinity of q but q is in equilibrium under the combined forces of charges at other places. The net electric field at the position P of q is zero but q experiences an electric force if it is moved away from P. You want to show that it is not possible to set up an electric field that pushes q back toward P for every direction of its displacement.

Assume q is at P and surround it with an extremely small Gaussian surface in the form of a sphere centered at P. Now displace q from P to some point on the Gaussian sphere. If an electric force pushes q back there must be an inward pointing electric field at that point on the surface. If an electric field pushes q toward P no matter where it is placed on the surface, then there is an inward pointing electric field at every point on the surface. The net flux through the surface is not zero and, according to Gauss' law there must be charge within the Gaussian surface. This is a contradiction. We conclude that the field acting on a charge cannot push the charge back toward P for every possible displacement and that therefore the charge cannot be in stable equilibrium.

If there are places on the Gaussian surface where the electric field points inward and pushes q back toward its original position, then there must be other places where the field points outward and pushes q away from its original position.

56P

Use $E(r) = \dfrac{q_{encl}}{4\pi\epsilon_0 r^2} = \dfrac{1}{4\pi\epsilon_0 r^2} \int_0^r \rho(r)4\pi r^2 dr$ to solve for $\rho(r)$:

$$\rho(r) = \frac{\epsilon_0}{r^2}\frac{d}{dr}[r^2 E(r)] = \frac{\epsilon_0}{r^2}\frac{d}{dr}(Kr^6) = 6K\epsilon_0 r^3.$$

57

(a) From

$$-e = \int_0^\infty \rho(r)4\pi r^2 dr = \int_0^\infty Ae^{-2r/a_0}4\pi r^2 dr = \pi a_0^3 A,$$

we get $A = -e/\pi a_0^3$.

(b)

$$E = \frac{q_{encl}}{4\pi\epsilon_0 a_0^2} = \frac{1}{4\pi\epsilon_0 a_0^2}\left[e + \int_0^{a_0} \rho(r)4\pi r^2 dr\right]$$

$$= \frac{e}{4\pi\epsilon_0 a_0^2}\left[1 - \frac{4}{a_0^3}\int_0^{a_0} e^{-2r/a_0}r^2 dr\right]$$

$$= \frac{5e\cdot\exp(-2)}{4\pi\epsilon_0 a_0^2}.$$

E points radially outward.

58

(a) Use the result from part (a) in problem 54. The force experienced by the electron would be

$$\mathbf{F} = -e\mathbf{E} = -e\left(\frac{\rho\mathbf{r}}{3\epsilon_0}\right) = -\left(\frac{e\mathbf{r}}{3\epsilon_0}\right)\left(\frac{q}{4\pi a_0^3/3}\right) = -\frac{e^2\mathbf{r}}{4\pi\epsilon_0 a_0^3}.$$

(b) Since $F(r) = -e^2 r/4\pi\epsilon_0 a_0^3 = -K_{\text{eff}} r$,

$$\omega = \sqrt{\frac{k_{\text{eff}}}{m}} = \sqrt{\frac{e^2}{4\pi\epsilon_0 m a_0^3}}.$$

59

$$\Phi = \oint \mathbf{E} \cdot d\mathbf{A} = \int \frac{\sigma}{\epsilon_0} dA = \int_0^\pi \frac{3\epsilon_0 E \cos\theta}{\epsilon_0} \pi a^2 \sin\theta d\theta$$
$$= 3\pi a^2 \int_0^\pi \sin\theta \cos\theta d\theta = 0.$$

60
(a)

$$E = \frac{\sigma}{\epsilon_0} = \frac{-qa}{2\pi\epsilon_0 r^3}.$$

(b) Convince yourself that Gauss's law should predict that the total charge induced is $-q$. Alternatively you may also perform the following integration:

$$q_{\text{induced}} = \int_{\text{plane}} \sigma dA = \int_0^\infty \frac{-qa}{2\pi(x^2+a^2)^{3/2}} 2\pi x dx = -q.$$

61
(a)

$$|F| = \frac{q}{4\pi\epsilon_0} \int_{\text{plane}} \frac{\sigma dA}{r^2} \frac{a}{r} = \frac{qa}{4\pi\epsilon_0} \int \frac{qa}{2\pi r^6} dA$$
$$= \frac{q^2 a^2}{4\pi\epsilon_0} \int_0^\infty \frac{2\pi x dx}{2\pi(x^2+a^2)^3}$$
$$= \frac{q^2}{16\pi\epsilon_0 a^2}.$$

(b) Let the magnitude of the other charge be q'. Then

$$|F| = \frac{1}{4\pi\epsilon_0} \frac{qq'}{(2a)^2} = \frac{q^2}{16\pi\epsilon_0 a^2},$$

or $q' = q$.

CHAPTER 26

1E

The magnitude is $\Delta U = e\Delta V = 1.2 \times 10^9\,\text{eV}$.

2E

(a) An ampere is a coulomb per second, so

$$84\,\text{A} \cdot \text{h} = \left(84\,\frac{\text{C}\cdot\text{h}}{\text{s}}\right)\left(3600\,\frac{\text{s}}{\text{h}}\right) = 3.0 \times 10^5\,\text{C}.$$

(b) The change in potential energy is $\Delta U = q\,\Delta V = (3.0 \times 10^5\,\text{C})(12\,\text{V}) = 3.6 \times 10^6\,\text{J}$.

3P

(a) When charge q moves through a potential difference ΔV its potential energy changes by $\Delta U = q\,\Delta V$. In this case, $\Delta U = (30\,\text{C})(1.0 \times 10^9\,\text{V}) = 3.0 \times 10^{10}\,\text{J}$.

(b) Equate the final kinetic energy of the automobile to the energy released by the lightning: $\Delta U = \frac{1}{2}mv^2$, where m is the mass of the automobile and v is its final speed. Thus

$$v = \sqrt{\frac{2\,\Delta U}{m}} = \sqrt{\frac{2(3.0 \times 10^{10}\,\text{J})}{1000\,\text{kg}}} = 7.7 \times 10^3\,\text{m/s}.$$

(c) Equate the energy required to melt mass m of ice to the energy released by the lightning: $\Delta U = mL_F$, where L_F is the heat of fusion for water. Thus

$$m = \frac{\Delta U}{L_F} = \frac{3.0 \times 10^{10}\,\text{J}}{3.3 \times 10^5\,\text{J/kg}} = 9.0 \times 10^4\,\text{kg}.$$

4E

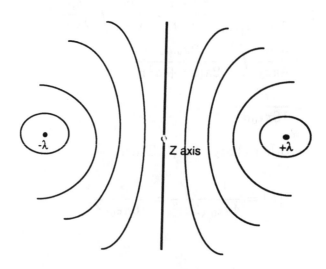

682

5E

(a) $V_B - V_A = \Delta U/(-e) = 3.94 \times 10^{-19}\,\mathrm{J}/ - 1.60 \times 10^{-19}\,\mathrm{C} = -2.46\,\mathrm{V}$.

(b) $V_C - V_A = V_B - V_A = -2.46\,\mathrm{V}$.

(c) $V_C - V_B = 0$ (Since C and B are on the same equipotential line).

6E

(a)

$$W = \int_i^f q_0 \mathbf{E} \cdot d\mathbf{s} = \frac{q_0 \sigma}{2\epsilon_0} \int_0^z dz = \frac{q_0 \sigma z}{2\epsilon_0}.$$

(b) Since $V - V_0 = -W/q_0 = -\sigma z/2\epsilon_0$, we get

$$V = V_0 - \frac{\sigma z}{2\epsilon_0}.$$

7E

$\Delta V = E \Delta s = (1.92 \times 10^5\,\mathrm{N/C})(0.0150\,\mathrm{m}) = 2.90 \times 10^3\,\mathrm{V}$.

8E

(a) $E = \dfrac{F}{e} = \dfrac{3.9 \times 10^{-15}\,\mathrm{N}}{1.60 \times 10^{-19}\,\mathrm{C}} = 2.4 \times 10^4\,\mathrm{N/C}$.

(b) $\Delta V = E \Delta S = (2.4 \times 10^4\,\mathrm{N/\dot{C}})(0.12\,\mathrm{m}) = 2.9 \times 10^3\,\mathrm{V}$.

9E The electric field produced by an infinite sheet of charge has magnitude $E = \sigma/2\epsilon_0$, where σ is the surface charge density. The field is normal to the sheet and is uniform. Place the origin of a coordinate system at the sheet and take the x axis to be parallel to the field and positive in the direction of the field. Then the electric potential is

$$V = V_s - \int_0^x E\,dx = V_s - Ex,$$

where V_s is the potential at the sheet. The equipotential surfaces are surfaces of constant x; that is, they are planes that are parallel to the plane of charge. If two surfaces are separated by Δx then their potentials differ by $\Delta V = -E\Delta x = (\sigma/2\epsilon_0)\Delta x$. Thus

$$\Delta x = \frac{2\epsilon_0\,\Delta V}{\sigma} = \frac{2(8.85 \times 10^{-12}\,\mathrm{C^2/N \cdot m^2})(50\,\mathrm{V})}{0.10 \times 10^{-6}\,\mathrm{C/m^2}} = 8.8 \times 10^{-3}\,\mathrm{m}.$$

10P

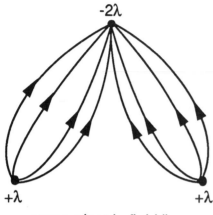

some electric field lines

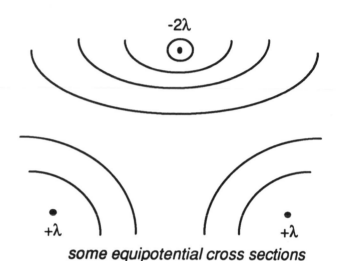

some equipotential cross sections

11P

(a)

$$V(r) = V(0) - \int_0^r E(r)dr = 0 - \int_0^r \frac{qr}{4\pi\epsilon_0 R^3}dr$$
$$= -\frac{qr^2}{8\pi\epsilon_0 R^3}.$$

(b) $\Delta V = V(0) - V(R) = q/8\pi\epsilon_0 R$.

(c) Since $\Delta V = V(0) - V(R) > 0$, the potential at the center of the sphere is higher.

12P

The potential difference between the wire and cylinder is given, not the linear charge density on the wire. Use Gauss' law to find an expression for the electric field a distance r from the center of the wire, between the wire and the cylinder, in terms of the linear charge density. Then integrate with respect to r to find an expression for the potential difference between the wire and cylinder in terms of the linear charge density. Use this result to obtain an expression for the linear charge density in terms of the potential difference and substitute the result into the equation for the electric field. This will give the electric field in terms of the potential difference and will allow you to compute numerical values for the field at the wire and at the cylinder.

For the Gaussian surface use a cylinder of radius r and length ℓ, concentric with the wire and cylinder. The electric field is normal to the rounded portion of the cylinder's surface and is uniform over that surface. This means the electric flux through the Gaussian surface is given by $2\pi r\ell E$, where E is the magnitude of the electric field. The charge enclosed by the Gaussian surface is $q = \lambda\ell$, where λ is the linear charge density on the wire. Gauss' law yields $2\pi\epsilon_0 r\ell E = \lambda\ell$. Thus

$$E = \frac{\lambda}{2\pi\epsilon_0 r}.$$

Since the field is radial, the difference in the potential V_c of the cylinder and the potential V_w of the wire is

$$\Delta V = V_w - V_c = -\int_{r_c}^{r_w} E\,dr = \int_{r_w}^{r_c} \frac{\lambda}{2\pi\epsilon_0 r}\,dr = \frac{\lambda}{2\pi\epsilon_0}\ln\frac{r_c}{r_w},$$

where r_w is the radius of the wire and r_c is the radius of the cylinder. This means that

$$\lambda = \frac{2\pi\epsilon_0\,\Delta V}{\ln(r_c/r_w)}$$

and

$$E = \frac{\lambda}{2\pi\epsilon_0 r} = \frac{\Delta V}{r\ln(r_c/r_w)}.$$

(a) Substitute r_w for r to obtain the field at the surface of the wire:

$$E = \frac{\Delta V}{r_w\ln(r_c/r_w)} = \frac{850\,\text{V}}{(0.65\times 10^{-6}\,\text{m})\ln\left[(1.0\times 10^{-2}\,\text{m})/(0.65\times 10^{-6}\,\text{m})\right]}$$
$$= 1.36\times 10^8\,\text{V/m}.$$

(b) Substitute r_c for r to find the field at the surface of the cylinder:

$$E = \frac{\Delta V}{r_w\ln(r_c/r_w)} = \frac{850\,\text{V}}{(1.0\times 10^{-2}\,\text{m})\ln\left[(1.0\times 10^{-2}\,\text{m})/(0.65\times 10^{-6}\,\text{m})\right]}$$
$$= 8.82\times 10^3\,\text{V/m}.$$

13P

(a) Use Gauss' law to find expressions for the electric field inside and outside the spherical charge distribution. Since the field is radial the electric potential can be written as an integral of the field along a sphere radius, extended to infinity. Since different expressions for the field apply in different regions the integral must be split into two parts, one from infinity to the surface of the distribution and one from the surface to a point inside.

Outside the charge distribution the magnitude of the field is $E = q/4\pi\epsilon_0 r^2$ and the potential is $V = q/4\pi\epsilon_0 r$, where r is the distance from the center of the distribution.

To find an expression for the magnitude of the field inside the charge distribution use a Gaussian surface in the form of a sphere with radius r, concentric with the distribution. The field is normal to the Gaussian surface and its magnitude is uniform over it, so the electric flux through the surface is $4\pi r^2 E$. The charge enclosed is qr^3/R^3. Gauss' law becomes

$$4\pi\epsilon_0 r^2 E = \frac{qr^3}{R^3},$$

so

$$E = \frac{qr}{4\pi\epsilon_0 R^3}.$$

If V_s is the potential at the surface of the distribution ($r = R$) then the potential at a point inside, a distance r from the center, is

$$V = V_s - \int_R^r E\, dr = V_s - \frac{q}{4\pi\epsilon_0 R^3}\int_R^r r\, dr = V_s - \frac{qr^2}{8\pi\epsilon_0 R^3} + \frac{q}{8\pi\epsilon_0 R}.$$

The potential at the surface can be found by replacing r with R in the expression for the potential at points outside the distribution. It is $V_s = q/4\pi\epsilon_0 R$. Thus

$$V = \frac{q}{4\pi\epsilon_0}\left[\frac{1}{R} - \frac{r^2}{2R^3} + \frac{1}{2R}\right] = \frac{q}{8\pi\epsilon_0 R^3}(3R^2 - r^2).$$

(b) In Problem 11 the electric potential was taken to be zero at the center of the sphere. In this problem it is zero at infinity. According to the expression derived in part (a) the potential at the center of the sphere is $V_c = 3q/8\pi\epsilon_0 R$. Thus $V - V_c = -qr^2/8\pi\epsilon_0 R^3$. This is the result of Problem 11.

(c) The potential difference is

$$\Delta V = V_s - V_c = \frac{2q}{8\pi\epsilon_0 R} - \frac{3q}{8\pi\epsilon_0 R} = -\frac{q}{8\pi\epsilon_0 R}.$$

The same value as is given by the expression obtained in Problem 11.

(d) Only potential differences have physical significance, not the value of the potential at any particular point. The same value can be added to the potential at every point without changing the electric field, for example. Changing the reference point from the center of the distribution to infinity changes the value of the potential at every point but it does not change any potential differences.

14P

(a) For $r > r_2$ the field is like that of a point charge and

$$V = \frac{1}{4\pi\epsilon_0}\frac{Q}{r},$$

where the zero of potential was taken to be at infinity.

(b) To find the potential in the region $r_1 < r < r_2$, first use Gauss's law to find an expression for the electric field, then integrate along a radial path from r_2 to r. The Gaussian surface is a sphere of radius r, concentric with the shell. The field is radial and therefore normal to the surface. Its magnitude is uniform over the surface, so the flux through the surface is $\Phi = 4\pi r^2 E$. The volume of the shell is $(4\pi/3)(r_2^3 - r_1^3)$, so the charge density is

$$\rho = \frac{3Q}{4\pi(r_2^3 - r_1^3)}$$

and the charge enclosed by the Gaussian surface is

$$q = \left(\frac{4\pi}{3}\right)(r^3 - r_1^3)\rho = Q\left(\frac{r^3 - r_1^3}{r_2^3 - r_1^3}\right).$$

Gauss' law yields

$$4\pi\epsilon_0 r^2 E = Q\left(\frac{r^3 - r_1^3}{r_2^3 - r_1^3}\right)$$

and the magnitude of the electric field is

$$E = \frac{Q}{4\pi\epsilon_0}\frac{r^3 - r_1^3}{r^2(r_2^3 - r_1^3)}.$$

If V_s is the electric potential at the outer surface of the shell ($r = r_2$) then the potential a distance r from the center is given by

$$V = V_s - \int_{r_2}^r E\,dr = V_s - \frac{Q}{4\pi\epsilon_0}\frac{1}{r_2^3 - r_1^3}\int_{r_2}^r\left(r - \frac{r_1^3}{r^2}\right)dr$$

$$= V_s - \frac{Q}{4\pi\epsilon_0}\frac{1}{r_2^3 - r_1^3}\left(\frac{r^2}{2} - \frac{r_2^2}{2} + \frac{r_1^3}{r} - \frac{r_1^3}{r_2}\right).$$

The potential at the outer surface is found by placing $r = r_2$ in the expression found in part (a). It is $V_s = Q/4\pi\epsilon_0 r_2$. Make this substitution and collect terms to find

$$V = \frac{Q}{4\pi\epsilon_0}\frac{1}{r_2^3 - r_1^3}\left(\frac{3r_2^2}{2} - \frac{r^2}{2} - \frac{r_1^3}{r}\right).$$

Since $\rho = 3Q/4\pi(r_2^3 - r_1^3)$ this can also be written

$$V = \frac{\rho}{3\epsilon_0}\left(\frac{3r_2^2}{2} - \frac{r^2}{2} - \frac{r_1^3}{r}\right).$$

(c) The electric field vanishes in the cavity, so the potential is everywhere the same inside and has the same value as at a point on the inside surface of the shell. Put $r = r_1$ in the result of part (b). After collecting terms the result is

$$V = \frac{Q}{4\pi\epsilon_0}\frac{3(r_2^2 - r_1^2)}{2(r_2^3 - r_1^3)},$$

or in terms of the charge density $V = (\rho/2\epsilon_0)(r_2^2 - r_1^2)$.

(d) The solutions agree at $r = r_1$ and at $r = r_2$.

15E

Let $V = 0$ at $r \to \infty$. Then $V(r) = q/4\pi\epsilon_0 r$. Thus

(a)

$$V_A - V_B = \frac{q}{4\pi\epsilon_0 r_A} - \frac{q}{4\pi\epsilon_0 r_B}$$

$$= (1.0 \times 10^{-6} \text{ C})(8.99 \times 10^9 \text{ N} \cdot \text{m}^2/\text{C}^2)\left(\frac{1}{2.0\,\text{m}} - \frac{1}{1.0\,\text{m}}\right) = -4500\,\text{V}.$$

(b) Since $V(r)$ depends only on the magnitude of $\mathbf{r}$, the result is unchanged.

16E

(a) From symmetry consideration, the equipotential surface with $V = 30\,\text{V}$ must be a sphere (of radius R) centered at q, where $V = q/4\pi\epsilon_0 R$. Solve for R:

$$R = \frac{q}{4\pi\epsilon_0 V} = \frac{(1.5 \times 10^{-8} \text{ C})(8.99 \times 10^9 \text{ N} \cdot \text{m}^2/\text{C}^2)}{30\,\text{V}} = 4.5\,\text{m}.$$

(b) Since $\Delta R = (q/4\pi\epsilon_0)\Delta(1/V)$, ΔR is not proportional to ΔV (but rather to ΔV^{-1}), so the surfaces are not evenly spaced.

17E

The potential raised would be

$$V = \frac{q}{4\pi\epsilon_0 R} = \frac{(8.99 \times 10^9 \text{ N} \cdot \text{m}^2/\text{C}^2)(1.50 \times 10^{-8} \text{ C})}{0.160\,\text{m}} = 843\,\text{V}.$$

18E

$$q = 4\pi\epsilon_0 RV = \frac{(10\,\text{m})(-1.0\,\text{V})}{8.99 \times 10^9 \text{ N} \cdot \text{m}^2/\text{C}^2} = -1.1 \times 10^{-9} \text{ C}.$$

19E

If the electric potential is zero at infinity then at the surface of a uniformly charged sphere it is $V = q/4\pi\epsilon_0 R$, where q is the charge on the sphere and R is the sphere radius. Thus $q = 4\pi\epsilon_0 RV$ and the number of electrons is

$$N = \frac{|q|}{e} = \frac{4\pi\epsilon_0 R|V|}{e} = \frac{(1.0 \times 10^{-6} \text{ m})(400\,\text{V})}{(8.99 \times 10^9 \text{ N} \cdot \text{m}^2/\text{C}^2)(1.60 \times 10^{-19} \text{ C})} = 2.8 \times 10^5.$$

(a)

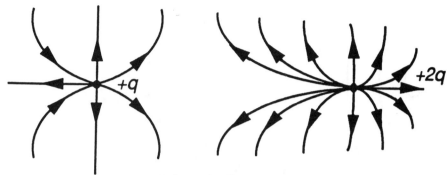

some electric field lines

(b)

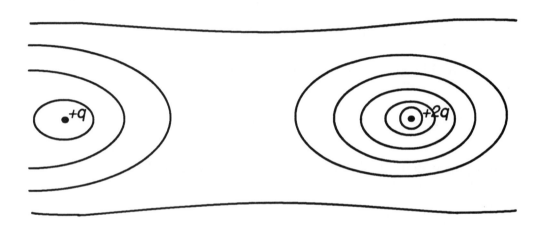

some equipotential cross sections

(a)

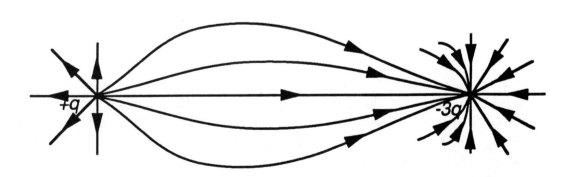

some electric field lines

(b)

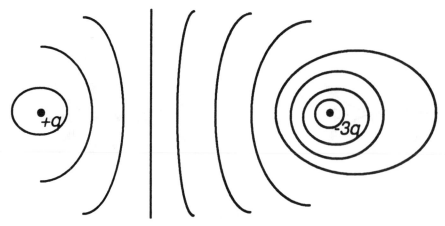

some equipotential cross sections

22E

(a) $V = \dfrac{q}{4\pi\epsilon_0 R} = \dfrac{(4.0 \times 10^{-6}\,\text{C})(8.99 \times 10^9\,\text{N}\cdot\text{m}^2/\text{C}^2)}{0.10\,\text{m}} = 3.6 \times 10^5\,\text{V}.$

(b) The field just outside the sphere would be

$$E = \frac{q}{4\pi\epsilon_0 R^2} = \frac{V}{R} = \frac{3.6 \times 10^5\,\text{V}}{0.10\,\text{m}} = 3.6\,\text{MV/m},$$

which would have exceeded $3.0\,\text{MV/m}$. So this situation cannot occur.

23E

(a)

$$q = 4\pi\epsilon_0 V R = \frac{(200\,\text{V})(0.15\,\text{m})}{8.99 \times 10^9\,\text{N}\cdot\text{m}^2/\text{C}^2} = 3.3 \times 10^{-9}\,\text{C}.$$

(b)

$$\sigma = \frac{q}{4\pi R^2} = \frac{3.3 \times 10^{-9}\,\text{C}}{4\pi(0.15\,\text{m})^2} = 1.2 \times 10^{-8}\,\text{C/m}^2.$$

24P

Assume the charge on the Earth is distributed with spherical symmetry. If the electric potential is zero at infinity then at the surface of the Earth it is $V = q/4\pi\epsilon_0 R$, where q is the charge on the Earth and $R\,(= 6.37\times10^6\text{ m})$ is the radius of the Earth. The magnitude of the electric field at the surface is $E = q/4\pi\epsilon_0 R^2$, so $V = ER = (100\,\text{V/m})(6.37 \times 10^6\,\text{m}) = 6.4 \times 10^8\,\text{V}.$

25P

Use $q = 137,000\,$C from Sample Problem 23-3 to find V,

$$V = \frac{q}{4\pi\epsilon_0 R} = \frac{(137,000\,\text{C})(8.99 \times 10^9\,\text{N} \cdot \text{m}^2/\text{C}^2)}{6.37 \times 10^6\,\text{m}} = 200\,\text{mV}.$$

26P

(a) The electric potential V at the surface of the drop, the charge q on the drop, and the radius R of the drop are related by $V = q/4\pi\epsilon_0 R$. Thus

$$R = \frac{q}{4\pi\epsilon_0 V} = \frac{(8.99 \times 10^9\,\text{N} \cdot \text{m}^2/\text{C}^2)(30 \times 10^{-12}\,\text{C})}{500\,\text{V}} = 5.4 \times 10^{-4}\,\text{m}.$$

(b) After the drops combine the total volume is twice the volume of an original drop, so the radius R' of the combined drop is given by $(R')^3 = 2R^3$ and $R' = 2^{1/3}R$. The charge is twice the charge of original drop: $q' = 2q$. Thus

$$V' = \frac{1}{4\pi\epsilon_0}\frac{q'}{R'} = \frac{1}{4\pi\epsilon_0}\frac{2q}{2^{1/3}R} = \frac{2V}{2^{1/3}} = \frac{2(500\,\text{V})}{2^{1/3}} = 790\,\text{V}.$$

27P

(a) The net charge carried by the sphere after a time t is $q = \frac{1}{2}aet$, where a is the activity of the nickel coating. Thus from $V = q/4\pi\epsilon_0 R = aet/8\pi\epsilon_0 R$ we solve for t:

$$t = \frac{8\pi\epsilon_0 VR}{ae} = \frac{2(1000\,\text{V})(0.010\,\text{m})}{(8.99 \times 10^9\,\text{N} \cdot \text{m}^2/\text{C}^2)(3.70 \times 10^8/\text{s})(1.60 \times 10^{-19}\,\text{C})}$$

$$= 38\,\text{s}.$$

(b) The time t' required satisfies $\frac{1}{2}aet' = C\Delta T$, where $\epsilon = 100\,\text{keV}$. Thus

$$t' = \frac{2C\Delta T}{ae} = \frac{2(14.3\,\text{J}/°\text{C})(5.0°\text{C})}{(3.70 \times 10^8/\text{s})(100 \times 10^3 \times 1.6 \times 10^{-19}\,\text{J})}$$

$$= 2.4 \times 10^9\,\text{s} = 280\,\text{da}.$$

28E

There are two such points, x_1 and x_2, where $x_1 > 0$ and $x_2 < 0$. To find x_1, let

$$V = \frac{q}{4\pi\epsilon_0}\left(\frac{1}{x_1} + \frac{-3}{d - x_1}\right) = 0,$$

we get $x_1 = d/4$. To find x_2, let

$$V = \frac{q}{4\pi\epsilon_0}\left(-\frac{1}{x_2} + \frac{-3}{d - x_2}\right) = 0,$$

we get $x_2 = -d/2$.

29E
Draw an x axis which originates at Q_1 and runs through Q_2 at $(d, 0, 0)$. From $E(x = d/4) = 0$ we have

$$\frac{Q_1}{(d/4)^2} = \frac{Q_2}{(3d/4)^2},$$

or $Q_2 = 9Q_1$. The rest follows analogously from the previous problem. The two points at which $V = 0$ are $x_1 = d/10$ and $x_2 = -d/8$.

30E
Use Eq. 26-23:

$$V = \frac{1}{4\pi\epsilon_0}\frac{p}{r^2} = (8.99 \times 10^9\,\mathrm{N\cdot m^2/C^2})\frac{1.47 \times 3.34 \times 10^{-30}\,\mathrm{C\cdot m}}{(52.0 \times 10^{-9}\,\mathrm{m})^2}$$

$$= 1.63 \times 10^{-5}\,\mathrm{V}.$$

31P
(a) Since both charges produce positive potentials, you cannot find a point other than infinity where $V = 0$.
(b) Let the point be at $(x, 0, 0)$ $(x > 0)$. Then

$$E = \frac{q}{4\pi\epsilon_0}\left[\frac{1}{x^2} - \frac{2}{(d - x)^2}\right] = 0,$$

or $x = d/(1 + \sqrt{2}) = 1.0\,\mathrm{m}/(1 + \sqrt{2}) = 0.41\,\mathrm{m}$.

32P
(a) and (b). Consider the two points $A(R + x_c,\ 0,\ 0)$ and $B(R - x_c,\ 0,\ 0)$ where the circle intersects the x axis. We have

$$\begin{cases} 4\pi\epsilon_0 V_A = \dfrac{q_1}{R + x_c} + \dfrac{q_2}{x_2 - (R + x_c)} = 0, \\[2mm] 4\pi\epsilon_0 V_B = \dfrac{q_1}{R - x_c} + \dfrac{q_2}{x_2 + (R - x_c)} = 0. \end{cases}$$

Solve for R and x_c:

$$
\begin{cases}
x_c = \dfrac{q_1^2 x_2}{q_1^2 - q_2^2} = \dfrac{(6.0\,\mathrm{e})^2(8.6\,\mathrm{nm})}{(6.0\,\mathrm{e})^2 - (-10\,\mathrm{e})^2} = -4.8\,\mathrm{nm}, \\[2mm]
R = \dfrac{q_1 q_2 x_2}{q_1^2 - q_2^2} = \dfrac{(6.0\,\mathrm{e})(-10\,\mathrm{e})(8.6\,\mathrm{nm})}{(6.0\,\mathrm{e})^2 - (-10\,\mathrm{e})^2} = 8.1\,\mathrm{nm}.
\end{cases}
$$

(c) No. In fact the $V = 0$ one is the only circular one.

33P A positive charge q is a distance $r - d$ from P, another positive charge q is a distance r from P, and a negative charge $-q$ is a distance $r + d$ from P. Sum the individual electric potentials created at P to find the total:

$$
V = \frac{q}{4\pi\epsilon_0}\left[\frac{1}{r-d} + \frac{1}{r} - \frac{1}{r+d}\right].
$$

Use the binomial theorem to approximate $1/(r - d)$ for r much larger than d:

$$
\frac{1}{r-d} = (r - d)^{-1} \approx (r)^{-1} - (r)^{-2}(-d) = \frac{1}{r} + \frac{d}{r^2}.
$$

Similarly,

$$
\frac{1}{r+d} \approx \frac{1}{r} - \frac{d}{r^2}.
$$

Only the first two terms of each expansion were retained. Thus

$$
V \approx \frac{q}{4\pi\epsilon_0}\left[\frac{1}{r} + \frac{d}{r^2} + \frac{1}{r} - \frac{1}{r} + \frac{d}{r^2}\right] = \frac{q}{4\pi\epsilon_0}\left[\frac{1}{r} + \frac{2d}{r^2}\right] = \frac{q}{4\pi\epsilon_0 r}\left[1 + \frac{2d}{r}\right].
$$

34P A charge $-5q$ is a distance $2d$ from P, a charge $-5q$ is a distance d from P, and two charges $+5q$ are each a distance d from P, so the electric potential at P is

$$
V = \frac{q}{4\pi\epsilon_0}\left[-\frac{5}{2d} - \frac{5}{d} + \frac{5}{d} + \frac{5}{d}\right] = -\frac{5q}{8\pi\epsilon_0}.
$$

The zero of the electric potential was taken to be at infinity.

35P

$$
\begin{aligned}
V_p &= \frac{1}{4\pi\epsilon_0}\left[\frac{5q}{\sqrt{d^2 + (d/2)^2}} + \frac{-2q}{d/2} + \frac{-3q}{\sqrt{d^2 + (d/2)^2}}\right.\\
&\quad \left. + \frac{3q}{\sqrt{d^2 + (d/2)^2}} + \frac{-2q}{d/2} + \frac{-5q}{\sqrt{d^2 + (d/2)^2}}\right]\\
&= \frac{-2q}{\pi\epsilon_0 d}.
\end{aligned}
$$

693

36E

(a) From Eq. 26-28,

$$V = 2\frac{\lambda}{4\pi\epsilon_0} \ln\left[\frac{L/2 + (L^2/4 + d^2)^{1/2}}{d}\right].$$

(b) $V = 0$ due to superposition.

37E

$$V_p = \frac{1}{4\pi\epsilon_0} \int_{\text{rod}} \frac{dq}{R} = \frac{-Q}{4\pi\epsilon_0 R}.$$

38P

(a) $V_p = Q/4\pi\epsilon_0 R$.
(b) and (c) $V_p = Q/4\pi\epsilon_0 R$ (see Exercise 37).
(d) $E_p(a) > E_p(b) > E_p(c)$.

39P

(a) All the charge is the same distance R from C, so the electric potential at C is

$$V = \frac{1}{4\pi\epsilon_0}\left[\frac{Q}{R} - \frac{6Q}{R}\right] = -\frac{5Q}{4\pi\epsilon_0 R},$$

where the zero was taken to be at infinity.

(b) All the charge is the same distance from P. That distance is $\sqrt{R^2 + z^2}$, so the electric potential at P is

$$V = \frac{1}{4\pi\epsilon_0}\left[\frac{Q}{\sqrt{R^2 + z^2}} - \frac{6Q}{\sqrt{R^2 + z^2}}\right] = -\frac{5Q}{4\pi\epsilon_0\sqrt{R^2 + z^2}}.$$

40P

The disk is uniformly charged. This means that when the full disk is present each quadrant contributes equally to the electric potential at P, so the potential at P due to a single quadrant is one-fourth the potential due to the entire disk. First find an expression for the potential at P due to the entire disk.

Consider a ring of charge with radius r and width dr. Its area is $2\pi r\, dr$ and it contains charge $dq = 2\pi\sigma r\, dr$. All the charge in it is a distance $\sqrt{r^2 + z^2}$ from P, so the potential it produces at P is

$$dV = \frac{1}{4\pi\epsilon_0}\frac{2\pi\sigma r\, dr}{\sqrt{r^2 + z^2}} = \frac{\sigma r\, dr}{2\epsilon_0\sqrt{r^2 + z^2}}.$$

The total potential at P is

$$V = \frac{\sigma}{2\epsilon_0} \int_0^R \frac{r\, dr}{\sqrt{r^2 + z^2}} = \frac{\sigma}{2\epsilon_0} \sqrt{r^2 + z^2}\Big|_0^R = \frac{\sigma}{2\epsilon_0} \left[\sqrt{R^2 + z^2} - z \right] \,.$$

The potential V_{sq} at P due to a single quadrant is

$$V_{sq} = \frac{V}{4} = \frac{\sigma}{8\epsilon_0} \left[\sqrt{R^2 + z^2} - z \right] \,.$$

41P
Put the origin at the left end of the rod. We have

$$V_p = \frac{1}{4\pi\epsilon_0} \int_{\text{rod}} \frac{dq}{L + d - x} = \frac{1}{4\pi\epsilon_0} \left(\frac{-Q}{L} \right) \int_0^L \frac{dx}{L + d - x}$$

$$= -\frac{Q}{4\pi\epsilon_0 L} \ln\left(1 + \frac{L}{d} \right).$$

42E
The electric field is $E = \Delta V/\Delta s = 2(5.0\,\text{V})/0.015\,\text{m} = 6.7 \times 10^2\,\text{V/m}$.

43E
Use $E_x = -dV/dx = -$local slope of the V vs. x curve. The results are:
$E_x(ab) = -6.0\,\text{V/m}$, $E_x(bc) = 0$, $E_x(cd) = E_x(de) = 3.0\,\text{V/m}$,
$E_x(ef) = 15\,\text{V/m}$, $E_x(fg) = 0$, $E_x(gh) = -3.0\,\text{V/m}$.

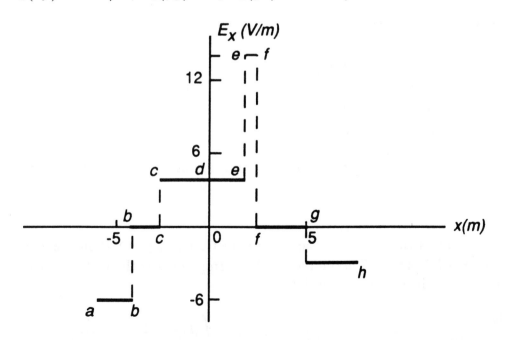

44E
On the dipole axis $\theta = 0$ or π so

$$E(r) = -\frac{\partial V}{\partial r} = \pm\frac{p}{4\pi\epsilon_0}\frac{d}{dr}\left(\frac{1}{r^2}\right) = \pm\frac{p}{4\pi\epsilon_0 r^3}.$$

45E
From symmetry $E_x = E_y = 0$. So

$$E = E_z = -\frac{dV}{dz} = -\frac{\sigma}{2\epsilon_0}\frac{d}{dz}\left(\sqrt{z^2 + R^2} - z\right)$$
$$= \frac{\sigma}{2\epsilon}\left(1 - \frac{z}{\sqrt{z^2 + R^2}}\right).$$

46E

$$\mathbf{E} = -\frac{dV}{dx}\mathbf{i} = -\frac{d}{dx}(1500x^2)\mathbf{i} = -3000x\mathbf{i}$$
$$= (-3000\,\mathrm{V/m^2})(0.0130\,\mathrm{m})\mathbf{i} = (39\,\mathrm{V/m})\mathbf{i}.$$

47E
(a) The E-field corresponding to V is

$$E = -\frac{dV}{dr} = -\frac{d}{dr}\left[\frac{Ze}{4\pi\epsilon_0}\left(\frac{1}{r} - \frac{3}{2R} + \frac{r^2}{2R^3}\right)\right]$$
$$= \frac{Ze}{4\pi\epsilon_0}\left(\frac{1}{r^2} - \frac{r}{R^3}\right).$$

(b) The expression for $V(r)$ is valid inside the atom only and cannot be extended to $r \to \infty$.

48P
(a) The charge on every part of the ring is the same distance from any point P on the axis. This distance is $r = \sqrt{z^2 + R^2}$, where R is the radius of the ring and z is the distance from the center of the ring to P. The electric potential at P is

$$V = \frac{1}{4\pi\epsilon_0}\int\frac{dq}{r} = \frac{1}{4\pi\epsilon_0}\int\frac{dq}{\sqrt{z^2 + R^2}} = \frac{1}{4\pi\epsilon_0}\frac{1}{\sqrt{z^2 + R^2}}\int dq = \frac{1}{4\pi\epsilon_0}\frac{q}{\sqrt{z^2 + R^2}}.$$

(b) The electric field is along the axis and its component is given by

$$E = -\frac{\partial V}{\partial z} = -\frac{q}{4\pi\epsilon_0}\frac{d}{dz}(z^2 + R^2)^{-1/2}$$

$$= -\frac{q}{4\pi\epsilon_0}\left(\frac{1}{2}\right)(z^2 + R^2)^{-3/2}(2z) = \frac{q}{4\pi\epsilon_0}\frac{z}{(z^2 + R^2)^{3/2}}.$$

This agrees with the result of Section 24–6.

49P
(a) Put the origin at the right end of the rod and consider an infinitesimal segment of the rod, located at $x = x'$ (a negative coordinate). It has length dx' and contains charge $dq = \lambda\,dx'$. Its distance from P is $d = x - x'$ and the potential it creates at P is

$$dV = \frac{1}{4\pi\epsilon_0}\frac{dq}{d} = \frac{1}{4\pi\epsilon_0}\frac{\lambda\,dx'}{x - x'}.$$

To find the total potential at P, integrate over the rod:

$$V = \frac{\lambda}{4\pi\epsilon_0}\int_{-L}^{0}\frac{dx'}{x - x'} = -\frac{\lambda}{4\pi\epsilon_0}\ln(x - x')\Big|_{-L}^{0} = \frac{\lambda}{4\pi\epsilon_0}\ln\frac{x + L}{x}.$$

(b) Differentiate the electric potential with respect to x to find the x component of the electric field:

$$E_x = -\frac{\partial V}{\partial x} = -\frac{\lambda}{4\pi\epsilon_0}\frac{\partial}{\partial x}\ln\frac{x + L}{x} = -\frac{\lambda}{4\pi\epsilon_0}\frac{x}{x + L}\left(\frac{1}{x} - \frac{x + L}{x^2}\right) = \frac{\lambda}{4\pi\epsilon_0}\frac{L}{x(x + L)}.$$

(c) Consider two points an equal distance on either side of P, along a line that is perpendicular to the x axis. The difference in the electric potential divided by their separation gives the transverse component of the electric field. Since the two points are situated symmetrically with respect to the rod, their potentials are the same and the potential difference is zero. Thus the transverse component of the electric field is zero.

50P
(a) Consider a segment of the rod from x to $x + dx$. Its contribution to the potential at point P is

$$dV_p = \frac{1}{4\pi\epsilon_0}\frac{\lambda(x)dx}{\sqrt{x^2 + y^2}} = \frac{k}{4\pi\epsilon_0}\frac{x}{\sqrt{x^2 + y^2}}dx.$$

Thus

$$V_p = \int_{\text{rod}}dV_p = \frac{k}{4\pi\epsilon_0}\int_{0}^{L}\frac{x}{\sqrt{x^2 + y^2}}dx$$

$$= \frac{k}{4\pi\epsilon_0}(\sqrt{L^2 + y^2} - y).$$

697

(b)

$$E_{p,y} = -\frac{dV_p}{dy} = -\frac{k}{4\pi\epsilon_0}\frac{d}{dy}(\sqrt{L^2 + y^2} - y)$$

$$= \frac{k}{4\pi\epsilon_0}\left(1 - \frac{y}{\sqrt{L^2 + y^2}}\right).$$

(c) All we obtained above for the potential is its value at point P, which is along the y-axis. In order to obtain $E_x(x, y)$ we need to first calculate $V(x, y)$, i.e. the potential as a function of both x and y. Then $E_x(x, y) = \partial V(x, y)/\partial x$.

51E
(a)

$$V_A - V_B = \frac{q}{4\pi\epsilon_0}\left[\left(\frac{1}{a} - \frac{1}{a+d}\right) - \left(\frac{1}{a+d} - \frac{1}{a}\right)\right]$$

$$= \frac{q}{2\pi\epsilon_0}\frac{d}{a(a+d)}.$$

(b) When $q = 0$ or $d = 0$, $V_A - V_B = 0$ as expected. For $a = 0$ we expect $V_A - V_B \to \infty$, since $V_A \to +\infty$ and $V_B \to -\infty$. This also agrees with the result in (a).

52E
(a) The charges are equal and are the same distance from C. Use the Pythagorean theorem to find the distance $r = \sqrt{(d/2)^2 + (d/2)^2} = d/\sqrt{2}$. The electric potential at C is the sum of the potential due to the individual charges but since they produce the same potential, it is twice that of either one:

$$V = \frac{2q}{4\pi\epsilon_0}\frac{\sqrt{2}}{d} = \frac{2\sqrt{2}q}{4\pi\epsilon_0 d}$$

$$= \frac{(8.99 \times 10^9 \text{ N} \cdot \text{m}^2/\text{C}^2)(2)\sqrt{2}(2.0 \times 10^{-6} \text{ C})}{0.020\,\text{m}} = 2.5 \times 10^6 \text{ V}.$$

(b) As you move the charge into position from far away the potential energy changes from zero to qV, where V is the electric potential at the final location of the charge. The change in the potential energy equals the work you must do to bring the charge in: $W = qV = (2.0 \times 10^{-6} \text{ C})(2.5 \times 10^6 \text{ V}) = 5.1 \text{ J}$.

(c) The work calculated in part (b) represents the potential energy of the interactions between the charge brought in from infinity and the other two charges. To find the total potential energy of the three-charge system you must add the potential energy of the interaction between the fixed charges. Their separation is d so this potential energy is $q^2/4\pi\epsilon_0 d$. The total potential energy is

$$U = W + \frac{q^2}{4\pi\epsilon_0 d}$$

$$= 5.1\,\text{J} + \frac{(8.99 \times 10^9\,\text{N} \cdot \text{m}^2/\text{C}^2)(2.0 \times 10^{-6}\,\text{C})^2}{0.020\,\text{m}} = 6.9\,\text{J}.$$

53E

The potential energy of the two-charge system is

$$U = \frac{q_1 q_2}{4\pi\epsilon_0} \frac{1}{\sqrt{(x_1 - x_2)^2 + (y_1 - y_2)^2}}$$

$$= (8.99 \times 10^9\,\text{N} \cdot \text{m}^2/\text{C}^2)(3.0 \times 10^{-6}\,\text{C})(-4.0 \times 10^{-6}\,\text{C})$$

$$\cdot \left[\frac{1}{\sqrt{(3.5 + 2.0)^2 + (0.50 - 1.5)^2}\,\text{cm}} \right]$$

$$= -1.9\,\text{J}.$$

Thus $-1.9\,\text{J}$ of work is needed.

54E

(a) Denote the side length of the triangle as a. Then the electric potential energy is

$$U = \frac{3(e/3)^2}{4\pi\epsilon_0 a} = \frac{(8.99 \times 10^9\,\text{N} \cdot \text{m}^2/\text{C}^2)(1.60 \times 10^{-19}\,\text{C})^2}{3(2.82 \times 10^{-31})}$$

$$= 2.72 \times 10^{-14}\,\text{J}.$$

(b) $U/c^2 = 2.72 \times 10^{-14}\,\text{J}/(3.00 \times 10^8\,\text{m/s})^2 = 3.02 \times 10^{-31}\,\text{kg}$. This is about a third of the accepted electron mass.

55E

Let the quark-quark separation be a. Then

(a)

$$U_{up-up} = \frac{1}{4\pi\epsilon_0} \frac{(2e/3)(2e/3)}{a} = \frac{4e^2}{4\pi\epsilon_0 a}$$

$$= \frac{4(8.99 \times 10^9\,\text{N} \cdot \text{m}^2/\text{C}^2)(1.60 \times 10^{-19}\,\text{C})e}{9(1.32 \times 10^{-15}\,\text{m})}$$

$$= 4.84 \times 10^5\,\text{eV} = 0.484\,\text{MeV}.$$

(b)

$$U = \frac{1}{4\pi\epsilon_0}\left(\frac{2e/3 \cdot 2e/3}{a} - 2 \cdot \frac{2e/3 \cdot 2e/3}{a}\right) = 0.$$

56E

The electric potential energy of the system is

$$U = \frac{q^2}{4\pi\epsilon_0}\left(-\frac{1}{a} - \frac{1}{a} + \frac{1}{\sqrt{2}a} - \frac{1}{a} - \frac{1}{a} + \frac{1}{\sqrt{2}a}\right)$$

$$= \frac{2q^2}{4\pi\epsilon_0 a}\left(\frac{1}{\sqrt{2}} - 2\right) = -\frac{0.21q^2}{\epsilon_0 a}.$$

Thus the above amount of work is required to set up the system.

57E

$$U = \frac{1}{4\pi\epsilon_0 d}\left(q_1 q_2 + q_1 q_3 + q_2 q_4 + q_3 q_4 + \frac{q_1 q_4}{\sqrt{2}} + \frac{q_2 q_3}{\sqrt{2}}\right)$$

$$= \frac{(8.99 \times 10^9 \, \text{N} \cdot \text{m}^2/\text{C}^2)}{1.3\,\text{m}}\left[(12)(-24) + (12)(31) + (-24)(17) + (31)(17)\right.$$

$$\left. + \frac{(12)(17)}{\sqrt{2}} + \frac{(-24)(31)}{\sqrt{2}}\right](10^{-19}\,\text{C})^2$$

$$= -1.2 \times 10^{-6}\,\text{J}.$$

58P

Let $q = 0.12\,\text{C}$ and $a = 1.7\,\text{m}$. The change in electric potential energy of the three-charge system as one of the charges is moved as described in the problem is

$$\Delta U = \frac{q^2}{4\pi\epsilon_0}\left(\frac{2}{a/2} - \frac{2}{a}\right) = \frac{2q^2}{4\pi\epsilon_0 a}$$

$$= \frac{2(0.12\,\text{C})^2(8.99 \times 10^9\,\text{N} \cdot \text{m}^2/\text{C}^2)}{1.7\,\text{m}} = 1.5 \times 10^8\,\text{J}.$$

Thus the number of days required would be

$$n = \frac{(1.5 \times 10^8\,\text{J})}{(0.83 \times 10^3\,\text{W})(86400\,\text{s/d})} = 2.1\,\text{d}.$$

59P

(a) Let ℓ ($= 0.15\,\text{m}$) be the length of the rectangle and w ($= 0.050\,\text{m}$) be its width. Charge q_1 is a distance ℓ from point A and charge q_2 is a distance w, so the electric potential at A is

$$V_A = \frac{1}{4\pi\epsilon_0}\left[\frac{q_1}{\ell} + \frac{q_2}{w}\right]$$

$$= (8.99 \times 10^9\,\text{N}\cdot\text{m}^2/\text{C}^2)\left[\frac{-5.0 \times 10^{-6}\,\text{C}}{0.15\,\text{m}} + \frac{2.0 \times 10^{-6}\,\text{C}}{0.050\,\text{m}}\right]$$

$$= 6.0 \times 10^4\,\text{V}.$$

(b) Charge q_1 is a distance w from point b and charge q_2 is a distance ℓ, so the electric potential at B is

$$V_B = \frac{1}{4\pi\epsilon_0}\left[\frac{q_1}{w} + \frac{q_2}{\ell}\right]$$

$$= (8.99 \times 10^9\,\text{N}\cdot\text{m}^2/\text{C}^2)\left[\frac{-5.0 \times 10^{-6}\,\text{C}}{0.050\,\text{m}} + \frac{2.0 \times 10^{-6}\,\text{C}}{0.15\,\text{m}}\right]$$

$$= -7.8 \times 10^5\,\text{V}.$$

(c) Since the kinetic energy is zero at the beginning and end of the trip, the work done by an external agent equals the change in the potential energy of the system. The potential energy is the product of the charge q_3 and the electric potential. If U_A is the potential energy when q_3 is at A and U_B is the potential energy when q_3 is at B, then the work done in moving the charge from B to A is $W = U_A - U_B = q_3(V_A - V_B) = (3.0 \times 10^{-6}\,\text{C})(6.0 \times 10^4\,\text{V} + 7.8 \times 10^5\,\text{V}) = 2.5\,\text{J}$.

(d) The work done by the external agent is positive, so the energy of the three-charge system increases.

(e) and (f) The electrostatic force is conservative, so the work is the same no matter what the path.

60P
The work required is

$$W = \Delta U = \frac{1}{4\pi\epsilon_0}\left[\frac{(4q)(5q)}{2d} + \frac{(5q)(-2q)}{d}\right] = 0.$$

61P
The particle with charge $-q$ has both potential and kinetic energy and both these change when the radius of the orbit is changed. Find an expression for the total energy in terms of the orbit radius. Q provides the centripetal force required for $-q$ to move in uniform

circular motion. The magnitude of the force is $F = Qq/4\pi\epsilon_0 r^2$, where r is the orbit radius. The acceleration of $-q$ is v^2/r, where v is its speed. Newton's second law yields $Qq/4\pi\epsilon_0 r^2 = mv^2/r$, so $mv^2 = Qq/4\pi\epsilon_0 r$ and the kinetic energy is $K = \frac{1}{2}mv^2 = Qq/8\pi\epsilon_0 r$. The potential energy is $U = -Qq/4\pi\epsilon_0 r$ and the total energy is

$$E = K + U = \frac{Qq}{8\pi\epsilon_0 r} - \frac{Qq}{4\pi\epsilon_0 r} = -\frac{Qq}{8\pi\epsilon_0 r}.$$

When the orbit radius is r_1 the energy is $E_1 = -Qq/8\pi\epsilon_0 r_1$ and when it is r_2 the energy is $E_2 = -Qq/8\pi\epsilon_0 r_2$. The difference $E_2 - E_1$ is the work W done by an external agent to change the radius:

$$W = E_2 - E_1 = -\frac{Qq}{8\pi\epsilon_0}\left(\frac{1}{r_2} - \frac{1}{r_1}\right) = \frac{Qq}{8\pi\epsilon_0}\left(\frac{1}{r_1} - \frac{1}{r_2}\right).$$

62P
(a)

$$V(r) = \frac{1}{4\pi\epsilon_0}\frac{e}{d\,r} = \frac{(8.99 \times 10^9 \,\text{N} \cdot \text{m}^2/\text{C}^2)(1.60 \times 10^{-19}\,\text{C})}{5.29 \times 10^{-11}\,\text{m}} = 27.2\,\text{V}.$$

(b) $U = -eV(r) = -27.2\,\text{eV}$.
(c) Since $mv^2/r = -e^2/4\pi\epsilon_0 r^2$, we have

$$K = \frac{1}{2}mv^2 = -\frac{1}{2}\left(\frac{e^2}{4\pi\epsilon_0 r}\right) = -\frac{1}{2}V(r) = \frac{27.2\,\text{eV}}{2} = 13.6\,\text{eV}.$$

(d) The energy required is

$$\Delta E = 0 - [V(r) + K] = 0 - (-27.2\,\text{eV} + 13.6\,\text{eV}) = 13.6\,\text{eV}.$$

63P
Let $r = 1.5\,\text{m}$, $x = 3.0\,\text{m}$, $q_1 = -9.0\,\text{nC}$, and $q_2 = -6.0\,\text{pC}$. The work done is

$$W = \Delta U = \frac{q_1 q_2}{4\pi\epsilon_0}\left(\frac{1}{r} - \frac{1}{\sqrt{r^2 + x^2}}\right)$$

$$= (-9.0 \times 10^{-9}\,\text{C})(-6.0 \times 10^{-12}\,\text{C})(8.99 \times 10^9 \,\text{N} \cdot \text{m}^2/\text{C}^2)$$

$$\left[\frac{1}{1.5\,\text{m}} - \frac{1}{\sqrt{(1.5\,\text{m})^2 + (3.0\,\text{m})^2}}\right]$$

$$= 1.8 \times 10^{-10}\,\text{J}.$$

64P Use the conservation of energy principle. The initial potential energy is $U_i = q^2/4\pi\epsilon_0 r_1$, the initial kinetic energy is $K_i = 0$, the final potential energy is $U_f = q^2/4\pi\epsilon_0 r_2$, and the final kinetic energy is $K_f = \frac{1}{2}mv^2$, where v is the final speed of the particle. Conservation of energy yields

$$\frac{q^2}{4\pi\epsilon_0 r_1} = \frac{q^2}{4\pi\epsilon_0 r_2} + \frac{1}{2}mv^2 \,.$$

The solution for v is

$$v = \sqrt{\frac{2q^2}{4\pi\epsilon_0 m}\left(\frac{1}{r_1} - \frac{1}{r_2}\right)}$$

$$= \sqrt{\frac{(8.99 \times 10^9 \, \text{N} \cdot \text{m}^2/\text{C}^2)(2)(3.1 \times 10^{-6} \, \text{C})^2}{20 \times 10^{-6} \, \text{kg}}\left(\frac{1}{0.90 \times 10^{-3} \, \text{m}} - \frac{1}{2.5 \times 10^{-3} \, \text{m}}\right)}$$

$$= 2.5 \times 10^3 \, \text{m/s} \,.$$

65P

(a) The potential energy is

$$U = \frac{q^2}{4\pi\epsilon_0 d} = \frac{(8.99 \times 10^9 \, \text{N} \cdot \text{m}^2/\text{C}^2)(5.0 \times 10^{-6} \, \text{C})^2}{1.00 \, \text{m}} = 0.225 \, \text{J} \,,$$

relative to the potential energy at infinite separation.

(b) Each sphere repels the other with a force that has magnitude

$$F = \frac{q^2}{4\pi\epsilon_0 d^2} = \frac{(8.99 \times 10^9 \, \text{N} \cdot \text{m}^2/\text{C}^2)(5.0 \times 10^{-6} \, \text{C})^2}{(1.00 \, \text{m})^2} = 0.225 \, \text{N} \,.$$

According to Newton's second law the acceleration of each sphere is the force divided by the mass of the sphere. Let m_A and m_B be the masses of the spheres. The acceleration of sphere A is

$$a_A = \frac{F}{m_A} = \frac{0.225 \, \text{N}}{5.0 \times 10^{-3} \, \text{kg}} = 45.0 \, \text{m/s}^2$$

and the acceleration of sphere B is

$$a_B = \frac{F}{m_B} = \frac{0.225 \, \text{N})}{10 \times 10^{-3} \, \text{kg}} = 22.5 \, \text{m/s}^2 \,.$$

(c) Energy is conserved. The initial potential energy is $U = 0.225 \, \text{J}$, as calculated in part (a). The initial kinetic energy is zero since the spheres start from rest. The final potential energy is zero since the spheres are then far apart. The final kinetic energy is $\frac{1}{2}m_A v_A^2 + \frac{1}{2}m_B v_B^2$, where v_A and v_B are the final velocities. Thus

$$U = \frac{1}{2}m_A v_A^2 + \frac{1}{2}m_B v_B^2 \,.$$

Momentum is also conserved, so

$$0 = m_A v_A + m_B v_B \,.$$

Solve these equations simultaneously for v_A and v_B.

Substitute $v_B = -(m_A/m_B)v_A$, from the momentum equation, into the energy equation and collect terms. You should obtain $U = \frac{1}{2}(m_A/m_B)(m_A + m_B)v_A^2$. Thus

$$v_A = \sqrt{\frac{2Um_B}{m_A(m_A + m_B)}}$$

$$= \sqrt{\frac{2(0.225\,\text{J})(10 \times 10^{-3}\,\text{kg})}{(5.0 \times 10^{-3}\,\text{kg})(5.0 \times 10^{-3}\,\text{kg} + 10 \times 10^{-3}\,\text{kg})}} = 7.75\,\text{m/s}.$$

Now calculate v_B:

$$v_B = -\frac{m_A}{m_B}v_A = -\left(\frac{5.0 \times 10^{-3}\,\text{kg}}{10 \times 10^{-3}\,\text{kg}}\right)(7.75\,\text{m/s}) = -3.87\,\text{m/s}.$$

66P

The initial speed v_i satisfies

$$K_i = \frac{1}{2}mv_i^2 = e\Delta V,$$

or

$$v_i = \sqrt{\frac{2e\Delta V}{m}} = \sqrt{\frac{2(1.60 \times 10^{-19}\,\text{J})(625\,\text{V})}{9.11 \times 10^{-31}\,\text{kg}}} = 1.48 \times 10^7\,\text{m/s}.$$

67P

(a) At the least center-to-center separation $r_{\min}$ the kinetic energy K_i of the proton is entirely converted to the electric potential energy between the proton and the neucleus. Thus

$$K_i = \frac{1}{4\pi\epsilon_0}\frac{e q_{\text{lead}}}{r_{\min}} = \frac{82e^2}{4\pi\epsilon_0 r_{\min}}.$$

Thus

$$r_{\min} = \frac{82e^2}{4\pi\epsilon_0 K_i} = \frac{82(1.6 \times 10^{-19}\,\text{J})(8.99 \times 10^9\,\text{N}\cdot\text{m}^2/\text{C}^2)}{4.80 \times 10^6\,\text{V}}$$

$$= 2.5 \times 10^{-14}\,\text{m} = 25\,\text{fm}.$$

(b) In this case

$$K_i = \frac{1}{4\pi\epsilon_0}\frac{q_\alpha q_{\text{lead}}}{r'_{\min}} = 2\left(\frac{82e^2}{4\pi\epsilon_0 r'_{\min}}\right) = \frac{82e^2}{4\pi\epsilon_0 r_{\min}},$$

so the new minimum separation is $r'_{\min} = 2r_{\min} = 50\,\text{fm}$.

68P

The idea is the same as that for problem 67. We have

$$K = \frac{1}{4\pi\epsilon_0} \frac{qQ}{r_{\min}},$$

or $r_{\min} = qQ/4\pi\epsilon_0 K$.

69P

The change in electric potential energy of the electron-shell system as the electron starts from its initial position and just reaches the shell is $\Delta U = (-e)(-V) = eV$. Thus from $\Delta U = K = \frac{1}{2}mv_i^2$ we find the initial electron speed to be

$$v_i = \sqrt{2\Delta U/m} = \sqrt{2eV/m}.$$

70P Use the conservation of energy principle. Take the potential energy to be zero when the moving electron is far away from the fixed electrons. The final potential energy is then $U_f = 2e^2/4\pi\epsilon_0 d$, where d is the half the distance between the fixed electrons. The initial kinetic energy is $K_i = \frac{1}{2}mv^2$, where m is the mass of an electron and v is the initial speed of the moving electron. The final kinetic energy is zero. Thus $K_i = U_f$ or $\frac{1}{2}mv^2 = 2e^2/4\pi\epsilon_0 d$. Hence

$$v = \sqrt{\frac{4e^2}{4\pi\epsilon_0 dm}} = \sqrt{\frac{(8.99 \times 10^9 \, \text{N} \cdot \text{m}^2/\text{C}^2)(4)(1.60 \times 10^{-19} \, \text{C})^2}{(0.010 \, \text{m})(9.11 \times 10^{-31} \, \text{kg})}} = 3.2 \times 10^2 \, \text{m/s}.$$

71P

The potential difference between the surface of the sphere of charge Q and radius r and a point infinitely far from it is $\Delta V = Q/4\pi\epsilon_0 r$. Thus the escape speed v_e satisfies $K = \frac{1}{2}mv_e^2 = e\Delta V$, or

$$v_e = \sqrt{\frac{2eQ}{4\pi\epsilon_0 mr}} = \sqrt{\frac{2(1.60 \times 10^{-19} \, \text{C})(1.60 \times 10^{-15} \, \text{C})(8.99 \times 10^9 \, \text{N} \cdot \text{m}^2/\text{C}^2)}{(9.11 \times 10^{-31} \, \text{kg})(1.0 \times 10^{-2} \, \text{m})}}$$

$$= 2.0 \times 10^4 \, \text{m/s}.$$

72P

Let the distance in question be r. The initial kinetic energy of the electron is $K_i = \frac{1}{2}mv_i^2$, where $v_i = 3.2 \times 10^5$ m/s. As the speed doubles, K becomes $4K_i$. Thus

$$\Delta U = \frac{-e^2}{4\pi\epsilon_0 r} = -\Delta K = -(4K_i - K_i) = -3K_i = -\frac{3mv_i^2}{2},$$

or

$$r = \frac{2e^2}{3(4\pi\epsilon_0)mv_i^2} = \frac{2(1.6 \times 10^{-19} \text{ C})^2(8.99 \times 10^9 \text{ N} \cdot \text{m}^2/\text{C}^2)}{3(9.11 \times 10^{-19} \text{ kg})(3.2 \times 10^5 \text{ m/s})^2}$$

$$= 1.6 \times 10^{-9} \text{ m}.$$

73E

Since the whole conductor is equipotential, the electric potential at its center is also $+400$ V.

74E

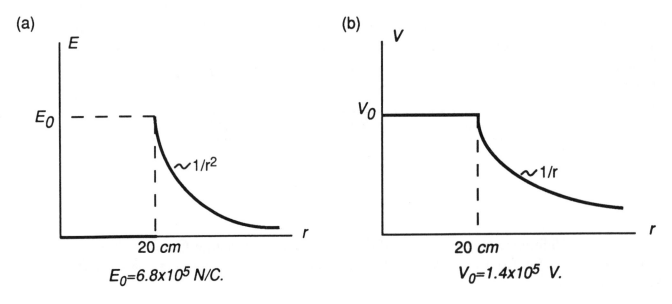

(a)

$E_0 = 6.8\times10^5$ N/C.

(b)

$V_0 = 1.4\times10^5$ V.

75E If the electric potential is zero at infinity, then the potential at the surface of the sphere is given by $V = q/4\pi\epsilon_0 r$, where q is the charge on the sphere and r is its radius. Thus

$$q = 4\pi\epsilon_0 r V = \frac{(0.15 \text{ m})(1500 \text{ V})}{8.99 \times 10^9 \text{ N} \cdot \text{m}^2/\text{C}^2} = 2.5 \times 10^{-8} \text{ C}.$$

76E

(a) V_1 and V_2 must be the same.

706

(b) Let $V_1 = q_1/4\pi\epsilon_0 R_1 = V_2 = q_2/4\pi\epsilon_0 R_2$ and note that $q_1 + q_2 = q$ and $R_2 = 2R_1$, we find $q_1 = q/3$ and $q_2 = 2q/3$.

(c)

$$\frac{\sigma_1}{\sigma_2} = \frac{q_1/4\pi R_1^2}{q_2/4\pi R_2^2} = \left(\frac{q_1}{q_2}\right)\left(\frac{R_2}{R_1}\right)^2 = 2.$$

77P

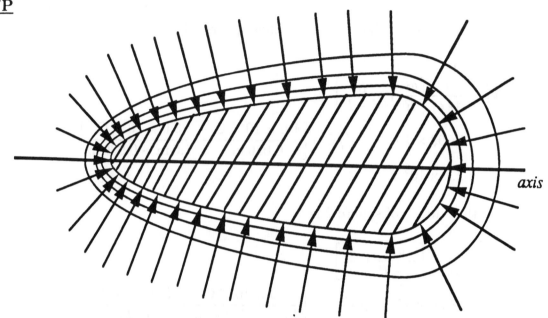

some equipotential lines and electric field lines(denoted with arrows)

78P

(a) The potential would be

$$V_e = \frac{Q_e}{4\pi\epsilon_0 R_e} = \frac{4\pi R_e^2 \sigma_e}{4\pi\epsilon_0 R_e}$$
$$= 4\pi(6.37 \times 10^6 \text{ m})(1.0 \text{ electron}/\text{ m}^2)(-1.6 \times 10^{-19} \text{ C}/\text{ electron})(8.99 \times 10^9 \text{ N} \cdot \text{ m}^2/\text{ C}^2)$$
$$= -0.12 \text{ V}.$$

(b)

$$E = \frac{\sigma_e}{\epsilon_0} = \frac{V_e}{R_e} = -\frac{0.12 \text{ V}}{6.37 \times 10^6 \text{ m}} = -1.8 \times 10^{-8} \text{ N/C},$$

where the minus sign indicates that **E** is radially inward.

79P

(a) The electric potential is the sum of the contributions of the individual spheres. Let q_1 be the charge on one and q_2 be the charge on the other. The point halfway between them is the same distance d $(= 1.0\,\mathrm{m})$ from the center of each sphere, so the potential at the halfway point is

$$V = \frac{q_1 + q_2}{4\pi\epsilon_0 d} = \frac{(8.99 \times 10^9\,\mathrm{N \cdot m^2/C^2})(1.0 \times 10^{-8}\,\mathrm{C} - 3.0 \times 10^{-8}\,\mathrm{C})}{1.0\,\mathrm{m}} = -1.80 \times 10^2\,\mathrm{V}\,.$$

(b) The distance from the center of one sphere to the surface of the other is $d - R$, where R is the radius of either sphere. The potential of either one of the spheres is due to the charge on that sphere and the charge on the other sphere. The potential at the surface of sphere 1 is

$$
\begin{aligned}
V_1 &= \frac{1}{4\pi\epsilon_0}\left[\frac{q_1}{R} + \frac{q_2}{d - R}\right] \\
&= (8.99 \times 10^9\,\mathrm{N \cdot m^2/C^2})\left[\frac{1.0 \times 10^{-8}\,\mathrm{C}}{0.030\,\mathrm{m}} - \frac{3.0 \times 10^{-8}\,\mathrm{C}}{1.0\,\mathrm{m} - 0.030\,\mathrm{m}}\right] \\
&= 2.7 \times 10^3\,\mathrm{V}\,.
\end{aligned}
$$

The potential at the surface of sphere 2 is

$$
\begin{aligned}
V_2 &= \frac{1}{4\pi\epsilon_0}\left[\frac{q_1}{d - R} + \frac{q_2}{R}\right] \\
&= (8.99 \times 10^9\,\mathrm{N \cdot m^2/C^2})\left[\frac{1.0 \times 10^{-8}\,\mathrm{C}}{1.0\,\mathrm{m} - 0.030\,\mathrm{m}} - \frac{3.0 \times 10^{-8}\,\mathrm{C}}{0.030\,\mathrm{m}}\right] \\
&= -8.9 \times 10^3\,\mathrm{V}\,.
\end{aligned}
$$

80P

(a)

$$E = \frac{\sigma}{\epsilon_0} = \frac{q}{4\pi\epsilon_0 R^2}$$

$$= \frac{(3.0 \times 10^{-8}\,\mathrm{C})(8.99 \times 10^9\,\mathrm{N \cdot m^2/C^2})}{(0.15\,\mathrm{m})^2} = 1.2 \times 10^4\,\mathrm{N/C}\,.$$

(b) $V = RE = (0.15\,\mathrm{m})(1.2 \times 10^4\,\mathrm{N/C}) = 1.8 \times 10^3\,\mathrm{V}$.

(c) Let the distance be x. Then

$$\Delta V = V(x) - V = \frac{q}{4\pi\epsilon_0}\left(\frac{1}{R + x} - \frac{1}{R}\right) = -500\,\mathrm{V}\,,$$

which gives

$$x = \frac{R\Delta V}{-V - \Delta V} = \frac{(0.15\,\mathrm{m})(-500\,\mathrm{V})}{-1800\,\mathrm{V} + 500\,\mathrm{V}} = 5.8 \times 10^{-2}\,\mathrm{m}\,.$$

For $r > R_2 > R_1$:

$$\begin{cases} V(r) = \dfrac{q_1 + q_2}{4\pi\epsilon_0 r}, \\[2mm] E(r) = \dfrac{q_1 + q_2}{4\pi\epsilon_0 r^2}. \end{cases}$$

For $R_2 > r > R_1$:

$$\begin{cases} V(r) = \dfrac{1}{4\pi\epsilon_0}\left(\dfrac{q_1}{r} + \dfrac{q_2}{R_2}\right), \\[2mm] E(r) = \dfrac{q_1}{4\pi\epsilon_0 r^2}. \end{cases}$$

For $R_2 > R_1 > r$:

$$\begin{cases} E = 0, \\[2mm] V(r) = \dfrac{1}{4\pi\epsilon_0}\left(\dfrac{q_1}{R_1} + \dfrac{q_2}{R_2}\right). \end{cases}$$

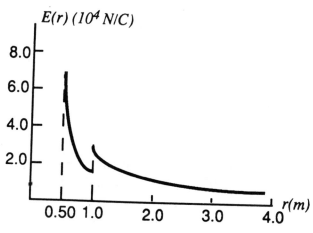
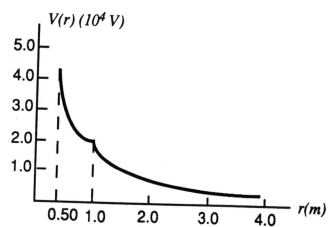

82E
(a) Use $V = q/4\pi\epsilon_0 R$ to calculate q:

$$q = 4\pi\epsilon_0 V R = \frac{(1.0 \times 10^6 \text{ V})(1.0 \text{ m})}{8.99 \times 10^9 \text{ N} \cdot \text{m}^2/\text{C}^2} = 1.1 \times 10^{-4} \text{ C}.$$

(b) Now

$$q' = 4\pi\epsilon_0 V R' = \frac{qR'}{R} = \frac{(1.1 \times 10^{-4} \text{ C})(1.0 \text{ cm})}{(1.0 \text{ m})} = 1.1 \times 10^{-6} \text{ C}.$$

(c) Since the electric field just outside the sphere is given by $E = V/R$, a large enough radius R is needed to prevent E from being so strong as to cause electrical breakdown in the air.

83E
The minimum power required is

$$P = \frac{d}{dt}(q\Delta V) = \frac{dq}{dt}\Delta V$$
$$= (2.80 \times 10^{-3} \text{ C/s})(3.40 \times 10^6 \text{ V}) = 9.52 \times 10^3 \text{ W}.$$

84E
(a) Since energy is conserved and the α particle starts from rest its final kinetic energy is the change in its potential energy: $K = \Delta U$. The change in its potential energy is $\Delta U = q\,\Delta V$, where q is its charge ($2e$) and ΔV is the difference in the electric potential along the accelerator. Thus $K = 2e\,\Delta V = 2(1.60 \times 10^{-19} \text{ C})(1.0 \times 10^6 \text{ V}) = 3.2 \times 10^{-13} \text{ J}$.

(b) The charge on the proton is e, so

$$K = e\,\Delta V = (1.60 \times 10^{-19} \text{ C})(1.0 \times 10^6 \text{ V}) = 1.6 \times 10^{-13} \text{ J}.$$

(c) Since $K = \frac{1}{2}mv^2$, where m is the mass of a particle and v is its speed,

$$v = \sqrt{\frac{2K}{m}} = \sqrt{\frac{2q\,\Delta V}{m}},$$

Now an α particle has twice the charge of a proton and 4 times the mass so the ratio of the final speeds is $v_p/v_\alpha = \sqrt{2}$. For $\Delta V = 1.0 \times 10^6$ V, $v_p = 1.4 \times 10^7$ m/s and $v_\alpha = 9.8 \times 10^6$ m/s.

85P
(a) Take $V = 0$ at infinity. Then

$$\begin{cases} V_r = \dfrac{1}{4\pi\epsilon_0}\left(\dfrac{Q}{R} + \dfrac{q}{r}\right), \\[2mm] V_R = \dfrac{1}{4\pi\epsilon_0}\left(\dfrac{q}{R} + \dfrac{Q}{R}\right). \end{cases}$$

Thus

$$V_r - V_R = \frac{q}{4\pi\epsilon_0}\left(\frac{1}{r} - \frac{1}{R}\right).$$

(b) Since $V_r - V_R \propto q$ must reduce to zero upon connection of the two sphere with a conducting wire, q must be zero.

710

86P

If Q is the charge on the shell and R is its radius, then the electric potential of the shell is given by $V = Q/4\pi\epsilon_0 R$ and the magnitude of the electric field just outside the shell is given by $E = Q/4\pi\epsilon_0 R^2$, so $V = RE$. Calculate R for the operating potential of the generator and the breakdown electric field:

$$R = \frac{V}{E} = \frac{9.0\,\text{MV}}{100\,\text{MV/m}} = 9.0 \times 10^{-2}\,\text{m}.$$

For larger values of R the electric field is smaller in magnitude so R must be larger than 9.0 cm to avoid breakdown.

(b) For each infinitesimal amount of charge dq that is transferred, work $dW = V\,dq$ must be done. The power required is the rate of doing work: $P = dW/dt = V\,dq/dt$, where dq/dt is the rate at which charge is transferred. Thus $P = (9.0 \times 10^6\,\text{V})(300 \times 10^{-6}\,\text{C/s}) = 2.7 \times 10^3\,\text{W}$.

(c) As the belt moves a distance $\Delta\ell$ it delivers charge $\Delta q = \sigma w \Delta\ell$, so the charge delivered per unit time is $\Delta q / \Delta t = \sigma w \Delta\ell / \Delta t$, where Δt is the time required for the belt to move the distance $\Delta\ell$. Now $\Delta\ell / \Delta t = v$, where v is the speed of the belt, so $\Delta q / \Delta t = \sigma w v$ and

$$\sigma = \frac{1}{wv}\frac{\Delta q}{\Delta t} = \frac{300 \times 10^{-6}\,\text{C/s}}{(0.50\,\text{m})(30\,\text{m/s})} = 2.0 \times 10^{-5}\,\text{C/m}^2.$$

87

(a) Let $x = 0$ be at the outer screen of the pair of screens at left, whose potential is arbitrarily set to be zero.

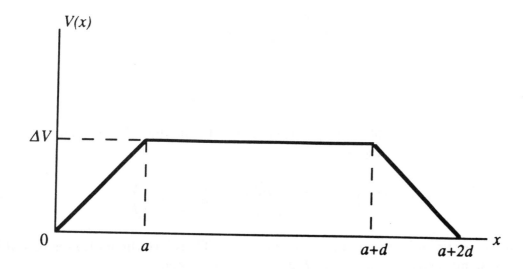

(b) As long as the proton can make it to the inner screen of the pair at left it will no longer encounter any resistance. So its minimum energy required is $E = e\Delta V = 100\,\text{eV}$.

(c) It would proceed to the right, speeding up between the left pair of screens, traveling at a constant speed between the two pairs, slowing down between the right pair, and leaving with its original velocity.

88

Consider the potential $V(r)$ at point r. The contribution to $V(r)$ from the charges located in the region between $(0, r)$ is $V_1(r) = Q(r)/4\pi\epsilon_0 r$, while the contribution to $V(r)$ due to the charges dQ located elsewhere (at $r' > r$) is

$$dV_2(r, r') = \frac{dQ(r')}{4\pi\epsilon_0 r'}.$$

Thus

$$V_2(r) = \int_r^\infty \frac{dQ(r')}{4\pi\epsilon_0 r'^2},$$

and

$$V(r) = V_1(r) + V_2(r) = \frac{Q(r)}{4\pi\epsilon_0 r} + \int_r^\infty \frac{dQ(r')}{4\pi\epsilon_0 r'}.$$

However

$$\int_r^\infty \frac{Q(r')}{4\pi\epsilon_0 r'^2} dr' = -\frac{1}{4\pi\epsilon_0} \int_r^\infty Q(r') d\left(\frac{1}{r'}\right)$$

$$= -\left. \frac{Q(r')}{4\pi\epsilon_0 r'} \right|_r^\infty + \int_0^\infty \frac{dQ(r')}{4\pi\epsilon_0 r'} = \frac{Q(r)}{4\pi\epsilon_0 r} + \int_r^\infty \frac{dQ(r')}{4\pi\epsilon_0 r'}.$$

Comparing the two equations above we find

$$V(r) = \int_r^\infty \frac{Q(r')}{4\pi\epsilon_0 r'^2} dr'.$$

89

(a) Consider a small displacement x for Q perpendicular to the line. The change in electric potential energy as a function of x is

$$\Delta U(x) = U(x) - U(0) = \frac{2qQ}{4\pi\epsilon_0}\left(\frac{1}{\sqrt{a^2 + x^2}} - \frac{1}{a}\right).$$

Obviously $\Delta U(x)$ assumes its maximum $(= 0)$ at $x = 0$. Therefore the motion is unstable. Now consider a small displacement x for Q along the line. Then

$$\Delta U(x) = \frac{qQ}{4\pi\epsilon_0}\left(\frac{1}{a+x} + \frac{1}{a-x} - \frac{2}{a}\right) = \frac{qQx^2}{2\pi\epsilon_0 a(a^2 - x^2)}.$$

For $x \ll a$, $\Delta U(x)$ obviously has a minimum at $x = 0$. Therefore the motion is stable.

(c) To lowest order in x

$$\Delta U(x) = \frac{qQx^2}{2\pi\epsilon_0 a^3}\left(1 + \frac{x^2}{a^2} + \cdots\right) \approx \frac{qQx^2}{2\pi\epsilon_0 a^3}.$$

Thus

$$|F| = \left|\frac{d}{dx}\Delta U(x)\right| = \frac{qQx}{\pi\epsilon_0 a^3}.$$

(d) Since $F = -k_{\text{eff}}x$ where $k_{\text{eff}} = qQ/\pi\epsilon_0 a^3$, we have

$$\omega = \sqrt{\frac{k_{\text{eff}}}{m}} = \sqrt{\frac{qQ}{\pi\epsilon_0 a^3 m}}.$$

90

(a) Set up a coodinate system on the surface of the conducting plane with its origin at the midpoint of the line joining $+q$ and $-q$. Thus with $V = 0$ at infinity,

$$V(x,y,0) = \frac{1}{4\pi\epsilon_0}\left(\frac{q}{\sqrt{x^2 + y^2 + d^2}} + \frac{-q}{\sqrt{x^2 + y^2 + d^2}}\right) = 0,$$

i.e. the plane is an equipotential surface.

(b)

$$F = \frac{1}{4\pi\epsilon_0}\frac{q^2}{(d+d)^2} = \frac{q^2}{16\pi\epsilon_0 d^2}.$$

91

(a) Since $V_1 = V_2$ we have $Q_1/4\pi\epsilon_0 R_1 = Q_2/4\pi\epsilon_0 R_2$. Also $Q_1 + Q_2 = Q$. Thus $Q_1 = QR_1/(R_1 + R_2)$ and $Q_2 = QR_2/(R_1 + R_2)$.

(b) The tension in the wire is

$$T = F_{12} = \frac{Q_1 Q_2}{4\pi\epsilon_0(L + R_1 + R_2)^2} = \frac{Q^2 R_1 R_2}{4\pi\epsilon_0(R_1 + R_2)^2(L + R_1 + R_2)^2}.$$

(Note that since $L \gg R_1, R_2$, we have $L + R_1 + R_2 \approx L$.)

CHAPTER 27

1E
The minimum charge measurabe is

$$Q_{min} = CV_{min} = (50\,\text{pF})(0.15\,\text{V}) = 7.5\,\text{pC}.$$

2E
(a)

$$C = \frac{Q}{\Delta V} = \frac{70\,\text{pC}}{20\,\text{V}} = 3.5\,\text{pF}.$$

(b) The capacitance is independent of Q, i.e. it is still $3.5\,\text{pF}$.
(c)

$$\Delta V = \frac{Q}{C} = \frac{200\,\text{pC}}{3.5\,\text{pF}} = 57\,\text{V}.$$

3E
Charge flows until the potential difference across the capacitor is the same as the emf of the battery. The charge on the capacitor is then $q = C\varepsilon$ and this is the same as the total charge that has passed through the battery. Thus $q = (25 \times 10^{-6}\,\text{F})(120\,\text{V}) = 3.0 \times 10^{-3}\,\text{C}$.

4E

$$[\epsilon_0] = \frac{\text{F}}{\text{m}} = \frac{\text{C}}{\text{V} \cdot \text{m}} = \frac{\text{C}}{(\text{N} \cdot \text{m}/\text{C})\,\text{m}} = \frac{\text{C}^2}{\text{N} \cdot \text{m}^2}.$$

5E
(a) The capacitance of a parallel plate capacitor is given by $C = \epsilon_0 A/d$, where A is the area of each plate and d is the plate separation. Since the plates are circular the plate area is $A = \pi R^2$, where R is the radius of a plate. Thus

$$C = \frac{\epsilon_0 \pi R^2}{d} = \frac{(8.85 \times 10^{-12}\,\text{F/m})\pi(8.2 \times 10^{-2}\,\text{m})^2}{1.3 \times 10^{-3}\,\text{m}} = 1.4 \times 10^{-10}\,\text{F} = 140\,\text{pF}.$$

(b) The charge on the positive plate is given by $q = CV$, where V is the potential difference across the plates. Thus $q = (1.4 \times 10^{-10}\,\text{F})(120\,\text{V}) = 1.7 \times 10^{-8}\,\text{C} = 17\,\text{nC}$.

6E
Use $C = A\epsilon_0/d$. Thus

$$d = \frac{A\epsilon_0}{C} = \frac{(1.00\,\text{m}^2)(8.85 \times 10^{-12}\,\text{F/m})}{1.00\,\text{F}} = 8.85 \times 10^{-12}\,\text{m}.$$

Since d is much less than the size of an atom ($\sim 10^{10}\,\text{m}$), this capacitor cannot be constructed.

7E
The capacitance of a cylindrical capacitor is given by $C = 2\pi\epsilon_0 L/\ln(b/a)$, where L is the length, a is the inner radius, and b is the outer radius. Thus

$$C = \frac{2\pi(8.85 \times 10^{-12}\,\text{F/m})(2.4 \times 10^{-2}\,\text{m})}{\ln\left[(18\,\text{mm})/(1.6\,\text{mm})\right]} = 5.5 \times 10^{-13}\,\text{F} = 0.55\,\text{pF}.$$

The diameters can be used instead of the radii since the radii enter the equation as a ratio.

8E
(a) Use Eq. 27-17:

$$C = 4\pi\epsilon_0\frac{ab}{b-a} = \frac{(40.0\,\text{mm})(38.0\,\text{mm})}{(8.99 \times 10^9\,\text{N}\cdot\text{m}^2/\,\text{C}^2)(40.0\,\text{mm} - 38.0\,\text{mm})} = 84.5\,\text{pF}.$$

(b) Let the area required be A. Then $C = \epsilon_0 A/(b-a)$, or

$$A = \frac{C(b-a)}{\epsilon_0} = \frac{(84.5\,\text{pF})(40.0\,\text{mm} - 38.0\,\text{mm})}{(8.85 \times 10^{-12}\,\text{F/m})} = 191\,\text{cm}^2.$$

9E
The charge accumulated is

$$Q = CV = 4\pi\epsilon_0 RV = \frac{(0.25\,\text{m})(15 \times 10^3\,\text{V})}{8.99 \times 10^9\,\text{N}\cdot\text{m}^2/\,\text{C}^2} = 4.1 \times 10^{-7}\,\text{C}.$$

10E
(a) Use $Q = CV = \epsilon_0 AV/d$:

$$A = \frac{cd}{\epsilon_0} = \frac{(10 \times 10^{-12}\,\text{F})(1.0 \times 10^{-3}\,\text{m})}{(8.85 \times 10^{-12}\,\text{F/m})} = 1.1 \times 10^{-3}\,\text{m}^2.$$

(b) Now

$$C' = C\left(\frac{d}{d'}\right) = (10\,\text{pF})\left(\frac{1.0\,\text{mm}}{0.9\,\text{mm}}\right) = 11\,\text{pF}.$$

(c) The new potential difference is $V' = Q/C = CV/C'$. Thus

$$\Delta V = V' - V = \frac{(10\,\text{pF})(12\,\text{V})}{11\,\text{pF}} - 12\,\text{V} = 1.2\,\text{V}.$$

In a microphone, mechanical pressure applied to the aluminum foil as a result of sound can cause the capacitance of the foil to change, therefore inducing a variable ΔV in response to the sound signal.

11E

You want to find the radius of the combined spheres, then use $C = 4\pi\epsilon_0 R$ to find the capacitance. When the drops combine the volume is doubled. It is then $V = 2(4\pi/3)R^3$. The new radius R' is given by

$$\frac{4\pi}{3}(R')^3 = 2\frac{4\pi}{3}R^3\,,$$

so

$$R' = 2^{1/3}R\,.$$

The new capacitance is $C' = 4\pi\epsilon_0 R' = 4\pi\epsilon_0 2^{1/3}R = 2^{1/3}C = 1.26C$.

12P

In Eq. 27-14, let $b = a + d$ with $d/a \ll 1$, we have

$$C = 2\pi\epsilon_0 \frac{L}{\ln(b/a)} = 2\pi\epsilon_0 \frac{L}{\ln(1 + d/a)} \approx \frac{2\pi\epsilon_0 L}{d/a}$$

$$= \frac{\epsilon_0(2\pi aL)}{d} \approx \frac{\epsilon_0 A}{d}\,,$$

where $A = 2\pi aL$ is roughly the surface area of either of the cylinders.

13P

From Eq. 27-17

$$C = 4\pi\epsilon_0 \frac{ab}{b - a} \approx \frac{\epsilon_0(4\pi a^2)}{d} = \frac{\epsilon_0 A}{d}\,.$$

14P

$$\frac{dC}{dT} = \frac{d}{dT}\left(\epsilon_0 \frac{A}{x}\right) = \frac{\epsilon_0}{x}\frac{dA}{dT} - \frac{\epsilon_0 A}{x^2}\frac{dx}{dT}$$

$$= \frac{\epsilon_0 A}{x}\left(\frac{1}{A}\frac{dA}{dT} - \frac{1}{x}\frac{dx}{dT}\right)$$

$$= C\left(\frac{1}{A}\frac{dA}{dT} - \frac{1}{x}\frac{dx}{dT}\right).$$

(b) Let $dC/dT = 0$:

$$\frac{1}{A}\frac{dA}{dT} = \beta_{Al} = 2\alpha_{Al} = \alpha_x.$$

So $\alpha_x = 2\alpha_{Al} = 2(2.3 \times 10^{-6}/°C) = 4.6 \times 10^{-5}/°C.$

15E

The equivalent capacitance is given by $C_{eq} = q/V$, where q is the total charge on all the capacitors and V is the potential difference across any one of them. For N identical capacitors in parallel $C_{eq} = NC$, where C is the capacitance of one of them. Thus $NC = q/V$ and

$$N = \frac{q}{VC} = \frac{1.00\,\text{C}}{(110\,\text{V})(1.00 \times 10^{-6}\,\text{F})} = 9090.$$

16P

$$C_{eq} = \frac{(C_1 + C_2)C_3}{C_1 + C_2 + C_3} = \frac{(10.0\mu\,\text{F} + 5.00\mu\,\text{F})(4.00\mu\,\text{F})}{10.0\mu\,\text{F} + 5.00\mu\,\text{F} + 4.00\mu\,\text{F}} = 3.16\mu\,\text{F}.$$

17E

$$C_{eq} = C_3 + \frac{C_1 C_2}{C_1 + C_2} = 4.00\mu\,\text{F} + \frac{(10.0\mu\,\text{F})(5.00\mu\,\text{F})}{10.0\mu\,\text{F} + 5.00\mu\,\text{F}} = 7.33\mu\,\text{F}$$

18E

The charge that passes through meter A is

$$q = C_{eq}V = 3CV = 3(25.0\mu\,\text{F})(4200\,\text{V}) = 0.315\,\text{C}.$$

19E

(a) $C_{eq} = \dfrac{C_1 C_2}{C_1 + C_2} = (6.00\mu\,\text{F})(4.00\mu\,\text{F})/6.00\mu\,\text{F} + 4.00\mu\,\text{F} = 2.40\mu\,\text{F}.$

(b) $q = C_{eq}V = (2.40\mu\,\mathrm{F})(200\,\mathrm{V}) = 4.8 \times 10^4\,\mathrm{C}$.

(c) $V_1 = q/C_1 = 4.8 \times 10^4\,\mathrm{C}/2.40\mu\,\mathrm{F} = 120\,\mathrm{V}$, and $V_2 = V - V_1 = 200\,\mathrm{V} - 120\,\mathrm{V} = 80\,\mathrm{V}$.

20E

(a) Now $C_{eq} = C_1 + C_2 = 6.00\mu\,\mathrm{F} + 4.00\mu\,\mathrm{F} = 10.0\mu\,\mathrm{F}$.

(b) $q_1 = C_1V = (6.00\mu\,\mathrm{F})(200\,\mathrm{V}) = 1.20 \times 10^{-3}\,\mathrm{C}$, $q_2 = C_2V = (4.00\mu\,\mathrm{F})(200\,\mathrm{V}) = 8.00 \times 10^{-4}\,\mathrm{C}$.

(c) $V_1 = V_2 = 200\,\mathrm{V}$.

21P

(a) The equivalent capacitance of the three capacitors connected in parallel is $C_{eq} = 3C = 3\epsilon_0 A/d$. Thus the required spacing is $d/3$.

(b) Now $C_{eq} = C/3 = \epsilon_0 A/3d$, so the spacing should be $3d$.

22P

(a) The equivalent capacitance is $C_{eq} = C_1C_2/(C_1 + C_2)$. Thus the charge q on each capacitor is

$$q = C_{eq}V = \frac{C_1C_2V}{C_1 + C_2} = \frac{(2.0\mu\,\mathrm{F})(8.0\mu\ \mathrm{F})(300\,\mathrm{V})}{2.0\mu\,\mathrm{F} + 8.0\mu\,\mathrm{F}} = 4.8 \times 10^{-4}\,\mathrm{C}.$$

The potential differences are: $V_1 = q/C_1 = 4.8 \times 10^{-4}\,\mathrm{C}/2.0\mu\,\mathrm{F} = 240\,\mathrm{V}$, $V_2 = V - V_1 = 300\,\mathrm{V} - 240\,\mathrm{V} = 60\,\mathrm{V}$.

(b) Now we have $q_1'/C_1 = q_2'/C_2 = V'$ (V' being the new potential difference across each capacitor) and $q_1' + q_2' = 2q$. Solve for q_1', q_2' and V:

$$\begin{cases} q_1' = \dfrac{2C_1q}{C_1 + C_2} = \dfrac{2(2.0\mu\,\mathrm{F})(4.8 \times 10^{-4}\,\mathrm{C})}{2.0\mu\,\mathrm{F} + 8.0\mu\,\mathrm{F}} = 1.9 \times 10^{-4}\,\mathrm{C}, \\[2mm] q_2' = 2q - q_1 = 7.7 \times 10^{-4}\,\mathrm{C}, \\[2mm] V' = \dfrac{q_1'}{C_1} = \dfrac{1.92 \times 10^{-4}\,\mathrm{C}}{2.0\mu\,\mathrm{F}} = 96\,\mathrm{V}. \end{cases}$$

(c) Now the capacitors will simply discharge themselves, leaving $q_1 = q_2 = 0$ and $V_1 = V_2 = 0$.

23P

For maximum capacitance the two groups of plates must face each other with maximum area. In this case the whole capacitor consists of $(n - 1)$ single capacitors of capacitance $C_0 = \epsilon_0 A/d$ each, connected in parallel, with surface area A and plate separation d. Thus

$$C = (n - 1)C_0 = \frac{(n - 1)\epsilon_0 A}{d}.$$

718

24P

(a) and (b) The original potential difference V_1 on C_1 is

$$V_1 = \frac{C_{eq}V}{C_1 + C_2} = \frac{(3.16\mu\,\mathrm{F})(100\,\mathrm{V})}{10.0\mu\,\mathrm{F} + 5.00\mu\,\mathrm{F}} = 21.1\,\mathrm{V}.$$

Thus $\Delta V_1 = 100\,\mathrm{V} - 21.1\,\mathrm{V} = 78.9\,\mathrm{V}$, and $\Delta q_1 = C_1\Delta V_1 = (10.0\mu\,\mathrm{F})(78.9\,\mathrm{V}) = 7.89 \times 10^{-4}\,\mathrm{C}$.

25P

(a) Put five such capacitors in a series. Obviously the equivalent capacitance is $2.0\mu\,\mathrm{F}/5 = 0.40\mu\,\mathrm{F}$, and with each capacitor taking a 200-V potential difference the equivalent capacitor can withstand 1000 V.

(b) As one possibility, you can take three arrays as in (a) above and hook them in parallel. The equivalent capacitance is now $C_{eq} = 3(0.40\mu\,\mathrm{F}) = 1.2\mu\,\mathrm{F}$, and with each capacitor taking a 200-V potential difference the equivalent capacitor can withstand 1000 V.

26P

Let x be the separation of the plates in the lower capacitor. Then the plate separation in the upper capacitor is $a - b - x$. The capacitance of the lower capacitor is $C_\ell = \epsilon_0 A/x$ and the capacitance of the upper capacitor is $C_u = \epsilon_0 A/(a - b - x)$, where A is the plate area. Since the two capacitors are in series the equivalent capacitance is determined from

$$\frac{1}{C_{eq}} = \frac{1}{C_\ell} + \frac{1}{C_u} = \frac{x}{\epsilon_0 A} + \frac{a - b - x}{\epsilon_0 A} = \frac{a - b}{\epsilon_0 A}.$$

Thus the equivalent capacitance is given by $C_{eq} = \epsilon_0 A/(a - b)$ and is independent of x.

27P

The charge initially carried by the 100-pF capacitor is $q_1 = C_1 V_1 = (100\,\mathrm{pF})(50\,\mathrm{V}) = 5.0 \times 10^{-9}\,\mathrm{C}$. When connected with the second capacitor, the charge on the first one reduces to $q_1' = C_1 V_1' = (100\,\mathrm{pF})(35\,\mathrm{V}) = 3.5 \times 10^{-9}\,\mathrm{C}$, which means that the second one now has a charge of $q_2 = q_1 - q_1' = 1.5 \times 10^{-9}\,\mathrm{C}$. Thus its capacitance is $C_2 = q_2/V_2 = 1.5 \times 10^{-9}\,\mathrm{C}/35\,\mathrm{V} = 43\,\mathrm{pF}$.

28P

(a) After the switches are closed the potential differences across the capacitors are the same and the two capacitors are in parallel. The potential difference from a to b is given by $V_{ab} = Q/C_{eq}$, where Q is the net charge on the combination and C_{eq} is the equivalent capacitance.

The equivalent capacitance is $C_{eq} = C_1 + C_2 = 4.0 \times 10^{-6}$ F. The total charge on the combination is the net charge on either pair of connected plates. The charge on capacitor 1 is

$$q_1 = C_1 V = (1.0 \times 10^{-6} \text{ F})(100 \text{ V}) = 1.0 \times 10^{-4} \text{ C}$$

and the charge on capacitor 2 is

$$q_2 = C_2 V = (3.0 \times 10^{-6} \text{ F})(100 \text{ V}) = 3.0 \times 10^{-4} \text{ C} \,,$$

so the net charge on the combination is 3.0×10^{-4} C $- 1.0 \times 10^{-4}$ C $= 2.0 \times 10^{-4}$ C. The potential difference is

$$V_{ab} = \frac{2.0 \times 10^{-4} \text{ C}}{4.0 \times 10^{-6} \text{ F}} = 50 \text{ V} \,.$$

(b) The charge on capacitor 1 is now $q_1 = C_1 V_{ab} = (1.0 \times 10^{-6} \text{ F})(50 \text{ V}) = 5.0 \times 10^{-5}$ C.

(c) The charge on capacitor 2 is now $q_2 = C_2 V_{ab} = (3.0 \times 10^{-6} \text{ F})(50 \text{ V}) = 1.5 \times 10^{-4}$ C.

29P

The charges on capacitors 2 and 3 are the same, so these capacitors may be replaced by an equivalent capacitance determined from

$$\frac{1}{C_{eq}} = \frac{1}{C_2} + \frac{1}{C_3} = \frac{C_2 + C_3}{C_2 C_3} \,.$$

Thus $C_{eq} = C_2 C_3 / (C_2 + C_3)$. The charge on the equivalent capacitor is the same as the charge on either of the two capacitors in the combination and the potential difference across the equivalent capacitor is given by q_2 / C_{eq}. The potential difference across capacitor 1 is q_1 / C_1, where q_1 is the charge on this capacitor.

The potential difference across the combination of capacitors 2 and 3 must be the same as the potential difference across capacitor 1, so $q_1 / C_1 = q_2 / C_{eq}$. Now some of the charge originally on capacitor 1 flows to the combination of 2 and 3. If q_0 is the original charge, conservation of charge yields $q_1 + q_2 = q_0 = C_1 V_0$, where V_0 is the original potential difference across capacitor 1.

Solve the two equations $q_1 / C_1 = q_2 / C_{eq}$ and $q_1 + q_2 = C_1 V_0$ for q_1 and q_2. The second equation yields

$$q_2 = C_1 V_0 - q_1$$

and, when this is substituted into the first, the result is

$$\frac{q_1}{C_1} = \frac{C_1 V_0 - q_1}{C_{eq}} \,.$$

Solve for q_1. You should get

$$q_1 = \frac{C_1^2 V_0}{C_{eq} + C_1} = \frac{C_1^2 V_0}{\dfrac{C_2 C_3}{C_2 + C_3} + C_1} = \frac{C_1^2 (C_2 + C_3) V_0}{C_1 C_2 + C_1 C_3 + C_2 C_3} \,.$$

720

The charges on capacitors 2 and 3 are

$$q_2 = q_3 = C_1 V_0 - q_1 = C_1 V_0 - \frac{C_1^2(C_2 + C_3)V_0}{C_1 C_2 + C_1 C_3 + C_2 C_3} = \frac{C_1 C_2 C_3 V_0}{C_1 C_2 + C_1 C_3 + C_2 C_3}.$$

30P
(a)

$$q_1 = q_3 = \frac{C_1 C_3 V}{C_1 + C_3} = \frac{(1.0\mu\,\mathrm{F})(3.0\mu\,\mathrm{F})(12\,\mathrm{V})}{1.0\mu\,\mathrm{F} + 3.0\mu\,\mathrm{F}} = 9.0\mu\,\mathrm{C},$$

$$q_2 = q_4 = \frac{C_2 C_4 V}{C_2 + C_4} = \frac{(2.0\mu\,\mathrm{F})(4.0\mu\,\mathrm{F})(12\,\mathrm{V})}{2.0\mu\,\mathrm{F} + 4.0\mu\,\mathrm{F}} = 16\mu\,\mathrm{C},$$

(b) Now the voltage difference V_1 across C_1 and C_2 is

$$V_1 = \frac{C_3 + C_4}{C_1 + C_2 + C_3 + C_4}V = \frac{(3.0\mu\,\mathrm{F} + 4.0\mu\,\mathrm{F})(12\,\mathrm{V})}{1.0\mu\,\mathrm{F} + 2.0\mu\,\mathrm{F} + 3.0\mu\,\mathrm{F} + 4.0\mu\,\mathrm{F}} = 8.4\,\mathrm{V}.$$

Thus $q_1 = C_1 V_1 = (1.0\mu\,\mathrm{F})(8.4\,\mathrm{V}) = 8.4\mu\,\mathrm{C}$, $q_2 = C_2 V_1 = (2.0\mu\,\mathrm{F})(8.4\,\mathrm{V}) = 17\mu\,\mathrm{C}$, $q_3 = C_3(V - V_1) = (3.0\mu\,\mathrm{F})(12\,\mathrm{V} - 8.4\,\mathrm{V}) = 11\mu\,\mathrm{C}$, $q_4 = C_4(V - V_1) = (4.0\mu\,\mathrm{F})(12\,\mathrm{V} - 8.4\,\mathrm{V}) = 14\mu\,\mathrm{C}$.

31P
In the first case the two capacitors are effectively in series so the output potential difference is $V_{\mathrm{out}} = CV_{\mathrm{in}}/2C = V_{\mathrm{in}}/2 = 50.0\,\mathrm{V}$. In the second case the lower diode acts as a wire so $V_{\mathrm{out}} = 0$.

32E
Let $V = 1.00\,\mathrm{m}^3$. The energy stored is

$$U = uV = \frac{1}{2}\epsilon_0 E^2 V$$

$$= \frac{1}{2}(8.85 \times 10^{-12}\,\mathrm{F/m})(150\,\mathrm{V/m})^2(1.00\,\mathrm{m}^3) = 9.96 \times 10^{-8}\,\mathrm{J}.$$

33E
(a)

$$U = \frac{1}{2}CV^2 = \frac{1}{2}(61.0 \times 10^{-3}\,\mathrm{F})(10.0 \times 10^3\,\mathrm{V})^2 = 3.05 \times 10^6\,\mathrm{J}.$$

(b)

$$U = (3.05 \times 10^6\,\mathrm{J})/(3.6 \times 10^6\,\mathrm{J/kW \cdot h}) = 0.847\,\mathrm{kW \cdot h}.$$

34E

The energy stored by a capacitor is given by $U = \frac{1}{2}CV^2$, where V is the potential difference across its plates. You must convert the given value of the energy to joules. Since a joule is a watt·second, simply multiply by $(10^3 \text{ W/kW})(3600 \text{ s/h})$ to obtain $10 \text{ kW} \cdot \text{h} = 3.6 \times 10^7 \text{ J}$. Thus

$$C = \frac{2U}{V^2} = \frac{2(3.6 \times 10^7 \text{ J})}{(1000 \text{ V})^2} = 72 \text{ F}.$$

35E

(a)

$$U = \frac{1}{2}CV^2 = \frac{1}{2}(130 \times 10^{-12} \text{ F})(56.0 \text{ V})^2 = 2.04 \times 10^{-7} \text{ J}.$$

(b) No, because we don't know the volume of the space inside the capacitor where the electric field is present.

36E

(a) $C = \dfrac{\epsilon_0 A}{d} = \dfrac{(8.85 \times 10^{-12} \text{ F/m})(40 \times 10^{-4} \text{ m}^2)}{1.0 \times 10^{-3} \text{ m}} = 3.5 \times 10^{-11} \text{ F} = 35 \text{ pF}.$

(b) $q = CV = (35 \text{ pF})(600 \text{ V}) = 2.1 \times 10^{-8} \text{ C} = 21 \text{ nC}.$

(c) $U = \dfrac{1}{2}CV^2 = \dfrac{1}{2}(35 \text{ pF})(21 \text{ nC})^2 = 6.3 \times 10^{-6} \text{ J} = 6.3\mu \text{ J}.$

(d) $E = V/d = 600 \text{ V}/1.0 \times 10^{-3} \text{ m} = 6.0 \times 10^5 \text{ V/m}.$

(e)

$$u = \frac{U}{v} = \frac{6.3 \times 10^{-6} \text{ J}}{(40 \times 10^{-4} \text{ m}^2)(1.0 \times 10^{-3} \text{ m})} = 1.6 \text{ J/m}^3.$$

37E

The total energy is the sum of the energies stored in the individual capacitors. Since they are connected in parallel the potential difference V across the capacitors is the same and the total energy is $U = \frac{1}{2}(C_1 + C_2)V^2 = \frac{1}{2}(2.0 \times 10^{-6} \text{ F} + 4.0 \times 10^{-6} \text{ F})(300 \text{ V})^2 = 0.27 \text{ J}.$

38E

(a)

$$u = \frac{1}{2}\epsilon_0 E^2 = \frac{1}{2}\epsilon_0 \left(\frac{e}{4\pi\epsilon_0 r^2}\right)^2 = \frac{e^2}{32\pi^2\epsilon_0 r^4}.$$

(b) For $r \to 0$, $u \to \infty$.

39E

Use $U = \frac{1}{2}CV^2$. As V is increased by ΔV we have $U + \Delta U = \frac{1}{2}C(V + \Delta V)^2$. Thus $(1 + \Delta V/V)^2 = 1 + \Delta U/U$, or

$$\frac{\Delta V}{V} = \sqrt{1 + \frac{\Delta U}{U}} - 1 = \sqrt{1 + 10\%} - 1 = 4.9\%.$$

40P

Use $E = q/4\pi\epsilon_0 R^2 = V/R$. Thus

$$u = \frac{1}{2}\epsilon_0 E^2 = \frac{1}{2}\epsilon_0 \left(\frac{V}{R}\right)^2 = \frac{1}{2}(8.85 \times 10^{-12}\,\text{F/m})\left(\frac{8000\,\text{V}}{0.050\,\text{m}}\right)^2 = 0.11\,\text{J/m}^3.$$

41P

The total energy stored in the bank is

$$U = \frac{1}{2}C_{\text{total}}V^2 = \frac{1}{2}(2000)(5.00 \times 10^{-6}\,\text{F})(50,000\,\text{V})^2 = 1.3 \times 10^7\,\text{J}.$$

Thus the cost is

$$\text{cost} = \frac{(1.3 \times 10^7\,\text{J})(3.0\,\text{cent/kW} \cdot \text{h})}{3.6 \times 10^6\,\text{J/kW} \cdot \text{h}} = 10\,\text{cent}.$$

42P

(a)

$$U_1 = \frac{q^2}{2C_1} = \frac{(4.8 \times 10^{-4}\,\text{C})^2}{2(2.0 \times 10^{-6}\,\text{F})} = 5.8 \times 10^{-2}\,\text{J},$$

$$U_2 = \frac{q^2}{2C_2} = \frac{(4.8 \times 10^{-4}\,\text{C})^2}{2(8.0 \times 10^{-6}\,\text{F})} = 1.4 \times 10^{-2}\,\text{J}.$$

(b)

$$U_1' = \frac{q_1'^2}{2C_1} = \frac{(1.9 \times 10^{-4}\,\text{C})^2}{2(2.0 \times 10^{-6}\,\text{F})} = 9.2 \times 10^{-3}\,\text{J},$$

$$U_2' = \frac{q_2'^2}{2C_2} = \frac{(7.7 \times 10^{-4}\,\text{C})^2}{2(8.0 \times 10^{-6}\,\text{F})} = 3.7 \times 10^{-2}\,\text{J}.$$

(c) $U_1'' = U_2'' = 0$.
Note that $U_1 + U_2 > U_1' + U_2' > U_1'' + U_2''$, since the system partially discharges as it goes from situation (a) to (b), and completely discharges in (c).

43P

(a) In the first case $U = q^2/2C$. In the second case $U = 2(q/2)^2/2C = q^2/4C$. So the energy is now $4.0\,\text{J}/2 = 2.0\,\text{J}$.

(b) It becomes the thermal energy generated in the wire connecting the capacitors during the discharging process.

44P

(a) and (b). The voltage difference across C_1 and C_2 is given by

$$V_1 = V_2 = \frac{C_3 V}{C_1 + C_2 + C_3} = \frac{(4.00\mu\,\text{F})(100\,\text{V})}{10.0\mu\,\text{F} + 5.00\mu\,\text{F} + 4.00\mu\,\text{F}} = 21.1\,\text{V}.$$

Also, $V_3 = V - V_1 = V - V_2 = 100\,\text{V} - 21.1\,\text{V} = 78.9\,\text{V}$. Thus $q_1 = C_1 V_1 = (10.0\mu\,\text{F})(21.1\,\text{V})$ $= 2.11 \times 10^{-4}\,\text{C}$, $q_2 = C_2 V_2 = (5.00\mu\ \text{F})(21.1\,\text{V}) = 1.05 \times 10^{-4}\,\text{C}$, and $q_3 = q_1 + q_2 = 2.11 \times 10^{-4}\,\text{C} + 1.05 \times 10^{-4}\,\text{C} = 3.16 \times 10^{-4}\,\text{C}$.

(c) $U_1 = \frac{1}{2} C_1 V_1^2 = \frac{1}{2}(10.0\mu\,\text{F})(21.1\,\text{V})^2 = 2.22 \times 10^{-3}\,\text{J}$, $U_2 = \frac{1}{2} C_2 V_2^2 = \frac{1}{2}(5.00\mu\,\text{F})$ $(21.1\,\text{V})^2 = 1.11 \times 10^{-3}\,\text{J}$, and $U_3 = \frac{1}{2} C_3 V_3^2 = \frac{1}{2}(4.00\mu\,\text{F})(78.9\,\text{V})^2 = 1.25 \times 10^{-2}\,\text{J}$.

45P

(a) $q_3 = C_3 V = (4.00\mu\,\text{F})(100\,\text{V}) = 4.00 \times 10^{-4}\,\text{mC}$,

$$q_1 = q_2 = \frac{C_1 C_2 V}{C_1 + C_2} = \frac{(10.0\mu\,\text{F})(5.00\mu\,\text{F})(100\,\text{V})}{10.0\mu\,\text{F} + 5.00\mu\,\text{F}} = 3.33 \times 10^{-4}\,\text{C}.$$

(b) $V_1 = q_1/C_1 = 3.33 \times 10^{-4}\,\text{C}/10.0\mu\,\text{F} = 33.3\,\text{V}$, $V_2 = V - V_1 = 100\,\text{V} - 33.3\,\text{V} = 66.7\,\text{V}$, and $V_3 = V = 100\,\text{V}$.

46P

(a) Let q be the charge on the positive plate. Since the capacitance of a parallel-plate capacitor is given by $\epsilon_0 A/d$, the charge is $q = CV = \epsilon_0 AV/d$. After the plates are pulled apart their separation is $2d$ and the potential difference is V'. Then $q = \epsilon_0 AV'/2d$ and

$$V' = \frac{2d}{\epsilon_0 A} q = \frac{2d}{\epsilon_0 A} \frac{\epsilon_0 A}{d} V = 2V.$$

(b) The initial energy stored in the capacitor is

$$U_i = \frac{1}{2} C V^2 = \frac{\epsilon_0 A V^2}{2d}$$

and the final energy stored is

$$U_f = \frac{1}{2} \frac{\epsilon_0 A}{2d} (V')^2 = \frac{1}{2} \frac{\epsilon_0 A}{2d} 4V^2 = \frac{\epsilon_0 A V^2}{d}.$$

This is twice the initial energy.

(*c*) The work done to pull the plates apart is the difference in the energy: $W = U_f - U_i = \epsilon_0 A V^2/2d$.

47P

You first need to find an expression for the energy stored in a cylinder of radius R and length L, whose surface lies between the inner and outer cylinders of the capacitor ($a < R < b$). The energy density at any point is given by $u = \frac{1}{2}\epsilon_0 E^2$, where E is the magnitude of the electric field at that point. If q is the charge on the surface of the inner cylinder then the magnitude of the electric field at a point a distance r from the cylinder axis is given by

$$E = \frac{q}{2\pi\epsilon_0 L r}$$

(see Eq. 27–12) and the energy density at that point is given by

$$u = \frac{1}{2}\epsilon_0 E^2 = \frac{q^2}{8\pi^2\epsilon_0 L^2 r^2}.$$

The energy in the cylinder is the volume integral

$$U_R = \int u \, dV.$$

Now $dV = 2\pi r L \, dr$, so

$$U_R = \int_a^R \frac{q^2}{8\pi^2\epsilon_0 L^2 r^2} 2\pi r \, dr = \frac{q^2}{4\pi\epsilon_0 L^2} \int_a^R \frac{dr}{r} = \frac{q^2}{4\pi\epsilon_0 L^2} \ln\frac{R}{a}.$$

To find an expression for the total energy stored in the capacitor, replace R with b:

$$U_b = \frac{q^2}{4\pi\epsilon_0 L^2} \ln\frac{b}{a}.$$

You want the ratio U_R/U_b to be $1/2$, so

$$\ln\frac{R}{a} = \frac{1}{2}\ln\frac{b}{a}$$

or, since $\frac{1}{2}\ln(b/a) = \ln(\sqrt{b/a})$, $\ln(R/a) = \ln(\sqrt{b/a})$. This means $R/a = \sqrt{b/a}$ or $R = \sqrt{ab}$.

48P

(a) The electric energy density as a function of r, the distance from the center of the electron, is given by

$$u(r) = \frac{1}{2}\epsilon_0 E^2(r) = \frac{1}{2}\epsilon_0\left(\frac{e}{4\pi\epsilon_0 r^2}\right)^2 = \frac{e^2}{32\pi^2\epsilon_0 r^4}.$$

725

Thus

$$U = \int_R^\infty u(r)4\pi r^2 dr = \frac{e^2}{8\pi\epsilon_0} \int_R^\infty \frac{dr}{r^2} = \frac{e^2}{8\pi\epsilon_0 R}.$$

(b) Let $U = mC^2$ we find

$$R = \frac{e^2}{8\pi\epsilon_0 mC^2} = \frac{(1.6\times 10^{-19}\,\text{C})^2(8.99\times 10^9\,\text{N}\cdot\text{m}^2/\text{C}^2)}{2(9.11\times 10^{-31}\,\text{kg})(3.00\times 10^8\,\text{m/s})^2}$$
$$= 1.41\times 10^{-15}\,\text{m} = 1.41\,\text{fm}.$$

49P

The charge is held constant while the plates are being separated, so write the expression for the stored energy as $U = q^2/2C$, where q is the charge and C is the capacitance. The capacitance of a parallel-plate capacitor is given by $C = \epsilon_0 A/x$, where A is the plate area and x is the plate separation, so

$$U = \frac{q^2 x}{2\epsilon_0 A}.$$

If the plate separation increases by dx the energy increases by $dU = (q^2/2\epsilon_0 A)\,dx$. Suppose the agent pulling the plate apart exerts force F. Then the agent does work $F\,dx$ and if the plates begin and end at rest this must equal the increase in stored energy. Thus

$$F\,dx = \left(\frac{q^2}{2\epsilon_0 A}\right) dx$$

and

$$F = \frac{q^2}{2\epsilon_0 A}.$$

The net force on a plate is zero so this must also be the magnitude of the force one plate exerts on the other.

The force can also be computed as the product of the charge q on one plate and the electric field E_1 due to the charge on the other plate. Recall that the field produced by a uniform plane surface of charge is $E_1 = q/2\epsilon_0 A$. Thus $F = q^2/2\epsilon_0 A$.

50P

According to the result of Problem 27–49 the force on either capacitor plate is given by $F = q^2/2\epsilon_0 A$, where q is the charge on one plate and A is the area of a plate. The electric field between the plates is $E = q/\epsilon_0 A$, so $q = \epsilon_0 AE$ and

$$F = \frac{\epsilon_0^2 A^2 E^2}{2\epsilon_0 A} = \frac{1}{2}\epsilon_0 AE^2.$$

726

The force per unit area of plate is

$$\frac{F}{A} = \frac{1}{2}\epsilon_0 E^2 .$$

Note that the field E that enters this equation is the total field, due to charges on both plates.

51P

According to the result of Problem 27–50 the electrostatic force acting on a small area ΔA is $F_e = \frac{1}{2}\epsilon_0 E^2 \Delta A$. The electric field at the surface is $E = q/4\pi\epsilon_0 R^2$, where q is the charge on the bubble. Thus

$$F_e = \frac{1}{2}\epsilon_0 \frac{q^2 \Delta A}{16\pi^2 \epsilon_0^2 R^4} = \frac{q^2 \Delta A}{32\pi^2 \epsilon_0 R^4} .$$

This force is outward. The force of the gas inside is the product of the pressure inside and the area: $F_g = p(V_0/V)\Delta A$. Since $V_0 = (4\pi/3)R_0^3$ and $V = (4\pi/3)R^3$,

$$F_g = p\left(\frac{R_0^3}{R^3}\right)\Delta A .$$

This force is outward. The force of the air outside is $F_a = p\,\Delta A$. This force is inward. Since the bubble surface is in equilibrium, the sum of the forces must vanish: $F_e + F_g - F_a = 0$. This means

$$\frac{q^2}{32\pi^2\epsilon_0 R^4} + p\frac{R_0^3}{R^3} - p = 0 .$$

Solve for q^2. You should get

$$q^2 = 32\pi^2\epsilon_0 R^4 p\left(1 - \frac{R_0^3}{R^3}\right) = 32\pi^2\epsilon_0 pR(R^3 - R_0^3) .$$

52E

If the original capacitance is given by $C = \epsilon_0 A/d$, then the new capacitance is $C' = \epsilon_0 \kappa A/2d$. Thus $C'/C = \kappa/2$ or $\kappa = 2C'/C = 2(2.6\,\text{pF}/1.3\,\text{pF}) = 4.0$.

53E

The capacitance with the dielectric in place is given by $C = \kappa C_0$, where C_0 is the capacitance before the dielectric is inserted. The energy stored is given by $U = \frac{1}{2}CV^2 = \frac{1}{2}\kappa C_0 V^2$, so

$$\kappa = \frac{2U}{C_0 V^2} = \frac{2(7.4 \times 10^{-6}\,\text{J})}{(7.4 \times 10^{-12}\,\text{F})(652\,\text{V})^2} = 4.7 .$$

According to Table 27–2 you should use pyrex.

54E

Use $C = \epsilon_0 \kappa A/d \propto \kappa/d$. To maximize C we need to choose the material with the greatest value of κ/d. It follows that the mica sheet should be chosen.

55E

(a) Use $C = \epsilon_0 A/d$. So

$$d = \frac{\epsilon_0 A}{C} = \frac{(8.85 \times 10^{-12}\,\text{F/m})(0.35\,\text{m}^2)}{50 \times 10^{-12}\,\text{F}} = 6.2 \times 10^{-2}\,\text{m}.$$

(b) Use $C \propto \kappa$. The new capacitance is $C' = C(\kappa/\kappa_{\text{air}}) = (50\,\text{pf})(5.6/1.0) = 280\,\text{pF}$.

56E

The capacitance of a cylindrical capacitor is given by

$$C = \kappa C_0 = \frac{2\pi \kappa \epsilon_0 L}{\ln(b/a)},$$

where C_0 is the capacitance without the dielectric, κ is the dielectric constant, L is the length, a is the inner radius, and b is the outer radius. The capacitance per unit length of the cable is

$$\frac{C}{L} = \frac{2\pi \kappa \epsilon_0}{\ln(b/a)} = \frac{2\pi(2.6)(8.85 \times 10^{-12}\,\text{F/m})}{\ln\left[(0.60\,\text{mm})/(0.10\,\text{mm})\right]} = 8.1 \times 10^{-11}\,\text{F/m} = 81\,\text{pF/m}.$$

57P

The capacitance is given by $C = \kappa C_0 = \kappa \epsilon_0 A/d$, where C_0 is the capacitance without the dielectric, κ is the dielectric constant, A is the plate area, and d is the plate separation. The electric field between the plates is given by $E = V/d$, where V is the potential difference between the plates. Thus $d = V/E$ and $C = \kappa \epsilon_0 AE/V$. Solve for A:

$$A = \frac{CV}{\kappa \epsilon_0 E}.$$

For the area to be a minimum, the electric field must be the greatest it can be without breakdown occurring. That is,

$$A = \frac{(7.0 \times 10^{-8}\,\text{F})(4.0 \times 10^3\,\text{V})}{2.8(8.85 \times 10^{-12}\,\text{F/m})(18 \times 10^6\,\text{V/m})} = 0.63\,\text{m}^2.$$

728

58P

(a) Use Eq. 27-14:

$$C = 2\pi\epsilon_0\kappa\frac{L}{\ln(b/a)} = \frac{(4.7)(0.15\,\mathrm{m})}{2(8.99\times10^9\,\mathrm{N\cdot m^2/C^2})\ln(3.8\,\mathrm{cm}/3.6\,\mathrm{cm})} = 0.73\,\mathrm{nF}.$$

(b) The breakdown potential is $(14\,\mathrm{kV/mm})(3.8\,\mathrm{cm} - 3.6\,\mathrm{cm}) = 28\,\mathrm{kV}$.

59P

(a) Since $u = \frac{1}{2}\kappa\epsilon_0 E^2$, we select the material with the greatest value of κE_{max}^2, when E_{max} is its dielectric strength. Thus we choose strontium titanate, with the corresponding minimum volume

$$V_{min} = \frac{U}{U_{max}} = \frac{2U}{\kappa\epsilon_0 E_{max}^2} = \frac{2(250\,\mathrm{kJ})}{(310)(8.85\times10^{-12}\,\mathrm{F/m})(8\,\mathrm{kV/mm})^2} = 2.85\,\mathrm{m^3}.$$

(b)

$$\kappa' = \frac{2U}{\epsilon_0 V'_{min} E_{max}^2} = \frac{2(250\,\mathrm{kJ})}{(8.85\times10^{-12}\,\mathrm{F/m})(0.0870\,\mathrm{m^3})(8\,\mathrm{kV/mm})^2} = 1.01\times10^4.$$

60P

(a)

$$C_{eq} = \frac{C_1 C_2}{C_1 + C_2} = \frac{(\epsilon_0 A/d)^2(\kappa + \Delta\kappa)(\kappa - \Delta\kappa)}{(\epsilon_0 A/d)(\kappa + \Delta\kappa + \kappa - \Delta\kappa)} = \frac{\epsilon_0 A}{d}\frac{\kappa^2 - (\Delta\kappa)^2}{2\kappa}.$$

(b)

$$q = \frac{C_1 Q}{C_1 + C_2} = \frac{(\epsilon_0 A/d)(\kappa + \Delta\kappa)Q}{(\epsilon_0 A/d)(\kappa + \Delta\kappa + \kappa - \Delta\kappa)} = \frac{1}{2}Q\left(1 + \frac{\Delta\kappa}{\kappa}\right).$$

61P

(a) The length d is effectively shortened by b so $C' = \epsilon_0 A/(d - b)$.

(b)

$$\frac{U}{U'} = \frac{q^2/2C}{q^2/2C'} = \frac{C'}{C} = \frac{\epsilon_0 A/(d-b)}{\epsilon_0 A/d} = \frac{d}{d-b}.$$

(c) The work done is

$$W = \Delta U = U' - U = \frac{q^2}{2}\left(\frac{1}{C'} - \frac{1}{C}\right) = \frac{q^2}{2\epsilon_0 A}(d - b - d) = -\frac{q^2 b}{2\epsilon_0 A}.$$

Since $W < 0$ the slab is sucked in.

62P

(a) $C' = \epsilon_0 A/(d - b)$, the same as part (a) in Problem 61.

(b)

$$\frac{U}{U'} = \frac{\frac{1}{2}CV^2}{\frac{1}{2}C'V^2} = \frac{C}{C'} = \frac{\epsilon_0 A/d}{\epsilon_0 A/(d - b)} = \frac{d - b}{d}.$$

(c) The work done is

$$W = \Delta U = U' - U = \frac{1}{2}(C' - C)V^2$$

$$= \frac{\epsilon_0 A}{2}\left(\frac{1}{d - b} - \frac{1}{d}\right)V^2 = \frac{\epsilon_0 AbV^2}{2d(d - b)}.$$

Since $W > 0$ the slab must be pushed in.

63P

The capacitor can be viewed as two capacitors C_1 and C_2 in parallel, each with surface area $A/2$ and plate separation d, filled with dielectric materials with dielectric constans κ_1 and κ_2, respectively. Thus

$$C = C_1 + C_2 = \frac{\epsilon_0(A/2)\kappa_1}{d} + \frac{\epsilon_0(A/2)\kappa_2}{d} = \frac{\epsilon_0 A}{d}\left(\frac{\kappa_1 + \kappa_2}{2}\right).$$

64P

Assume there is charge q on one plate and charge $-q$ on the other. Calculate the electric field at points between the plates and use the result to find an expression for the potential difference V between the plates, in terms of q. The capacitance is $C = q/V$.

The electric field in the upper half of the region between the plates is

$$E_1 = \frac{q}{\kappa_1 \epsilon_0 A},$$

where A is the plate area. The electric field in the lower half is

$$E_2 = \frac{q}{\kappa_2 \epsilon_0 A}.$$

Take $d/2$ to be the thickness of each dielectric. Since the field is uniform in each region the potential difference between the plates is

$$V = \frac{E_1 d}{2} + \frac{E_2 d}{2} = \frac{qd}{2\epsilon_0 A}\left[\frac{1}{\kappa_1} + \frac{1}{\kappa_2}\right] = \frac{qd}{2\epsilon_0 A}\frac{\kappa_1 + \kappa_2}{\kappa_1 \kappa_2},$$

so

$$C = \frac{q}{V} = \frac{2\epsilon_0 A}{d}\frac{\kappa_1 \kappa_2}{\kappa_1 + \kappa_2}.$$

Notice that this expression is exactly the same as the expression for the equivalent capacitance of two capacitors in series, one with dielectric constant κ_1 and the other with dielectric constant κ_2. Each has plate area A and plate separation $d/2$. Also notice that if $\kappa_1 = \kappa_2$ the expression reduces to $C = \kappa_1 \epsilon_0 A/d$, the correct result for a parallel plate capacitor with plate area A, plate separation d, and dielectric constant κ_1.

65P

Let $C_1 = \epsilon_0(A/2)\kappa_1/2d = \epsilon_0 A\kappa_1/4d$, $C_2 = \epsilon_0(A/2)\kappa_2/d = \epsilon_0 A\kappa_2/2d$, and $C_3 = \epsilon_0 A\kappa_3/2d$. Then

$$
\begin{aligned}
C = C_1 + \frac{C_2 C_3}{C_2 + C_3} &= \frac{\epsilon_0 A\kappa_1}{4d} + \frac{(\epsilon_0 A/d)(\kappa_2/2)(\kappa_3/2)}{\kappa_2/2 + \kappa_3/2} \\
&= \frac{\epsilon_0 A}{4d}\left(\kappa_1 + \frac{2\kappa_2\kappa_3}{\kappa_2 + \kappa_3}\right).
\end{aligned}
$$

66E

(a) The electric field in the region between the plates is given by $E = V/d$, where V is the potential difference between the plates and d is the plate separation. The capacitance is given by $C = \kappa\epsilon_0 A/d$, where A is the plate area and κ is the dielectric constant, so $d = \kappa\epsilon_0 A/C$ and

$$
E = \frac{VC}{\kappa\epsilon_0 A} = \frac{(50\,\text{V})(100 \times 10^{-12}\,\text{F})}{5.4(8.85 \times 10^{-12}\,\text{F/m})(100 \times 10^{-4}\,\text{m}^2)} = 1.0 \times 10^4\,\text{V/m}\,.
$$

(b) The free charge on the plates is $q_f = CV = (100 \times 10^{-12}\,\text{F})(50\,\text{V}) = 5.0 \times 10^{-9}\,\text{C}$.

(c) The electric field is produced by both the free and induced charge. Since the field of a large uniform layer of charge is $q/2\epsilon_0 A$, the field between the plates is

$$
E = \frac{q_f}{2\epsilon_0 A} + \frac{q_f}{2\epsilon_0 A} - \frac{q_i}{2\epsilon_0 A} - \frac{q_i}{2\epsilon_0 A}\,,
$$

where the first term is due to the positive free charge on one plate, the second is due to the negative free charge on the other plate, the third is due to the positive induced charge on one dielectric surface, and the fourth is due to the negative induced charge on the other dielectric surface. Note that the field due to the induced charge is opposite the field due to the free charge, so they tend to cancel. The induced charge is therefore

$$
\begin{aligned}
q_i &= q_f - \epsilon_0 AE \\
&= 5.0 \times 10^{-9}\,\text{C} - (8.85 \times 10^{-12}\,\text{F/m})(100 \times 10^{-4}\,\text{m}^2)(1.0 \times 10^4\,\text{V/m}) \\
&= 4.1 \times 10^{-9}\,\text{C} = 4.1\,\text{nC}\,.
\end{aligned}
$$

67E

(a) The electric field E_1 in the free space between the two plates is $E_1 = q/\epsilon_0 A$ while that inside the slab is $E_2 = E_1/\kappa = q/\kappa\epsilon_0 A$. Thus $V_0 = E_1(d-b) + E_2 b = (q/\epsilon_0 A)(d-b+b/\kappa)$, and the capacitance is

$$
\begin{aligned}
C = \frac{q}{V_0} &= \frac{\epsilon_0 A \kappa}{\kappa(d-b)+b} \\
&= \frac{(8.85 \times 10^{-12}\,\text{F/m})(115 \times 10^{-4}\,\text{m}^2)(2.61)}{(2.61)(1.24-0.780)(10^{-2}\,\text{m})+(0.780 \times 10^{-2})} = 13.4\,\text{pF}.
\end{aligned}
$$

(b) $q = CV = (13.4 \times 10^{-12}\,\text{F})(85.5\,\text{V}) = 1.15\,\text{nC}.$

(c)

$$
E_1 = \frac{q}{\epsilon_0 A} = \frac{1.15 \times 10^{-9}\,\text{C}}{(8.85 \times 10^{-12}\,\text{F/m})(115 \times 10^{-4}\,\text{m}^2)} = 1.13 \times 10^4\,\text{N/C}.
$$

(d)

$$
E_2 = \frac{E_1}{\kappa} = \frac{1.13 \times 10^4\,\text{N/C}}{2.61} = 4.33 \times 10^3\,\text{N/C}.
$$

68P

(a) Apply Gauss's law with a dielectric: $q/\epsilon_0 = \kappa E A$, we get

$$
\kappa = \frac{q}{\epsilon_0 E A} = \frac{8.9 \times 10^{-7}\,\text{C}}{(8.85 \times 10^{-12}\,\text{F/m})(1.4 \times 10^{-6}\,\text{V/m})(100 \times 10^{-4}\,\text{m}^2)} = 7.1.
$$

(b) The charge induced is

$$
q' = q\left(1 - \frac{1}{\kappa}\right) = (8.9 \times 10^{-7}\,\text{C})\left(1 - \frac{1}{7.1}\right) = 7.6 \times 10^{-7}\,\text{C}.
$$

69P

(a)

$$
C_0 = \frac{\epsilon_0 A}{d} = \frac{(8.85 \times 10^{-12}\,\text{F/m})(0.12\,\text{m}^2)}{1.2 \times 10^{-2}\,\text{m}} = 89\,\text{pF}.
$$

(b) Use the result of Exercise 67, part (a):

$$
C = \frac{\epsilon_0 A \kappa}{\kappa(d-b)+b} = \frac{(8.85 \times 10^{-12}\,\text{F/m})(0.12\,\text{m}^2)(4.8)}{(4.8)(1.2-0.40)(10^{-2}\,\text{m})+(4.0 \times 10^{-3}\,\text{m})} = 120\,\text{pF}.
$$

(c) Before the insertion: $q = C_0 V (89\,\text{pF})(120\,\text{V}) = 11\,\text{nC}$. Since the battery is disconnected, q will remain the same after the insertion of the slab.

(d) $E = q/\epsilon_0 A = 11\,\text{nC}/(8.85 \times 10^{-12}\,\text{F/m})(0.12\,\text{m}^2) = 10\,\text{kV/m}.$

(e) $E' = E/\kappa = (10\,\text{kV/m})/4.8 = 2.1\,\text{kV/m}$.

(f)

$$V = E(d - b) + E'b = (10\,\text{kV/m})(1.2 - 0.40)(10^{-2}\,\text{m}) + (2.1\,\text{kV/m})(0.40 \times 10^{-3}\,\text{m})$$
$$= 88\,\text{V}.$$

(g) The work done is

$$W_{\text{ext}} = \Delta U = \frac{q^2}{2}\left(\frac{1}{C} - \frac{1}{C_0}\right)$$
$$= \frac{(11 \times 10^{-9}\,\text{C})^2}{2}\left(\frac{1}{89 \times 10^{-12}\,\text{F}} - \frac{1}{120 \times 10^{-12}\,\text{F}}\right) = 1.7 \times 10^{-7}\,\text{J}.$$

70P

(a) Since $u = \dfrac{1}{2}\epsilon_0 E^2$, the fraction of energy stored in the air gaps is

$$\text{frac} = \frac{E_{\text{air}}^2 A(d - b)}{E_{\text{air}}^2 A(d - b) + E_{slab}^2 Ab} = \frac{1}{1 + (E_{\text{slab}}/E_{\text{air}})^2[b/(d - b)]}$$
$$= \frac{1}{1 + (1/2.61)^2[0.780/(1.24 - 0.780)]} = 0.800.$$

(b) The fraction of energy stored in the slab is $1 - 0.800 = 0.200$.

71P

Assume the charge on one plate is $+q$ and the charge on the other plate is $-q$. Find an expression for the electric field in each region, in terms of q, then use the result to find an expression for the potential difference V between the plates. The capacitance is $C = q/V$.

The electric field in the dielectric is $E_d = q/\kappa\epsilon_0 A$, where κ is the dielectric constant and A is the plate area. Outside the dielectric (but still between the capacitor plates) the field is $E = q/\epsilon_0 A$. The field is uniform in each region so the potential difference across the plates is

$$V = E_d b + E(d - b) = \frac{qb}{\kappa\epsilon_0 A} + \frac{q(d - b)}{\epsilon_0 A} = \frac{q}{\epsilon_0 A}\frac{b + \kappa(d - b)}{\kappa}.$$

The capacitance is

$$C = \frac{q}{V} = \frac{\kappa\epsilon_0 A}{\kappa(d - b) + b} = \frac{\kappa\epsilon_0 A}{\kappa d - b(\kappa - 1)}.$$

The result does not depend on where the dielectric is located between the plates; it might be touching one plate or it might have a vacuum gap on each side.

For the capacitor of Sample Problem 27–10, $\kappa = 2.61$, $A = 115\,\text{cm}^2 = 115 \times 10^{-4}\,\text{m}^2$, $d = 1.24\,\text{cm} = 1.24 \times 10^{-2}\,\text{m}$, and $b = 0.78\,\text{cm} = 0.78 \times 10^{-2}\,\text{m}$, so

$$C = \frac{2.61(8.85 \times 10^{-12}\,\text{F/m})(115 \times 10^{-4}\,\text{m}^2)}{2.61(1.24 \times 10^{-2}\,\text{m} - 0.78 \times 10^{-2}\,\text{m}) + 0.78 \times 10^{-2}\,\text{m}}$$
$$= 1.34 \times 10^{-11}\,\text{F} = 13.4\,\text{pF}\,,$$

in agreement with the result found in the sample problem.

If $b = 0$ and $\kappa = 1$, then the expression derived above yields $C = \epsilon_0 A/d$, the correct expression for a parallel-plate capacitor with no dielectric. If $b = d$ then the derived expression yields $C = \kappa \epsilon_0 A/d$, the correct expression for a parallel-plate capacitor completely filled with a dielectric.

72P

(a) Consider a "strip" capacitor located from x to $x + dx$. Its contribution to C is $dC = \epsilon_0 dA/w$, where $dA = A\,dx/L$ and $w = d + 2x\Delta/L$ is the plate separation at x. Thus

$$C = \int dC = \int_0^L \frac{\epsilon_0 A\,dx}{(d - \Delta + 2x\Delta/L)L} = \frac{\epsilon_0 A}{2\Delta} \ln \frac{d + \Delta}{d - \Delta}.$$

(b) For $\Delta \to 0$,

$$C = \frac{A\epsilon_0}{2\Delta} \ln \left(\frac{1 + \Delta/d}{1 - \Delta/d} \right) = \frac{\epsilon_0 A}{2\Delta} \ln \left(1 + \frac{2\Delta}{d} \right) = \frac{\epsilon_0 A}{d},$$

where we use $(1 - x)^{-1} \approx 1 + x$ and $\ln(1 + x) \simeq x$ for $|x| \ll 1$.

73

(a) Use $C = C_0 \kappa$ where C_0 is given by Eq. 27-17:

$$C = 4\pi\epsilon_0 \kappa \frac{ab}{b - a}.$$

(b) $q = CV = 4\pi\epsilon_0 \kappa V ab/(b - a)$.
(c)
$$q' = q\left(1 - \frac{1}{\kappa}\right) = \frac{4\pi\epsilon_0(\kappa - 1)Vab}{b - a}.$$

74

(a) Interior to the conductor: $E = 0$.
(b) Exterior to the conductor: $E = Q/4\pi\epsilon_0 R^2$, pointing radially outward (if $Q > 0$).

(c)

$$dU = \frac{1}{2}\epsilon_0 E(r)^2 \cdot 4\pi r^2 dr = \frac{\epsilon_0}{2}\left(\frac{Q}{4\pi\epsilon_0 r^2}\right)^2 \cdot 4\pi r^2 dr = \frac{Q^2 dr}{8\pi\epsilon_0 r^2}.$$

(d)

$$U = \int dU = \frac{Q^2}{8\pi\epsilon_0}\int_R^\infty \frac{1}{r^2}dr = \frac{Q^2}{8\pi\epsilon_0 R}.$$

(e)

$$\Delta U = \frac{Q^2}{8\pi\epsilon_0}\left(\frac{1}{R+\Delta R} - \frac{1}{R}\right) = -\frac{Q^2 \Delta R}{8\pi\epsilon_0 R(R+\Delta R)}.$$

(f) The pressure is

$$p = -\frac{dU}{dV} = -\left(\frac{1}{4\pi R^2 dR}\right)\left(-\frac{Q^2 dR}{8\pi\epsilon_0 R^2}\right) = \frac{Q^2}{32\pi^2\epsilon_0 R^4}.$$

But

$$u(R) = \frac{1}{2}\epsilon_0 E(R)^2 = \frac{1}{2}\epsilon_0\left(\frac{Q}{4\pi\epsilon_0 R^2}\right)^2 = \frac{Q^2}{32\pi^2\epsilon_0 R^4},$$

Hence $p = u(R)$.

CHAPTER 28

1E

(a) The charge that passes through any cross section is the product of the current and time. Since $4.0 \, \text{min} = (4.0 \, \text{min})(60 \, \text{s/min}) = 240 \, \text{s}$, $q = it = (5.0 \, \text{A})(240 \, \text{s}) = 1200 \, \text{C}$.

(b) The number of electrons N is given by $q = Ne$, where e is the magnitude of the charge on an electron. Thus $N = q/e = (1200 \, \text{C})/(1.60 \times 10^{-19} \, \text{C}) = 7.5 \times 10^{21}$.

2E

The number of electrons is

$$n = \frac{q}{e} = \frac{it}{e} = \frac{(200 \times 10^{-6} \, \text{A})(1 \, \text{s})}{1.60 \times 10^{-19} \, \text{C}} = 1.25 \times 10^{15}.$$

3P

Suppose the charge on the sphere increases by Δq in time Δt. Then in that time its potential increases by

$$\Delta V = \frac{\Delta q}{4\pi\epsilon_0 r},$$

where r is the radius of the sphere. This means

$$\Delta q = 4\pi\epsilon_0 r \, \Delta V.$$

Now $\Delta q = (i_{\text{in}} - i_{\text{out}}) \Delta t$, where i_{in} is the current entering the sphere and i_{out} is the current leaving. Thus

$$\Delta t = \frac{\Delta q}{i_{\text{in}} - i_{\text{out}}} = \frac{4\pi\epsilon_0 r \, \Delta V}{i_{\text{in}} - i_{\text{out}}}$$

$$= \frac{(0.10 \, \text{m})(1000 \, \text{V})}{(8.99 \times 10^9 \, \text{F}/m)(1.0000020 \, \text{A} - 1.0000000 \, \text{A})} = 5.6 \times 10^{-3} \, \text{s}.$$

4P

Use $i = \sigma v l$:

$$\sigma = \frac{i}{vl} = \frac{100 \times 10^{-6} \, \text{A}}{(30 \, \text{m/s})(50 \times 10^{-2} \, \text{m})} = 6.7 \times 10^{-6} \, \text{C/m}^2.$$

5E

(a) The magnitude of the current density is given by $J = nqv_d$, where n is the number of particles per unit volume, q is the charge on each particle, and v_d is the drift speed of the particles. The particle concentration is $n = 2.0 \times 10^8 \, \text{cm}^{-3} = 2.0 \times 10^{14} \, \text{m}^{-3}$, the charge is $q = 2e = 2(1.60 \times 10^{-19} \, \text{C}) = 3.20 \times 10^{-19} \, \text{C}$, and the drift speed is $1.0 \times 10^5 \, \text{m/s}$. Thus

$$J = (2 \times 10^{14} \, \text{m}^{-3})(3.2 \times 10^{-19} \, \text{C})(1.0 \times 10^5 \, \text{m/s}) = 6.4 \, \text{A/m}^2 \, .$$

Since the particles are positively charged the current density is in the same direction as their motion, to the north.

(b) The current cannot be calculated unless the cross-sectional area of the beam is known. Then $i = JA$ can be used.

6E

(a) $J = i/A = i/(\pi D^2/4) = 4(1.2 \times 10^{-10} \, \text{A})/[\pi(2.5 \times 10^{-3} \, \text{m})^2] = 2.4 \times 10^{-5} \, \text{A/m}^2$.

(b)

$$v_d = \frac{J}{ne} = \frac{2.4 \times 10^{-5} \, \text{A/m}^2}{(8.47 \times 10^{28}/\text{m}^3)(1.60 \times 10^{-19} \, \text{C})} = 1.8 \times 10^{-15} \, \text{m/s}.$$

7E

The cross-sectional area of wire is given by $A = \pi r^2$, where r is its radius. The magnitude of the current density is $J = i/A = i/\pi r^2$, so

$$r = \sqrt{\frac{i}{\pi J}} = \sqrt{\frac{0.50 \, \text{A}}{\pi(440 \times 10^4 \, \text{A/m}^2)}} = 1.9 \times 10^{-4} \, \text{m} \, .$$

The diameter is $D = 2r = 2(1.9 \times 10^{-4} \, \text{m}) = 3.8 \times 10^{-4} \, \text{m}$.

8E

Use $J = i/A = 4i/\pi D^2$. The 4-gauge wire has the maximum safe current density.

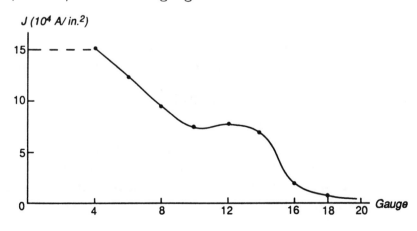

9E

The magnitude of the current is

$$i = (n_p + n_e)e = (1.1 \times 10^{18}/s + 3.1 \times 10^{18}/s)(1.60 \times 10^{-19}\,C) = 1.67\,A.$$

The current flows toward the negative terminal.

10E

(a) $i = (n_h + n_e)e = (2.25 \times 10^{15}/s + 3.50 \times 10^{15}/s)(1.60 \times 10^{-19}\,C) = 9.20 \times 10^4\,A.$
(b) $J = i/A = 9.20 \times 10^{-4}\,A/[\pi(0.165 \times 10^{-3}\,m)^2] = 1.08 \times 10^4\,A/m^2.$

11P

(a) $J = n_p e v_p = (8.70/10^{-6}\,m^3)(1.60 \times 10^{-19}\,C)(470 \times 10^5\,m/s) = 6.54 \times 10^{-7}\,A/m^2.$
(b) $i = JA = \pi R_e^2 J = \pi(6.37 \times 10^6\,m)^2(6.54 \times 10^{-7}\,A/m^2) = 8.34 \times 10^7\,A.$

12P

$$
\begin{aligned}
J &= q_\alpha n_\alpha v_\alpha + e n_e v_e = (2e)n_\alpha v_\alpha + e(2n_\alpha)v_e \\
&= 2(1.60 \times 10^{-19}\,C)(2.8 \times 10^{15}/cm^3)(25\,m/s + 88\,m/s) \\
&= 10\,A/cm^2.
\end{aligned}
$$

The direction of the current is to the east.

13P

Use $v_d = J/ne = i/Ane$. Thus

$$
\begin{aligned}
t &= \frac{L}{v_d} = \frac{L}{i/Ane} = \frac{LAne}{i} \\
&= \frac{(0.85\,m)(0.21 \times 10^{-4}\,m^2)(8.47 \times 10^{28}/m^3)(1.60 \times 10^{-19}\,C)}{300\,A} \\
&= 8.1 \times 10^2\,s = 13\,min.
\end{aligned}
$$

14P

(a) The charge that strikes the surface in time Δt is given by $\Delta q = i\,\Delta t$, where i is the current. Since each particle carries charge $2e$, the number of particles that strike the surface is

$$N = \frac{\Delta q}{2e} = \frac{i\,\Delta t}{2e} = \frac{(0.25 \times 10^{-6}\,A)(3.0\,s)}{2(1.6 \times 10^{-19}\,C)} = 2.3 \times 10^{12}.$$

(b) Now let N be the number of particles in a length L of the beam. They will all pass through the beam cross section at one end in time $t = L/v$, where v is the particle speed. The current is the charge that moves through the cross section per unit time. That is, $i = 2eN/t = 2eNv/L$. Thus $N = iL/2ev$.

Now find the particle speed. The kinetic energy of a particle is

$$K = 20\,\text{MeV} = (20 \times 10^6\,\text{eV})(1.60 \times 10^{-19}\,\text{J/eV}) = 3.2 \times 10^{-12}\,\text{J}.$$

Since $K = \frac{1}{2}mv^2$, $v = \sqrt{2K/m}$. The mass of an alpha particle is 4 times the mass of a proton or $m = 4(1.67 \times 10^{-27}\,\text{kg}) = 6.68 \times 10^{-27}\,\text{kg}$, so

$$v = \sqrt{\frac{2(3.2 \times 10^{-12}\,\text{J})}{6.68 \times 10^{-27}\,\text{kg}}} = 3.1 \times 10^7\,\text{m/s}$$

and

$$N = \frac{iL}{2ev} = \frac{(0.25 \times 10^{-6})(20 \times 10^{-2}\,\text{m})}{2(1.60 \times 10^{-19}\,\text{C})(3.1 \times 10^7\,\text{m/s})} = 5.0 \times 10^3.$$

(c) Use conservation of energy. The initial kinetic energy is zero, the final kinetic energy is $20\,\text{MeV} = 3.2 \times 10^{-12}\,\text{J}$, the initial potential energy is $qV = 2eV$, and the final potential energy is zero. Here V is the electric potential through which the particles are accelerated. Conservation of energy leads to $K_f = U_i = 2eV$, so

$$V = \frac{K_f}{2e} = \frac{3.2 \times 10^{-12}\,\text{J}}{2(1.60 \times 10^{-19}\,\text{C})} = 10 \times 10^6\,\text{V}.$$

15P
(a)

$$i = \int_{\text{cylinder}} J\,dA = \int_0^R J_0 \left(1 - \frac{r}{R}\right) 2\pi r\,dr$$

$$= \frac{1}{3}\pi R^2 J_0 = \frac{1}{3} A J_0.$$

(b) Now

$$i = \int_{\text{cylinder}} J\,dA = \frac{J_0}{R} \int_0^R r \cdot 2\pi r\,dr = \frac{2\pi R^2 J_0}{3} = \frac{2}{3} A J_0.$$

The result is different from that in (a) because the current density in (b) is lower near the center of the cylinder (where the area is smaller for the same radial interval) and higher outward, resulting in a greater current than that in (a).

16E
$R = \rho L/A = (3.00 \times 10^{-7}\,\Omega \cdot \text{m})(10.0 \times 10^3\,\text{m})/(56.0 \times 10^{-4}\,\text{m}^2) = 0.536\,\Omega.$

17E

The resistance of the wire is given by $R = \rho L/A$, where ρ is the resistivity of the material, L is the length of the wire, and A is the cross-sectional area of the wire. The cross-sectional area is $A = \pi r^2 = \pi(0.50 \times 10^{-3}\,\text{m})^2 = 7.85 \times 10^{-7}\,\text{m}^2$. Here $r = 0.50\,\text{mm} = 0.50 \times 10^{-3}\,\text{m}$ is the radius of the wire. Thus

$$\rho = \frac{RA}{L} = \frac{(50 \times 10^{-3}\,\Omega)(7.85 \times 10^{-7}\,\text{m}^2)}{2.0\,\text{m}} = 2.0 \times 10^{-8}\,\Omega \cdot \text{m}.$$

18E

Since the potential difference V and current i are related by $V = iR$, where R is the resistance of the electrician, the fatal voltage is $V = (50 \times 10^{-3}\,\text{A})(2000\,\Omega) = 100\,\text{V}$.

19E

The resistance of the coil is given by $R = \rho L/A$, where L is the length of the wire, ρ is the resistivity of copper, and A is the cross-sectional area of the wire. Since each turn of wire has length $2\pi r$, where r is the radius of the coil, $L = (250)2\pi r = (250)(2\pi)(0.12\,\text{m}) = 188.5\,\text{m}$. If r_w is the radius of the wire, its cross-sectional area is $A = \pi r_w^2 = \pi(0.65 \times 10^{-3}\,\text{m})^2 = 1.33 \times 10^{-6}\,\text{m}^2$. According to Table 28–1, the resistivity of copper is $1.69 \times 10^{-8}\,\Omega \cdot \text{m}$. Thus

$$R = \frac{\rho L}{A} = \frac{(1.69 \times 10^{-8}\,\Omega \cdot \text{m})(188.5\,\text{m})}{1.33 \times 10^{-6}\,\text{m}^2} = 2.4\,\Omega.$$

20E

(a) $i = V/R = 23.0\,\text{V}/15.0 \times 10^{-3}\Omega = 1.53 \times 10^3\,\text{A}.$
(b) $J = i/A = 4i/\pi D^2 = 4(1.53 \times 10^{-3}\,\text{A})/[\pi(6.00 \times 10^{-3}\,\text{m})^2] = 5.41 \times 10^7\,\text{A}/\text{m}^2.$
(c) $\rho = RA/L = (15.0 \times 10^{-3}\Omega)(\pi)(6.00 \times 10^{-3}\,\text{m})^2/[4(4.00\,\text{m})] = 10.6 \times 10^{-8}\Omega \cdot \text{m}.$
The material is platinum.

21E

$$\sigma = \frac{1}{\rho} = \frac{L}{RA} = \frac{L}{(V/i)A} = \frac{Li}{VA}$$

$$= \frac{(1.0\,\text{m})(4.0\,\text{A})}{(2.0\,\text{V})(1.0 \times 10^{-6}\,\text{m}^2)} = 2.0 \times 10^6\,(\Omega \cdot \text{m})^{-1}.$$

22E

In Eq. 28-16, Let $\rho(T) = 2\rho_0$ where ρ_0 is the resistivity at 20°C: $\rho - \rho_0 = 2\rho_0 - \rho_0 = \rho_0\alpha(T - T_0)$, and solve for T:

$$T = T_0 + \frac{1}{\alpha} = 20°\text{C} + \frac{1}{(4.3 \times 10^{-3}\text{ K}^{-1})} = 2.5 \times 10^2 °\text{C}.$$

This agrees well with Fig. 28-10, from which you can deduce $T = 5.2 \times 10^2$ K, or $2.5 \times 10^2 °$C.

23E

Use Eq. 28-16: $\rho - \rho_0 = \rho\alpha(T - T_0)$, and solve for T:

$$T = T_0 + \frac{1}{\alpha}\left(\frac{\rho}{\rho_0} - 1\right)$$

$$= 20°\text{C} + \frac{1}{4.3 \times 10^{-3}\text{ K}^{-1}}\left(\frac{58\Omega}{50\Omega} - 1\right) = 57°\text{C}.$$

Here we noted that $\rho/\rho_0 = R/R_0$.

24E

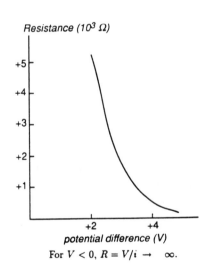

For $V < 0$, $R = V/i \rightarrow \infty$.

25E

(a)

$$V = iR = i\rho\frac{L}{A}$$

$$= \frac{(12\text{ A})(1.69 \times 10{-8}\Omega \cdot \text{m})(4.0 \times 10^{-2}\text{ m})}{\pi(5.2 \times 10^{-3}\text{ m}/2)^2} = 3.8 \times 10^{-4}\text{ V}.$$

(b) Since it moves in the direction of the electron drift which is against the direction of the current, its trail is negative compared to its head.

(c) Use the result in Problem 13:

$$t = \frac{l}{v_d} = \frac{lAne}{i} = \frac{\pi l D^2 ne}{4i}$$

$$= \frac{\pi(1.0 \times 10^{-2}\,\text{m})(5.2 \times 10^{-3}\,\text{m})^2(8.47 \times 10^{28}/\text{m}^3)(1.60 \times 10^{-19}\,\text{C})}{4(12\,\text{A})}$$

$$= 238\,\text{s} = 3\,\text{min}58\,\text{s}.$$

26E
(a) The new area is $A' = AL/L' = A/2$.
(b) The new resistance is $R' = R(A/A')(L'/L) = 4R$.

27E
Since the mass and density of the material do not change, the volume remains the same. If L_0 is the original length, L is the new length, A_0 is the original cross-sectional area, and A is the new cross-sectional area, then $L_0 A_0 = LA$ and $A = L_0 A_0/L = L_0 A_0/3L_0 = A_0/3$. The new resistance is

$$R = \frac{\rho L}{A} = \frac{\rho 3 L_0}{A_0/3} = 9\frac{\rho L_0}{A_0} = 9R_0\,,$$

where R_0 is the original resistance. Thus $R = 9(6.0\,\Omega) = 54\,\Omega$.

28E
The resistance of the second wire is

$$R_2 = R\left(\frac{A_1}{A_2}\right)\left(\frac{L_2}{L_1}\right) = R = \left(\frac{D_1}{D_2}\right)^2\left(\frac{L_2}{L_1}\right) = R(2)^2(1/2) = 2R.$$

29P
Let $R_i = \rho_i L_i/A_i = R_c = \rho_c L_c/A_c$, we get

$$D_i = \sqrt{\frac{A_i}{A_c}}D_c = \sqrt{\frac{\rho_i}{\rho_c}}D_c = \sqrt{\frac{9.68 \times 10^8}{1.69 \times 10^8}}(1.2\,\text{mm}) = 2.9\,\text{mm}.$$

30P
The resistance of conductor A is given by

$$R_A = \frac{\rho L}{\pi r_A^2}\,,$$

where r_A is the radius of the conductor. If r_o is the outside diameter of conductor B and r_i is its inside diameter, then its cross-sectional area is $\pi(r_o^2 - r_i^2)$ and its resistance is

$$R_B = \frac{\rho L}{\pi(r_o^2 - r_i^2)}.$$

The ratio is

$$\frac{R_A}{R_B} = \frac{r_o^2 - r_i^2}{r_A^2} = \frac{(1.0\,\text{mm})^2 - (0.50\,\text{mm})^2}{(0.50\,\text{mm})^2} = 3.0.$$

31P
(a) Let $i_c = V/R_c = i_i = V/R_i$, or $R_c = R_i$, we get $\rho_c L_c/\pi r_c^2 = \rho_i L_i/\pi r_i^2$, i.e.

$$\frac{r_i}{r_c} = \sqrt{\frac{\rho_i}{\rho_c}} = \sqrt{\frac{9.68 \times 10^8}{1.69 \times 10^8}} = 2.39.$$

(b) If $J_i = i/A_i = J_c = i/A_c$ we must have $A_i = A_c$, which is inconsistent with the result in (a). So this is impossible.

32P
(a)

$$R = \rho_a \frac{L}{A} = \frac{(2.75 \times 10^{-8}\Omega \cdot \text{m})(1.3\,\text{m})}{(5.2 \times 10^{-3}\,\text{m})^2} = 1.3 \times 10^{-3}\Omega.$$

Let $R = \rho_c L/(\pi D^2/4)$ and solve for D:

$$D = \sqrt{\frac{4\rho_c L}{\pi R}} = \sqrt{\frac{4(1.69 \times 10^{-8}\Omega \cdot \text{m})(1.3\,\text{m})}{\pi(1.3 \times 10^{-3}\Omega)}} = 4.6 \times 10^{-3}\,\text{m}.$$

33P
(a) Since $\rho = RA/L = \pi RD^2/4L = \pi(1.09 \times 10^{-3}\Omega)(5.50 \times 10^{-3}\,\text{m})^2/[4(1.60\,\text{m})] = 1.62 \times 10^{-8}\Omega \cdot \text{m}$, the material is silver.
(b)

$$R = \rho \frac{L}{A} = \frac{4\rho L}{\pi D^2}$$
$$= \frac{4(1.62 \times 10^{-8}\Omega \cdot \text{m})(1.00 \times 10^{-3}\,\text{m})}{\pi(2.00 \times 10^{-2}\,\text{m})^2} = 5.16 \times 10^{-8}\Omega.$$

34P

(a) The current in each strand is $i = 0.750\,\mathrm{A}/125 = 6.00 \times 10^{-3}\,\mathrm{A}$.

(b) The potential difference is $V = iR = (6.00 \times 10^{-3}\,\mathrm{A})(2.65 \times 10^{-6}\Omega) = 1.59 \times 10^{-8}\,\mathrm{V}$.

(c) The resistance is $R_{\mathrm{total}} = 2.65 \times 10^{-6}\Omega/125 = 2.12 \times 10^{-8}\Omega$.

35P

The resistance at operating temperature T is $R = V/i = 2.9\,\mathrm{V}/0.30\,\mathrm{A} = 9.67\Omega$. Thus from $R - R_0 = R_0\alpha(T - T_0)$ we find

$$T = T_0 + \frac{1}{\alpha}\left(\frac{R}{R_0} - 1\right)$$

$$= 20°\mathrm{C} + \left(\frac{1}{4.5 \times 10^{-3}\,\mathrm{K}^{-1}}\right)\left(\frac{9.67\Omega}{1.1\Omega} - 1\right) = 1.8 \times 10^{3}°\mathrm{C}.$$

36P

Use $J = E/\rho$, where E is the magnitude of the electric field in the wire, J is the magnitude of the current density, and ρ is the resistivity of the material. The electric field is given by $E = V/L$, where V is the potential difference along the wire and L is the length of the wire. Thus $J = V/L\rho$ and

$$\rho = \frac{V}{LJ} = \frac{115\,\mathrm{V}}{(10\,\mathrm{m})(1.4 \times 10^4\,\mathrm{A/m^2})} = 8.2 \times 10^{-4}\,\Omega\cdot\mathrm{m}.$$

37P

(a) $i = V/R = 35.8\,\mathrm{V}/935\Omega = 3.83 \times 10^{-2}\,\mathrm{A}$.

(b) $J = i/A = 3.83 \times 10^{-2}\,\mathrm{A}/(3.50 \times 10^{-4}\,\mathrm{m^2}) = 109\,\mathrm{A/m^2}$.

(c) $v_d = J/ne = (109\,\mathrm{A/m^2})/[(5.33 \times 10^{22}/\mathrm{m^3})(1.60 \times 10^{-19}\,\mathrm{C})] = 1.28 \times 10^{-2}\,\mathrm{m/s}$.

(d) $E = V/L = 35.8\,\mathrm{V}/0.158\,\mathrm{m} = 227\,\mathrm{V/m}$.

38P

Use $R/L = \rho/A = 0.150\,\Omega/\mathrm{km}$. Thus

(a) For copper: $J = i/A = (60.0\,\mathrm{A})(0.150\,\Omega/\mathrm{km})/(1.69 \times 10^{-8}\,\Omega\cdot\mathrm{m}) = 5.32 \times 10^5\,\mathrm{A/m^2}$,

For aluminum: $J = (60.0\,\mathrm{A})(0.150\,\Omega/\mathrm{km})/(2.75 \times 10^{-8}\,\Omega\cdot\mathrm{m}) = 3.27 \times 10^5\,\mathrm{A/m^2}$.

(b) Denote the mass densities as ρ_m's. For copper: $(m/L)_c = (\rho_m A)_c = (8960\,\mathrm{kg/m^3})$ $(1.69 \times 10^{-8}\,\Omega\cdot\mathrm{m})/(0.150\,\Omega/\mathrm{km}) = 1.01\,\mathrm{kg/m}$,

For aluminum: $(m/L)_a = (\rho_m A)_a = (2700\,\mathrm{kg/m^3})(2.75 \times 10^{-8}\,\Omega\cdot\mathrm{m})/(0.150\,\Omega/\mathrm{km}) = 0.495\,\mathrm{kg/m}$.

39P

Use $J = \sigma E = (n_+ + n_-)ev_d$.

(a)

$$v_d = \frac{\sigma E}{(n_+ + n_-)e} = \frac{(2.70 \times 10^{-14}/\,\Omega \cdot \mathrm{m})(120\,\mathrm{V/m})}{[(620 + 550)/\,\mathrm{cm}^3](1.60 \times 10^{-19}\,\mathrm{C})} = 1.73\,\mathrm{cm/s}.$$

(b) $J = \sigma E = (2.70 \times 10{-}14/\,\Omega \cdot \mathrm{m})(120\,\mathrm{V/m}) = 3.24 \times 10^{-12}\,\mathrm{A/m}^2$.

40P

The diameter of a 22-gauge wire is 1/4 that of 10-gauge wire. Thus from $R = \rho L/A$, the resistance of 25 ft of 22-gauge copper wire is $R = (1.00\,\Omega)(25\,\mathrm{ft}/1000\,\mathrm{ft})(4)^2 = 0.40\,\Omega$.

41P

(a) Let ΔT be the change in temperature and β be the coefficient of linear expansion for copper. Then $\Delta L = \beta L \, \Delta T$ and

$$\frac{\Delta L}{L} = \beta \, \Delta T = (1.7 \times 10^{-5}\,/^\circ\mathrm{C})(1.0^\circ\,\mathrm{C}) = 1.7 \times 10^{-5}.$$

This is 0.0017%.

The fractional change in area is

$$\frac{\Delta A}{A} = 2\beta \, \Delta T = 2(1.7 \times 10^{-5}\,/^\circ\mathrm{C})(1.0^\circ\,\mathrm{C}) = 3.4 \times 10^{-5}.$$

This is 0.0034%.

For small changes in the resistivity ρ, length L, and area A of a wire, the change in the resistance is given by

$$\Delta R = \frac{\partial R}{\partial \rho}\,\Delta\rho + \frac{\partial R}{\partial L}\,\Delta L + \frac{\partial R}{\partial A}\,\Delta A.$$

Since $R = \rho L/A$, $\partial R/\partial \rho = L/A = R/\rho$, $\partial R/\partial L = \rho/A = R/L$, and $\partial R/\partial A = -\rho L/A^2 = -R/A$. Furthermore, $\Delta\rho/\rho = \alpha\,\Delta T$, where α is the temperature coefficient of resistivity for copper ($4.3 \times 10^{-3}\,/^\circ\mathrm{C}$, according to Table 28–1). Thus

$$\frac{\Delta R}{R} = \frac{\Delta\rho}{\rho} + \frac{\Delta L}{L} - \frac{\Delta A}{A} = (\alpha + \beta - 2\beta)\,\Delta T = (\alpha - \beta)\,\Delta T$$
$$= (4.3 \times 10^{-3}\,/^\circ\mathrm{C} - 1.7 \times 10^{-5}\,/^\circ\mathrm{C})(1.0^\circ\,\mathrm{C}) = 4.3 \times 10^{-3}.$$

This is 0.43%.

(b) The fractional change in resistivity is much larger than the fractional change in length and area. Changes in length and area affect the resistance much less than changes in resistivity.

745

42P

(a) Assume, as in Fig. 28-20, that the cone has current i, from bottom to top. The current is the same through every cross-section. We can find an expression for the electric field at every cross section, in terms of the current and then use this expression to find the potential difference V from bottom to top of the cone. The resistance of the cone is given by $R = V/i$.

Consider any cross section of the cone. Let J denote the current density at that cross section and assume it is uniform over the cross section. Then the current through the cross section is given by $i = \int J\, dA = \pi r^2 J$, where r is the radius of the cross section. Now $J = E/\rho$, where ρ is the resistivity and E is the magnitude of the electric field at the cross section. Thus $i = \pi r^2 E/\rho$ and $E = i\rho/\pi r^2$. The current density and electric field have different values on different cross sections because different cross sections have different radii.

Let x measure distance downward from the upper surface of the cone. The radius increases linearly with x, so we may write

$$r = a + \frac{b-a}{L}\, x \,.$$

The coefficients in this function have been chosen so $r = a$ when $x = 0$ and $r = b$ when $x = L$. Thus

$$E = \frac{i\rho}{\pi}\left[a + \frac{b-a}{L}\, x\right]^{-2} \,.$$

The potential difference between the upper and lower surfaces of the cone is given by

$$V = -\int_0^L E\, dx = -\frac{i\rho}{\pi}\int_0^L \left[a + \frac{b-a}{L}\, x\right]^{-2} dx$$

$$= \frac{i\rho}{\pi}\frac{L}{b-a}\left[a + \frac{b-a}{L}\, x\right]^{-1}\Bigg|_0^L = \frac{i\rho}{\pi}\frac{L}{b-a}\left[\frac{1}{a} - \frac{1}{b}\right]$$

$$= \frac{i\rho}{\pi}\frac{L}{b-a}\frac{b-a}{ab} = \frac{i\rho L}{\pi ab} \,.$$

The resistance is

$$R = \frac{V}{i} = \frac{\rho L}{\pi ab} \,.$$

(b) If $b = a$ then $R = \rho L/\pi a^2 = \rho L/A$, where $A = \pi a^2$ is the cross-sectional area of the cylinder.

43P

From Eq. 28-19, $\rho \propto \tau^{-1} \propto \bar{v}$. But $\bar{v} \propto \sqrt{T}$ from Eq. 21-23. Thus $\rho \propto \sqrt{T}$.

44E

$q = it = Pt/V = (7.0\,\text{W})(5.0\,\text{hr})(3600\,\text{s/hr})/9.0\,\text{V} = 1.4 \times 10^4\,\text{C}.$

45E

The power dissipated is given by the product of the current and the potential difference:

$$P = iV = (7.0 \times 10^{-3}\,\text{A})(80 \times 10^3\,\text{V}) = 560\,\text{W}.$$

46E

$R = P/i^2 = 100\,\text{W}/(3.00\,\text{A})^2 = 11.1\,\Omega.$

47E

The horse power required is

$$P = \frac{iV}{80\%} = \frac{(10\,\text{A})(12\,\text{V})}{(81\%)(746\,\text{W/hp})} = 0.20\,\text{hp}.$$

48E

(a) Electrical energy is transferred to heat at a rate given by

$$P = \frac{V^2}{R},$$

where V is the potential difference across the heater and R is the resistance of the heater. Thus

$$P = \frac{(120\,\text{V})^2}{14\,\Omega} = 1.0 \times 10^3\,\text{W} = 1.0\,\text{kW}.$$

(b) The cost is given by

$$C = (1.0\,\text{kW})(5.0\,\text{h})(5.0\,\text{cents/kW} \cdot \text{h}) = 25\,\text{cents}.$$

49E

Use $P = V^2/R$. The power dissipated in the second case is

$$P = (1.50\,\text{V}/3.00\,\text{V})^2(0.540\,\text{W}) = 0.135\,\text{W}.$$

50E

(a) $R = V^2/P = (120\,\text{V})^2/500\,\text{W} = 28.8\,\Omega$.

(b) The rate is given by $i/e = P/eV = 500\,\text{W}/[1.60 \times 10^{-19}\,\text{C}(120\,\text{V})] = 2.60 \times 10^{19}/\text{s}$.

51E

(a)

$$J = \frac{i}{A} = \frac{4(25\,\text{A})}{\pi[(0.10\,\text{in.})(2.54 \times 10^{-2}\,\text{m/in.})]^2} = 4.9 \times 10^6\,\text{A/m}^2.$$

(b) $E = J/\sigma = \rho J = (1.69 \times 10^{-8}\,\Omega \cdot \text{m})(4.9 \times 10^6\,\text{A/m}^2) = 8.3 \times 10^{-2}\,\text{V/m}$.

(c) $V = EL = (8.3 \times 10^{-2}\,\text{V/m})(1000\,\text{ft})(0.3048\,\text{m/ft}) = 25\,\text{V}$.

(d) $P = Vi = (25\,\text{V})(25\,\text{A}) = 6.3 \times 10^2\,\text{W}$.

52E

(a)

$$i = \frac{V}{R} = \frac{V}{\rho L/A} = \frac{\pi V D^2}{4\rho L}$$

$$= \frac{\pi(1.20\,\text{V})[(0.0400\,\text{in.})(2.54 \times 10^{-2}\,\text{m/in.})]^2}{4(1.69 \times 10^{-8}\,\Omega \cdot \text{m})(33.0\,\text{m})} = 1.74\,\text{A}.$$

(b)

$$J = \frac{i}{A} = \frac{4i}{\pi D^2} = \frac{4(1.74\,\text{A})}{\pi[(0.0400\,\text{in.})(2.54 \times 10^{-2}\,\text{m/in.})]^2} = 2.15 \times 10^6\,\text{A/m}^2.$$

(c) $E = V/L = 1.20\,\text{V}/33.0\,\text{m} = 3.63 \times 10^{-2}\,\text{V/m}$.

(d) $P = Vi = (1.20\,\text{V})(1.74\,\text{A}) = 2.09\,\text{W}$.

53P

Use $P = i^2 R = i^2 \rho L/A$, or $L/A = P/i^2\rho$. So the new values of L and A should be such that

$$\left(\frac{L}{A}\right)_{\text{new}} = \left(\frac{P}{i^2\rho}\right)_{\text{new}} = \frac{30}{4^2}\left(\frac{P}{i^2\rho}\right)_{\text{old}} = \frac{30}{16}\left(\frac{L}{A}\right)_{\text{old}},$$

i.e. $(L/A)_{\text{new}} = 1.875(L/A)_{\text{old}}$. Also note that $(LA)_{\text{new}} = (LA)_{\text{old}}$.

Solve the above two equations for L_{new} and A_{new}: $L_{\text{new}} = \sqrt{1.875}L_{\text{old}} = 1.369L_{\text{old}}$, $A_{\text{new}} = \sqrt{1/1.875}A_{\text{old}} = 0.730A_{\text{old}}$.

748

54P

(a) Since $P = i^2 R = J^2 A^2 R$, the current density is

$$J = \frac{1}{A}\sqrt{\frac{P}{R}} = \frac{1}{A}\sqrt{\frac{P}{\rho L/A}} = \sqrt{\frac{P}{\rho L A}}$$

$$= \sqrt{\frac{1.0\,\text{W}}{\pi(3.5 \times 10^{-5}\,\Omega \cdot \text{m})(2.0 \times 10^{-2}\,\text{m})(5.0 \times 10^{-3}\,\text{m})^2}} = 1.3 \times 10^5\,\text{A}/\text{m}^2.$$

(b) From $P = iV = JAV$ we get

$$V = \frac{P}{JA} = \frac{P}{\pi r^2 J}$$

$$= \frac{1.0\,\text{W}}{\pi(5.0 \times 10^{-3}\,\text{m})^2(1.3 \times 10^5\,\text{A}/\text{m}^2)} = 9.4 \times 10^{-2}\,\text{V}.$$

55P

(a) From $P = V^2/R = AV^2/\rho L$ we solve for L:

$$L = \frac{AV^2}{\rho P} = \frac{(2.60 \times 10^{-6}\,\text{m}^2)(75.0\,\text{V})^2}{(5.00 \times 10^{-7}\,\Omega \cdot \text{m})(5000\,\text{W})} = 5.85\,\text{m}.$$

(b) Since $L \propto V^2$ the new length should be

$$L' = L(V'/V)^2 = (5.85\,\text{m})(100\,\text{V}/75.0\,\text{V})^2 = 10.4\,\text{m}.$$

56P

(a) Let P be the power dissipated, i be the current in the heater, and V be the potential difference across the heater. They are related by $P = iV$. Solve for i:

$$i = \frac{P}{V} = \frac{1250\,\text{W}}{115\,\text{V}} = 10.9\,\text{A}.$$

(b) According to Ohm's law $V = iR$, where R is the resistance of the heater. Solve for R:

$$R = \frac{V}{i} = \frac{115\,\text{V}}{10.9\,\text{A}} = 10.6\,\Omega.$$

(c) The thermal energy E generated by the heater in time $t\,(= 1.0\,\text{h} = 3600\,\text{s})$ is

$$E = Pt = (1250\,\text{W})(3600\,\text{s}) = 4.5 \times 10^6\,\text{J}.$$

57P

(a) The monthly cost is $(100\,\mathrm{W})(24\,\mathrm{h/d})(31\,\mathrm{d/month})(6\,\mathrm{cents/kW \cdot h}) = 446\,\mathrm{cents} = \$4.46$, assuming a 31-day month.

(b) $R = V^2/P = (120\,\mathrm{V})^2/100\,\mathrm{W} = 144\,\Omega$.

(c) $i = P/V = 100\,\mathrm{W}/120\,\mathrm{V} = 0.833\,\mathrm{A}$.

58P

Let R_H be the resistance at the higher temperature ($800°\,\mathrm{C}$) and let R_L be the resistance at the lower temperature ($200°\,\mathrm{C}$). Since the potential difference is the same for the two temperatures, the power dissipated at the lower temperature is $P_L = V^2/R_L$, and the power dissipated at the higher temperature is $P_H = V^2/R_H$, so $P_L = (R_H/R_L)P_H$. Now $R_L = R_H + \alpha R_H\,\Delta T$, where ΔT is the temperature difference $T_L - T_H = -600°\,\mathrm{C}$. Thus

$$P_L = \frac{R_H}{R_H + \alpha R_H\,\Delta T}\,P_H = \frac{P_H}{1 + \alpha\,\Delta T} = \frac{500\,\mathrm{W}}{1 + (4.0 \times 10^{-4}\,/°\mathrm{C})(-600°\,\mathrm{C})} = 660\,\mathrm{W}\,.$$

59P

(a) The rate n is given by $n = i/e = (15 \times 10^{-6}\,\mathrm{A})/(1.60 \times 10^{-19}\,\mathrm{C}) = 9.4 \times 10^{13}\,/\mathrm{s}$.

(b) The rate is $P = (9.4 \times 10^{13}\,/\mathrm{s})(16 \times 10^6\,\mathrm{eV})(1.60 \times 10{-}19\,\mathrm{J/eV}) = 2.4 \times 10^2\,\mathrm{W}$.

60P

(a) The charge q that flows past any cross section of the beam in time Δt is given by $q = i\,\Delta t$ and the number of electrons is $N = q/e = (i/e)\,\Delta t$. This is the number of electrons that are accelerated. Thus

$$N = \frac{(0.50\,\mathrm{A})(0.10 \times 10^{-6}\,\mathrm{s})}{1.60 \times 10^{-19}\,\mathrm{C}} = 3.1 \times 10^{11}\,.$$

(b) Over a long time t the total charge is $Q = nqt$, where n is the number of pulses per unit time and q is the charge in one pulse. The average current is given by $\bar{i} = Q/t = nq$. Now $q = i\,\Delta t = (0.50\,\mathrm{A})(0.10 \times 10^{-6}\,\mathrm{s}) = 5.0 \times 10^{-8}\,\mathrm{C}$, so

$$\bar{i} = (500\,\mathrm{s}^{-1})(5.0 \times 10^{-8}\,\mathrm{C}) = 2.5 \times 10^{-5}\,\mathrm{A}\,.$$

(c) The accelerating potential difference is $V = K/e$, where K is the final kinetic energy of an electron. Since $K = 50\,\mathrm{MeV}$, the accelerating potential is $V = 50\,\mathrm{kV} = 5.0 \times 10^7\,\mathrm{V}$. During a pulse the power output is

$$P = iV = (0.50\,\mathrm{A})(5.0 \times 10^7\,\mathrm{V}) = 2.5 \times 10^7\,\mathrm{W}\,.$$

This is the peak power. The average power is

$$\overline{P} = \bar{i}V = (2.5 \times 10^{-5}\,\mathrm{A})(5.0 \times 10^7\,\mathrm{V}) = 1.3 \times 10^3\,\mathrm{W}\,.$$

61P

Let the heat of vaporization be L_v. Then $mL_v = P = iV$, where $m = 21\,\mathrm{mg/s}$. So

$$L_v = \frac{iV}{m} = \frac{(5.2\,\mathrm{A})(12\,\mathrm{V})}{(21 \times 10^{-3}\,\mathrm{g/s})(4.17\,\mathrm{J/cal})} = 7.1 \times 10^2\,\mathrm{cal/g}.$$

62P

The rate of change of mechanical energy of the piston-earth system, mgv, must be equal to the rate at which heat is generated from the coil, $i^2 R$: $mgv = i^2 R$. Thus

$$v = \frac{i^2 R}{mg} = \frac{(0.240\,\mathrm{A})^2(550\,\Omega)}{(12\,\mathrm{kg})(9.8\,\mathrm{m/s^2})} = 0.27\,\mathrm{m/s}.$$

63P

Use $P = V^2/R \propto V^2$. The percentage change is roughly $\Delta P/P = 2\Delta V/V = 2(110 - 115)/115 = -8.6\%$.

(b) At a lower temperature R will decrease, thus partially offsetting the decrease in P. So the actual drop will be smaller.

CHAPTER 29

1E

(a) $W = eV = e(12\,\text{V}) = 12\,\text{eV} = (12\,\text{eV})(1.6 \times 10^{-19}\,\text{J/eV}) = 1.9 \times 10^{-18}\,\text{J}$.

(b) $P = iV = neV = (3.4 \times 10^{18}/\text{s})(1.6 \times 10^{-19}\,\text{C})(12\,\text{V}) = 6.5\,\text{W}$.

2E

The chemical energy of the battery is reduced by $\Delta E = q\varepsilon$, where q is the charge that passes through in time $\Delta t = 6.0\,\text{min}$ and ε is the emf of the battery. If i is the current, then $q = i\,\Delta t$ and $\Delta E = i\varepsilon\,\Delta t = (5.0\,\text{A})(6.0\,\text{V})(6.0\,\text{min})(60\,\text{s/min}) = 1.1 \times 10^4\,\text{J}$. Notice the conversion of time from minutes to seconds.

3E

(a) The cost is $(100\,\text{W} \cdot 8.0\,\text{h})/(2.0\,\text{W} \cdot \text{h})(\$0.80) = \$320$.

(b) The cost is $(100\,\text{W} \cdot 8.0\,\text{h})/(10^3\,\text{W} \cdot \text{h})(\$0.12) = \$0.096$.

4P

If P is the rate at which the battery delivers energy and Δt is the time, the $\Delta E = P\,\Delta t$ is the energy delivered in time Δt. If q is the charge that passes through the battery in time Δt and ε is the emf of the battery, then $\Delta E = q\varepsilon$. Equate the two expressions for ΔE and solve for Δt:

$$\Delta t = \frac{q\varepsilon}{P} = \frac{(120\,\text{A} \cdot \text{h})(12\,\text{V})}{100\,\text{W}} = 14.4\,\text{h}.$$

5E

(a) Since $\varepsilon_1 > \varepsilon_2$ the current flows counterclockwise.

(b) Battery 1.

(c) Point B, since the current flows from B to A.

6E

(a) The energy transferred is

$$U = Pt = \frac{\varepsilon^2 t}{r + R} = \frac{(2.0\,\text{V})^2(2.0\,\text{min})(60\,\text{s/min})}{1.0\Omega + 5.0\Omega} = 80\,\text{J}.$$

(b) The amount of thermal energy generated is

$$U' = i^2 R t = \left(\frac{\varepsilon}{r + R}\right)^2 R t$$

$$= \left(\frac{2.0\,\text{V}}{1.0\Omega + 5.0\Omega}\right)^2 (5.0\Omega)(2.0\,\text{min})(60\,\text{s/min}) = 67\,\text{J}.$$

(c) The difference between U and U' is the thermal energy that appears in the battery due to its internal resistance.

7E

(a) and (b)

(C)

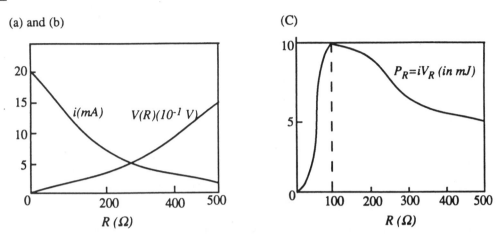

The curve in (c) above is the power P_R consumed by R as a function of R.

8E

(a) Let i be the current in the circuit and take it to be positive if it is to the left in R_1. Use Kirchhoff's loop rule: $\varepsilon_1 - iR_2 - iR_1 - \varepsilon_2 = 0$. Solve for i:

$$i = \frac{\varepsilon_1 - \varepsilon_2}{R_1 + R_2} = \frac{12\,\text{V} - 6.0\,\text{V}}{4.0\,\Omega + 8.0\,\Omega} = 0.50\,\text{A} .$$

A positive value was obtained, so the current is counterclockwise around the circuit.

(b) If i is the current in a resistor R, then the power dissipated by that resistor is given by $P = i^2 R$. For R_1, $P_1 = (0.50\,\text{A})^2(4.0\,\Omega) = 1.0\,\text{W}$ and for R_2, $P_2 = (0.50\,\text{A})^2(8.0\,\Omega) = 2.0\,\text{W}$.

(c) If i is the current in a battery with emf ε, then the battery supplies energy at the rate $P = i\varepsilon$ provided the current and emf are in the same direction. The battery absorbs energy at the rate $P = i\varepsilon$ if the current and emf are in opposite directions. For ε_1, $P_1 = (0.50\,\text{A})(12\,\text{V}) = 6.0\,\text{W}$ and for ε_2, $P_2 = (0.50\,\text{A})(6.0\,\text{V}) = 3.0\,\text{W}$. In battery 1 the current is in the same direction as the emf so this battery supplies energy to the circuit. The battery is discharging. The current in battery 2 is opposite the direction of the emf, so this battery absorbs energy from the circuit. It is charging.

9E

(a) The potential difference is $V = \varepsilon + ir = 12\,\text{V} + (0.040\Omega)(50\,\text{A}) = 14\,\text{V}$.
(b) $P = i^2 r = (50\,\text{A})^2(0.040\Omega) = 100\,\text{W}$.
(c) $P' = iV = (50\,\text{A})(12\,\text{V}) = 600\,\text{W}$.
(d) In this case $V = \varepsilon - ir = 12\,\text{V} - (0.040\Omega)(50\,\text{A}) = 10\,\text{V}$ and $P = i^2 r = 100\,\text{W}$.

10E

The current in the circuit is $i = (150\,\text{V} - 50\,\text{V})/(3.0\,\Omega + 2.0\,\Omega) = 20\,\text{A}$. So from $V_Q + 150\,\text{V} - (2.0\,\Omega)i = V_P$ we get $V_Q = 100\,\text{V} + (2.0\,\Omega)(20\,\text{A}) - 150\,\text{V} = -10\,\text{V}$.

11E

(a) If i is the current and ΔV is the potential difference then the power absorbed is given by $P = i\,\Delta V$. Thus

$$\Delta V = \frac{P}{i} = \frac{50\,\text{W}}{1.0\,\text{A}} = 50\,\text{V}.$$

Since the energy of the charge decreases, point A is at a higher potential than point B; that is $V_A - V_B = 50\,\text{V}$.

(b) The end-to-end potential difference is given by $V_A - V_B = +iR + \varepsilon$, where ε is the emf of element C and is taken to be positive if it is to the left in the diagram. Thus $\varepsilon = V_A - V_B - iR = 50\,\text{V} - (1.0\,\text{A})(2.0\,\Omega) = 48\,\text{V}$.

(c) A positive value was obtained for ε, so it is toward the left. The negative terminal is at B.

12E

The potential difference across R_2 is

$$V_2 = iR_2 = \frac{\varepsilon R_2}{R_1 + R_2 + R_3} = \frac{(12\,\text{V})(4.0\,\Omega)}{3.0\,\Omega + 4.0\,\Omega + 5.0\,\Omega} = 4.0\,\text{V}.$$

13E

From $V_a - \varepsilon_1 - ir_1 = V_c$ and $i = (\varepsilon_2 - \varepsilon_1)/(R + r_1 + r_2)$ we get

$$V_a - V_c = \varepsilon_1 + ir_1 = \varepsilon_1 + \frac{(\varepsilon_2 - \varepsilon_1)r_1}{R + r_1 + r_2}$$

$$= 2.1\,\text{V} + \frac{(4.4\,\text{V} - 2.1\,\text{V})(1.8\,\Omega)}{5.5\,\Omega + 1.8\,\Omega + 2.3\,\Omega} = 2.5\,\text{V}.$$

14E

(a) Now $R_{\text{tank}} = 140\,\Omega$ so $i = 12\,\text{V}/(10\,\Omega + 140\,\Omega) = 8.0 \times 10^{-2}\,\text{A}$.
(b) Now $R_{\text{tank}} = (140\,\Omega - 20\,\Omega)/2 = 60\,\Omega$ so $i = 12\,\text{V}/(10\,\Omega + 60\,\Omega) = 0.17\,\text{A}$.
(c) Now $R_{\text{tank}} = 20\,\Omega$ so $i = 12\,\text{V}/(10\,\Omega + 20\,\Omega) = 0.40\,\text{A}$.

15P
(a) Solve $i = (\varepsilon_2 - \varepsilon_1)/(r_1 + r_2 + R)$ for R:

$$R = \frac{\varepsilon_2 - \varepsilon_1}{i} - r_1 - r_2 = \frac{3.0\,\text{V} - 2.0\,\text{V}}{1.0 \times 10^{-3}\,\text{A}} - 3.0\,\Omega - 3.0\,\Omega = 9.9 \times 10^2\,\Omega.$$

(b) $P = i^2 R = (1.0 \times 10^{-3}\,\text{A})^2 (9.9 \times 10^2\,\Omega) = 9.9 \times 10^{-4}\,\text{W}.$

16P
(a) From $P = V^2/R$ we find $V = \sqrt{PR} = \sqrt{(10\,\text{W})(0.10\,\Omega)} = 1.0\,\text{V}.$
(b) From $i = V/R = (\varepsilon - V)/r$ we find $r = R(\varepsilon - V)/V = (0.10\,\Omega)(1.5\,\text{V} - 1.0\,\text{V})/(1.0\,\text{V}) = 0.050\,\Omega.$

17P
Let the emf be V. Then we have $V = iR = (5.0\,\text{A})R = i'(R + R') = (4.0\,\text{A})(R + 2.0\,\Omega).$
Solve for R: $R = 8.0\,\Omega.$

18P
Let the power supplied be P_s and that dissipated be P_d. Since $P_d = i^2 R$ and $i = P_s/\varepsilon$, we have $P_d = P_s^2/\varepsilon^2 R \propto \varepsilon^{-2}$. The ratio is then

$$\frac{P_d(\varepsilon = 110,000\,\text{V})}{P_d(\varepsilon = 110\,\text{V})} = \left(\frac{110\,\text{V}}{110,000\,\text{V}}\right)^2 = 1.0 \times 10^{-6}.$$

19P
The internal resistance of the battery is $r = (12\,\text{V} - 11.4\,\text{V})/50\,\text{A} = 0.012\,\Omega < 0.020\,\Omega$, so the battery is OK. The resistance of the cable is $R = 3.0\,\text{V}/50\,\text{A} = 0.060\,\Omega > 0.040\,\Omega$, so the cable is defective.

20P
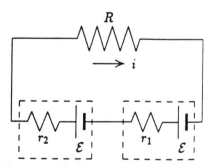

(a) The circuit is shown in the diagram to the right. The current is taken to be positive if it is clockwise. The potential difference across battery 1 is given by $V_1 = \varepsilon - ir_1$ and for this to be 0 the current must be $i = \varepsilon/r_1$. Kirchhoff's loop rule gives $2\varepsilon - ir_1 - ir_2 - iR = 0$. Substitute $i = \varepsilon/r_1$ and solve for R. You should get $R = r_1 - r_2$.

(b) Since R must be positive, r_1 must be greater than r_2. The potential difference across the battery with the larger internal resistance can be made to vanish with the proper choice

755

of R, the potential difference across the battery with the smaller potential difference cannot be made to vanish.

21P

(a) and (b) Let the emf of the solar cell be ε and the output voltage be V, then $V = \varepsilon - ir = \varepsilon - (V/R)r$ for both cases. Numerically we get $0.10\,\text{V} = \varepsilon - (0.10\,\text{V}/500\,\Omega)r$ and $0.15\,\text{V} = \varepsilon - (0.15\,\text{V}/1000\,\Omega)r$. Solve for ε and r: $\varepsilon = 0.30\,\text{V}$, $r = 1000\,\Omega$.
(c) The efficiency is $e = (V^2/R)/P_{\text{received}} = (0.15\,\text{V})/[(1000\,\Omega)(5.0\,\text{cm}^2)$
$(2.0 \times 10^{-3}\,\text{W/cm}^2)] = 2.3 \times 10^{-3}$.

22P

(a) The current in the circuit is

$$i = \frac{\varepsilon}{r + R},$$

so the rate of energy dissipation in R is

$$P = i^2 R = \frac{\varepsilon^2 R}{(r + R)^2}.$$

You want to find the value of R that maximizes P. To do this find an expression for the derivative with respect to R, set it equal to 0, and solve for R. The derivative is

$$\frac{dP}{dR} = \frac{\varepsilon^2}{(r + R)^2} - \frac{2\varepsilon^2 R}{(r + R)^3} = \frac{\varepsilon^2 (r - R)}{(r + R)^3}.$$

Thus $r - R = 0$ and $R = r$. For R very small P increases with R. For R large P decreases with increasing R. So $R = r$ is a maximum, not a minimum.
(b) Substitute $R = r$ into $P = \varepsilon^2 R/(r + R)^2$ to obtain $P = \varepsilon^2/4r$.

23P

(a)

$$J_A = J_B = \frac{i}{A} = \frac{V}{(R_1 + R_2)A} = \frac{4V}{(R_1 + R_2)\pi D^2}$$

$$= \frac{4(60.0\,\text{V})}{\pi(0.127\,\Omega + 0.729\,\Omega)(2.60 \times 10^{-3}\,\text{m})^2} = 1.32 \times 10^7\,\text{A/m}^2.$$

(b) $V_A = VR_1/(R_1 + R_2) = (60.0\,\text{V})(0.127\,\Omega)/(0.127\,\Omega + 0.729\,\Omega) = 8.90\,\text{V}$, and $V_B = V - V_A = 60.0\,\text{V} - 8.9\,\text{V} = 51.1\,\text{V}$.
(c) Calculate the resistivity from $R = \rho L/A$ for both materials: $\rho_A = R_A A/L_A = \pi R_A D^2/4L_A = \pi(0.127\,\Omega)(2.60 \times 10^{-3}\,\text{m})^2/[4(40.0\,\text{m})] = 1.69 \times 10^{-8}\,\Omega \cdot \text{m}$. So A is made of copper. Similarly we find $\rho_B = 9.68 \times 10^{-8}\,\Omega \cdot \text{m}$, so B is made of iron.

24P

(a) The power delivered by the motor is $P = (2.00\,\text{V})(0.500\,\text{m/s}) = 1.00\,\text{W}$. From $P = i^2 R_{\text{motor}}$ and $\varepsilon = i(r + R_{\text{motor}})$ we then find $i^2 r - i\varepsilon + P = 0$ (which also follows directly from the conservation of energy principle). Solve for i:

$$i = \frac{\varepsilon \pm \sqrt{\varepsilon^2 - 4rP}}{2r}$$

$$= \frac{2.00\,\text{V} \pm \sqrt{(2.00\,\text{V})^2 - 4(0.500\,\Omega)(1.00\,\text{W})}}{2(0.500\,\Omega)} = 3.41\,\text{A or } 0.586\,\text{A}.$$

(b) Use $V = \varepsilon - ir = 2.00\,\text{V} - i(0.500\,\Omega)$. Substitute the two values of i obtained in (a) into the above formula to get $V = 0.293\,\text{V or } 1.71\,\text{V}$.

(c) The power P delivered by the motor is the same for either solution. Since $P = iV$ we may have a lower i and higher V or, reversely, a lower V and higher i, while keeping $P = iV$ a constant.

25P

Denote $T_0 = 20°$. If $R(T) = R_s(T) + R_i(T) = R_s(T_0)[1 + \alpha(T - T_0)] + R_i(T_0)[1 + \alpha_i(T - T_0)] = [R_s(T)_0 \alpha_s + R_i(T_0)\alpha_i] + (\text{temperature-independent terms})$ is to be temperature-independent, we must require that $R_s(T_0)\alpha_s + R_i(T_0)\alpha_i = 0$. Also note that $R_s(T_0) + R_i(T_0) = R = 1000\,\Omega$. Solve for $R_s(T_0)$ and $R_i(T_0)$:
$R_s(T_0) = R\alpha_i/(\alpha_i - \alpha_s) = (1000\,\Omega)(6.5 \times 10^{-3})/(6.5 \times 10^{-3} + 70 \times 10^{-3}) = 85.0\,\Omega$,
$R_i(T_0) = 1000\,\Omega - 85.0\,\Omega = 915\,\Omega$.

26E

The potential difference across each resistor is $V = 25.0\,\text{V}$. Since the resistors are identical, the current in each one is $i = V/R = (25.0\,\text{V})/(18.0\,\Omega) = 1.39\,\text{A}$. The total current through the battery is $i_{\text{total}} = 4(1.39\,\text{A}) = 5.56\,\text{A}$.

You might use the idea of equivalent resistance. For 4 identical resistors in parallel the equivalent resistance is given by

$$\frac{1}{R_{\text{eq}}} = \frac{4}{R}.$$

When a potential difference of $25.0\,\text{V}$ is applied to the equivalent resistor the current through it is the same as the total current through the 4 resistors in parallel. Thus $i_{\text{total}} = V/R_{\text{eq}} = 4V/R = 4(25.0\,\text{V})/(18.0\,\Omega) = 5.56\,\text{A}$.

27E

Since $R_{\text{eq}} < R$ the two resistors ($R = 12.0\,\Omega$ and R_x) must be connceted in parallel:
$R_{\text{eq}} = 3.00\,\Omega = R_x R/(R + R_x) = R_x/(12.0\,\Omega + R_x)$. Solve for R_x: $R_x = R_{\text{eq}}R/(R - R_{\text{eq}}) = (3.00\,\Omega)(12.0\,\Omega)/(12.0\,\Omega - 3.00\,\Omega) = 4.00\,\Omega$.

28E

Let the resistances of the two resistors be R_1 and R_2. Note that the smallest valuve of the possible R_{eq}'s must be the result of connecting R_1 and R_2 in parallel, while the largest one must be that of connecting them in series. Thus $R_1 R_2/(R_1 + R_2) = 3.0\,\Omega$ and $R_1 + R_2 = 16\,\Omega$. So R_1, R_2 must be $4.0\,\Omega$ and $12\,\Omega$.

29E

Let i_1 be the current in R_1 and take it to be positive if it is to the right. Let i_2 be the current in R_2 and take it to be positive if it is upward. When the loop rule is applied to the lower loop, the result is

$$\varepsilon_2 - i_1 R_1 = 0.$$

and when it is applied to the upper loop, the result is

$$\varepsilon_1 - \varepsilon_2 - \varepsilon_3 - i_2 R_2 = 0.$$

The first equation yields

$$i_1 = \frac{\varepsilon_2}{R_1} = \frac{5.0\,\text{V}}{100\,\Omega} = 0.050\,\text{A}.$$

The second yields

$$i_2 = \frac{\varepsilon_1 - \varepsilon_2 - \varepsilon_3}{R_2} = \frac{6.0\,\text{V} - 5.0\,\text{V} - 4.0\,\text{V}}{50\,\Omega} = -0.060\,\text{A}.$$

The negative sign indicates that the current in R_2 is actually downward.

If V_b is the potential at point b, then the potential at point a is $V_a = V_b + \varepsilon_3 + \varepsilon_2$, so $V_a - V_b = \varepsilon_3 + \varepsilon_2 = 4.0\,\text{V} + 5.0\,\text{V} = 9.0\,\text{V}$.

30E

s_1, s_2 and s_3 all open: $i_a = 0.00\,\text{A}$.
s_1 closed, s_2 and s_3 open: $i_a = \varepsilon/2R_1 = 120\,\text{V}/40.0\,\Omega = 3.00\,\text{A}$.
s_2 closed, s_1 and s_3 open: $i_a = \varepsilon/(2R_1 + R_2) = 120\,\text{V}/50.0\,\Omega = 2.40\,\text{A}$.
s_3 closed, s_1 and s_2 open: $i_a = \varepsilon/(2R_1 + R_2) = 120\,\text{V}/60.0\,\Omega = 2.00\,\text{A}$.
s_1 open, s_2 and s_3 closed: $R_{eq} = R_1 + R_2 + R_1(R_1 + R_2)/(2R_1 + R_2) = 20.0\,\Omega + 10.0\,\Omega + (20.0\,\Omega)(30.0\,\Omega)/(50.0\,\Omega) = 42.0\,\Omega$, so $i_a = \varepsilon/R_{eq} = 120\,\text{V}/42.0\,\Omega = 2.86\,\text{A}$.
s_2 open, s_1 and s_3 closed: $R_{eq} = R_1 + R_1(R_1 + 2R_2)/(2R_1 + 2R_2) = 20.0\,\Omega + (20.0\,\Omega)(40.0\,\Omega)/(60.0\,\Omega) = 33.3\,\Omega$, so $i_a = \varepsilon/R_{eq} = 120\,\text{V}/33.3\,\Omega = 3.60\,\text{A}$.
s_3 open, s_1 and s_2 closed: $R_{eq} = R_1 + R_1(R_1 + R_2)/(2R_1 + R_2) = 20.0\,\Omega + (20.0\,\Omega)(30.0\,\Omega)/(50.0\,\Omega) = 32.0\,\Omega$, so $i_a = \varepsilon/R_{eq} = 120\,\text{V}/32.0\,\Omega = 3.75\,\text{A}$.
s_1, s_2 and s_3 all closed: $R_{eq} = R_1 + R_1 R'/(R_1 + R')$ where $R' = R_2 + R_1(R_1 + R_2)/(2R_1 + R_2) = 22.0\,\Omega$, i.e. $R_{eq} = 20.0\,\Omega + (20.0\,\Omega)(22.0\,\Omega)/(20.0\,\Omega + 22.0\,\Omega) = 30.5\,\Omega$; so $i_a = \varepsilon/R_{eq} = 120\,\text{V}/30.5\,\Omega = 3.94\,\text{A}$.

31E

(a) $R_{eq}(AB) = 20.0\,\Omega/3 = 6.67\,\Omega$ (Three 20.0-Ω resistors in parallel).

(b) $R_{eq}(AC) = 20.0\text{-}\Omega/3 = 6.67\,\Omega$ (Three $20.0 - \Omega$ resistors in parallel).

(c) $R_{eq}(BC) = 0$ (as B and C are connected by a conducting wire).

32E

$R_{eq} = 2.50\,\Omega + (4.00\,\Omega)(4.00\,\Omega)/(4.00\,\Omega + 4.00\,\Omega) = 4.50\,\Omega.$

33E

(a) Let ε be the emf of the battery. When the bulbs are connected in parallel the potential difference across them is the same and is the same as the emf of the battery. The power dissipated by bulb 1 is $P_1 = \varepsilon^2/R_1$ and the power dissipated by bulb 2 is $P_2 = \varepsilon^2/R_2$. Since R_1 is greater than R_2, bulb 2 dissipates energy at a greater rate than bulb 1 and is the brighter of the two.

(b) When the bulbs are connected in series the current in them is the same. The power dissipate by bulb 1 is now $P_1 = i^2 R_1$ and the power dissipated by bulb 2 is $P_2 = i^2 R_2$. Since R_1 is greater than R_2 greater power is dissipated by bulb 1 than by bulb 2 and bulb 1 is the brighter of the two.

34E

The currents i_1, i_2 and i_3 are obatined from Eqs. 29-14 through 29-16:

$$
\begin{cases}
i_1 = \dfrac{\varepsilon_1(R_2 + R_3) - \varepsilon_2 R_3}{R_1 R_2 + R_2 R_3 + R_1 R_3} = \dfrac{(4.0\,\text{V})(10\,\Omega + 5.0\,\Omega) - (1.0\,\text{V})(5.0\,\Omega)}{(10\,\Omega)(10\,\Omega) + (10\,\Omega)(5.0\,\Omega) + (10\,\Omega)(5.0\,\Omega)} \\
\quad = 0.275\,\text{A}, \\
i_2 = \dfrac{\varepsilon_1 R_3 - \varepsilon_2(R_1 + R_2)}{R_1 R_2 + R_2 R_3 + R_1 R_3} = \dfrac{(4.0\,\text{V})(5.0\,\Omega) - (1.0\,\text{V})(10\,\Omega + 5.0\,\Omega)}{(10\,\Omega)(10\,\Omega) + (10\,\Omega)(5.0\,\Omega) + (10\,\Omega)(5.0\,\Omega)} \\
\quad = 0.025\,\text{A}, \\
i_3 = i_2 - i_1 = 0.025\,\text{A} - 0.275\,\text{A} = -0.250\,\text{A}.
\end{cases}
$$

$V_d - V_c$ can now be calculated by taking various paths. Two examples: from $V_d - i_2 R_2 = V_c$ we get $V_d - V_c = i_2 R_2 = (0.0250\,\text{A})(10\,\Omega) = 0.25\,\text{V}$; or from $V_d + i_3 R_3 + \varepsilon_2 = V_c$ we get $V_d - V_c = -i_3 R_3 - \varepsilon_2 = -(-0.250\,\text{A})(5.0\,\Omega) - 1.0\,\text{V} = 0.25\,\text{V}.$

35E

Let r be the resistance of each of the narrow wires. Since they are in parallel the resistance R of the composite is given by

$$\frac{1}{R} = \frac{9}{r},$$

or $R = r/9$. Now $r = 4\rho\ell/\pi d^2$ and $R = 4\rho\ell/\pi D^2$, where ρ is the resistivity of copper. $A = \pi d^2/4$ was used for the cross-sectional area of a single wire and a similar expression was used for the cross-sectional area of the thick wire. Since the single thick wire is to have the same resistance as the composite,

$$\frac{4\rho\ell}{\pi D^2} = \frac{4\rho\ell}{9\pi d^2}.$$

Solve for D and obtain $D = 3d$.

36E
The maximum power output is $(120\,\text{V})(15\,\text{A}) = 1800\,\text{W}$. Since $1800\,\text{W}/500\,\text{W} = 3.6$, the maximum number of 500-W lamps allowed is **3**.

37E
Consider the lowest branch with the $R_1 = 3.0\text{-}\Omega$ and the $R_2 = 5.0\text{-}\Omega$ resistors. The voltage difference across the $5.0\text{-}\Omega$ resistor is

$$V = i_2 R_2 = \frac{\varepsilon R_2}{R_1 + R_2} = \frac{(120\,\text{V})(5.0\,\Omega)}{3.0\,\Omega + 5.0\,\Omega} = 7.5\,\text{V}.$$

38P
When connected in series, the electric energy dissipation is $P_s = \varepsilon^2/(R_1 + R_2)$. When connected in parallel $P_p = \varepsilon^2(R_1 + R_2)/R_1 R_2$. Let $P_p/P_s = 5$, we get $(R_1 + R_2)^2/R_1 R_2 = 5$, where $R_1 = 100\,\Omega$. Solve for R_2: $R_2 = 38\,\Omega$ or $260\,\Omega$.

39P
Divide the resistors into groups of n resistors each, with all the resistors of a group connected in series. Suppose there are m such groups, with the groups connected in parallel. The scheme is shown in the diagram on the right for $n = 3$ and $m = 2$. Let R be the resistance of any one the resistors. Then the resistance of a series group is nR and the resistance of the total array is given by

$$\frac{1}{R_{\text{total}}} = \frac{m}{nR}.$$

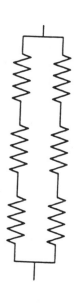

Since we want $R_{\text{total}} = R$, we must select $n = m$.

The current is the same in every resistor and there are n^2 resistors, so the maximum total power that can be dissipated is $P_{\text{total}} = n^2 P$, where P is the maximum power that can be dissipated by any one of the resistors.

You want $P_{total} > 5.0P$, so n^2 must be larger than 5.0. Since n must be an integer, the smallest it can be is 3. The least number of resistors is $n^2 = 9$.

40P

(a) The batteries are identical and, because they are connected in parallel, the potential differences across them are the same. This means the currents in them are the same. Let i be the current in either battery and take it to be positive to the left. According to the junction rule the current in R is $2i$ and it is positive to the right. The loop rule applied to either loop containing a battery and R yields $\varepsilon - ir - 2iR = 0$, so

$$i = \frac{\varepsilon}{r + 2R}.$$

The power dissipated in R is

$$P = i^2 R = \frac{\varepsilon^2 R}{(r + 2R)^2}.$$

Find the maximum by setting the derivative with respect to R equal to zero. The derivative is

$$\frac{dP}{dR} = \frac{\varepsilon^2}{(r + 2R)^2} - \frac{4\varepsilon^2 R}{(r + 2R)^3} = \frac{\varepsilon^2(r - 2R)}{(r + 2R)^3}.$$

It vanishes and P is a maximum if $R = r/2$.
(b) Substitute $R = r/2$ into $P = \varepsilon^2 R/(r + 2R)^2$ to obtain

$$P_{max} = \frac{\varepsilon^2 r/2}{(2r)^2} = \frac{\varepsilon^2}{8r}.$$

41P

When connected in parallel: by symmetry the current i going through either battery is the same. So from $\varepsilon = ir + (2i)R$ we get $i_R = 2i = 2\varepsilon/(r + 2R)$.
When connected in series: $2\varepsilon - i_R r - i_R r - i_R R = 0$, or $i_R = 2\varepsilon/(2r + R)$.
(b) In series, since $R > r$.
(c) In parallel, since $R < r$.

42P

When all the batteries are connected in parallel, each supplies a current i and therefore $i_R = Ni$. Then from $\varepsilon = ir + i_R R = ir + Nir$, we get $i_R = N\varepsilon/[(N + 1)r]$.
When all the batteries are connected in series $\varepsilon_{total} = N\varepsilon = Ni_r r + i_R R = Ni_R r + i_R r$, or $i_R = N\varepsilon/[(N + 1)r]$.

43P

(a) Since $\varepsilon_2 = \varepsilon_3$ and $R_2 = 2R_1$, from symmetry we know that the currents through ε_2 and ε_3 are the same: $i_2 = i_3 = i$. Therefore the current through ε_1 is $i_1 = 2i$. Then from $V_b - V_a = \varepsilon_2 - iR_2 = \varepsilon_1 + (2R_1)(2i)$ we get

$$i = \frac{\varepsilon_2 - \varepsilon_1}{4R_1 + R_2} = \frac{4.0\,\text{V} - 2.0\,\text{V}}{4(1.0\,\Omega) + 2.0\,\Omega} = 0.33\,\text{A}.$$

So the current through ε_1 is $i_1 = 2i = 0.67\,\text{A}$, flowing downward; the current through either ε_2 and ε_3 is $0.33\,\text{A}$, flowing upward.

(b) $V_a - V_b = -iR_2 + \varepsilon_2 = -(0.333\,\text{A})(2.0\,\Omega) + 4.0\,\text{V} = 3.3\,\text{V}.$

44P

(a) Since $P = \varepsilon^2/R_{eq}$, the higher the power rating the smaller R_{eq}. To achieve this, we can let the low position connect the larger resistance (R_1), middle position connect the smaller resistance (R_2), and the high position connect both in parallel.

(b) For $P = 100\,\text{W}$, $R_{eq} = R_1 = \varepsilon^2/P = (120\,\text{V})^2/100\,\text{W} = 144\,\Omega$.

(c) For $P = 300\,\text{W}$, $R_{eq} = R_1 R_2/(R_1 + R_2) = (144\,\Omega)R_2/(144\,\Omega + R_2) = (120\,\text{V})^2/300\,\text{W}$. Solve for R_2: $R_2 = 72\,\Omega$.

45P

(a) R_2, R_3 and R_4 are in parallel with an equivalent resistance of

$$R = \frac{R_2 R_3 R_4}{R_2 R_3 + R_2 R_4 + R_3 R_4} = \frac{(50\,\Omega)(50\,\Omega)(75\,\Omega)}{(50\,\Omega)(50\,\Omega) + (50\,\Omega)(75\,\Omega) + (50\,\Omega)(75\,\Omega)} = 19\,\Omega.$$

Thus $R_{eq} = R_1 + R = 100\,\Omega + 19\,\Omega = 1.2 \times 10^2\,\Omega$.

(b) $i_1 = \varepsilon/R_{eq} = 6.0\,\text{V}/(1.2 \times 10^2\,\Omega) = 5.0 \times 10^{-2}\,\text{A}$.

$i_2 = (\varepsilon - V_1)/R_2 = (\varepsilon - i_1 R_1)/R_2 = [6.0\,\text{V} - (5.0 \times 10^{-2}\,\text{A})(100\,\Omega)]/50\,\Omega = 2.0 \times 10^{-2}\,\text{A}$.

$i_3 = (\varepsilon - V_1)/R_3 == i_2 R_2/R_3 = (2.0 \times 10^{-2}\,\text{A})(50\,\Omega/50\,\Omega) = 2.0 \times 10^{-2}\,\text{A}$.

$i_4 = i_1 - i_2 - i_3 = 5.0 \times 10^{-2}\,\text{A} - 2(2.0 \times 10^{-2}\,\text{A}) = 1.0 \times 10^{-2}\,\text{A}$.

46P

(a) First find the currents. Let i_1 be the current in R_1 and take it to be positive if it is upward. Let i_2 be the current in R_2 and take it to be positive if it is to the left. Let i_3 be the current in R_3 and take it to be positive if it is to the right. The junction rule produces

$$i_1 + i_2 + i_3 = 0.$$

The loop rule applied to the left-hand loop produces

$$\varepsilon_1 - i_3 R_3 + i_1 R_1 = 0$$

762

and applied to the right-hand loop produces

$$\varepsilon_2 - i_2 R_2 + i_1 R_1 = 0.$$

Substitute $i_1 = -i_2 - i_3$, from the first equation, into the other two to obtain

$$\varepsilon_1 - i_3 R_3 - i_2 R_1 - i_3 R_1 = 0$$

and

$$\varepsilon_2 - i_2 R_2 - i_2 R_1 - i_3 R_1 = 0.$$

The first of these yields

$$i_3 = \frac{\varepsilon_1 - i_2 R_1}{R_1 + R_3}.$$

Substitute this into the second equation and solve for i_2. You should obtain

$$
\begin{aligned}
i_2 &= \frac{\varepsilon_2(R_1 + R_3) - \varepsilon_1 R_1}{R_1 R_2 + R_1 R_3 + R_2 R_3} \\
&= \frac{(1.00\,\text{V})(5.00\,\Omega + 4.00\,\Omega) - (3.00\,\text{V})(5.00\,\Omega)}{(5.00\,\Omega)(2.00\,\Omega) + (5.00\,\Omega)(4.00\,\Omega) + (2.00\,\Omega)(4.00\,\Omega)} = -0.158\,\text{A}.
\end{aligned}
$$

Substitute into the expression for i_3 to obtain

$$i_3 = \frac{\varepsilon_1 - i_2 R_1}{R_1 + R_3} = \frac{3.00\,\text{V} - (-0.158\,\text{A})(5.00\,\Omega)}{5.00\,\Omega + 4.00\,\Omega} = 0.421\,\text{A}.$$

Finally,

$$i_1 = -i_2 - i_3 = -(-0.158\,\text{A}) - (0.421\,\text{A}) = -0.263\,\text{A}.$$

Note that the current in R_1 is actually downward and the current in R_2 is to the right. The current in R_3 is also to the right.

The power dissipated in R_1 is $P_1 = i_1^2 R_1 = (-0.263\,\text{A})^2(5.00\,\Omega) = 0.346\,\text{W}$, the power dissipated in R_2 is $P_2 = i_2^2 R_2 = (-0.158\,\text{A})^2(2.00\,\Omega) = 0.0499\,\text{W}$, and the power dissipated in R_3 is $P_3 = i_3^2 R_3 = (0.421\,\text{A})^2(4.00\,\Omega) = 0.709\,\text{W}$.

(b) The power supplied by ε_1 is $i_3 \varepsilon_1 = (0.421\,\text{A})(3.00\,\text{V}) = 1.26\,\text{W}$ and the power supplied by ε_2 is $i_2 \varepsilon_2 = (-0.158\,\text{A})(1.00\,\text{V}) = -0.158\,\text{W}$. The negative sign indicates that ε_2 is actually absorbing energy from the circuit.

47P

(a) Use $P = \varepsilon^2 / R_{\text{eq}}$, where

$$R_{\text{eq}} = 7.00\,\Omega + \frac{(12.0\,\Omega)(4.00\,\Omega)R}{(12.0\,\Omega)(4.0\,\Omega) + (12.0\,\Omega)R + (4.00\,\Omega)R}.$$

Put $P = 60.0\,\text{W}$ and $\varepsilon = 24.0\,\text{V}$ and solve for R: $R = 19.5\,\Omega$.

(b) Since $P \propto R_{eq}$, we must minimize R_{eq}, which means $R = 0$.

(c) Now we must maximize R_{eq}, or set $R = \infty$.

(d) Since $R_{eq, max} = 7.00\,\Omega + (12.0\,\Omega)(4.00\,\Omega)/(12.0\,\Omega + 4.00\,\Omega) = 10.0\,\Omega$, $P_{min} = \varepsilon^2/R_{eq, max} = (24.0\,V)^2/10.0\,\Omega = 57.6\,W$.

Since $R_{eq, min} = 7.00\,\Omega$, $P_{max} = \varepsilon^2/R_{eq, min} = (24.0\,V)^2/7.00\,\Omega = 82.3\,W$.

48P

The voltage difference across R is $V_R = \varepsilon R'/(R' + 2.00\,\Omega)$, where $R' = (5.00\,\Omega R)/(5.00\,\Omega + R)$. So

$$P_R = \frac{V_R^2}{R} = \frac{1}{R}\left(\frac{\varepsilon R'}{R' + 2.00\,\Omega}\right)^2 = \frac{1}{R}\left(\frac{\varepsilon}{1 + 2.00\,\Omega/R'}\right)^2$$

$$= \frac{\varepsilon^2}{R}\left[1 + \frac{(2.00\,\Omega)(5.00\,\Omega + R)}{(5.00\,\Omega)R}\right]^{-2} \equiv \frac{\varepsilon^2}{f(R)}.$$

To maximize P_R we need to minimize the expression $f(R)$. Let

$$\frac{df(R)}{dR} = -\frac{4.00\,\Omega^2}{R^2} + \frac{49}{25} = 0,$$

we get $R = \sqrt{(4.00\,\Omega^2)(25)/49} = 1.43\,\Omega$.

49P

(a) $R_{eq}(FH) = (10.0\,\Omega)(10.0\,\Omega)(5.00\,\Omega)/[(10.0\,\Omega)(10.0\,\Omega) + 2(10.0\,\Omega)(5.00\,\Omega)] = 2.50\,\Omega$.

(b) $R_{eq}(FG) = (5.00\,\Omega)R/(R + 5.00\,\Omega)$, where $R = 5.00\,\Omega + (5.00\,\Omega)(10.0\,\Omega)/(5.00\,\Omega + 10.0\,\Omega) = 8.33\,\Omega$. So $R_{eq}(FG) = (5.00\,\Omega)(8.33\,\Omega)/(5.00\,\Omega + 8.33\,\Omega) = 3.13\,\Omega$.

50P

(a) The copper wire and the aluminum sheath are connected in parallel, so the potential difference is the same for them. Since the potential difference is the product of the current and the resistance, $i_C R_C = i_A R_A$, where i_C is the current in the copper, I_A is the current in the aluminum, R_C is the resistance of the copper, and R_A is the resistance of the aluminum. The resistance of either component is given by $R = \rho L/A$, where ρ is the resistivity, L is the length, and A is the cross-sectional area. The resistance of the copper wire is $R_C = \rho_C L/\pi a^2$ and the resistance of the aluminum sheath is $R_A = \rho_A L/\pi(b^2 - a^2)$. Substitute these expressions into $i_C R_C = i_A R_A$, and cancel the common factors L and π to obtain

$$\frac{i_C \rho_C}{a^2} = \frac{i_A \rho_A}{b^2 - a^2}.$$

Solve this equation simultaneously with $i = i_C + i_A$, where i is the total current. You should get

$$i_C = \frac{r_C^2 \rho_C i}{(r_A^2 - r_C^2)\rho_C + r_C^2 \rho_A}$$

and

$$i_A = \frac{(r_A^2 - r_C^2)\rho_C i}{(r_A^2 - r_C^2)\rho_C + r_C^2 \rho_A} \; .$$

The denominators are the same and each has the value

$$(b^2 - a^2)\rho_C + a^2 \rho_A = [(0.380 \times 10^{-3}\,\text{m})^2 - (0.250 \times 10^{-3}\,\text{m})^2] \times (1.69 \times 10^{-8}\,\Omega \cdot \text{m})$$
$$+ (0.250 \times 10^{-3}\,\text{m})^2 (2.75 \times 10^{-8}\,\Omega \cdot \text{m})$$
$$= 3.10 \times 10^{-15}\,\Omega \cdot \text{m}^3 \; .$$

Thus

$$i_C = \frac{(0.250 \times 10^{-3}\,\text{m})^2 (2.75 \times 10^{-8}\,\Omega \cdot \text{m})(2.00\,\text{A})}{3.10 \times 10^{-15}\,\Omega \cdot \text{m}^3} = 1.11\,\text{A}$$

and

$$i_A = \frac{\left[(0.380 \times 10^{-3}\,\text{m})^2 - (0.250 \times 10^{-3}\,\text{m})^2\right](1.69 \times 10^{-8}\,\Omega \cdot \text{m})(2.00\,\text{A})}{3.10 \times 10^{-15}\,\Omega \cdot \text{m}^3}$$
$$= 0.893\,\text{A} \; .$$

(b) Consider the copper wire. If V is the potential difference, then the current is given by $V = i_C R_C = i_C \rho_C L / \pi a^2$, so

$$L = \frac{\pi a^2 V}{i_C \rho_C} = \frac{\pi \times (0.250 \times 10^{-3}\,\text{m})^2 (12.0\,\text{V})}{(1.11\,\text{A})(1.69 \times 10^{-8}\,\Omega \cdot \text{m})} = 126\,\text{m} \; .$$

51P
The part of R_0 connected in parallel with R is given by $R_1 = R_0 x / L$, where $L = 10\,\text{cm}$. The voltage difference across R is then $V_R = \varepsilon R' / R_{\text{eq}}$, where $R' = RR_1/(R + R_1)$ and $R_{\text{eq}} = R_0(i - x/L) + R'$. Thus

$$P_R = \frac{V_R^2}{R} = \frac{1}{R}\left[\frac{\varepsilon RR_1/(R + R_1)}{R_0(1 - x/L) + RR_1/(R + R_1)}\right]^2 \; .$$

Some simple algebra then leads to

$$P_R = \frac{100R(\varepsilon x/R_0)^2}{(100R/R_0 + 10x - x^2)^2} \; ,$$

where x is measured in cm.

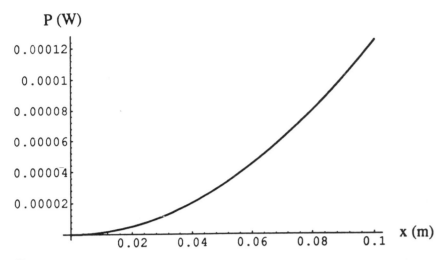

P (W)

0.00012

0.0001

0.00008

0.00006

0.00004

0.00002

0.02   0.04   0.06   0.08   0.1   x (m)

52P

(*a*) A potential difference is applied across points 1 and 3 in the diagram of the text. Notice that the point labelled 2 is one cube edge from 1 and one cube edge from 3. So is the point labelled 4. These points must be at the same potential. Similarly the points labelled 6 and 8 must be at the same potential. The cube can be distorted so that points 2 and 4 come together and points 6 and 8 come together, without changing the current in any branch. When this is done the circuit can be drawn as in the figure shown to the right. The numbered points correspond to points on the original diagram of the text. Each of the resistors has the same value, R.

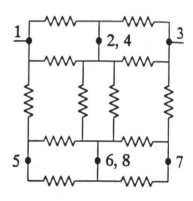

Notice that the two resistors in the upper left of the diagram are in parallel and can be replaced by a resistor with their equivalent resistance, $R/2$. So can the pair in the upper right, the pair in the lower left, the pair in the lower right, and the vertical pair in the center. When this is done the circuit looks like that shown on the left below. Now the resistor on the left and the one on the bottom left are in series and have an equivalent resistance of $3R/2$. Similarly, the resistor on the right and the one on the bottom right have the same equivalent resistance. When these pairs of resistors are replaced with their equivalents the circuit looks like that shown on the right below. Be sure you understand why neither of the two resistors along the top of the circuit are in series with any of the others.

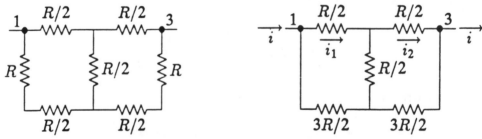

This is as far as we can go by combining resistors in parallel and series. Find the equivalent resistance by assuming a current i enters the circuit at point 1 and leaves at point 3. Find the current in resistors, then use the results to calculate the potential difference V between points 1 and 3. The equivalent resistance of the circuit is $R_{13} = V/i$.

Let i_1 be the current in the upper left resistor and take it to be positive to the right. Let i_2 be the current in the upper right resistor and take it to be positive to the right. Then the current in the bottom left resistor is $i - i_1$ and it is positive if it is to the right. The current in the bottom right resistor is $i - i_2$ and it is positive if it is to the right. Finally the current in the central resistor is $i_2 - i_1$ and it is positive if it is upward. These currents automatically satisfy the junction rule. When the loop rule is applied to the left-hand loop the result is

$$-i_1 \frac{R}{2} + (i_2 - i_1)\frac{R}{2} + (i - i_1)\frac{3R}{2} = 0$$

and when it is applied to the right-hand loop the result is

$$-i_2 \frac{R}{2} + (i - i_2)\frac{3R}{2} - (i_2 - i_1)\frac{R}{2} = 0.$$

The solution to these equation is $i_1 = i_2 = 3i/4$. The potential difference between points 1 and 3 is $V = i_1(R/2) + i_2(R/2) = 3iR/4$ and the equivalent resistance is $R_{13} = V/i = 3R/4$.

(b) Now a potential difference is applied across the points 1 and 7 on the diagram of the text. Points 3 and 6 must be at the same potential and points 4 and 5 must be at the same potential. Once the points in each of these pairs are placed together, the circuit can be drawn as in the diagram on the right.

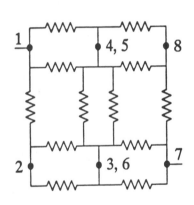

Again 5 pairs of parallel resistors can be identified and each pair can be replaced by an equivalent resistor. When this is done the circuit on the left below is obtained. There are now two series connections, each with an equivalent resistance of $3R/2$. When these replacements are made the circuit on the right below is obtained.

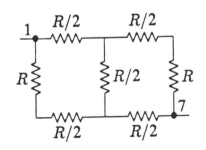
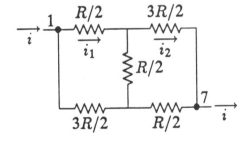

Now find the equivalent resistance of this circuit. Suppose current i enters at 1 and leaves at 7. Let i_1 be the current in the upper left resistor and take it to be positive if it is to the right. Let i_2 be the current in the upper right resistor and take it to be positive if it is to the right. The current in the lower left resistor is $i - i_1$ and it is positive if it is to the right. The current in the lower right resistor is $i - i_2$ and it is positive if it is to the right.

The current in the central resistor is $i_2 - i_1$ and it is positive if it is upward. The loop rule applied to the left-hand loop yields

$$-i_1 \frac{R}{2} + (i_2 - i_1)\frac{R}{2} + (i - i_1)\frac{3R}{2} = 0$$

and applied to the right-hand loop yields

$$-i_2 \frac{3R}{2} + (i - i_2)\frac{R}{2} - (i_2 - i_1)\frac{R}{2} = 0.$$

The solution to these equations is $i_1 = 2i/3$ and $i_2 = i/3$.

The potential difference between points 1 and 7 is $V = i_1(R/2) + i_2(3R/2) = i(R/3) + i(R/2) = 5iR/6$ and the equivalent resistance is $R_{17} = V/i = 5R/6$.

53P
Since $i = \varepsilon/(r + R_{ext})$ and $i_{max} = \varepsilon/r$, we have $R_{ext} = R(i_{max}/i - 1)$ where $r = 1.50\,V/1.00\,mA = 1.50 \times 10^3\,\Omega$. Thus
(a) $R_{ext} = (1.5 \times 10^3\,\Omega)(1/10\% - 1) = 1.35 \times 10^4\,\Omega$.
(b) $R_{ext} = (1.5 \times 10^3\,\Omega)(1/50\% - 1) = 1.50 \times 10^3\,\Omega$.
(c) $R_{ext} = (1.5 \times 10^3\,\Omega)(1/90\% - 1) = 167\,\Omega$.
(d) Since $r = 20.0\,\Omega + R$, we have $R = 1.50 \times 10^3\,\Omega - 20.0\,\Omega = 1.48 \times 10^3\,\Omega$.

54P
(a) Put r roughly in the middle of its range; adjust current roughly with B; make fine adjustment with A.
(b) Relatively large percentage changes in A causes only small percentage charges in the resistance of the parallel combination, thus permitting fine adjustment; any change in A causes half as much change in this combination.

55P
(a) The current in R_1 is given by $i_1 = \varepsilon/[R_1 + R_2 R_3/(R_2 + R_3)] = (5.0\,V)/[2.0\,\Omega + (4.0\,\Omega)(6.0\,\Omega)/(4.0\,\Omega + 6.0\,\Omega)] = 1.13\,A$. Thus

$$i_3 = \frac{\varepsilon - V_1}{R_3} = \frac{\varepsilon - i_1 R_1}{R_3}$$
$$= \frac{5.0\,V - (1.13\,A)(2.0\,\Omega)}{6.0\,\Omega} = 0.46\,A.$$

(b) All we need to do is to interchange the subscripts 1 and 3 above. Now $i_3 = \varepsilon/[R_3 + R_2 R_1/(R_2 + R_1)] = (5.0\,V)[6.0\,\Omega + (2.0\,\Omega)(4.0\,\Omega)/(2.0\,\Omega + 4.0\,\Omega)] = 0.682\,A$, and $i_1 = [(5.0\,V) - (0.682\,A)(6.0\,\Omega)]/2.0\,\Omega = 0.46\,A$.

56P

From $V_{ab} = \varepsilon = 2Ri_1 + R(i_1 + i_A) = Ri_2 + R(i_2 - i_A)$, and $V_{ac} = 2i_1R = V_{ad} = i_2R$, we solve for i_A : $i_A = \varepsilon/7R$.

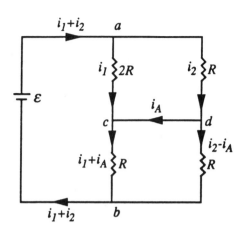

57P

(a) $\varepsilon = V + ir = 12\,\text{V} + (10\,\text{A})(0.050\,\Omega) = 12.5\,\text{V}$.

(b) Now $\varepsilon = V' + (i_{\text{motor}} + 8.0\,\text{A})r$, where $V' = i'_A R_{\text{light}} = (8.0\,\text{A})(12\,\text{V}/10\,\text{A}) = 9.6\,\text{V}$. Solve for i_{motor}: $i_{\text{motor}} = (\varepsilon - V')/r - 8.0\,\text{A} = (12.5\,\text{V} - 9.6\,\text{V})/0.050\,\Omega - 8.0\,\text{A} = 50\,\text{A}$.

58P

The current in R_2 is i. Let i_1 be the current in R_1 and take it to be downward. According to the junction rule the current in the voltmeter is $i - i_1$ and it is downward. Apply the loop rule to the left-hand loop to obtain

$$\varepsilon - iR_2 - i_1R_1 - ir = 0\,.$$

Apply the loop rule to the right-hand loop to obtain

$$i_1R_1 - (i - i_1)R_V = 0\,.$$

Solve these equations for i_1. The second equation yields

$$i = \frac{R_1 + R_V}{R_V}\, i_1\,.$$

Substitute this into the first equation to obtain

$$\varepsilon - \frac{(R_2 + r)(R_1 + R_V)}{R_V}\, i_1 + R_1 i_1 = 0\,.$$

This has the solution

$$i_1 = \frac{\varepsilon R_V}{(R_2 + r)(R_1 + R_V) + R_1 R_V}\,.$$

769

The reading on the voltmeter is

$$i_1 R_1 = \frac{\varepsilon R_V R_1}{(R_2 + r)(R_1 + R_V) + R_1 R_V}$$

$$= \frac{(3.0\,\text{V})(5.0 \times 10^3\,\Omega)(250\,\Omega)}{(300\,\Omega + 100\,\Omega)(250\,\Omega + 5.0 \times 10^3\,\Omega) + (250\,\Omega)(5.0 \times 10^3\,\Omega)} = 1.12\,\text{V}.$$

The current in the absence of the voltmeter can be obtained by taking the limit as R_V becomes infinitely large. Then

$$i_1 R_1 = \frac{\varepsilon R_1}{R_1 + R_2 + r} = \frac{(3.0\,\text{V})(250\,\Omega)}{250\,\Omega + 300\,\Omega + 100\,\Omega} = 1.15\,\text{V}.$$

The fractional error is
$$\frac{1.15 - 1.12}{1.15} = 0.030.$$

This is 3.0%.

59P
The current in the ammeter is given by $i_A = \varepsilon/(r + R_1 + R_2 + R_A)$. The current in R_1 and R_2 without the ammeter is $i = \varepsilon/(r + R_1 + R_2)$. The percent error is then

$$\frac{\Delta i}{i} = \frac{i - i_A}{i} = 1 - \frac{r + R_1 + R_2}{r + R_1 + R_2 + R_A} = \frac{R_A}{r + R_1 + R_2 + R_A}$$

$$= \frac{0.10\,\Omega}{2.0\,\Omega + 5.0\,\Omega + 4.0\,\Omega + 0.10\,\Omega} = 0.90\%.$$

60P
The currents in R and R_V are i and $i' - i$, respectively. Since $V = iR = (i' - i)R_V$ we have, by dividing both sides with V, $1 = (i'/V - i/V)R_V = (1/R' - 1/R)R_V$, i.e.

$$\frac{1}{R} = \frac{1}{R'} - \frac{1}{R_V}.$$

61P
Let the current in the ammeter be i'. We have $V = i'(R + R_A)$, or $R = V/i' - R_A = R' - R_A$, where $R' = V/i'$ is the apparent reading of the resistance.

62P

(a) In the first case $i' = \varepsilon/R_{eq} = \varepsilon/[R_A + R_0 + R_V R/(R + R_V)] = 12.0\,\text{V}/[3.00\,\Omega + 100\,\Omega + (300\,\Omega)(85.0\,\Omega)/(300\,\Omega + 85.0\,\Omega)] = 7.09 \times 10^{-2}\,\text{A}$, and $V = \varepsilon - i'(R_A + R_0) = 12.0\,\text{V} - (0.0709\,\text{A})(103.00\,\Omega) = 4.70\,\text{V}$. In the second case $V = \varepsilon R'/(R' + R_0)$, where $R' = R_V(R + R_A)/(R_V + R + R_A) = (300\,\Omega)(300\,\Omega + 85.0\,\Omega)/(300\,\Omega + 85.0\,\Omega + 3.00\,\Omega) = 68.0\,\Omega$. So $V = (12.0\,\text{V})(68.0\,\Omega)/(68.0\,\Omega + 100\,\Omega) = 4.86\,\text{V}$, and $i' = V(R + R_A) = 4.86\,\text{V}/(300\,\Omega + 85.0\,\Omega) = 5.52 \times 10^{-2}\,\text{A}$.

(b) In the first case $R' = V/i' = 4.70\,\text{V}/(7.09 \times 10^{-2}\,\text{A}) = 66.3\,\Omega$.
In the second case $R' = V/i' = 4.86\,\text{V}/(5.52 \times 10^{-2}\,\text{A}) = 88.0\,\Omega$.

63P

Let i_1 be the current in R_1 and R_2 and take it to be positive if it is toward point a in R_1. Let i_2 be the current in R_s and R_x and take it to be positive if it is toward b in R_s. The loop rule yields $(R_1 + R_2)i_1 - (R_x + R_s)i_2 = 0$. Since points a and b are at the same potential $i_1 R_1 = i_2 R_s$. The second equation gives $i_2 = i_1 R_1/R_s$. This expression is substituted into the first equation to obtain

$$(R_1 + R_2)i_1 = (R_x + R_s)\frac{R_1}{R_s} i_1.$$

Solve for R_x. You should get $R_x = R_2 R_s/R_1$.

64P

Refer to the figure to the right.
From

$$\varepsilon = V_c - V_d = i_1 R + (i_1 - i)R$$
$$= i_2 R_s + (i_2 + i)R_x$$

and

$$V_a - V_b = (V_a - V_c) - (V_b - V_c)$$
$$= -i_1 R + i_2 R_s = ir,$$

we solve for i:

$$i = \frac{\varepsilon(R_s - R_x)}{(R + 2r)(R_s + R_x) + 2R_s R_x}.$$

The condition for $i = 0$ is $R_s = R_x$. Since $R_1 = R_2 = R$, this is equivalent to $R_x = R_s(R_2/R_1)$, consistent with the result of Problem 63.

65E

(a) $\tau = RC = (1.40 \times 10^6 \, \Omega)(1.80 \times 10^{-6} \, \text{F}) = 2.52 \, \text{s}$.

(b) $q_o = \varepsilon C = (12.0 \, \text{V})(1.80 \, \mu\text{F}) = 21.6 \, \mu\text{C}$.

(c) The time t satisfies $q = q_0(1 - e^{-t/RC})$, or

$$t = RC \ln\left(\frac{q_0}{q_0 - q}\right) = (2.52 \, \text{s}) \ln\left(\frac{21.6 \, \mu\text{C}}{21.6 \, \mu\text{C} - 16.0 \, \mu\text{C}}\right) = 3.40 \, \text{s}.$$

66E

During charging the charge on the positive plate of the capacitor is given by

$$q = C\varepsilon \left[1 - e^{-t/\tau}\right],$$

where C is the capacitance, ε is applied emf, and τ is the time constant. The equilibrium charge is $q_{eq} = C\varepsilon$. You want $q = 0.99q_{eq} = 0.99C\varepsilon$, so

$$0.99 = 1 - e^{-t/\tau}.$$

Thus

$$e^{-t/\tau} = 0.01.$$

Take the natural logarithm of both sides to obtain $t/\tau = -\ln 0.01 = 4.6$ and $t = 4.6\tau$.

67E

Use $q = q_0 e^{-t/\tau}$, or $t = \tau \ln(q_0/q)$.

(a) $t_{1/3} = \tau \ln[q_0/(2q_0/3)] = \tau \ln(3/2) = 0.41\tau$.

(b) $t_{2/3} = \tau \ln[q_0/(q_0/3)] = \tau \ln 3 = 1.1\tau$.

68E

(a) The voltage difference V across the capacitor varies with time as $V(t) = \varepsilon(1 - e^{-t/RC})$. At $t = 1.30 \, \mu\text{s}$ we have $V(t) = 5.00 \, \text{V}$, so $5.00 \, \text{V} = (12.0 \, \text{V})(1 - e^{-1.30 \, \mu\text{s}/RC})$, which gives $\tau = (1.30 \, \mu\text{s})/\ln(12/7) = 2.41 \, \mu\text{s}$.

(b) $C = \tau/R = 2.41 \, \mu\text{s}/15.0 \, \text{k}\Omega = 161p \, \text{F}$.

69P

(a) The potential difference V across the plates of a capacitor is related to the charge q on the positive plate by $V = q/C$, where C is capacitance. Since the charge on a discharging capacitor is given by $q = q_0 e^{-t/\tau}$, where q_0 is the charge at time $t = 0$ and τ is the time constant, this means

$$V = V_0 e^{-t/\tau},$$

where q_0/C was replaced by V_0, the initial potential difference. Solve for τ by dividing the equation by V_0 and taking the natural logarithm of both sides. The result is:

$$\tau = -\frac{t}{\ln(V/V_0)} = -\frac{10.0\,\text{s}}{\ln[(1.00\,\text{V})/(100\,\text{V})]} = 2.17\,\text{s}.$$

At $t = 17.0\,\text{s}$, $t/\tau = (17.0\,\text{s})/(2.17\,\text{s}) = 7.83$ and

$$V = V_0\,e^{-t/\tau} = (100\,\text{V})\,e^{-7.83} = 3.96 \times 10^{-2}\,\text{V}.$$

70P
The time it takes for the voltage difference across the capacitor to reach V_L is given by $V_L = \varepsilon(1 - e^{-t/RC})$. Solve for R:

$$R = \frac{t}{C\ln[\varepsilon/(\varepsilon - V_L)]} = \frac{0.500\,\text{s}}{(0.150 \times 10^{-6}\,\text{F})\ln[95.0\,\text{V}/(95.0\,\text{V} - 72.0\,\text{V})]}$$
$$= 2.35 \times 10^6\,\Omega,$$

where we used $t = 0.500\,\text{s}$ given in the problem.

71P
(a) The initial energy stored in a capacitor is given by

$$U_C = \frac{q_0^2}{2C},$$

where C is the capacitance and q_0 is the initial charge on one plate. Thus

$$q_0 = \sqrt{2CU_C} = \sqrt{2(1.0 \times 10^{-6}\,\text{F})(0.50\,\text{J})} = 1.0 \times 10^{-3}\,\text{C}.$$

(b) The charge as a function of time is given by $q = q_0\,e^{-t/\tau}$, where τ is the time constant. The current is the derivative of the charge:

$$i = -\frac{dq}{dt} = \frac{q_0}{\tau}\,e^{-t/\tau}$$

and the initial current is given by this function evaluated for $t = 0$: $i_0 = q_0/\tau$. The time constant is $\tau = RC = (1.0 \times 10^{-6}\,\text{F})(1.0 \times 10^6\,\Omega) = 1.0\,\text{s}$. Thus $i_0 = (1.0 \times 10^{-3}\,\text{C})/(1.0\,\text{s}) = 1.0 \times 10^{-3}\,\text{A}$.

(c) Substitute $q = q_0\, e^{-t/\tau}$ into $V_C = q/C$ to obtain

$$V_C = \frac{q_0}{C}\, e^{-t/\tau}\,.$$

Substitute $i = (q_0/\tau)\, e^{-t/\tau}$ into $V_R = iR$ to obtain

$$V_R = \frac{q_0 R}{\tau}\, e^{-t/\tau}\,.$$

(d) Substitute $i = (q_0/\tau)\, e^{-t/\tau}$ into $P = i^2 R$ to obtain

$$P = \frac{q_0^2 R}{\tau^2}\, e^{-2t/\tau}\,.$$

72P

(a) The charge on the positive plate of the capacitor is given by

$$q = C\varepsilon\left[1 - e^{-t/\tau}\right],$$

where ε is the emf of the battery, C is the capacitance, and τ is the time constant. The value of τ is $\tau = RC = (3.00 \times 10^6\,\Omega)(1.00 \times 10^{-6}\,\text{F}) = 3.00\,\text{s}$. At $t = 1.00\,\text{s}$, $t/\tau = (1.00\,\text{s})/(3.00\,\text{s}) = 0.333$ and the rate at which the charge is increasing is

$$\frac{dq}{dt} = \frac{C\varepsilon}{\tau}\, e^{-t/\tau} = \frac{(1.00 \times 10^{-6})(4.00\,\text{V})}{3.00\,\text{s}}\, e^{-0.333} = 9.55 \times 10^{-7}\,\text{C/s}\,.$$

(b) The energy stored in the capacitor is given by

$$U_C = \frac{q^2}{2C}\,.$$

and its rate of change is

$$\frac{dU_c}{dt} = \frac{q}{C}\frac{dq}{dt}\,.$$

Now

$$q = C\varepsilon\left[1 - e^{-t/\tau}\right] = (1.00 \times 10^{-6})(4.00\,\text{V})\left[1 - e^{-0.333}\right] = 1.13 \times 10^{-6}\,\text{C}\,,$$

so

$$\frac{dU_C}{dt} = \frac{1.13 \times 10^{-6}\,\text{C}}{1.00 \times 10^{-6}\,\text{F}}(9.55 \times 10^{-7}\,\text{C/s}) = 1.08 \times 10^{-6}\,\text{W}\,.$$

(c) The rate at which energy is being dissipated in the resistor is given by $P = i^2 R$. The current is $9.55 \times 10^{-7}\,\text{A}$, so

$$P = (9.55 \times 10^{-7}\,\text{A})^2(3.00 \times 10^6\,\Omega) = 2.74 \times 10^{-6}\,\text{W}\,.$$

(d) The rate at which energy is delivered by the battery is

$$i\varepsilon = (9.55 \times 10^{-7}\,\text{A})(4.00\,\text{V}) = 3.82 \times 10^{-6}\,\text{W}.$$

The energy delivered by the battery is either stored in the capacitor or dissipated in the resistor. Conservation of energy requires that $i\varepsilon = (q/C)(dq/dt) + i^2 R$. Except for some round-off error the numerical results support the conservation principle.

73P

The potential difference across the capacitor varies as a function of t as $V(t) = V_0 e^{-t/RC}$, which gives

$$R = \frac{t}{C\ln(V_0/V)} = \frac{2.0\,\text{s}}{(2.0 \times 10^{-6}\,\text{F})\ln 4} = 7.2 \times 10^5\,\Omega,$$

where we used $V = V_0/4$ at $t = 2.0\,\text{s}$.

74P

The electric energy stored in the fully charged capacitor is $U_E = \frac{1}{2}C\varepsilon^2$. At time t after the switch is thrown from a to b the voltage difference across R is $V_R(t) = \varepsilon e^{-t/RC}$, so the instantaneous rate at which thermal energy is generated in R is $P(t) = V_R(t)^2/R = \varepsilon^2 e^{-2t/RC}/R$. The total amount of thermal energy generated in the discharging process is then

$$U_{\text{th}} = \int_0^\infty P(t)dt = \frac{\varepsilon^2}{R}\int_0^\infty e^{-2t/RC}dt = \frac{1}{2}C\varepsilon^2.$$

Thus $U_E = U_{\text{th}}$.

75P

(a) The charge q on the capacitor as a function of time is $q(t) = (\varepsilon C)(1 - e^{-t/RC})$, so the charging current is $i(t) = dq/dt = (\varepsilon/R)e^{-t/RC}$. The energy supplied by the emf is then

$$U = \int_0^\infty \varepsilon i dt = \frac{\varepsilon^2}{R}\int_0^\infty e^{-t/RC}dt = C\varepsilon^2 = 2U_c,$$

where $U_c = \frac{1}{2}C\epsilon^2$ is the energy stored in the capacitor.
(b)

$$U_R = \int_0^\infty i^2 R dt = \frac{\varepsilon^2}{R}\int_0^\infty e^{-2t/RC} \cdot dt = \frac{1}{2}C\varepsilon^2.$$

76P

Use the result of Problem 73: $R = t/[C\ln(V_0/V)]$. For $t_{min} = 10.0\,\mu\text{s}$ we then get $R_{min} = 10.0\,\mu\text{s}/[(0.220\,\mu\text{F})\ln(5.00/0.800)] = 24.8\,\Omega$; and for $t_{max} = 6.00\,\text{ms}$ we get $R_{max} = (6.00\,\text{ms}/10.0\,\mu\text{s})(24.8\,\Omega) = 1.49 \times 10^4\,\Omega$.

77P

When S is open for a long time, the charge on C is $q_i = \varepsilon_2 C$. When S is closed for a long time, the current i in R_1 and R_2 is $i = (\varepsilon_2 - \varepsilon_1)/(R_1 + R_2) = (3.0\,\text{V} - 1.0\,\text{V})/(0.20\,\Omega + 0.40\,\Omega) = 3.33\,\text{A}$. The voltage difference V across the capacitor is then $V = \varepsilon_2 - iR_2 = 3.0\,\text{V} - (3.33\,\text{A})(0.40\,\Omega) = 1.67\,\text{V}$. Thus the final charge on C is $q_f = VC$. So the charge is $\Delta q = q_f - q_i = (V - \varepsilon_2)C = (1.67\,\text{V} - 3.0\,\text{V})(10\,\mu\text{F}) = -13\,\mu\text{C}$.

78P

(a) At $t = 0$ the capacitor is completely uncharged and the current in the capacitor branch is as it would be if the capacitor were replaced by a wire. Let i_1 be the current in R_1 and take it to be positive if it is to the right. Let i_2 be the current in R_2 and take it to be positive if it is downward. Let i_3 be the current in R_3 and take it to be positive if it is downward. The junction rule produces

$$i_1 = i_2 + i_3\,,$$

the loop rule applied to the left-hand loop produces

$$\varepsilon - i_1 R_1 - i_2 R_2 = 0\,,$$

and the loop rule applied to the right-hand loop produces

$$i_2 R_2 - i_3 R_3 = 0\,.$$

Since the resistances are all the same you can simplify the mathematics by replacing R_1, R_2, and R_3 with R. The solution to the three simultaneous equations is

$$i_1 = \frac{2\varepsilon}{3R} = \frac{2(1.2 \times 10^3\,\text{V})}{3(0.73 \times 10^6\,\Omega)} = 1.1 \times 10^{-3}\,\text{A}$$

and

$$i_2 = i_3 = \frac{\varepsilon}{3R} = \frac{1.2 \times 10^3\,\text{V}}{3(0.73 \times 10^6\,\Omega)} = 5.5 \times 10^{-4}\,\text{A}\,.$$

At $t = \infty$ the capacitor is fully charged and the current in the capacitor branch is 0. Then $i_1 = i_2$ and the loop rule yields

$$\varepsilon - i_1 R_1 - i_1 R_2 = 0\,.$$

776

The solution is

$$i_1 = i_2 = \frac{\varepsilon}{2R} = \frac{1.2 \times 10^3 \text{ V}}{2(0.73 \times 10^6 \ \Omega)} = 8.2 \times 10^{-4} \text{ A}.$$

(b) Take the upper plate of the capacitor to be positive. This is consistent with current into that plate. The junction and loop equations are

$$i_1 = i_2 + i_3,$$

$$\varepsilon - i_1 R - i_2 R = 0,$$

and

$$-\frac{q}{C} - i_3 R + i_2 R = 0.$$

Use the first equation to substitute for i_1 in the second and obtain $\varepsilon - 2i_2 R - i_3 R = 0$. Thus $i_2 = (\varepsilon - i_3 R)/2R$. Substitute this expression into the third equation above to obtain $-(q/C) - (i_3 R) + (\varepsilon/2) - (i_3 R/2) = 0$. Now replace i_3 with dq/dt and obtain

$$\frac{3R}{2}\frac{dq}{dt} + \frac{q}{C} = \frac{\varepsilon}{2}.$$

This is just like the equation for an RC series circuit, except that the time constant is $\tau = 3RC/2$ and the impressed potential difference is $\varepsilon/2$. The solution is

$$q = \frac{C\varepsilon}{2}\left[1 - e^{-2t/3RC}\right].$$

The current in the capacitor branch is

$$i_3 = \frac{dq}{dt} = \frac{\varepsilon}{3R} e^{-2t/3RC}.$$

The current in the center branch is

$$i_2 = \frac{\varepsilon}{2R} - \frac{i_3}{2} = \frac{\varepsilon}{2R} - \frac{\varepsilon}{6R}e^{-2t/3RC}$$
$$= \frac{\varepsilon}{6R}\left[3 - e^{-2t/3RC}\right]$$

and the potential difference across R_2 is

$$V_2 = i_2 R = \frac{\varepsilon}{6}\left[3 - e^{-2t/3RC}\right].$$

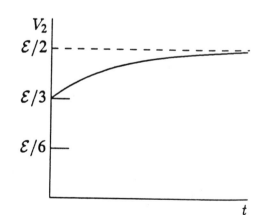

The graph is shown to the right.

(c) For $t = 0$, $e^{-2t/3RC}$ is 1 and $V_R = \varepsilon/3 = (1.2 \times 10^3 \text{ V})/3 = 400 \text{ V}$. For $t = \infty$, $e^{-2t/3RC}$ is 0 and $V_R = \varepsilon/2 = (1.2 \times 20^3 \text{ V})/2 = 600 \text{ V}$.

(*d*) "A long time" means after several time constants. Then the current in the capacitor branch is very small and can be approximated by 0.

79P

(a) and (b) Denote $L = 10\,\text{km}$ and $\alpha = 13\,\Omega/\text{km}$. Measured from the east end we have $R_1 = 100\,\Omega = 2\alpha(L - x) + R$, and measured from the west end $R_2 = 200\,\Omega = 2\alpha x + R$. Solve for x and R:

$$x = \frac{R_2 - R_1}{4\alpha} + \frac{L}{2} = \frac{200\,\Omega - 100\,\Omega}{4(13\,\Omega/\text{km})} + \frac{10\,\text{km}}{2} = 6.9\,\text{km},$$

$$R = \frac{R_1 + R_2}{2} - \alpha L = \frac{100\,\Omega + 200\,\Omega}{2} - (13\,\Omega/\text{km})(10\,\text{km}) = 20\,\Omega.$$

CHAPTER 30

1E
One way to do this is through Eq. 30-6: $\mathbf{F}_B = q\mathbf{v} \times \mathbf{B}$, which gives

$$[\mathbf{B}] = \frac{[\mathbf{F}]}{[q][v]} = \frac{ML/T^2}{Q\,L/T} = \frac{M}{QT}.$$

2E
You can determine whether the charges are positive, negative or zero by noting that $\mathbf{F}_B = q\mathbf{v} \times \mathbf{B}$. It follows that particle 1 is positive, particle 2 and 4 are negative, and particle 3 is neutral.

3E
(a) $F_{B,\text{max}} = q|\mathbf{v} \times \mathbf{B}|_{\text{max}} = qvB|\sin(\mathbf{v}, \mathbf{B})|_{\text{max}} = qvB = (1.60 \times 10^{-19}\,\text{C})(7.20 \times 10^6\,\text{m/s})$ $(83.0 \times 10^{-3}\,\text{T}) = 9.56 \times 10^{-14}\,\text{N}$; $F_{B,\text{min}} = q|\mathbf{v} \times \mathbf{B}|_{\text{min}} = qvB|\sin(\mathbf{v}, \mathbf{B})|_{\text{min}} = 0$.
(b) $a = F_B/m = qvB\sin(\mathbf{v}, \mathbf{B})/m$ so the angle between $\mathbf{v}$ and $\mathbf{B}$ is

$$\theta = \sin^{-1}\left(\frac{ma}{qvB}\right) = \sin^{-1}\left[\frac{(9.11 \times 10^{-31}\,\text{kg})(4.90 \times 10^{14}\,\text{m/s}^2)}{(1.60 \times 10^{-16}\,\text{C})(7.20 \times 10^6\,\text{m/s})(83.0 \times 10^{-3}\,\text{T})}\right] = 0.267°.$$

4E
(a) The magnitude of the magnetic force on the proton is given by $F_B = evB\sin\phi$, where v is the speed of the proton, B is the magnitude of the magnetic field, and ϕ is the angle between the particle velocity and the field when they are drawn with their tails at the same point. Thus

$$v = \frac{F_B}{eB\sin\phi} = \frac{6.50 \times 10^{-17}\,\text{N}}{(1.60 \times 10^{-19}\,\text{C})(2.60 \times 10^{-3}\,\text{T})\sin 23.0°} = 4.00 \times 10^5\,\text{m/s}.$$

(b) The kinetic energy of the proton is

$$K = \frac{1}{2}mv^2 = \frac{1}{2}(1.67 \times 10^{-27}\,\text{kg})(4.00 \times 10^5\,\text{m/s})^2 = 1.34 \times 10^{-16}\,\text{J}.$$

This is $(1.34 \times 10^{-16}\,\text{J})/(1.60 \times 10^{-19}\,\text{J/eV}) = 835\,\text{eV}$.

5E

(a) $\mathbf{F}_B = q\mathbf{v} \times \mathbf{B} = q(v_x\mathbf{i} + v_y\mathbf{j}) \times (B_x\mathbf{i} + B_y\mathbf{j}) = q(v_xB_y - v_yB_x)\mathbf{k} = (-1.6 \times 10^{-19}\,\text{C})[(2.0 \times 10^6\,\text{m/s})(-0.15\,\text{T}) - (3.0 \times 10^6\,\text{m/s})(0.030\,\text{T})] = 6.2 \times 10^{-14}\,\text{N}\mathbf{k}$. So the magnitude of $\mathbf{F}_B$ is $6.2 \times 10^{14}\,\text{N}$, and $\mathbf{F}_B$ points in the $+z$ direction.

(b) All you need to do is to change in sign in q. So now $\mathbf{F}_B$ still has the same magnitude but points in the $-z$ diretion.

6P

Let $\mathbf{B} = B_y\mathbf{j} + B_z\mathbf{k}$, then $\mathbf{F}_B = q\mathbf{v} \times \mathbf{B} = q(v_x\mathbf{i} + v_y\mathbf{j}) \times (B_y\mathbf{j} + B_z\mathbf{k}) = q(v_yB_z\mathbf{i} - v_xB_z\mathbf{j} + v_xB_y\mathbf{k}) = F_x\mathbf{i} + F_y\mathbf{j}$. Thus $qv_yB_z = F_x$, $-qv_xB_z = F_y$, and $qv_xB_y = 0$. The last equation gives $B_y = 0$. So

$$\mathbf{B} = B_z\mathbf{k} = \frac{F_x\mathbf{k}}{qv_y} = \frac{(-4.2 \times 10^{-15}\,\text{N})\mathbf{k}}{(-1.60 \times 10^{-19}\,\text{C})(35 \times 10^3\,\text{m/s})} = (0.75\mathbf{k})\,\text{T}.$$

7P

(a) The diagram shows the electron traveling to the north. The magnetic field is into the page. The right-hand rule tells us that $\mathbf{v} \times \mathbf{B}$ is to the west, but since the electron is negatively charged the magnetic force on it is to the east.

(b) Use $F = ma$, with $F = evB\sin\phi$. Here v is the speed of the electron, B is the magnitude of the magnetic field, and ϕ is the angle between the electron velocity and the magnetic field. The velocity and field are perpendicular to each other so $\phi = 90°$ and $\sin\phi = 1$. Thus $a = evB/m$.

The electron speed can be found from its kinetic energy. Since $K = \frac{1}{2}mv^2$,

$$v = \sqrt{\frac{2K}{m}} = \sqrt{\frac{2(12.0 \times 10^3\,\text{eV})(1.60 \times 10^{-19}\,\text{J/eV})}{9.11 \times 10^{-31}\,\text{kg}}} = 6.49 \times 10^7\,\text{m/s}.$$

Thus

$$a = \frac{evB}{m} = \frac{(1.60 \times 10^{-19}\,\text{C})(6.49 \times 10^7\,\text{m/s})(55.0 \times 10^{-6}\,\text{T})}{9.11 \times 10^{-31}\,\text{kg}} = 6.27 \times 10^{14}\,\text{m/s}^2.$$

(c) The electron follows a circular path. Its acceleration is given by v^2/R, where R is the radius of the path. Thus

$$R = \frac{v^2}{a} = \frac{(6.49 \times 10^7\,\text{m/s})^2}{6.27 \times 10^{14}\,\text{m/s}^2} = 6.72\,\text{m}.$$

The solid curve on the diagram is the path. Suppose it subtends the angle θ at the center. ℓ $(= 0.200\,\text{m})$ is the length of the tube and d is the deflection. The right triangle yields $d = R - R\cos\theta$ and $\ell = R\sin\theta$. Thus $R\cos\theta = R - d$ and $R\sin\theta = \ell$. Square both these equations and add the results to obtain $R^2 = (R - d)^2 + \ell^2$, or $d^2 - 2Rd + \ell^2 = 0$. The solution is $d = R \pm \sqrt{R^2 - \ell^2}$. The plus sign corresponds to an angle of $180° - \theta$; the minus sign corresponds to the correct solution.

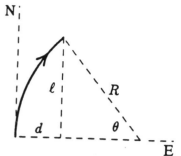

Since ℓ is much less than R, use the binomial theorem to expand $\sqrt{R^2 - \ell^2}$. The first two terms are $R - \frac{1}{2}\ell^2/R$, so $d = \frac{1}{2}\ell^2/R$ and when numerical values are substituted, $d = 0.00298\,\text{m}$ is obtained.

8P*

Apply $\mathbf{F} = q(\mathbf{E} + \mathbf{v} \times \mathbf{B}) = m\mathbf{a}$ to solve for $\mathbf{E}$:

$$\mathbf{E} = \frac{m\mathbf{a}}{q} + \mathbf{B} \times \mathbf{v}$$

$$= \frac{(9.11 \times 10^{-31}\,\text{kg})(2.00 \times 10^{12}\,\text{m/s}^2)\mathbf{i}}{-1.60 \times 10^{-19}\,\text{C}} + (400\,\mu\,\text{T})\mathbf{i} \times [(12.0\,\text{km/s})\mathbf{j} + (15.0\,\text{km/s})\mathbf{k}]$$

$$= (-11.4\mathbf{i} - 6.00\mathbf{j} + 4.80\mathbf{k})(\text{V/m}).$$

9E

Apply $\mathbf{F}_B = -|e|\mathbf{v} \times \mathbf{B}$ to determine the direction in which the electron beam deflects. The correct result is line no. 2.

10E

(a) The total force on the electron is $\mathbf{F} = -e(\mathbf{E} + \mathbf{v} \times \mathbf{B})$, where $\mathbf{E}$ is the electric field, $\mathbf{B}$ is the magnetic field and $\mathbf{v}$ is the electron velocity. The magnitude of the magnetic force is $evB\sin\phi$, where ϕ is the angle between the velocity and the field. Since the total force must vanish, $B = E/v\sin\phi$. The force is the smallest it can be when the field is perpendicular to the velocity and $\phi = 90°$. Then $B = E/v$. Use $K = \frac{1}{2}mv^2$ to find the speed:

$$v = \sqrt{\frac{2K}{m}} = \sqrt{\frac{2(2.5 \times 10^3\,\text{eV})(1.60 \times 10^{-19}\,\text{J/eV})}{9.11 \times 10^{-31}\,\text{kg}}} = 2.96 \times 10^7\,\text{m/s}.$$

Thus

$$B = \frac{E}{v} = \frac{10 \times 10^3\,\text{V/m}}{2.96 \times 10^7\,\text{m/s}} = 3.37 \times 10^{-4}\,\text{T}.$$

The magnetic field must be perpendicular to both the electric field and the velocity of the electron.

(b) A proton will pass undeflected if its velocity is the same as that of the electron. Both the electric and magnetic forces reverse direction, but they still cancel.

11E
(a) Let $\mathbf{F} = q(\mathbf{E} + \mathbf{v} \times \mathbf{B}) = 0$, we get $vB\sin(\mathbf{v}, \mathbf{B}) = E$. So $v_{min} = E/B = (1.50 \times 10^3\,\mathrm{V/m})/(0.400\,\mathrm{T}) = 3.75 \times 10^3\,\mathrm{m/s}$.

12P
(a) Let $\mathbf{F} = q(\mathbf{E} + \mathbf{v} \times \mathbf{B}) = 0$ and note that $\mathbf{v} \perp \mathbf{B}$, we get

$$B = \frac{E}{v} = \frac{E}{\sqrt{2mK}} = \frac{100\,\mathrm{V}/(20 \times 10^{-3}\,\mathrm{m})}{\sqrt{2(9.11 \times 10^{-31}\,\mathrm{kg})(1.0 \times 10^3\,\mathrm{V})(1.60 \times 10^{-19}\,\mathrm{C})}}$$
$$= 2.7 \times 10^{-4}\,\mathrm{T}.$$

13P
Since the total force, given by $\mathbf{F} = e(\mathbf{E} + \mathbf{v} \times \mathbf{B})$, vanishes, the electric field $\mathbf{E}$ must be perpendicular to both the particle velocity $\mathbf{v}$ and the magnetic field $\mathbf{B}$. The magnetic field is perpendicular to the velocity so $\mathbf{v} \times \mathbf{B}$ has magnitude vB and the magnitude of the electric field is given by $E = vB$. Since the particle has charge e and is accelerated through a potential difference V, $\frac{1}{2}mv^2 = eV$ and $v = \sqrt{2eV/m}$. Thus

$$E = B\sqrt{\frac{2eV}{m}} = (1.2\,\mathrm{T})\sqrt{\frac{2(1.60 \times 10^{-19}\,\mathrm{C})(10 \times 10^3\,\mathrm{V})}{(6.0\,\mathrm{u})(1.661 \times 10^{-27}\,\mathrm{kg/u})}} = 6.8 \times 10^5\,\mathrm{V/m}.$$

14E
(a) As the charge carriers move out of the page they are subject to a magnetic field in the $-y$ direction. So an electric field is established in the y direction. i.e. Terminals a and c should be used, with point a at a higher potential.
(b) Analogously, now we should use terminals b and d, with point b at a higher potential.
(c) Since $\mathbf{v} \parallel \mathbf{B}$, $\mathbf{F}_B = q\mathbf{v} \times \mathbf{B} = 0$ and there is no Hall voltage.

15E
Let $\mathbf{F} = q(\mathbf{E} + \mathbf{v} \times \mathbf{B}) = 0$, we get $v = E/B$. Also note that $J = nev$, so $J = ne(E/B)$, or $n = JB/eE$.

16P
(a) $v = E/B = (10 \times 10^{-6}\,\mathrm{V}/1.0 \times 10^{-2}\,\mathrm{m})/(1.5\,\mathrm{T}) = 6.7 \times 10^{-4}\,\mathrm{m/s}$.

(b)

$$n = \frac{JB}{eE} = \frac{iB}{AeE} = \frac{i}{Aev}$$

$$= \frac{3.0\,\text{A}}{(1.0 \times 10^{-2}\,\text{m})(10 \times 10^{-6}\,\text{m})(1.60 \times 10^{-19}\,\text{C})(6.7 \times 10^{-4}\,\text{m/s})} = 2.8 \times 10^{29}/\text{m}^3.$$

(c) As shown in the diagram to the right, if the electrons move out of the page and the magnetic field **B** is in the $+x$ direction, then $V_a > V_b$.

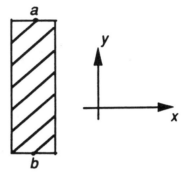

17P

Since $J = \sigma E_c = E_c/\rho$ and $J = neE/B$ (from Exercise 15), we get $J = E_c/\rho = neE/B$, i.e. $E/E_c = B/ne\rho$.

(b)

$$\frac{E}{E_c} = \frac{B}{ne\rho} = \frac{0.65\,\text{T}}{(8.47 \times 10^{28}/\text{m}^3)(1.60 \times 10^{-19}\,\text{C})(1.69 \times 10^{-8}\,\Omega \cdot \text{m})} = 2.84 \times 10^{-3}.$$

18P

For a free charge q inside the metal strip with velocity **v** we have $\mathbf{F} = q(\mathbf{E} + \mathbf{v} \times \mathbf{B})$ or

$$v = \frac{E}{B} = \frac{|V_x - V_y|/d_{xy}}{B} = \frac{(3.90 \times 10^{-9}\,\text{V})}{(1.20 \times 10^{-3}\,\text{T})(0.850 \times 10^{-2}\,\text{m})} = 0.382\,\text{m/s}.$$

19E

Since the magnetic field is perpendicular to the particle velocity the magnitude of the magnetic force is given by $F_B = evB$ and the acceleration of the electron has magnitude $a = F_B/m$, where v is the speed of the electron and m is its mass. B is the magnitude of the magnetic field. Since the electron is traveling with uniform speed in a circle, its acceleration is $a = v^2/r$, where r is the radius of the circle. Thus $evB/m = v^2/r$ and

$$B = \frac{mv}{er} = \frac{(9.11 \times 10^{-31}\,\text{kg})(1.3 \times 10^6\,\text{m/s})}{(1.60 \times 10^{-19}\,\text{C})(0.35\,\text{m})} = 2.1 \times 10^{-5}\,\text{T}.$$

20P

(a) Use Eq. 30-17 to calculate r:

$$r = \frac{mv}{qB} = \frac{(9.11 \times 10^{-31}\,\text{kg})(10\%)(3.00 \times 10^8\,\text{m/s})}{(1.60 \times 10^{-19}\,\text{C})(0.50\,\text{T})} = 3.4 \times 10^{-4}\,\text{m}.$$

(b)

$$K = \frac{1}{2}mv^2 = \frac{(9.11 \times 10^{-31}\,\text{kg})(3.0 \times 10^7\,\text{m/s})^2}{2(1.6 \times 10^{-19}\,\text{J/eV})} = 2.6 \times 10^3\,\text{eV}.$$

21E

Use Eq. 30-17 to calculate B:

$$B = \frac{mv}{qr} = \frac{(1.67 \times 10^{-27}\,\text{kg})(1.0 \times 10^7\,\text{m/s})}{(1.60 \times 10^{-19}\,\text{C})(6.37 \times 10^6\,\text{m})} = 1.6 \times 10^{-8}\,\text{T}.$$

22E

(a) From $K = \frac{1}{2}mv^2$ we get

$$v = \sqrt{\frac{2K}{m}} = \sqrt{\frac{2(1.20 \times 10^3\,\text{eV})(1.60 \times 10^{-19}\,\text{eV/J})}{9.11 \times 10^{-31}\,\text{kg}}} = 2.05 \times 10^7\,\text{m/s}.$$

(b) From $r = mv/qB$ we get

$$B = \frac{mv}{qr} = \frac{(9.11 \times 10^{-31}\,\text{kg})(2.05 \times 10^7\,\text{m/s})}{(1.60 \times 10^{-19}\,\text{C})(25.0 \times 10^{-2}\,\text{m})} = 4.67 \times 10^{-4}\,\text{T}.$$

(c)

$$f = \frac{v}{2\pi r} = \frac{2.07 \times 10^7\,\text{m/s}}{2\pi(25.0 \times 10^{-2}\,\text{m})} = 1.31 \times 10^7\,\text{Hz}.$$

(d) $T = 1/f = (1.31 \times 10^7\,\text{Hz})^{-1} = 7.63 \times 10^{-8}\,\text{s}.$

23E

(a) In the accelerating process the electron loses potential energy eV and gains the same amount of kinetic energy. Since it starts from rest, $\frac{1}{2}mv^2 = eV$ and

$$v = \sqrt{\frac{2eV}{m}} = \sqrt{\frac{2(1.60 \times 10^{-19}\,\text{C})(350\,\text{V})}{9.11 \times 10^{-31}\,\text{kg}}} = 1.11 \times 10^7\,\text{m/s}.$$

(b) The electron travels with constant speed around a circle. The magnetic force on it has magnitude $F_B = evB$ and its acceleration is v^2/R, where R is the radius of the circle. Newton's second law yields $evB = mv^2/R$, so

$$R = \frac{mv}{eB} = \frac{(9.11 \times 10^{-31}\,\text{kg})(1.11 \times 10^7\,\text{m/s})}{(1.60 \times 10^{-19}\,\text{C})(200 \times 10^{-3}\,\text{T})} = 3.16 \times 10^{-4}\,\text{m}.$$

24E

The period of revolution for the iodine ion is $T = 2\pi r/v = 2\pi m/Bq$, which gives

$$m = \frac{BqT}{2\pi} = \frac{(45.0 \times 10^{-3}\,\text{T})(1.60 \times 10^{-19}\,\text{C})(1.29 \times 10^{-3}\,\text{s})}{(7)(2\pi)(1.66 \times 10^{-27}\,\text{kg/u})} = 127\,\text{u}.$$

25E
(a)

$$v = \frac{rqB}{m} = \frac{2eB}{4.00\,\mu} = \frac{2(4.50 \times 10^{-2}\,\text{m})(1.60 \times 10^{-19}\,\text{C})(1.20\,\text{T})}{[(4.00\,\mu)(1.66 \times 10^{-27}\,\text{kg}/\mu)]} = 2.60 \times 10^6\,\text{m/s}.$$

(b) $T = 2\pi r/v = 2\pi(4.50 \times 10^{-2}\,\text{m})/(2.60 \times 10^6\,\text{m/s}) = 1.09 \times 10^{-7}\,\text{s}$.
(c)

$$K = \frac{1}{2}mv^2 = \frac{(4.00\,\mu)(1.66 \times 10^{-27}\,\text{kg}/\mu)(2.60 \times 10^6\,\text{m/s})^2}{2(1.60 \times 10^{-19}\,\text{J/eV})} = 1.40 \times 10^5\,\text{eV}.$$

(d) $\Delta V = K/q = 1.40 \times 10^5\,\text{ev}/2e = 7.00 \times 10^4\,\text{V}$.

26E
(a)

$$f = \frac{Bq}{2\pi m} = \frac{(35.0 \times 10^{-6}\,\text{T})(1.60 \times 10^{-19}\,\text{C})}{2\pi(9.11 \times 10^{-31}\,\text{kg})} = 9.78 \times 10^5\,\text{Hz}.$$

(b)

$$r = \frac{mv}{qB} = \frac{\sqrt{2mK}}{qB} = \frac{\sqrt{2(9.11 \times 10^{-31}\,\text{kg})(100\,\text{eV})(1.60 \times 10^{-19}\,\text{J/eV})}}{(1.60 \times 10^{-19}\,\text{C})(35.0 \times 10^{-6}\,\text{T})} = 0.964\,\text{m}.$$

27E

Orient the magnetic field so it is perpendicular to the plane of page. Then the electron will travel with constant speed around a circle in the plane of the page. The magnetic force on an electron has magnitude $F_B = evB$, where v is the speed of the electron and B is the magnitude of the magnetic field. If r is the radius of the circle, the acceleration of the electron has magnitude $a = v^2/r$. Newton's second law yields $evB = mv^2/r$, so the radius of the circle is given by $r = mv/eB$. The kinetic energy of the electron is $K = \frac{1}{2}mv^2$, so $v = \sqrt{2K/m}$. Thus

$$r = \frac{m}{eB}\sqrt{\frac{2K}{m}} = \sqrt{\frac{2mK}{e^2B^2}} .$$

This must be less than d, so

$$\sqrt{\frac{2mK}{e^2B^2}} \leq d$$

or

$$B \geq \sqrt{\frac{2mK}{e^2d^2}} .$$

If the electrons are to travel as shown in Fig. 30-32 the magnetic field must be out of the page. Then the magnetic force is toward the center of the circular path.

28P

From Exercise 26, part (b) we see that $r = \sqrt{2mK}/qB$, or $K = (rqB)^2/2m \propto q^2m^{-1}$. Thus:

(a) $K_\alpha = (q_\alpha/q_p)^2(m_p/m_\alpha)K_p = (2)^2(1/4)K_p = K_p = 1.0\,\text{MeV}$.
(b) $K_d = (q_d/q_p)^2(m_p/m_d)K_p = (1)^2(1/2)K_p = 1.0\,\text{MeV}/2 = 0.50\,\text{MeV}$.

29P

(a) Since $K = qV$ we have $K_p = K_d = \dfrac{1}{2}K_\alpha$ (as $q_\alpha = 2K_d = 2K_p$).

(b) Since $r = \sqrt{2mK}/qB \propto \sqrt{mK}/q$ we have

$$r_d = \sqrt{\frac{m_dK_d}{m_pK_p}}\frac{q_pr_p}{q_d} = \sqrt{\frac{(2.00\,\text{u})K_p}{(1.00\,\text{u})K_p}}r_p = 10\sqrt{2}\,\text{cm} = 14\,\text{cm}.$$

(c)

$$r_\alpha = \sqrt{\frac{m_\alpha K_\alpha}{m_pK_p}}\frac{q_pr_p}{q_\alpha} = \sqrt{\frac{(4.00\,\text{u})K_\alpha}{(1.00\,\text{u})(K_\alpha/2)}}\frac{er_p}{2e} = 10\sqrt{2}\,\text{cm} = 14\,\text{cm}.$$

30P

Use the result of the previous problem: $r \propto \sqrt{mK}/qB$. Thus

$$r_\alpha = \sqrt{\frac{m_\alpha K_\alpha}{m_pK_p}}\frac{q_p}{q_\alpha}r_P = \sqrt{\frac{4.0\,\text{u}}{1.0\,\text{u}}}\frac{er_p}{2e} = r_p,$$

$$r_d = \sqrt{\frac{m_d K_d}{m_p K_p} \frac{q_p}{q_d}} r_d = \sqrt{\frac{2.0 \text{ u}}{1.0 \text{ u}}} \frac{e r_d}{e} = \sqrt{2} r_p.$$

31P

During acceleration by the electric field, outside the magnetic field, the ion loses potential energy qV, where V is the accelerating potential difference and q is the charge on the ion. Since it starts from rest it gains kinetic energy $\frac{1}{2}mv^2$, where v is its final speed and m is its mass. Energy is conserved, so $qV = \frac{1}{2}mv^2$ and $v = \sqrt{2qV/m}$. While in the magnetic field it travels with constant speed around a circle of radius $x/2$. The magnetic force is qvB and its acceleration is $v^2/(x/2)$, so $qvB = 2mv^2/x$ or $qB = 2mv/x$. Substitute $v = \sqrt{2qV/m}$ and solve for m. You should get $m = qB^2x^2/8V$.

32P

(a) From $m = B^2qx^2/8V$ we have $\Delta m = (B^2q/8V)(2x\,\Delta x)$, where $x = \sqrt{8Vm/B^2q}$, which we sbustitute into the experssion for Δm:

$$\Delta m = \left(\frac{B^2 q}{8V}\right) 2 \sqrt{\frac{8mV}{B^2 q}} \Delta x = B\sqrt{\frac{mq}{2V}} \Delta x.$$

(b)

$$\Delta x = \frac{\Delta m}{B} \sqrt{\frac{2V}{mq}}$$

$$= \frac{(37 \text{ u} - 35 \text{ u})(1.66 \times 10^{-27} \text{ kg/u})}{0.50 \text{ T}} \sqrt{\frac{2(7.3 \times 10^3 \text{ V})}{(36 \text{ u})(1.66 \times 10^{-27} \text{ kg/u})(1.60 \times 10^{-19} \text{ C})}}$$

$$= 8.2 \times 10^{-3} \text{ m}.$$

33P

(a) Solve the result of Problem 31 for B. You should get

$$B = \sqrt{\frac{8Vm}{qx^2}}.$$

Evaluate this expression using $x = 2.00 \text{ m}$:

$$B = \sqrt{\frac{8(100 \times 10^3 \text{ V})(3.92 \times 10^{-25} \text{ kg})}{(3.20 \times 10^{-19} \text{ C})(2.00 \text{ m})^2}} = 0.495 \text{ T}.$$

(b) Let N be the number of ions that are separated by the machine per unit time. The current is $i = qN$ and the mass that is separated per unit time is $M = mN$, where m is the mass of a single ion. M has the value

$$M = 100 \, \text{mg/h} = \frac{100 \times 10^{-6} \, \text{kg}}{3600 \, \text{s}} = 2.78 \times 10^{-8} \, \text{kg/s} \,.$$

Since $N = M/m$ we have

$$i = \frac{qM}{m} = \frac{(3.20 \times 10^{-19} \, \text{C})(2.78 \times 10^{-8} \, \text{kg/s})}{3.92 \times 10^{-25} \, \text{kg}} = 2.27 \times 10^{-2} \, \text{A} \,.$$

(c) Each ion deposits an energy of qV in the cup, so the energy deposited in time Δt is given by

$$E = NqV \, \Delta t = \frac{iqV}{q} \Delta t = iV \, \Delta t \,.$$

For $\Delta t = 1.0 \, \text{h}$,

$$E = (2.27 \times 10^{-2} \, \text{A})(100 \times 10^{3} \, \text{V})(3600 \, \text{s}) = 8.17 \times 10^{8} \, \text{J} \,.$$

To obtain the second expression, i/q was substituted for N.

34P

For the ion beam to be undeviated we have $v = E/B$. Then as the ion beam enters the magnetic field $\mathbf{B}'$ we have $r = mv/(qB') = mE/(qBB')$, or $q/m = E/(rBB')$.

35P

(a) If v is the speed of the positron then $v \sin \phi$ is the component of its velocity in the plane that is perpendicular to the magnetic field. Here ϕ is the angle between the velocity and the field (89°). Newton's second law yields $eBv \sin \phi = m(v \sin \phi)^2/r$, where r is the radius of the orbit. Thus $r = (mv/eB) \sin \phi$. The period is given by

$$T = \frac{2\pi r}{v \sin \phi} = \frac{2\pi m}{eB} = \frac{2\pi(9.11 \times 10^{-31} \, \text{kg})}{(1.60 \times 10^{-19} \, \text{C})(0.10 \, \text{T})} = 3.58 \times 10^{-10} \, \text{s} \,.$$

The equation for r was substituted to obtain the second expression for T.

(b) The pitch is the distance traveled along the line of the magnetic field in a time interval of one period. Thus $p = vT \cos \phi$. Use the kinetic energy to find the speed: $K = \frac{1}{2}mv^2$ means

$$v = \sqrt{\frac{2K}{m}} = \sqrt{\frac{2(2.0 \times 10^{3} \, \text{eV})(1.60 \times 10^{-19} \, \text{J/eV})}{9.11 \times 10^{-31} \, \text{kg}}} = 2.651 \times 10^{7} \, \text{m/s} \,.$$

Thus
$$p = (2.651 \times 10^7 \, \text{m/s})(3.58 \times 10^{-10} \, \text{s}) \cos 89° = 1.66 \times 10^{-4} \, \text{m}.$$

(c) The orbit radius is

$$R = \frac{mv \sin \phi}{eB} = \frac{(9.11 \times 10^{-31} \, \text{kg})(2.651 \times 10^7 \, \text{m/s}) \sin 89°}{(1.60 \times 10^{-19} \, \text{C})(0.10 \, \text{T})} = 1.51 \times 10^{-3} \, \text{m}.$$

36P
(a) $-q$, from conservation of charges.
(b) Each of the two particlse will move in the same circular path, initially going in the opposite direction. After traveling half of the circular path each they will collide. So the time is given by $t = T/2 = \pi m / Bq$.

37P
(a) The radius r of the circular orbit is given by $r = p/eB$, where B is the magnitude of the magnetic field. The relativisitic expression $p = mv/\sqrt{1 - v^2/c^2}$ must be used for the magnitude of the momentum. Here v is the speed of the proton, m is its mass, and c is the speed of light. Hence

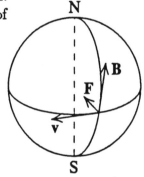

$$r = \frac{mv}{eB\sqrt{1 - v^2/c^2}}.$$

Square both sides and solve for v. The result is

$$v = \frac{reBc}{\sqrt{m^2c^2 + r^2e^2B^2}}.$$

Substitute $r = 6.37 \times 10^6 \, \text{m}$ (the radius of the Earth), $e = 1.6022 \times 10^{-19} \, \text{C}$ (the charge on a proton), $B = 41 \times 10^{-6} \, \text{T}$, $m = 1.6726 \times 10^{-27} \, \text{kg}$ (the mass of a proton), and $c = 2.9979 \times 10^8 \, \text{m/s}$ to obtain $v = 2.9977 \times 10^8 \, \text{m/s}$.

38E
(a)
$$f_{osc} = \frac{qB}{2\pi m} = \frac{(1.60 \times 10^{-19} \, \text{C})(1.2 \, \text{T})}{2\pi(1.67 \times 10^{-27} \, \text{kg})} = 1.8 \times 10^7 \, \text{Hz}.$$

(b) From $r = mv/qB = \sqrt{2mK}/qB$ we have

$$K = \frac{(rqB)^2}{2m} = \frac{[(0.50 \, \text{m})(1.60 \times 10^{-19} \, \text{C})(1.2 \, \text{T})]^2}{2(1.67 \times 10^{-27} \, \text{kg})(1.60 \times 10^{-19} \, \text{J/eV})} = 1.7 \times 10^7 \, \text{eV}.$$

39E

(a)
$$r = \frac{mv}{qB} = \frac{(1.67 \times 10^{-27}\,\text{kg})(3.00 \times 10^8\,\text{m/s})/10}{(1.60 \times 10^{-19}\,\text{C})(1.4\,\text{T})} = 0.22\,\text{m}.$$

(b) $f_{osc} = v/2\pi r = (3.00 \times 10^7\,\text{m/s})/[2\pi(0.22\,\text{m})] = 2.1 \times 10^7\,\text{Hz}.$

40P

(a) Since $K = \frac{1}{2}mv^2 = \frac{1}{2}m(2\pi R f_{osc})^2 \propto m$, $K_p = (m_p/m_d)K_d = \frac{1}{2}K_d = \frac{17}{2}\,\text{MeV} =$ 8.5 MeV.

(b) $B_p = B_d/2 = 1.6\,\text{T}/2 = 0.80\,\text{T}.$

(c) Since $K \propto B^2/m$ we have $K'_p = K_d(m_d/m_p) = 2K_d = 2(17\,\text{MeV}) = 34\,\text{MeV}.$

(d) Since $f_{osc} = Bq/(2\pi m) \propto m^{-1}$, we have

$$f_{osc,\,p} = \left(\frac{m_d}{m_P}\right)f_{osc,\,p} = 2(12 \times 10^6\,\text{s}^{-1}) = 2.4 \times 10^7\,\text{s}^{-1}.$$

(e) Now $K_\alpha = (m_\alpha/m_d)K_d = 2K_d = 2(17\,\text{MeV}) = 34\,\text{MeV},$

$$B_\alpha = \left(\frac{m_\alpha}{m_d}\right)\left(\frac{q_d}{q_\alpha}\right)B_d = 2\left(\frac{1}{2}\right)(1.6\,\text{T}) = 1.6\,\text{T},$$

$K'_\alpha = K_\alpha = 34\,\text{MeV}$ (Since $B_\alpha = B_d = 1.6\,\text{T}$),
and

$$f_{osc,\,\alpha} = \left(\frac{q_\alpha}{a_d}\right)\left(\frac{m_d}{m_\alpha}\right)f_{osc,\,d} = 2\left(\frac{2}{4}\right)(12 \times 10^6\,\text{s}^{-1}) = 1.2 \times 10^7\,\text{s}^{-1}.$$

41P

The speed of the deuteron before it breaks up is

$$v_d = \frac{rqB}{m_d} = \frac{(50 \times 10^{-2}\,\text{m}))(1.60 \times 10^{-19}\,\text{C})(1.5\,\text{T})}{2(1.66 \times 10^{-27}\,\text{kg})} = 3.6 \times 10^5\,\text{m/s}.$$

Since $K_d = \frac{1}{2}m_d v_d^2 = K_p + K_n = \frac{1}{2}m_n v_n^2 + \frac{1}{2}m_p v_p^2$ and $m_d v_d = m_n v_n + m_p v_p$ (conservation of linear momentum) we find $v_p \approx v_n \approx v_d$, where we noted that $m_n \approx m_p \approx m_d/2$. So the neutron will proceed with speed $v_n \approx v_d = 3.6 \times 10^5\,\text{m/s}$, moving in a straight line tangent to the original path of the deuteron (since $q_n = 0$). The proton will move in a circle with radius

$$r_p = \left(\frac{m_p}{m_d}\right)\left(\frac{q_d}{q_p}\right)r_d = \left(\frac{1}{2}\right)(1)(50\,\text{cm}) = 25\,\text{cm}.$$

42P

Approximate the total distance by the number of revolutions times the circumference of the orbit corresponding to the average energy. This should be a good approximation since the deuteron receives the same energy each revolution and its period does not depend on its energy. The deuteron accelerates twice in each cycle and each time it receives an energy of $qV = 80 \times 10^3$ eV. Since its final energy is 16.6 MeV the number of revolutions it makes is

$$n = \frac{16.6 \times 10^6 \text{ eV}}{2(80 \times 10^3 \text{ eV})} = 104 .$$

Its average energy during the accelerating process is 8.3 MeV. The radius of the orbit is given by $r = mv/qB$, where v is the deuteron's speed. Since this is given by $v = \sqrt{2K/m}$, the radius is

$$r = \frac{m}{qB}\sqrt{\frac{2K}{m}} = \frac{1}{qB}\sqrt{2Km} .$$

For the average energy

$$r = \frac{\sqrt{2(8.3 \times 10^6 \text{ eV})(1.60 \times 10^{-19} \text{ J/eV})(3.34 \times 10^{-27} \text{ kg})}}{(1.60 \times 10^{-19} \text{ C})(1.57 \text{ T})} = 0.375 \text{ m} .$$

The total distance traveled is about $n2\pi r = (104)(2\pi)(0.375) = 245$ m.

43E

Use $\mathbf{F}_B = q\mathbf{v} \times \mathbf{B}$. Tha answer is (b).

44E

The magnitude of the magnetic force on the wire is given by $F_B = iLB \sin\phi$, where i is the current in the wire, L is the length of the wire, B is the magnitude of the magnetic field, and ϕ is the angle between the current and the field. In this case $\phi = 70°$. Thus

$$F_B = (5000 \text{ A})(100 \text{ m})(60.0 \times 10^{-6} \text{ T}) \sin 70° = 28.2 \text{ N} .$$

Apply the right-hand rule to the vector product $\mathbf{F}_B = i\mathbf{L} \times \mathbf{B}$ to show that the force is to the west.

45E

$F_B = iBL \sin\theta = (13.0 \text{ A})(1.50 \text{ T})(1.80 \text{ m})(\sin 35.0°) = 20.1 \text{ N}.$

46P

The magnetic force on the wire must be upward and have a magnitude equal to the gravitational force mg on the wire. Apply the right-hand rule to show that the current must be from left to right. Since the field and the current are perpendicular to each other the magnitude of the magnetic force is given by $F_B = iLB$, where L is the length of the wire. The condition that the tension in the supports vanish is $iLB = mg$, which yields

$$i = \frac{mg}{LB} = \frac{(0.0130\,\mathrm{kg})(9.8\,\mathrm{m/s^2})}{(0.620\,\mathrm{m})(0.440\,\mathrm{T})} = 0.467\,\mathrm{A}\,.$$

47P

$$\begin{aligned}
\mathbf{F}_B &= i\mathbf{L} \times \mathbf{B} = iL\mathbf{i} \times (B_y\mathbf{j} + B_z\mathbf{k}) = iL(-B_z\mathbf{j} + B_y\mathbf{k}) \\
&= (0.50\,\mathrm{A})(0.50\,\mathrm{m})[-(0.010\,\mathrm{T})\mathbf{j} + (0.0030\,\mathrm{T})\mathbf{k}] \\
&= (-2.5 \times 10^{-3}\mathbf{j} + 0.75 \times 10^{-3}\mathbf{k})\,\mathrm{N}.
\end{aligned}$$

48P
The magnetic force on the wire is $F_B = idB$, pointing to the left. Thus $v = at = F_B t/m = idBt/m$, to the left.

49P
(a) Since $\mathbf{B}$ is uniform,

$$\mathbf{F}_B = \int_{\mathrm{wire}} id\mathbf{L} \times \mathbf{B} = i\left(\int_{\mathrm{wire}} d\mathbf{L}\right) \times \mathbf{B} = i\mathbf{L}_{ab} \times \mathbf{B},$$

where we noted that $\int_{\mathrm{wire}} d\mathbf{L} = \mathbf{L}_{ab}$, $\mathbf{L}_{ab}$ being the displacement vector from a to b.
(b) Now $\mathbf{L}_{ab} = 0$, so $\mathbf{F}_B = i\mathbf{L}_{ab} \times \mathbf{B} = 0$.

50P
Use $d\mathbf{F}_B = id\mathbf{L} \times \mathbf{B}$:

$$\begin{aligned}
\mathbf{F}_B &= \int_{x_i}^{x_f} idx\mathbf{i} \times (B_x\mathbf{i} + B_y\mathbf{j}) = i \int_{x_i}^{x_f} B_y\,dx\mathbf{k} \\
&= (-5.0\,\mathrm{A}) \int_{1.0}^{3.0} 8.0x^2\,dx\mathbf{k}(mT) = (-0.35\mathbf{k})\,\mathrm{N}.
\end{aligned}$$

51P
(a) From $F_B = iLB$ we get

$$i = \frac{F_B}{LB} = \frac{10 \times 10^3\,\mathrm{N}}{(3.0\,\mathrm{m})(10 \times 10^{-6}\,\mathrm{T})} = 3.3 \times 10^8\,\mathrm{A}.$$

(b) $P = i^2 R = (3.3 \times 10^8 \text{ A})^2 (1.0\,\Omega) = 1.0 \times 10^{17}$ W.

(c) It is totally unrealistic because of the huge current and the consequent high power loss.

52P

The magnetic force must push horizontally on the rod to overcome the force of friction. But it can be oriented so it also pulls up on the rod and thereby reduces both the normal force and the force of friction.

Suppose the magnetic field makes the angle θ with the vertical. The diagram to the right shows the view from the end of the sliding rod. The forces are also shown: F_B is the force of the magnetic field if the current is out of the page, mg is the force of gravity, N is the normal force of the stationary rails on the rod, and f is the force of friction. Notice that the magnetic force makes the angle θ with the *horizontal*. When the rod is on the verge of sliding, the net force acting on it is zero and the magnitude of the frictional force is given by $f = \mu_s N$, where μ_s is the coefficient of static friction. The magnetic field is perpendicular to the wire so the magnitude of the magnetic force is given by $F_B = iLB$, where i is the current in the rod and L is the length of the rod.

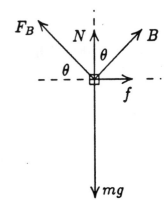

The vertical component of Newton's second law yields

$$N + iLB\sin\theta - mg = 0$$

and the horizontal component yields

$$iLB\cos\theta - \mu_s N = 0.$$

Solve the second equation for N and substitute the resulting expression into the first equation, then solve for B. You should get

$$B = \frac{\mu_s mg}{iL(\cos\theta + \mu_s \sin\theta)}.$$

The minimum value of B occurs when $\cos\theta + \mu_s \sin\theta$ is a maximum. Set the derivative of $\cos\theta + \mu_s \sin\theta$ equal to zero and solve for θ. You should get $\theta = \tan^{-1}\mu_s = \tan^{-1}(0.60) = 31°$. Now evaluate the expression for the minimum value of B:

$$B_{\min} = \frac{0.60(1.0\,\text{kg})(9.8\,\text{m/s}^2)}{(50\,\text{A})(1.0\,\text{m})(\cos 31° + 0.60\sin 31°)} = 0.10\,\text{T}.$$

(a) Choose a coordinate system as shown. Then
$\mathbf{B} = B\mathbf{i}$. We have

$$\begin{cases}
\mathbf{F}_c = i\mathbf{C} \times \mathbf{B} = (iC)\mathbf{i} \times (B)\mathbf{i} = 0, \\
\mathbf{F}_b = i\mathbf{b} \times \mathbf{B} = ibB \sin\theta\,\mathbf{k} \\
\quad = (4.00\,\mathrm{A})(1.20\,\mathrm{m})(0.0750\,\mathrm{T})(50.0/130)\mathbf{k} \\
\quad = (0.138\,\mathrm{N})\mathbf{k}, \\
\mathbf{F}_a = i\mathbf{a} \times \mathbf{B} = (-iaB \sin\phi)\mathbf{k} = (-ibB \sin\theta)\mathbf{k} \\
\quad = -\mathbf{F}B = -(0.138\,\mathrm{N})\mathbf{k}.
\end{cases}$$

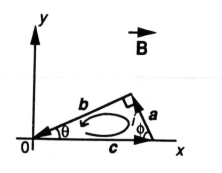

(b) $\mathbf{F}_a + \mathbf{F}_b + \mathbf{F}_c = (-iaB \sin\phi)\mathbf{k} + (ibB \sin\theta)\mathbf{k} + \vec{0} = 0$, where we noted that $a \sin\phi = b \sin\theta = ab/c$. This is in fact a special case of Problem 49, part (b).

54P

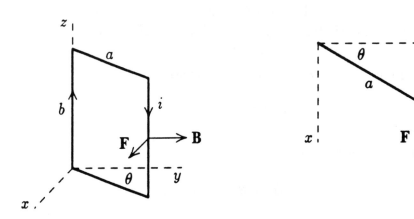

The situation is shown in the left diagram above. The z axis is along the hinge and the magnetic field is in the positive y direction. A torque around the hinge is associated with the wire opposite the hinge and not with the other wires. The force on this wire is in the positive x direction and has magnitude $F = NibB$, where N is the number of turns.

The right diagram shows the view from above. The magnitude of the torque is given by

$$\begin{aligned}
\tau &= Fa \cos\theta = NibBa \cos\theta \\
&= 20(0.10\,\mathrm{A})(0.10\,\mathrm{m})(0.50 \times 10^{-3}\,\mathrm{T})(0.050\,\mathrm{m}) \cos 30° \\
&= 4.33 \times 10^{-3}\,\mathrm{N \cdot m}.
\end{aligned}$$

Use the right-hand rule to show that the torque is directed downward, in the negative z direction.

55E

(a) Use $\tau = \vec{\mu} \times \mathbf{B}$. From the diagram it is apparent that τ points at the 20-minute mark. So the time interval is 20 min.

(b)

$$\tau = |\vec{\mu} \times \mathbf{B}| = \mu B \sin(\vec{\mu}, \mathbf{B})$$
$$= NiAB \sin 90° = \pi Nir^2 B$$
$$= 6\pi(2.0\,\text{A})(0.15\,\text{m})^2(70 \times 10^{-3}\,\text{T})$$
$$= 5.9 \times 10^{-2}\,\text{N} \cdot \text{m}.$$

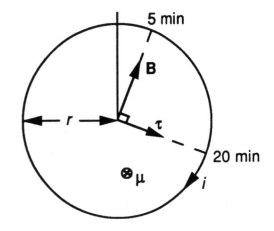

56P

If N closed loops are formed from the wire of length L, the circumference of each loop is L/N, the radius of each loop is $R = L/2\pi N$, and the area of each loop is $A = \pi R^2 = \pi(L/2\pi N)^2 = L^2/4\pi N^2$. For maximum torque, orient the plane of the loops parallel to the magnetic field, so the dipole moment is perpendicular to the field. The magnitude of the torque is then

$$\tau = NiAB = (Ni)\left(\frac{L^2}{4\pi N^2}\right)B = \frac{iL^2 B}{4\pi N}.$$

To maximize the torque take N to have the smallest possible value, 1. Then

$$\tau = \frac{iL^2 B}{4\pi}.$$

57P

Replace the loop of arbitrary shape with an assembly of adjacent long, thin, rectangular loops, each with N turns and carrying a current i, as shown. As the widths of these rectangles shrink to infinitesimally samll values the assembly gives equivalent current distribution as the original loop. The torque $\Delta\tau$ exerted by $\mathbf{B}$ on the nth rectangular loop of area ΔA_n is given by

$$\Delta\tau_n = NiB \sin\theta \Delta A_n.$$

Thus for the whole assembly

$$\tau = \sum_n \Delta\tau_n = NiB \sum_n \Delta A_n = NiAB \sin\theta.$$

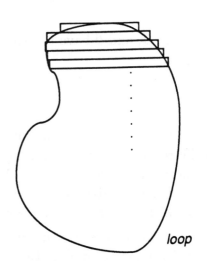

loop

58P

The total magnetic force on the loop L is

$$\mathbf{F}_B = i \oint_L (d\mathbf{L} \times \mathbf{B}) = i(\oint_L d\mathbf{L}) \times \mathbf{B} = 0,$$

where we noted that $\oint_L d\mathbf{L} = 0$. If $\mathbf{B}$ is not a constant then the equality

$$\oint_L (d\mathbf{L} \times \mathbf{B}) = (\oint_L d\mathbf{L}) \times \mathbf{B}$$

is not necessarily valid so $\mathbf{F}_B$ is not always zero.

59P

Consider an infinitesimal segment of the loop, of length ds. The magnetic field is perpendicular to the segment so the mag- netic force on it is has magnitude $dF = iB\,ds$. The diagram shows the direction of the force for the segment on the far right of the loop. The horizontal component of the force has magnitude $dF_h = (iB\cos\theta)\,ds$ and points inward toward the center of the loop. The vertical component has magnitude $dF_v = (iB\sin\theta)\,ds$ and points upward.

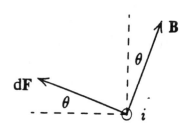

Now sum the forces on all the segments of the loop. The horizontal component of the total force vanishes since each segment of wire can be paired with another, diametrically opposite, segment. The horizontal components of these forces are both toward the center of the loop and thus in opposite directions. The vertical component of the total force is

$$F_v = iB\sin\theta \int ds = (iB\sin\theta)2\pi a\,.$$

Notice the i, B, and θ have the same value for every segment and so can be factored from the integral.

60P

(a) The current in the galvanometer should be $1.62\,\mathrm{mA}$ when the potential difference across the resistor-galvanometer combination is $1.00\,\mathrm{V}$. The potential difference across the galvanometer alone is $iR_g = (1.62 \times 10^{-3}\,\mathrm{A})(75.3\,\Omega) = 0.122\,\mathrm{V}$ so the resistor must be in series with the galvanometer and the potential difference across it must be $1.00\,\mathrm{V} - 0.122\,\mathrm{V} = 0.878\,\mathrm{V}$. The resistance should be $R = (0.878\,\mathrm{V})/(1.62 \times 10^{-3}\,\mathrm{A}) = 542\,\Omega$.

(b) The current in the galvanometer should be $1.62\,\mathrm{mA}$ when the total current in the resistor-galvanometer combination is $50.0\,\mathrm{mA}$. The resistor should be in parallel with the galvanometer and the current through it should be $50\,\mathrm{mA} - 1.62\,\mathrm{mA} = 48.38\,\mathrm{mA}$. The potential difference across the resistor is the same as that across the galvanometer, $0.122\,\mathrm{V}$, so the resistance should be $R = (0.122\,\mathrm{V})/(48.38 \times 10^{-3}\,\mathrm{A}) = 2.52\,\Omega$.

61P

In the diagram to the right $\vec{\mu}$ is the magnetic dipole moment of the wire loop and **B** is the magnetic field. Since the plane of the loop is parallel to the incline the dipole moment is normal to the incline. The forces acting on the cylinder are the force of gravity mg, acting downward from the center of mass, the normal force of the incline N, acting perpendicularly to the incline through the center of mass, and the force of friction f, acting up the incline at the point of contact.

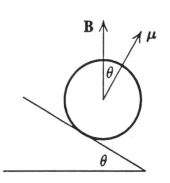

Take the x axis to be positive down the incline. Then the x component of Newton's second law for the center of mass yields

$$mg \sin\theta - f = ma.$$

For purposes of calculating the torque take the axis of the cylinder to be the axis of rotation. The magnetic field produces a torque with magnitude $\mu B \sin\theta$ and the force of friction produces a torque with magnitude fr, where r is the radius of the cylinder. The first tends to produce an angular acceleration in the counterclockwise direction and the second tends to produce an angular acceleration in the clockwise direction. Newton's second law for rotation about the center of the cylinder, $\tau = I\alpha$, gives

$$fr - \mu B \sin\theta = I\alpha.$$

Since you want the current that holds the cylinder in place, set $a = 0$ and $\alpha = 0$, then use one equation to eliminate f from the other. You should obtain $mgr = \mu B$. The loop is rectangular with two sides of length L and two of length $2r$, so its area is $A = 2rL$ and the dipole moment is $\mu = NiA = 2NirL$. Thus $mgr = 2NirLB$ and

$$i = \frac{mg}{2NLB} = \frac{(0.250\,\text{kg})(9.8\,\text{m/s}^2)}{2(10.0)(0.100\,\text{m})(0.500\,\text{T})} = 2.45\,\text{A}.$$

62E

(a) The magnitude of the magnetic dipole moment is given by $\mu = NiA$, where N is the number of turns, i is the current in each turn, and A is the area of a loop. In this case the loops are circular, so $A = \pi r^2$, where r is the radius of a turn. Thus

$$i = \frac{\mu}{N\pi r^2} = \frac{2.30\,\text{A} \cdot \text{m}^2}{(160)(\pi)(0.0190\,\text{m})^2} = 12.7\,\text{A}.$$

(b) The maximum torque occurs when the dipole moment is perpendicular to the field (or the plane of the loop is parallel to the field). It is given by $\tau = \mu B = (2.30\,\text{A} \cdot \text{m}^2)(35.0 \times 10^{-3}\,\text{T}) = 8.05 \times 10^{-2}\,\text{N} \cdot \text{m}.$

63E

(a) From $\mu = NiA = i\pi r^2$ we get

$$i = \frac{\mu}{\pi r^2} = \frac{8.00 \times 10^{22}\,\text{J/T}}{\pi(3500 \times 10^3\,\text{m})^2} = 2.08 \times 10^9\,\text{A}.$$

64E

(a) $\mu = NiA = \pi r^2 A = \pi r^2 i = \pi(0.150\,\text{m})^2(2.60\,\text{A}) = 0.184\,\text{A}\cdot\text{m}^2.$

(b) $\tau = |\vec{\mu} \times \mathbf{B}| = \mu B \sin\theta = (0.184\,\text{A}\cdot\text{m}^2)(12.0\,\text{T})(\sin 41.0°) = 1.45\,\text{N}\cdot\text{m}.$

65E

(a) The area A of the current loop is $A = \frac{1}{2}(30\,\text{cm})(40\,\text{cm}) = 6.0 \times 10^2\,\text{cm}^2$, so $\mu = iA = (5.0\,\text{A})(6.0 \times 10^{-2}\,\text{m}^2) = 0.30\,\text{A}\cdot\text{m}^2.$

(b) $\tau = \mu B \sin\theta = (0.30\,\text{A}\cdot\text{m}^2)(80 \times 10^3\,\text{T})(\sin 90°) = 2.4 \times 10^{-2}\,\text{N}\cdot\text{m}.$

66E

(a)

$$\mu = \sum_n i_n A_n = \pi r_1^2 i_1 + \pi r_2^2 i_2 = (\pi)(7.00\,\text{A})[(0.300\,\text{m})^2 + (0.200\,\text{m})^2] = 2.86\,\text{A}\cdot\text{m}^2.$$

Now $\mu = \pi r_1^2 i_1 - \pi r_2^2 i_2 = (\pi)(7.00\,\text{A})[(0.300\,\text{m})^2 - (0.200\,\text{m})^2] = 1.10\,\text{A}\cdot\text{m}^2.$

67P

The magnetic dipole moment is $\vec{\mu} = \mu(0.60\,\mathbf{i} - 0.80\,\mathbf{j})$, where $\mu = NiA = Ni\pi r^2 = 1(0.20\,\text{A})\pi(0.080\,\text{m})^2 = 4.02 \times 10^{-4}\,\text{A}\cdot\text{m}^2$. Here i is the current in the loop, N is the number of turns, A is the area of the loop, and r is its radius.

(a) The torque is

$$\begin{aligned}
\tau &= \vec{\mu} \times \mathbf{B} = \mu(0.60\,\mathbf{i} - 0.80\,\mathbf{j}) \times (0.25\,\mathbf{i} + 0.30\,\mathbf{k}) \\
&= \mu\left[(0.60)(0.30)(\mathbf{i} \times \mathbf{k}) - (0.80)(0.25)(\mathbf{j} \times \mathbf{i}) - (0.80)(0.30)(\mathbf{j} \times \mathbf{k})\right] \\
&= \mu[-0.18\,\mathbf{j} + 0.20\,\mathbf{k} - 0.24\,\mathbf{i}].
\end{aligned}$$

Here $\mathbf{i} \times \mathbf{k} = -\mathbf{j}$, $\mathbf{j} \times \mathbf{i} = -\mathbf{k}$, and $\mathbf{j} \times \mathbf{k} = \mathbf{i}$ were used. We also used $\mathbf{i} \times \mathbf{i} = 0$. Substitute the value for μ to obtain

$$\tau = [-0.97 \times 10^{-4}\,\mathbf{i} - 7.2 \times 10^{-4}\,\mathbf{j} + 8.0 \times 10^{-4}\,\mathbf{k}]\,\text{N}\cdot\text{m}.$$

798

(b) The potential energy of the dipole is given by

$$U = -\vec{\mu} \cdot \mathbf{B} = -\mu(0.60\,\mathbf{i} - 0.80\,\mathbf{j}) \cdot (0.25\,\mathbf{i} + 0.30\,\mathbf{k})$$
$$= -\mu(0.60)(0.25) = -0.15\mu = -6.0 \times 10^{-4}\,\text{J}.$$

Here $\mathbf{i} \cdot \mathbf{i} = 1$, $\mathbf{i} \cdot \mathbf{k} = 0$, $\mathbf{j} \cdot \mathbf{i} = 0$, and $\mathbf{j} \cdot \mathbf{k} = 0$ were used.

68E

Let $a = 30.0\,\text{cm}$, $b = 20.0\,\text{cm}$, and $c = 10.0\,\text{cm}$. From the hint given we write

$$\vec{\mu} = \vec{\mu}_1 + \vec{\mu}_2 = iab(-\mathbf{k}) + iab(\mathbf{j}) = ia(c\mathbf{j} - b\mathbf{k})$$
$$= (5.00\,\text{A})(0.300\,\text{m})[(0.100\,\text{m})\mathbf{j} - (0.200\,\text{m})\mathbf{k}]$$
$$= (0.150\mathbf{j} - 0.300\mathbf{k})\,\text{A} \cdot \text{m}^2.$$

Thus $\mu = \sqrt{(0.150)^2 + (0.300)^2}\,\text{A} \cdot \text{m}^2 = 0.335\,\text{A} \cdot \text{m}^2$, and $\vec{\mu}$ is in the yz plane at angle θ to the $+y$ direction, where

$$\theta = \tan^{-1}\left(\frac{\mu_y}{\mu_x}\right) = \tan^{-1}\left(\frac{-0.300}{0.150}\right) = -63.4°.$$

69

Let $v_{\parallel} = v\cos\theta$. The electron will proceed with a uniform speed $v_{\parallel}$ in the direction of $\mathbf{B}$ while undergoing uniform cirular motion with frequency f in the direction perpendicular to B: $f = eB/2\pi m$. The distance d is then

$$d = v_{\parallel}T = \frac{v_{\parallel}}{f} = \frac{(v\cos\theta)2\pi m}{eB}$$
$$= \frac{2\pi(1.5 \times 10^7\,\text{m/s})(9.11 \times 10^{-31}\,\text{kg})(\cos 10°)}{(1.60 \times 10^{-19}\,\text{C})(1.0 \times 10^{-3}\,\text{T})} = 0.53\,\text{m}.$$

70

The electron will accelerate in the direction of $\mathbf{E}$ while moving around (due to the magnetic field) with frequency $f = eB/2\pi m$. At $t = \frac{1}{4}f$ its velocity will be parallel to the plates. We require that its displacement toward the upper plate be less than d at that time:

$$d \lesssim \frac{1}{2}at^2 = \frac{1}{2}\left(\frac{eV}{dm}\right)\left(\frac{\pi m}{2eB}\right)^2,$$

which gives

$$B > B_{\min} \approx \sqrt{\frac{\pi^2 V m}{8ed^2}}.$$

71

Use $\tau_{\text{max}} = |\vec{\mu} \times \mathbf{B}|_{\text{max}} = \mu B = i\pi a^2 B$. Note that $i = qf = qv/2\pi a$. So

$$\tau_{\text{max}} = \left(\frac{qv}{2\pi a}\right)\pi a^2 B = \frac{qvaB}{2}.$$

72

The equation of motion for the proton is

$$\mathbf{F} = q\mathbf{v} \times \mathbf{B} = q(v_x\mathbf{i} + v_y\mathbf{j} + v_z\mathbf{k}) \times B\mathbf{i} = qB(v_z\mathbf{j} - v_y\mathbf{k})$$
$$= m\mathbf{a} = m\left[\left(\frac{dv_x}{dt}\right)\mathbf{i} + \left(\frac{dv_y}{dt}\right)\mathbf{j} + \left(\frac{dv_z}{dt}\right)\mathbf{k}\right].$$

Thus

$$\begin{cases} \dfrac{dv_x}{dt} = 0 \\[2mm] \dfrac{dv_y}{dt} = \omega v_z \\[2mm] \dfrac{dv_z}{dt} = -\omega v_y. \end{cases}$$

Here $\omega = eB/m_0$. The solution is $v_x = v_{0x}$, $v_y = v_{0y}\cos\omega t$ and $v_z = -v_{0y}\sin\omega t$; i.e.
$\mathbf{v}(t) = v_{0x}\mathbf{i} + v_{0y}\cos(\omega t)\mathbf{j} - v_{0y}(\sin\omega t)\mathbf{k}$.

CHAPTER 31

1E
Use Eq. 31-8:

$$B = \frac{\mu_0 i}{2\pi r} = \frac{(1.26 \times 10^{-6}\,\text{T} \cdot \text{m/A})(50\,\text{A})}{2\pi(2.6 \times 10^{-3}\,\text{m}/2)} = 7.7 \times 10^{-3}\,\text{T}.$$

2E
Solve i from Eq. 31-8:

$$i = \frac{2\pi r B}{\mu_0} = \frac{2\pi(88.0 \times 10^{-2}\,\text{m})(7.30 \times 10^{-6}\,\text{T})}{1.26 \times 10^{-6}\,\text{T} \cdot \text{m/A}} = 32.1\,\text{A}.$$

3E
(a) The magnitude of the magnetic field due to the current in the wire, at a point a distance r from the wire, is given by

$$B = \frac{\mu_0 i}{2\pi r}.$$

Put $r = 20\,\text{ft} = 6.10\,\text{m}$. Then

$$B = \frac{(4\pi \times 10^{-7}\,\text{T} \cdot \text{m/A})(100\,\text{A})}{2\pi(6.10\,\text{m})} = 3.3 \times 10^{-6}\,\text{T} = 3.3\,\mu\text{T}.$$

(b) This is about one-sixth the magnitude of the Earth's field. It will affect the compass reading.

4E
The current i due to the electron flow is $i = ne = (5.6 \times 10^{14}/\text{s})(1.6 \times 10^{-19}\,\text{C}) = 9.0 \times 10^{-5}\,\text{A}$. Thus

$$B = \frac{\mu_0 i}{2\pi r} = \frac{(1.26 \times 10^{-6}\,\text{T} \cdot \text{m/A})(9.0 \times 10^{-5}\,\text{A})}{2\pi(1.5 \times 10^{-3}\,\text{m})} = 1.2 \times 10^{-8}\,\text{T}.$$

5E
Use $B(x, y, z) = (\mu_0/4\pi)i\Delta s \times r/r^3$, where $\Delta s = \Delta s\mathbf{j}$ and $\mathbf{r} = x\mathbf{i} + y\mathbf{j} + z\mathbf{k}$. Thus

$$\mathbf{B}(x, y, z) = \left(\frac{\mu_0}{4\pi}\right)\frac{i\Delta s\mathbf{j} \times (x\mathbf{i} + y\mathbf{j} + z\mathbf{k})}{(x^2 + y^2 + z^2)^{3/2}}$$

$$= \frac{\mu_0 i\Delta s(z\mathbf{i} - x\mathbf{k})}{4\pi(x^2 + y^2 + z^2)^{3/2}}.$$

(a)

$$\mathbf{B}(0, 0, 5.0\,\text{m}) = \frac{(1.26 \times 10^{-6}\,\text{T} \cdot \text{m/A})(2.0\,\text{A})(3.0 \times 10^{-2}\,\text{m})(5.0\,\text{m})\mathbf{i}}{4\pi[0^2 + 0^2 + (5.0\,\text{m})^2]^{3/2}} = (2.4 \times 10^{-10}\mathbf{i})\,\text{T}.$$

(b) $\mathbf{B}(0, 6.0\,\text{m}, 0)$, since $x = z = 0$.
(c)

$$\mathbf{B}(7.0\,\text{m}, 7.0\,\text{m}, 0) = \frac{(1.26 \times 10^{-6}\,\text{T} \cdot \text{m/A})(2.0\,\text{A})(3.0 \times 10^{-2}\,\text{m})(-7.0\,\text{m})\mathbf{k}}{4\pi[(7.0\,\text{m})^2 + (7.0\,\text{m})^2 + 0^2]^{3/2}}$$

$$= (4.3 \times 10^{-11}\mathbf{k})\,\text{T}.$$

(d)

$$\mathbf{B}(-3.0\,\text{m}, -4.0\,\text{m}, 0) = \frac{(1.26 \times 10^{-6}\,\text{T} \cdot \text{m/A})(2.0\,\text{A})(3.0 \times 10^{-2}\,\text{m})(3.0\,\text{m})\mathbf{k}}{4\pi[(-3.0\,\text{m})^2 + (-4.0\,\text{m})^2 + 0^2]^{3/2}}$$

$$= (1.4 \times 10^{-10}\mathbf{k})\,\text{T}.$$

6E
The points must be along a line parallel to the wire and a distance r from it, where r satisfies

$$B_{\text{wire}} = \frac{\mu_0 i}{2\pi r} = B_{\text{ext}},$$

or

$$r = \frac{\mu_0 i}{2\pi B_{\text{ext}}} = \frac{(1.26 \times 10^{-6}\,\text{T} \cdot \text{m/A})(100\,\text{A})}{2\pi(5.0 \times 10^{-3}\,\text{T})} = 4.0 \times 10^{-3}\,\text{m}.$$

7E
(a) The field due to the wire, at a point 8.0 cm from the wire, must be $39\,\mu\text{T}$ and must be directed toward due south. Since $B = \mu_0 i/2\pi r$,

$$i = \frac{2\pi r B}{\mu_0} = \frac{2\pi(0.080\,\text{m})(39 \times 10^{-6}\,\text{T})}{4\pi \times 10^{-7}\,\text{T} \cdot \text{m/A}} = 16\,\text{A}.$$

(b) The current must be from west to east to produce a field to the south at points below it.

8E

Set up a coordinate system as shown. The **B**-field at the location of the charge q is

$$\mathbf{B} = \frac{\mu_0 i}{2\pi d}(-\mathbf{k}).$$

Thus

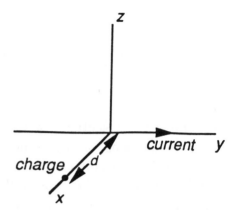

$$\mathbf{F}_q = q\mathbf{v} \times \mathbf{B}$$
$$= \frac{\mu_0 i}{2\pi d}(\mathbf{k} \times \mathbf{v}).$$

(a) Now $\mathbf{v} = v(-\mathbf{i})$ so

$$\mathbf{F}_q = \frac{\mu_0 i v}{2\pi d}\mathbf{k} \times (-\mathbf{i}) = \frac{\mu_0 i q v}{2\pi d}(-\mathbf{j}),$$

i.e. $\mathbf{F}_e$ has a magnitude of $\mu_0 i q v/2\pi d$, and it is directed against the current direction.
(b) Now $\mathbf{v}$ is reversed so $\mathbf{F}_q = \mu_0 i q v \mathbf{j}/2\pi d$.

9E

Use the same coordinated system as in Exercise 8. Then $\mathbf{F}_e = (-e\mu_0 i v/2\pi d)(\mathbf{k} \times \mathbf{v})$, as obtained there.
(a) Now $\mathbf{v} = v(-\mathbf{i})$ so

$$\mathbf{F}_e = \frac{\mu_0 i e v \mathbf{j}}{2\pi d} = \frac{(1.26 \times 10^{-6}\,\text{T} \cdot \text{m/A})(50\,\text{A})(1.6 \times 10^{-19}\,\text{C})(1.0 \times 10^7\,\text{m/s})\mathbf{j}}{2\pi(5.0 \times 10^{-2}\,\text{m})}$$
$$= (3.2 \times 10^{-16}\,\text{N})\mathbf{j}.$$

(c) Now $\mathbf{v} = \pm v\mathbf{k}$ so $\mathbf{F}_e \propto \mathbf{k} \times \mathbf{v} = 0$.

10E

The straight segment of the wire produces no magnetic fields at C. The field from the two semi-circular loop cancel at C. So $B_C = 0$.

11P

(a) The straignt segment of the wire produces no magnetic field at C.

(b) For the simicircular loop

$$B_C = \frac{\mu_0 i}{4\pi} \int_{\text{loop}} \frac{|d\mathbf{s} \times \mathbf{r}|}{r^3} = \frac{\mu_0 i}{4\pi} \int_{\text{loop}} \frac{r\,ds}{r^3}$$

$$= \frac{(\mu_0 i)(\pi r)}{4\pi R^2} = \frac{\mu_0 i}{4R}.$$

B points into the page.

(c) The same as (b), since the straight segments do not contribute to **B**.

12P

Label the various sections of the wires as shown. Firstly, the sections a_2 and c_2 do not coutribute to **B** at point O, as point O lies on the straight lines coinciding with a_2 and c_2. Secondly, the **B**-field due to the curved sections b_1 and b_2 cancel each other at point O. This leaves us just a_1 and c_1. Finally, if we relocate c_1 to c_1', its contribution to the **B**-field at O will not change. Note that a_1 and c_1' together do form an infinite straight wire carrying a current i to the left.

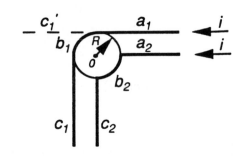

13P

Since sections AH and JD do not contribute to $\mathbf{B}_c$, we only need to consider the two arcs. For the smaller are

$$\mathbf{B}_{c1} = \left(\frac{\mu_0}{4\pi}\right) \int \frac{i\,d\mathbf{s}_1 \times \mathbf{r}}{r^3} = \frac{\mu_0 i}{4\pi} \int \frac{R_1\,ds_1}{R_1^3}\mathbf{e}$$

$$= \frac{\mu_0 i\mathbf{e}}{4R_1},$$

where **e** is a unit vector pointing into the page. For the larger arc

$$\mathbf{B}_{c2} = -\frac{\mu_0 i\mathbf{e}}{4R_2}.$$

Thus

$$\mathbf{B}_c = \mathbf{B}_{c1} + \mathbf{B}_{c2} = \frac{\mu_0 i(R_2 - R_1)\mathbf{e}}{4R_1 R_2}.$$

14P

(a) The contribution to $\mathbf{B}_a$ due to the straight sections of the wire is

$$\mathbf{B}_{a1} = \frac{\mu_0 i \mathbf{e}}{2\pi R},$$

where $\mathbf{e}$ is a unit vector which points out of the page. For the bent section (see Problem 13)

$$\mathbf{B}_{a2} = \frac{\mu_0 i \mathbf{e}}{4R}.$$

Thus

$$\mathbf{B}_a = \mathbf{B}_{a1} + \mathbf{B}_{a2} = \frac{\mu_0 i}{2R}\left(\frac{1}{\pi} + \frac{1}{2}\right)\mathbf{e}$$

$$= \frac{(1.26 \times 10^{-6}\ \text{T} \cdot \text{m/A})(10\,\text{A})}{2(5.0 \times 10^{-3}\ \text{m})}\left(\frac{1}{\pi} + \frac{1}{2}\right)\mathbf{e} = (1.0 \times 10^{-3}\ \text{T})\mathbf{e}.$$

(b) Now we only need to consider the two straight wires:

$$\mathbf{B}_b = \frac{2\mu_0 i \mathbf{e}}{2\pi R} = \frac{2(1.26 \times 10^{-6}\ \text{T} \cdot \text{m/A})(10\,\text{A})\mathbf{e}}{2\pi(5.0 \times 10^{-3}\ \text{m})} = (8.0 \times 10^{-4}\ \text{T})\mathbf{e}.$$

Here the factor of 2 in the numerator is due to the fact that two wires are involved.

15P

Sum the fields of the two straight wires and the circular arc. Look at the derivation of the expression for the field of a long straight wire, leading to Eq. 31–10. Since the wires we are considering are infinite in only one direction the field of either of them is half the field of an infinite wire. That is, the magnitude is $\mu_0 i/4\pi r$, where r is the distance from the end of the wire to the center of the arc. It is the radius of the arc. The fields of both wires are out of the page at the center of the arc.

Now find an expression for the field of the arc, at its center. Divide the arc into infinitesimal segments. Each segment produces a field in the same direction. If ds is the length of a segment the magnitude of the field it produces at the arc center is $(\mu_0 i/4\pi r^2)\,ds$. If θ is the angle subtended by the arc in radians, then $r\theta$ is the length of the arc and the total field of the arc is $\mu_0 i\theta/4\pi r$. For the arc of the diagram the field is into the page. The total field at the center, due to the wires and arc together, is

$$B = \frac{\mu_0 i}{4\pi r} + \frac{\mu_0 i}{4\pi r} - \frac{\mu_0 i\theta}{4\pi r} = \frac{\mu_0 i}{4\pi r}\left(2 - \theta\right).$$

For this to vanish θ must be 2 radians.

805

16P

First find the magnetic field of a circular arc at its center. Let ds be an infinitesimal segment of the arc and **r** be the vector from the segment to the arc center. ds and **r** are perpendicular to each other, so the contribution of the segment to the field at the center has magnitude

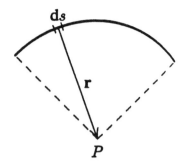

$$dB = \frac{\mu_0 i \, ds}{4\pi r^2} \, .$$

The field is into the page if the current is from left to right in the diagram and out of the page if the current is from right to left. All segments contribute magnetic fields in the same direction. Furthermore r is the same for all of them. Thus the magnitude of the total field at the center is given by

$$B = \frac{\mu_0 i s}{4\pi r^2} = \frac{\mu_0 i \theta}{4\pi r} \, .$$

Here s is the arc length and θ is the angle (in radians) subtended by the arc at its center. The second expression was obtained by replacing s with $r\theta$. θ must be in radians for this expression to be valid.

Now consider the circuit of Fig. 31-36. The magnetic field produced by the inner arc has magnitude $\mu_0 i \theta / 4\pi b$ and is out of the page. The field produced by the outer arc has magnitude $\mu_0 i \theta / 4\pi a$ and is into the page. The two straight segments of the circuit do not produce fields at the center of the arcs because the vector **r** from any point on them to the center is parallel or antiparallel to the current at that point. If the positive direction is out of the page then the total magnetic field at the center is

$$B = \frac{\mu_0 i \theta}{4\pi} \left[\frac{1}{b} - \frac{1}{a} \right] \, .$$

Since $b < a$ the total field is out of the page.

17P

Put the x axis along the wire with the origin at the midpoint and the current in the positive x direction. All segments of the wire produce magnetic fields at P that are into the page so we simply divide the wire into infinitesimal segments and sum the fields due to all the segments. The diagram shows one infinitesimal segment, with width dx. According to the Biot-Savart law the magnitude of the field it produces at P is given by

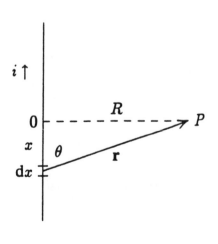

$$dB = \frac{\mu_0 i}{4\pi} \frac{\sin\theta}{r^2} \, dx \, .$$

806

θ and r are functions of x. Replace r with $\sqrt{x^2 + R^2}$ and $\sin\theta$ with $R/r = R/\sqrt{x^2 + R^2}$, then integrate from $x = -L/2$ to $x = L/2$. The total field is

$$B = \frac{\mu_0 i R}{4\pi} \int_{-L/2}^{L/2} \frac{dx}{(x^2 + R^2)^{3/2}} = \frac{\mu_0 i R}{4\pi} \frac{1}{R^2} \frac{x}{(x^2 + R^2)^{1/2}} \bigg|_{-L/2}^{L/2} = \frac{\mu_0 i}{2\pi R} \frac{L}{\sqrt{L^2 + 4R^2}}.$$

If $L \gg R$ then R^2 in the denominator can be ignored and

$$B = \frac{\mu_0 i}{2\pi R}$$

is obtained. This is the field of a long straight wire. For points close to a finite wire the field is quite similar to that of an infinitely long wire.

18P

You can easily check that each of the four sides produces the same magnetic field B_1 at the center of the square. Apply the result in Problem 17 for B_1 and let $R = a/2$ and $L = a$, we get

$$B = 4B_1 = \frac{4\mu_0 i}{2\pi(a/2)} \frac{a}{(a^2 + a^2)^{1/2}} = \frac{2\sqrt{2}\mu_0 i}{\pi a}.$$

19P

The **B**-fields produced by the four sides of the rectangle have the same direction. For each of the two longer sides (see Problem 17)

$$B_L = \frac{\mu_0 i}{2\pi(W/2)} \frac{L}{(L^2 + W^2)^{1/2}}.$$

Similarly for each of the shorter sides

$$B_W = \frac{\mu_0 i}{2\pi(L/2)} \frac{W}{W^2 + L^2)^{1/2}}.$$

Thus

$$B = 2B_L + 2B_W = \frac{2\mu_0 i L}{\pi W(L^2 + W^2)^{1/2}} + \frac{2\mu_0 W}{\pi L(L^2 + W^2)^{1/2}}$$

$$= \frac{2\mu_0 i(L^2 + W^2)^{1/2}}{\pi L W}.$$

For $L \gg W$

$$B \rightarrow \frac{2\mu_0 i L}{\pi L W} = \frac{2\mu_0 i}{\pi W},$$

807

which is consistent with Eq. 31-15 for $W = 2d$ and $x = 0$.

20P
When the fields of the four sides are summed vectorially the horizontal components add to zero. The vertical components are all the same, so the total field is given by

$$B_{\text{total}} = 4B\cos\theta = \frac{4Ba}{2R} = \frac{4Ba}{\sqrt{4x^2 + a^2}}.$$

Thus

$$B_{\text{total}} = \frac{4\mu_0 i a^2}{\pi(4x^2 + a^2)\sqrt{4x^2 + 2a^2}}.$$

For $x = 0$ the expression reduces to

$$B_{\text{total}} = \frac{4\mu_0 i a^2}{\pi a^2 \sqrt{2}a} = \frac{2\sqrt{2}\mu_0 i}{\pi a},$$

in agreement with the result of Problem 18.

21P
The square has sides of length $L/4$. The magnetic field at the center of the square is given by the result of Problem 20, with $a = L/4$ and $x = 0$. It is

$$B_{\text{sq}} = \frac{8\sqrt{2}\mu_0 i}{\pi L} = 11.31 \frac{\mu_0 i}{\pi L}.$$

The radius of the circle is $R = L/2\pi$. Use Eq. 31–24 of the text, with $R = L/2\pi$ and $z = 0$. The field is

$$B_{\text{circ}} = \frac{\pi^2 \mu_0 i}{\pi L} = 9.87 \frac{\mu_0 i}{\pi L}.$$

The square produces the larger magnetic field.

22P
Follow the same steps as in the solution of Problem 17 above but replace R with D, change the lower limit of integration to $-L$, and change the upper limit to 0. The magnitude of the total field is

$$B = \frac{\mu_0 i D}{4\pi} \int_{-L}^{0} \frac{dx}{(x^2 + D^2)^{3/2}} = \frac{\mu_0 i D}{4\pi} \frac{1}{D^2} \left. \frac{x}{(x^2 + D^2)^{1/2}} \right|_{-L}^{0} = \frac{\mu_0 i}{4\pi D} \frac{L}{\sqrt{L^2 + D^2}}.$$

808

23P
Since $ds \parallel \mathbf{r}$,

$$\mathbf{B}_Q \propto \int \frac{i ds \times \mathbf{r}}{r^3} = 0.$$

Let $\mathbf{e}$ be a unit vector unit vector pointing into the page. At point P,

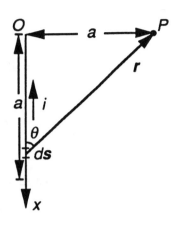

$$\mathbf{B}_P = \frac{\mu_0}{4\pi} \int \frac{i ds \times \mathbf{r}}{r^3} = \frac{\mu_0 i \mathbf{e}}{4\pi} \int \frac{\sin\theta ds}{r^2}$$

$$= \frac{\mu_0 i \mathbf{e}}{4\pi} \int_0^a \frac{a dx}{r^3} = \frac{\mu_0 i \mathbf{e}}{4\pi} \int_0^a \frac{a dx}{(a^2 + x^2)^{3/2}}$$

$$= \frac{\sqrt{2}\mu_0 i \mathbf{e}}{8\pi a}.$$

24P
Obviously, $B_{P3} = B_{P6} = 0$,

$$B_{P1} = B_{P2} = \frac{\sqrt{2}\mu_0 i}{8\pi a},$$

and

$$B_{P4} = P_{P5} = \frac{\sqrt{2}\mu_0 i}{8\pi(2a)}$$

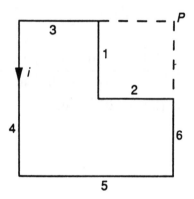

(see Problem 23). Thus

$$\mathbf{B}_P = \sum_{n=1}^{6} \mathbf{B}_{Pn} = (B_{p1} + B_{p2})\mathbf{e} - (B_{p4} + B_{p5})\mathbf{e} = 2\left(\frac{\sqrt{2}\mu_0 i}{8\pi a} - \frac{\sqrt{2}\mu_0 i}{16\pi a} \right)\mathbf{e}$$

$$= \frac{\sqrt{2}\mu_0 i \mathbf{e}}{8\pi a},$$

where $\mathbf{e}$ is a unit vector pointing into the page.

25P
Let $\mathbf{e}$ be a unit vector pointing into the page. Use the results of Problems 22 and 23 to calculate B_{P1} through B_{P8}:

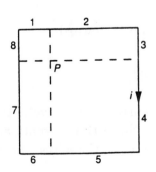

$$B_{P1} = B_{P8} = \frac{\sqrt{2}\mu_0 i}{8\pi(a/4)} = \frac{\sqrt{2}\mu_0 i}{2\pi a},$$

809

$$B_{P4} = B_{P5} = \frac{\sqrt{2}\mu_0 i}{8\pi(3a/4)} = \frac{\sqrt{2}\mu_0 i}{6\pi a},$$

$$B_{P2} = B_{P7} = \frac{\mu_0 i}{4\pi(a/4)} = \frac{3a/4}{[(3a/4)^2 + (a/4)^2]^{1/2}}$$

$$= \frac{3\mu_0 i}{\sqrt{10}\pi a},$$

and

$$B_{P3} = B_{P6} = \frac{\mu_0 i}{4\pi(3a/4)} = \frac{a/4}{[(a/4)^2 + (3a/4)^2]^{1/2}} = \frac{\mu_0 i}{3\sqrt{10}\pi a}.$$

Finally,

$$\mathbf{B}_P = \sum_{n=1}^{8} B_{Pn}\mathbf{e}$$

$$= 2\frac{\mu_0 i}{\pi a}\left(\frac{\sqrt{2}}{2} + \frac{\sqrt{2}}{6} + \frac{3}{\sqrt{10}} + \frac{1}{3\sqrt{10}}\right)\mathbf{e}$$

$$= \frac{2(1.26 \times 10^{-6}\,\text{T}\cdot\text{m/A})(10\,\text{A})}{\pi(8.0 \times 10^{-2}\,\text{m})}\left(\frac{\sqrt{2}}{2} + \frac{\sqrt{2}}{6} + \frac{3}{\sqrt{10}} + \frac{1}{3\sqrt{10}}\right)\mathbf{e}$$

$$= (2.0 \times 10^{-4}\,\text{T})\mathbf{e}.$$

26P

Consider a section of the ribbon of thickness dx located a distance x away from P. The current it carries is $di = i\,dx/w$, and its contribution to B_P is

$$dB_P = \frac{\mu_0\,di}{2\pi x} = \frac{\mu_0 i\,dx}{2\pi xw}.$$

Thus

$$B_P = \int dB_P = \frac{\mu_0 i}{2\pi w}\int_d^{d+w}\frac{dx}{x} = \frac{\mu_0 i}{2\pi w}\ln\left(1 + \frac{w}{d}\right),$$

and $\mathbf{B}_P$ points upward.

27E

(a) If the currents are parallel the two fields are in opposite directions in the region between the wires. Since the currents are the same the total field is zero along the line that runs halfway between the wires. There is no possible current for which the field does not vanish.

(b) If the currents are antiparallel the fields are in the same direction in the region between the wires. At a point halfway between they have the same magnitude, $\mu_0 i/2\pi r$. Thus the total field at the midpoint has magnitude $B = \mu_0 i/\pi r$ and

$$i = \frac{\pi r B}{\mu_0} = \frac{\pi(0.040\,\text{m})(300 \times 10^{-6}\,\text{T})}{4\pi \times 10^{-7}\,\text{T} \cdot \text{m/A}} = 30\,\text{A}\,.$$

28E

The current i_2 carried by wire 2 must be out of the page. Since $B_{P1} \propto i_1/r_1$ where $i_1 = 6.5\,\text{A}$ and $r_1 = 0.75\,\text{cm} + 1.5\,\text{cm} = 2.25\,\text{cm}$, and $B_{P2} \propto i_2/r_2$ where $r_2 = 1.5\,\text{cm}$, from $B_{P1} = B_{P2}$ we get

$$i_2 = i_1 \left(\frac{r_2}{r_1}\right) = (6.5\,\text{A})\left(\frac{1.5\,\text{cm}}{2.25\,\text{cm}}\right) = 4.3\,\text{A}.$$

29E

The point P at which $B_P = 0$ form a line parallel to both currents passing through the line joining the two wires, as shown. Note that $B_{P1} \propto i_1/r_1$, and $B_{P2} \propto i_2/(d-r_1)$. Let $B_{P1} = B_{P2}$ to obtain $i_1/r_1 = i_2/(d - r_1)$. Solve for r_1:

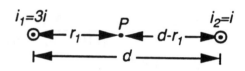

$$r_1 = \frac{i_1 d}{i_1 + i_2} = \frac{3id}{3i + i} = \frac{3d}{4}.$$

30E

Lable these wires 1 through 5, left to right. Then

$$\mathbf{F}_1 = \frac{\mu_0 i^2}{2\pi}\left(\frac{1}{d} + \frac{1}{2d} + \frac{1}{3d} + \frac{1}{4d}\right)\mathbf{j} = \left(\frac{25\mu_0 i^2}{24\pi d}\right)\mathbf{j}$$

$$= \frac{(13)(1.26 \times 10^{-6}\,\text{T} \cdot \text{m/A})(3.00\,\text{A})^2(1.00\,\text{m})\mathbf{j}}{24\pi(8.00 \times 10^{-2}\,\text{m})} = (4.69 \times 10^{-5}\,\text{T})\mathbf{j};$$

$$\mathbf{F}_2 = \frac{\mu_0 i^2}{2\pi}\left(\frac{1}{2d} + \frac{1}{3d}\right)\mathbf{j} = \left(\frac{5\mu_0 i^2}{12\pi d}\right)\mathbf{j} = (1.88 \times 10^{-5}\,\text{T})\mathbf{j};$$

$\mathbf{F}_3 = 0$ (because of symmetry); $\mathbf{F}_4 = -\mathbf{F}_2$, and $\mathbf{F}_5 = -\mathbf{F}_1$.

31E

Consider, for example, $x > d$. Then in Fig. 31-10 the direction of $\mathbf{B}_b$ is reversed, and

$$B(x) = \left| B_a(x) - B_b(x) \right| = \left| \frac{\mu_0 i}{2\pi(a+x)} - \frac{\mu_0 i}{2\pi(x-d)} \right|$$

$$= \frac{\mu_0 i d}{\pi(a^2 - x^2)}.$$

32E

(a) Refer to the figure to the right. We have

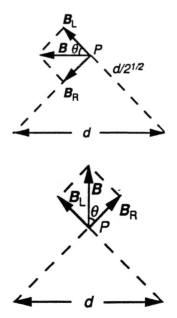

$$B = |\mathbf{B}_L + \mathbf{B}_R|$$

$$= 2B_L \cos\theta$$

$$= 2\left(\frac{\mu_0 i}{2\pi d/\sqrt{2}}\right)\cos\theta$$

$$= \frac{(1.26 \times 10^{-6}\,\text{T}\cdot\text{m/A})(100\,\text{A})(\cos 45°)\sqrt{2}}{\pi(10 \times 10^{-2}\,\text{m})}$$

$$= 4.0 \times 10^{-4}\,\text{T}.$$

$\mathbf{B}$ points to the left.

(b) From the figure to the right we see that B still has a magnitude of 4.0×10^{-4} T but now points upward.

33P

For $0 < x < d$ we have

$$B(x) = B_a(x) - B_b(x) = \frac{\mu_0 i}{2\pi(d+x)} - \frac{\mu_0 i}{2\pi(d-x)}$$

$$= \frac{\mu_0 i x}{\pi(d^2 - x^2)}.$$

For $x > d$

$$B(x) = B_a(x) + B_b(x) = \frac{\mu_0 i}{2\pi(d+x)} + \frac{\mu_0 i}{2\pi(d-x)}$$

$$= \frac{\mu_0 i x}{\pi(d^2 - x^2)}.$$

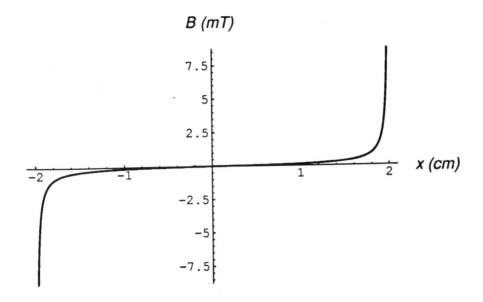

B (mT)

The same expression for $B(x)$ is valid for $x < 0$ due to symmetry.

34P

Each wire produces a field with magnitude given by $B = \mu_0 i/2\pi r$, where r is the distance from the corner of the square to the center. According to the Pythagorean theorem the diagonal of the square has length $\sqrt{2}a$, so $r = a/\sqrt{2}$ and $B = \mu_0 i/\sqrt{2}\pi a$. The fields due to the wires at the upper left and lower right corners both point toward the upper right corner of the square. The fields due to the wires at the upper right and lower left corners both point toward the upper left corner. The horizontal components cancel and the vertical components sum to

$$
\begin{aligned}
B_{\text{total}} &= 4\frac{\mu_0 i}{\sqrt{2}\pi a} \cos 45° = \frac{2\mu_0 i}{\pi a} \\
&= \frac{2(4\pi \times 10^{-7}\,\text{T} \cdot \text{m/A})(20\,\text{A})}{\pi(0.20\,\text{m})} = 8.0 \times 10^{-5}\,\text{T}.
\end{aligned}
$$

In the calculation $\cos 45°$ was replaced with $1/\sqrt{2}$. The total field points upward.

35P

Refer to the figure as shown. For example, the force on wire 1 is

$$
\begin{aligned}
F_1 &= |\mathbf{F}_{12} + \mathbf{F}_{13} + \mathbf{F}_{14}| \\
&= 2F_{12}\cos\theta + F_{13} \\
&= 2\left(\frac{\mu_0 i^2}{2\pi a}\right)\cos 45° + \frac{\mu_0 i^2}{2\sqrt{2}\pi a} \\
&= \frac{0.338\mu_0 i^2}{a}.
\end{aligned}
$$

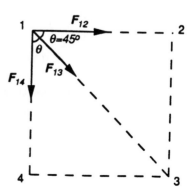

813

$\mathbf{F}_1$ points from wire 1 to the center of the squre.

36P

Use $\mathbf{F}_4 = \mathbf{F}_{14} + \mathbf{F}_{24} + \mathbf{F}_{34}$. Thus

$$\begin{aligned} F_{4x} &= -F_{43} - F_{42}\cos\theta \\ &= -\frac{\mu_0 i^2}{2\pi a} - \frac{\mu_0 i^2 \cos 45^\circ}{2\sqrt{2}\pi a} \\ &= -\frac{3\mu_0 i^2}{4\pi a}, \end{aligned}$$

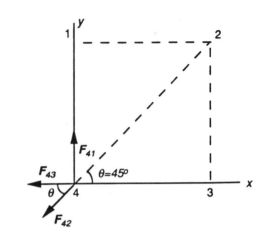

and

$$F_{4y} = F_{41} - F_{42}\sin\theta = \frac{\mu_0 i}{2\pi a} - \frac{\mu_0 i^2 \sin 45^\circ}{2\sqrt{2}\pi a} = \frac{\mu_0 i^2}{4\pi a}.$$

Thus

$$F_4 = (F_{4x}^2 + F_{4y}^2)^{1/2} = \left[\left(-\frac{3\mu_0 i^2}{4\pi a}\right)^2 + \left(\frac{\mu_0 i^2}{4\pi a}\right)^2\right]^{1/2} = \frac{\sqrt{10}\mu_0 i^2}{4\pi a},$$

and $\mathbf{F}_4$ makes an angle ϕ with $+x$ axis, where

$$\phi = \tan^{-1}\left(\frac{F_{4y}}{F_{4x}}\right) = \tan^{-1}\left(-\frac{1}{3}\right) = 162^\circ.$$

37P

(a) Refer to the figure to the right. We have

$$\begin{aligned} B_p &= |\mathbf{B}_1 + \mathbf{B}_2| = 2B_1 \cos\theta \\ &= 2\left(\frac{\mu_0 i}{2\pi r}\right)\left(\frac{d/2}{r}\right) \\ &= \frac{\mu_0 i d}{2\pi[R^2 + (d/2)^2]} \\ &= \frac{2\mu_0 i d}{\pi(4R^2 + d^2)}. \end{aligned}$$

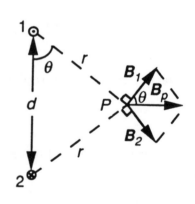

(b) $\mathbf{B}_p$ points to the right, as shown.

38P

The forces on the two sides of length b cancel out. For the remaining two sides

$$F = \frac{\mu_0 i_1 i_2 L}{2\pi}\left(\frac{1}{a} - \frac{1}{a+d}\right) = \frac{\mu i_1 i_2 b}{2\pi a(a+b)}$$

$$= \frac{(1.26 \times 10^{-6}\,\text{T}\cdot\text{m/A})(30\,\text{A})(20\,\text{A})(8.0\,\text{cm})(30\times 10^{-2}\,\text{m})}{2\pi(1.0\,\text{cm} + 8.0\,\text{cm})} = 3.2 \times 10^{-3}\,\text{N},$$

toward the wire.

39P

Consider a segment of the projectile between x and $x + dx$. Use Eq. 31-11 to obtain the force on the segment:

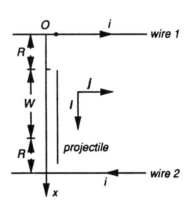

$$\begin{aligned}
d\mathbf{F} &= d\mathbf{F}_1 + d\mathbf{F}_2 \\
&= i(dx\mathbf{i}) \times \mathbf{B}_1(x) + i(dx\mathbf{i}) \times \mathbf{B}_2(x) \\
&= i[B_1(x) + B_2(x)]\mathbf{j}\,dx \\
&= i\left[\frac{\mu_0 i}{2\pi x} + \frac{\mu_0 i}{2\pi(2R + w - x)}\right]\mathbf{j}\,dx,
\end{aligned}$$

where $\mathbf{j}$ is a unit vector pointing to the right. Thus

$$\mathbf{F} = \int d\mathbf{F} = \frac{i^2\mu}{2\pi}\int_R^{R+w}\left(\frac{1}{x} + \frac{1}{2R+w-x}\right)\mathbf{j}\,dx$$

$$= \frac{\mu_0 i^2}{\pi}\ln\left(1 + \frac{w}{R}\right)\mathbf{j}.$$

(b) Use $\Delta K = \frac{1}{2}mv_f^2 = W_{\text{ext}} = \int \mathbf{F}\cdot d\mathbf{s}$ for the projectile:

$$\begin{aligned}
v_f &= \left(\frac{2W_{\text{ext}}}{m}\right)^{1/2} = \left[\frac{2}{m}\int_0^L \frac{\mu_0 i^2}{\pi}\ln\left(1 + \frac{w}{R}\right)dy\right]^{1/2} \\
&= \left[\frac{2(1.26 \times 10^{-6}\,\text{T}\cdot\text{m/A})(450 \times 10^3\,\text{A})^2(4.0\,\text{m})\ln(1 + 1.2\,\text{cm}/6.7\,\text{cm})}{(10 \times 10^{-3}\,\text{kg})\pi}\right]^{1/2} \\
&= 3.27 \times 10^3\,\text{m/s}.
\end{aligned}$$

40E

(a) Two of the currents are out of the page and one is into the page, so the net current enclosed by the path is 2.0 A, out of the page. Since the path is traversed in the clockwise

815

sense a current into the page is positive and a current out of the page is negative, as indicated by the right-hand rule associated with Ampere's law. Thus

$$\oint \mathbf{B} \cdot d\mathbf{s} = -\mu_0 i = -(2.0\,\text{A})(4\pi \times 10^{-7}\,\text{T} \cdot \text{m/A}) = -2.5 \times 10^{-6}\,\text{T} \cdot \text{m}.$$

(b) The net current enclosed by the path is zero (two currents are out of the page and two are into the page), so $\oint \mathbf{B} \cdot d\mathbf{s} = \mu_0 i = 0$.

41E
A close look at the path reveals that only currents no.1 and no.6 are enclosed. Thus

$$\oint \mathbf{B} \cdot d\mathbf{s} = \mu_0(6i_0 - i_0) = 5\mu_0 i.$$

42E
Use Eq. 31-18 for the B-field inside the wire and Eq. 37-17 for that outside the wire. The plot is as follows.

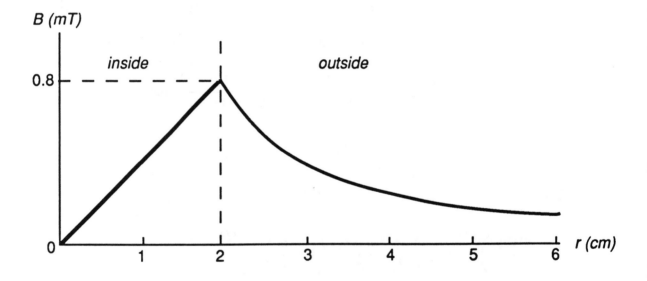

43E
The area enclosed by the loop L is $A = \dfrac{1}{2}(4d)(3d) = 6d^2$. Thus

$$\oint_c \mathbf{B} \cdot d\mathbf{s} = \mu_0 i = \mu_0 j A$$

$$= (1.26 \times 10^{-6}\,\text{T} \cdot \text{m/A})(15\,\text{A/m}^2)(6)(0.20\,\text{m})^2 = 4.5 \times 10^{-6}\,\text{T} \cdot \text{m}.$$

44P
Path 1:

$$\oint_1 \mathbf{B} \cdot d\mathbf{s} = \mu_0(-5.0\,\text{A} + 3.0\,\text{A}) = (-2.0\,\text{A})(1.26 \times 10^{-6}\,\text{T} \cdot \text{m/A})$$

$$= -2.5 \times 10^{-6}\,\text{m} \cdot \text{T}.$$

Path 2:

$$\oint_1 \mathbf{B} \cdot d\mathbf{s} = \mu_0(-5.0\,\text{A} - 5.0\,\text{A} - 3.0\,\text{A}) = (-13\,\text{A})(1.26 \times 10^{-6}\,\text{T} \cdot \text{m/A})$$

$$= -1.6 \times 10^{-5}\,\text{m} \cdot \text{T}.$$

45P
Use Ampere's law: $\oint \mathbf{B} \cdot d\mathbf{s} = \mu_0 i$, where the integral is around a closed loop and i is the net current through the loop. For the dotted loop shown on the diagram $i = 0$. The integral $\int \mathbf{B} \cdot d\mathbf{s}$ is zero along the bottom, right, and top sides of the loop. Along the right side the field is zero, along the top and bottom sides the field is perpendicular to $d\mathbf{s}$. If ℓ is the length of the left edge then direct integration yields $\oint \mathbf{B} \cdot d\mathbf{s} = B\ell$, where B is the magnitude of the field at the left side of the loop. Since neither B nor ℓ is zero, Ampere's law is contradicted. We conclude that the geometry shown for the magnetic field lines is in error. The lines actually bulge outward and their density decreases gradually, not precipitously as shown.

46P
(a) Consider the circular path L of radius r concentric with the cnductor:

$$\oint_L \mathbf{B} \cdot d\mathbf{s} = 2\pi r B(r) = \mu_0 i_{\text{enclosed}} = \mu_0 i \frac{\pi(r^2 - b^2)}{\pi(a^2 - b^2)}.$$

Thus

$$B(r) = \frac{\mu_0 i}{2\pi(a^2 - b^2)} \left(\frac{r^2 - b^2}{r} \right).$$

(b) At $r = a$,

$$B(a) = \frac{\mu_0 i}{2\pi(a^2 - b^2)} \left(\frac{a^2 - b^2}{a} \right) = \frac{\mu_0 i}{2\pi a}.$$

At $r = b$, $B(b) \propto r^2 - b^2 = 0$. For $b = 0$

$$B(r) = \frac{\mu_0 i}{2\pi a^2} \frac{r^2}{r} = \frac{\mu_0 i r}{2\pi a^2}.$$

817

47P

Use $\oint \mathbf{s} \cdot d\mathbf{B} = 2\pi r B = \mu_0 i_{\text{enclosed}}$, or $B = \mu_0 i_{\text{enclosed}}/2\pi r$.

(a) $r < c$:

$$B(r) = \frac{\mu_0 i_{\text{encl}}}{2\pi r} = \frac{\mu_0 i}{2\pi r}\left(\frac{\pi r^2}{\pi c^2}\right) = \frac{\mu_0 i r}{2\pi c^2}.$$

(b) $c < r < b$:

$$B(r) = \frac{\mu_0 i_{\text{encl}}}{2\pi r} = \frac{\mu_0 i}{2\pi r}.$$

(c) $b < r < a$:

$$B(r) = \frac{\mu_0 i_{\text{encl}}}{2\pi r} = \frac{\mu_0 i}{2\pi r}\left[1 - \frac{\pi(r^2 - b^2)}{\pi(a^2 - b^2)}\right]$$

$$= \frac{\mu_0 i (a^2 - r^2)}{2\pi r (a^2 - b^2)}.$$

(d) $r > a$:

$$B(r) = \frac{\mu_0 i_{\text{encl}}}{2\pi r} = 0.$$

(e) For example, check what happens if $b = c$. In this case the expressions in (a), (b) and (c) above should yield the same result at $r = b = c$. This is indeed the case.

(f)

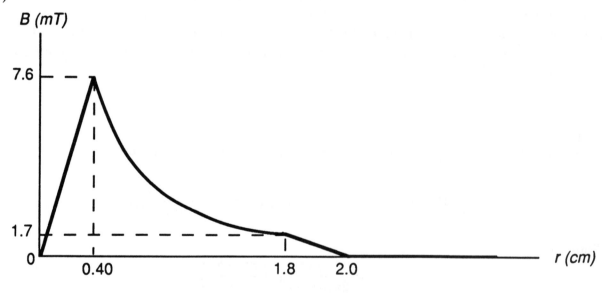

48P

For $r < a$,

$$B(r) = \frac{\mu_0 i_{\text{enclosed}}}{2\pi r} = \frac{\mu_0}{2\pi r}\int_0^r J(r)2\pi r\,dr = \frac{\mu_0}{2\pi}\int_0^r J_0\left(\frac{r}{a}\right)2\pi r\,dr$$

$$= \frac{\mu_0 J_0 r^2}{3a}.$$

818

49P

The field at the center of the pipe (point c) is due to the wire alone, with a magnitude of

$$B_c = \frac{\mu_0 i_{\text{wire}}}{2\pi(3R)} = \frac{\mu_0 i_{\text{wire}}}{6\pi R}.$$

For the wire we have $B_{p,\,\text{wire}} > B_{c,\,\text{wire}}$, so for $B_p = B_c = B_{c,\,\text{wire}}$, i_{wire} must be into the page:

$$B_p = B_{p,\,\text{wire}} - B_{p,\,\text{pipe}} = \frac{\mu_0 i_{\text{wire}}}{2\pi R} - \frac{\mu_0 i_0}{2\pi(2R)}.$$

Let $B_c = -B_p$ to obtain $i_{\text{wire}} = 3i_0/8$.

50P

(a) Take the magnetic field at a point within the hole to be the sum of the fields due to two current distributions. The first is the solid cylinder obtained by filling the hole and has a current density that is the same as that in the original cylinder with the hole. The second is the solid cylinder that fills the hole. It has a current density with the same magnitude as that of the original cylinder but it is in the opposite direction. Notice that if these two situations are superposed the total current in the region of the hole is zero.

Recall that a solid cylinder carrying current i, uniformly distributed over a cross section, produces a magnetic field with magnitude $B = \mu_0 ir/2\pi R^2$ a distance r from its axis, inside the cylinder. Here R is the radius of the cylinder.

For the cylinder of this problem the current density is

$$J = \frac{i}{A} = \frac{i}{\pi(a^2 - b^2)},$$

where A $(= \pi(a^2 - b^2))$ is the cross-sectional area of the cylinder with the hole. The current in the cylinder without the hole is

$$I_1 = JA = \pi J a^2 = \frac{ia^2}{a^2 - b^2}$$

and the magnetic field it produces at a point inside, a distance r_1 from its axis, has magnitude

$$B_1 = \frac{\mu_0 I_1 r_1}{2\pi a^2} = \frac{\mu_0 i r_1 a^2}{2\pi a^2 (a^2 - b^2)} = \frac{\mu_0 i r_1}{2\pi(a^2 - b^2)}.$$

The current in the cylinder that fills the hole is

$$I_2 = \pi J b^2 = \frac{ib^2}{a^2 - b^2}$$

and the field it produces at a point inside, a distance r_2 from the its axis, has magnitude

$$B_2 = \frac{\mu_0 I_2 r_2}{2\pi b^2} = \frac{\mu_0 i r_2 b^2}{2\pi b^2 (a^2 - b^2)} = \frac{\mu_0 i r_2}{2\pi(a^2 - b^2)}.$$

At the center of the hole this field is zero and the field there is exactly the same as it would be if the hole were filled. Place $r_1 = d$ in the expression for B_1 and obtain

$$B = \frac{\mu_0 i d}{2\pi(a^2 - b^2)}.$$

for the field at the center of the hole. The field points upward in the diagram if the current is out of the page.

(b) If $b = 0$ the formula for the field becomes

$$B = \frac{\mu_0 i d}{2\pi a^2}.$$

This correctly gives the field of a solid cylinder carrying a uniform current i, at a point inside the cylinder a distance d from the axis. If $d = 0$ the formula gives $B = 0$. This is correct for the field on the axis of a cylindrical shell carrying a uniform current.

(c) The diagram shows the situation in a cross-sectional plane of the cylinder. P is a point within the hole, A is on the axis of the cylinder, and C is on the axis of the hole. The magnetic field due to the cylinder without the hole, carrying a uniform current out of the page, is labeled $\mathbf{B_1}$ and the magnetic field of the cylinder that fills the hole, carrying a uniform current into the page, is labeled $\mathbf{B_2}$. The line from A to P makes the angle θ_1 with the line that joins the centers of the cylinders and the line from C to P makes the angle θ_2 with that line, as shown. $\mathbf{B_1}$ is perpendicular to the line from A to P and so makes the angle θ_1 with the vertical. Similarly, $\mathbf{B_2}$ is perpendicular to the line from C to P and so makes the angle θ_2 with the vertical.

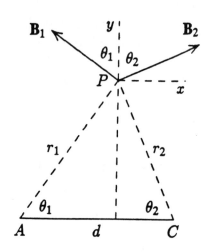

The x component of the total field is

$$B_x = B_2 \sin\theta_2 - B_1 \sin\theta_1 = \frac{\mu_0 i r_2}{2\pi(a^2 - b^2)} \sin\theta_2 - \frac{\mu_0 i r_1}{2\pi(a^2 - b^2)} \sin\theta_1$$

$$= \frac{\mu_0 i}{2\pi(a^2 - b^2)} [r_2 \sin\theta_2 - r_1 \sin\theta_1].$$

As the diagram shows $r_2 \sin\theta_2 = r_1 \sin\theta_1$, so $B_x = 0$. The y component is given by

$$B_y = B_2 \cos\theta_2 + B_1 \cos\theta_1 = \frac{\mu_0 i r_2}{2\pi(a^2 - b^2)} \cos\theta_2 + \frac{\mu_0 i r_1}{2\pi(a^2 - b^2)} \cos\theta_1$$

$$= \frac{\mu_0 i}{2\pi(a^2 - b^2)} [r_2 \cos\theta_2 + r_1 \cos\theta_1].$$

The diagram shows that $r_2 \cos\theta_2 + r_1 \cos\theta_1 = d$, so

$$B_y = \frac{\mu_0 i d}{2\pi(a^2 - b^2)}.$$

820

This is identical to the result found in part (a) for the field on the axis of the hole. It is independent of r_1, r_2, θ_1, and θ_2, showing that the field is uniform in the hole.

<u>**51P**</u>

(a) Suppose the field is not parallel to the sheet, as shown in the upper diagram. Reverse the direction of the current. According to the Biot-Savart law the field reverses, so it will be as in the second diagram. Now rotate the sheet by 180° about a line that perpendicular to the sheet. The field, of course, will rotate with it and end up in the direction shown in the bottom diagram. The current distribution is now exactly as it was originally, so the field must also be as it was originally. But it is not. Only if the field is parallel to the sheet will be final direction of the field be the same as the original direction. If the current is out of the page any infinitesimal portion of the sheet, in the form of a long straight wire, produces a field that is to the left above the sheet and to the right below the sheet. The field must be as drawn in Fig. 31–59.

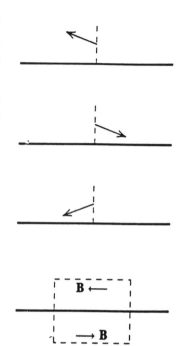

Integrate the tangential component of the magnetic field around the rectangular loop shown with dotted lines. The upper and lower edges are the same distance from the current sheet and each has length L. This means the field has the same magnitude along these edges. It points to the left along the upper edge and to the right along the lower.

If the integration is carried out in the counterclockwise sense the contribution of the upper edge is BL, the contribution of the lower edge is also BL, and the contribution of each of the sides is zero because the field is perpendicular to the sides. Thus $\oint \mathbf{B} \cdot d\mathbf{s} = 2BL$. The total current through the loop is λL. Ampere's law yields $2BL = \mu_0 \lambda L$, so $B = \mu_0 \lambda/2$.

<u>**52P***</u>

(a)

$$\oint_L \mathbf{B} \cdot d\mathbf{s} = \left(\int_1 + \int_2 + \int_3 + \int_4 \right) \mathbf{B} \cdot d\mathbf{s}$$

$$= \int_0^d [3.0\mathbf{i} + 8.0(x^2/d^2)\mathbf{j}] \cdot \mathbf{i}\,dx|_{y=0}$$

$$+ \int_0^d [3.0\mathbf{i} + 8.0(x^2/d^2)\mathbf{j}] \cdot \mathbf{j}\,dy|_{x=d}$$

$$+ \int_d^0 [3.0\mathbf{i} + 8.0(x^2/d^2)\mathbf{j}] \cdot \mathbf{i}\,dx|_{y=d}$$

$$+ \int_d^0 [3.0\mathbf{i} + 8.0(x^2/d^2)\mathbf{j}] \cdot \mathbf{j}\,dy|_{x=0}$$

$$= 3.0d + 8.0d - 3.0d = (8.0d)\,\text{mT},$$

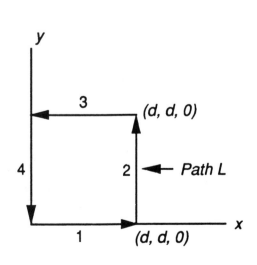

821

where d is in meters.

(b) From $\oint_L \mathbf{B} \cdot d\mathbf{s} = (8.0d)\,\text{mT} = \mu_0 i_{\text{enclosed}}$, we get

$$i_{\text{enclosed}} = \frac{(8.0d)\,\text{mT}}{\mu_0} = \frac{(8.0)(0.50)(10^{-3}\,\text{T})}{1.26 \times 10^{-6}\,\text{T}\cdot\text{m/A}} = 3.2 \times 10^3\,\text{A}.$$

(c) Since $\oint_L \mathbf{B} \cdot d\mathbf{s} > 0$, $i_{\text{enclosed}} > 0$ is in the $+\mathbf{k}$ direction.

53E

$$B = \mu_0 i_0 n = (1.26 \times 10^{-6}\,\text{T}\cdot\text{m/A})(3.60\,\text{A})(1200/0.950\,\text{m}) = 5.73 \times 10^{-3}\,\text{T}.$$

54E

The magnetic field inside an ideal solenoid is given by Eq. 31–21. The number of turns per unit length is $n = (200\,\text{turns})/(0.25\,\text{m}) = 800\,\text{turns/m}$. Thus

$$B = \mu_0 n i_0 = (4\pi \times 10^{-7}\,\text{T}\cdot\text{m/A})(800\,\text{m}^{-1})(0.30\,\text{A}) = 3.0 \times 10^{-4}\,\text{T}.$$

55E

Solve N, the number of turns of the solenoid, from $B = \mu_0 i n = \mu_0 i N/L$: $N = BL/\mu_0 i$. Thus the length of the wire is

$$l = 2\pi r N = \frac{2\pi r B L}{\mu_0 i}$$

$$= \frac{2\pi(2.60 \times 10^{-2}\,\text{m})(23.0 \times 10^{-3}\,\text{T})(1.30\,\text{m})}{2(1.26 \times 10^{-6}\,\text{T}\cdot\text{m/A})(18.0\,\text{A})} = 108\,\text{m}.$$

56E

(a) Use Eq. 31–22. The inner radius is $r = 15.0\,\text{cm}$ so the field there is

$$B = \frac{\mu_0 i_0 N}{2\pi r} = \frac{(4\pi \times 10^{-7}\,\text{T}\cdot\text{m/A})(0.800\,\text{A})(500)}{2\pi(0.150\,\text{m})} = 5.33 \times 10^{-4}\,\text{T}.$$

(b) The outer radius is $r = 20.0\,\text{cm}$. The field there is

$$B = \frac{\mu_0 i_0 N}{2\pi r} = \frac{(4\pi \times 10^{-7}\,\text{T}\cdot\text{m/A})(0.800\,\text{A})(500)}{2\pi(0.200\,\text{m})} = 4.00 \times 10^{-4}\,\text{T}.$$

57E

In this case $L = 2\pi r$ is roughly the length of the toroid so

$$B = \mu_0 i_0 \left(\frac{N}{2\pi r} \right) = \mu_0 n i_0.$$

This result is expected because from the perspective of a point inside the toroid, the portion of the toroid in the vicinity of the point resembles part of a long solenoid.

58P

Use $B = \mu_0 i_0 n$ and note that $n i_0 = \lambda$. Thus $B = \mu_0 \lambda$. Also from Problem 51 we have $\Delta B = \frac{1}{2}\mu_0 \lambda - (-\frac{1}{2}\mu_0 \lambda) = \mu_0 \lambda$ as we move through an infinite plane current sheet of current density λ.

59P

Consider a circle of radius r, inside the toroid and concentric with it. The current that passes through the region between the circle and the outer rim of the toroid is $N i_0$, where N is the number of turns and i_0 is the current. The current per unit length of circle is $\lambda = N i_0 / 2\pi r$ and $\mu_0 \lambda$ is $\mu_0 N i_0 / 2\pi r$, the magnitude of the magnetic field at the circle. Since the field is zero outside a toroid, this is also the change in the magnitude of the field encountered as you move from the circle to the outside.

The equality is not really surprising in light of Ampere's law. You are moving perpendicularly to the magnetic field lines. Consider an extremely narrow loop, with the narrow sides along field lines and the two long sides perpendicular to the field lines. If B_1 is the field at one end and B_2 is the field at the other end then $\oint \mathbf{B} \cdot d\mathbf{s} = (B_2 - B_1)w$, where w is the width of the loop. The current through the loop is $w\lambda$, so Ampere's law yields $(B_2 - B_1)w = \mu_0 w\lambda$ and $B_2 - B_1 = \mu_0 \lambda$.

60P

(a) Denote the B-fields at point P due to the solenoid and the wire as $\mathbf{B}_s$ and $\mathbf{B}_w$. Since $\mathbf{B}_s$ is along the axis of the solenoid and $\mathbf{B}_w$ is perpendicular to it, $\mathbf{B}_s \perp \mathbf{B}_w$. For the net field $\mathbf{B}$ to be at 45° with the axis we then must have $B_s = B_w$. Thus

$$B_s = \mu_0 i_s n = B_w = \frac{\mu_0 i_w}{2\pi d},$$

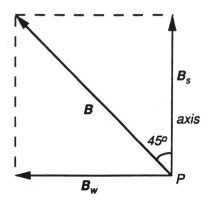

which gives the separation d fo point P the axis:

$$d = \frac{i_w}{2\pi i_s n} = \frac{6.00\,\text{A}}{2\pi(20.0 \times 10^{-3}\,\text{A})(10\,\text{turns}/\,\text{cm})} = 4.77\,\text{cm}.$$

(b) $B = \sqrt{2}B_s = \sqrt{2}(1.26 \times 10^{-6}\,\text{T} \cdot \text{m/A})(20.0 \times 10^{-3}\,\text{A})(10\,\text{turns}/0.0100\,\text{m}) = 3.55 \times 10^{-5}\,\text{T}$.

61P

Let

$$r = \frac{mv}{eB} = \frac{mv}{e\mu_0 ni}$$

and solve for i:

$$i = \frac{mv}{e\mu_0 nr}$$

$$= \frac{(9.11 \times 10^{-31}\,\text{kg})(0.0460)(3.00 \times 10^8\,\text{m/s})}{(1.60 \times 10^{-19}\,\text{C})(1.26 \times 10^{-6}\,\text{T} \cdot \text{m/A})(100/0.0100\,\text{m})(2.30 \times 10^{-2}\,\text{m})}$$

$$= 0.272\,\text{A}.$$

62P

(a) The magnetic force must be directed toward the center of the orbit. For the particle orbit shown $\mathbf{v} \times \mathbf{B}$ is away from the orbit center, so the particle must be negative.

(b) The radius of curvature is given by

$$R = \frac{mv}{qB} \,,$$

where B is the local magnitude of the magnetic field, v is the particle speed, m is the particle mass, and q is the particle charge. The magnetic field does no work on the particle and so does not change its kinetic energy or speed. This means for two different points in the toroid $R_1 B_1 = R_2 B_2$. The magnetic field is given by

$$B = \frac{\mu_0 i_0 N}{2\pi r} \,,$$

where r is the distance from the toroid center. This means $r_1 B_1 = r_2 B_2$. Divide the first equation by the second to obtain $R_1/r_1 = R_2/r_2$. Thus

$$R_2 = \frac{r_2}{r_1} R_1 = \frac{110\,\text{cm}}{125\,\text{cm}}(11.0\,\text{cm}) = 9.68\,\text{cm} \,.$$

63E

The magnitude of the dipole moment is given by $\mu = NiA$, where N is the number of turns, i is the current, and A is the area. Use $A = \pi R^2$, where R is the radius. Thus

$$\mu = (200)(0.30\,\text{A})\pi(0.050\,\text{m})^2 = 0.47\,\text{A} \cdot \text{m}^2 \,.$$

64E

(a) Use Eq. 31-24 and set $z = 0$: $B(0) \propto i/R$. Since case b has two loops, we have

$$\frac{B_b}{B_a} = \frac{2i/R_b}{i/R_a} = \frac{2R_a}{R_b} = 4.$$

(b)

$$\frac{\mu_b}{\mu_a} = \frac{2iA_b}{iA_a} = \frac{2R_b^2}{R_a^2} = 2\left(\frac{1}{2}\right)^2 = \frac{1}{2}.$$

65E

Use Eq. 31-24 and note that the contribute to $\mathbf{B}_p$ due to the two coils are the same. Thus

$$B_p = \frac{2\mu_0 i R^2 N}{2[R^2 + (R/2)^2]^{3/2}} = \frac{8\mu_0 N i}{5\sqrt{5}R}.$$

$\mathbf{B}_p$ is in the $+x$ direction.

66E

(a) As for Exercise 63, the magnitude of the dipole moment is given by $\mu = NiA$, where N is the number of turns, i is the current, and A is the area. Use $A = \pi R^2$, where R is the radius. Thus

$$\mu = Ni\pi R^2 = (300)(4.0 \, \text{A})\pi(0.025 \, \text{m})^2 = 2.36 \, \text{A} \cdot \text{m}^2 \, .$$

(b) The magnetic field on the axis of a magnetic dipole, a distance z away, is given by Eq. 31–25:

$$B = \frac{\mu_0}{2\pi} \frac{\mu}{z^3} \, .$$

Solve for z:

$$z = \left[\frac{\mu_0}{2\pi} \frac{\mu}{B}\right]^{1/3} = \left[\frac{4\pi \times 10^{-7} \, \text{T} \cdot \text{m/A}}{2\pi} \frac{2.36 \, \text{A} \cdot \text{m}^2}{5.0 \times 10^{-6} \, \text{T}}\right]^{1/3} = 46 \, \text{cm}.$$

67E

(a) For $x \gg a$ the result of Problem 20 reduces to

$$B(x) \approx \frac{4\mu_0 i a^2}{\pi(4x^2)(4x^2)^{1/2}} = \frac{\mu_0(ia^2)}{4\pi x^3},$$

indeed the B-field of a magnetic dipole (see Eq. 31-25).

(b) $\mu = ia^2$, by comparision between Eq. 31-25 and the result above.

68P

(a) The two straight segments of the wire do not contribute to $\mathbf{B}_p$. For the larger semicircular loop $B_{p1} = \mu_0 i / 4b$ (see Problem 13) and for the smaller one $B_{p2} = \mu_0 i / 4a$. Thus

$$B_p = B_{p1} + B_{p2} = \frac{\mu_0 i}{4}\left(\frac{1}{a} + \frac{1}{b}\right).$$

$\mathbf{B}_p$ points into the page.

(b) $\mu = A_{\text{loop}} i = \frac{1}{2}(\pi a^2 + \pi b^2)i$, pointing into the page.

69P

Use Eq. 31-24 to obtain

$$B(x) = \frac{\mu_0 i R^2}{2}\left[\left(\frac{1}{R^2 + (x - R/2)^2}\right)^{3/2} + \left(\frac{1}{R^2 + (x + R/2)^2}\right)^{3/2}\right].$$

The plot of B(x) is as follows. Note that $B(x)$ is almost a constant in the vicinity of $x = 0$.

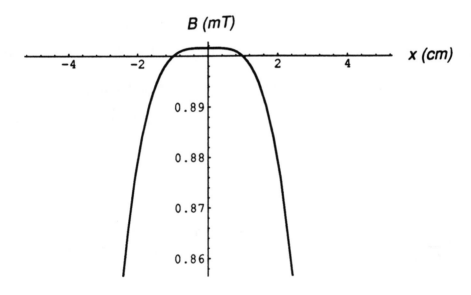

70P

(a) The magnitude of the magnetic field on the axis of a circular loop, a distance z from the loop center, is given by Eq. 31–24:

$$B = \frac{N\mu_0 i R^2}{2(R^2 + z^2)^{3/2}},$$

where R is the radius of the loop, N is the number of turns, and i is the current. Both of the loops in the problem have the same radius, the same number of turns, and carry the same current. The currents are in the same sense and the fields they produce are in the same direction in the region between them. Place the origin at the center of the left-hand loop and let x be the coordinate of a point on the axis between the loops. To calculate the field of the left-hand loop set $z = x$ in the equation above. The chosen point on the axis is a distance $s - x$ from the center of the right-hand loop. To calculate the field it produces put $z = s - x$ in the equation above. The total field at the point is therefore

$$B = \frac{N\mu_0 i R^2}{2}\left[\frac{1}{(R^2 + x^2)^{3/2}} + \frac{1}{(R^2 + x^2 - 2sx + s^2)^{3/2}}\right].$$

Its derivative with respect to x is

$$\frac{dB}{dx} = -\frac{N\mu_0 i R^2}{2}\left[\frac{3x}{(R^2 + x^2)^{5/2}} + \frac{3(x - s)}{(R^2 + x^2 - 2sx + s^2)^{5/2}}\right].$$

When this is evaluated for $x = s/2$ (the midpoint between the loops) the result is

$$\left.\frac{dB}{dx}\right|_{s/2} = -\frac{N\mu_0 i R^2}{2}\left[\frac{3s/2}{(R^2 + s^2/4)^{5/2}} - \frac{3s/2}{(R^2 + s^2/4 - s^2 + s^2)^{5/2}}\right] = 0,$$

independently of the value of s.

(b) The second derivative is

$$\frac{d^2 B}{dx^2} = \frac{N\mu_0 i R^2}{2}\left[-\frac{3}{(R^2 + x^2)^{5/2}} + \frac{15x^2}{(R^2 + x^2)^{7/2}}\right.$$

$$\left. - \frac{3}{(R^2 + x^2 - 2sx + s^2)^{5/2}} + \frac{15(x - s)^2}{(R^2 + x^2 - 2sx + s^2)^{7/2}}\right].$$

At $x = s/2$,

$$\left.\frac{d^2 B}{dx^2}\right|_{s/2} = \frac{N\mu_0 i R^2}{2}\left[-\frac{6}{(R^2 + s^2/4)^{5/2}} + \frac{30s^2/4}{(R^2 + s^2/4)^{7/2}}\right]$$

$$= \frac{N\mu_0 R^2}{2}\frac{-6(R^2 + s^2/4) + 30s^2/4}{(R^2 + s^2/4)^{7/2}} = 3N\mu_0 i R^2 \frac{s^2 - R^2}{(R^2 + s^2/4)^{7/2}}.$$

Clearly, this is zero if $s = R$.

71P
Denote the large/small loops with subscripts 1 and 2.

(a)

$$B_1 = \frac{\mu_0 i_1}{2R_1} = \frac{(1.26 \times 10^{-6}\,\text{T} \cdot \text{m/A})(15\,\text{A})}{2(0.12\,\text{m})} = 7.9 \times 10^{-5}\,\text{T}.$$

(b)

$$\tau = |\vec{\mu}_2 \times \mathbf{B}_1| = \mu B_1 \sin 90° = N_2 i_2 A_2 B_1 = \pi N_2 i_2 r_2^2 B_1$$
$$= \pi(50)(1.3\,\text{A})(0.82 \times 10^{-2}\,\text{m})^2(7.9 \times 10^{-5}\,\text{T}) = 1.1 \times 10^{-6}\,\text{N} \cdot \text{m}.$$

72P

(a) By imagining that both bg and cf have a pair of currents of the same magnitude $(= i)$ and opposite direction, you can justify the superposition.

(b)

$$\vec{\mu} = \vec{\mu}_{bcfgb} + \vec{\mu}_{abgha} + \vec{\mu}_{cdefc}$$
$$= (ia^2)(\mathbf{j} - \mathbf{i} + \mathbf{i}) = ia^2\mathbf{j}$$
$$= (6.0\,\text{A})(0.10\,\text{m})^2\mathbf{j} + (6.0 \times 10^{-2}\,\text{m}^2 \cdot \text{A})\mathbf{j}.$$

(c) Since both the points are far from the cube we can use the dipole approximation. For $(x, y, z) = (0, 5.0\,\text{m}, 0)$

$$\mathbf{B}(0, 5.0\,\text{m}, 0) = \frac{\mu_0}{2\pi}\frac{\vec{\mu}}{y^3} = \frac{(1.26 \times 10^{-6}\,\text{T} \cdot \text{m/A})(6.0 \times 10^{-2}\,\text{m}^2 \cdot \text{A})\mathbf{j}}{2\pi(5.0\,\text{m})^3} = (9.6 \times 10^{-11}\,\text{T})\mathbf{j}.$$

For $(x, y, z) = (5.0\,\text{m}, 0, 0)$, note that the line joining the and point of interest and the location of the dipole is perpendicular to the axis of the dipole. You can check easily that if an electric dipole is used, the field would be $E \approx (1/4\pi\epsilon_0)(p/x^3)$, which is half of the value of E for a point on the axis the same distance from the dipole. By analogy, in our case B is also half the value of $(B(0, 5.0\,\text{m}, 0)$, i.e.

$$B(5.0\,\text{m}, 0, 0) = \frac{1}{2}B(0, 5.0\,\text{m}, 0) = \frac{9.6 \times 10^{-11}\,\text{T}}{2} = 4.8 \times 10^{-11}\,\text{T}.$$

$\mathbf{B}(5.0\,\text{m}, 0, 0)$ points in the $+x$ direction.

73P

(a) Contribution to B_c from the straight segment of the wire:

$$B_{c1} = \frac{\mu_0 i}{2\pi R}.$$

Contribution from the circular loop:

$$B_{c2} = \frac{\mu_0 i}{2R}.$$

Thus

$$B_c = B_{c1} + B_{c2} = \frac{\mu_0 i}{2R}\left(1 + \frac{1}{\pi}\right).$$

$\mathbf{B}_c$ points out of the page.

(b) Now $\mathbf{B}_{c1} \perp \mathbf{B}_{c2}$ so

$$B_c = \sqrt{B_{c1}^2 + B_{c2}^2} = \frac{\mu_0 i}{2R}\sqrt{1 + \frac{1}{\pi^2}},$$

and $\mathbf{B}_c$ is at an angle θ out of the page, where

$$\theta = \tan^{-1}\left(\frac{B_{c1}}{B_{c2}}\right) = \tan^{-1}\left(\frac{1}{\pi}\right) = 18°.$$

CHAPTER 32

1E

$$\Phi_B = \int \mathbf{B} \cdot d\mathbf{A} = BA \cos 57° = (4.2 \times 10^{-6}\,\text{T})(2.5\,\text{m}^2)(\cos 57°) = 5.7 \times 10^{-5}\,\text{Wb}.$$

2E

$$\varepsilon = -\frac{d\Phi_B}{dt} = -\frac{d(BA)}{dt} = -A\frac{dB}{dt} = -A\frac{dB}{dt} = -A\frac{d}{dt}(\mu_0 in) = -A\mu_0 n\frac{d}{dt}(i_0 \sin\omega t)$$
$$= -A\mu_0 n i_0 \omega \cos\omega t.$$

3E

The magnetic field is normal to the plane of the loop and is uniform over the loop. Thus at any instant the magnetic flux through the loop is given by $\Phi_B = AB = \pi r^2 B$, where A $(= \pi r^2)$ is the area of the loop. According to Faraday's law the magnitude of the emf in the loop is

$$\varepsilon = \frac{d\Phi_B}{dt} = \pi r^2 \frac{dB}{dt} = \pi(0.055\,\text{m})^2(0.16\,\text{T/s}) = 1.5 \times 10^{-3}\,\text{V}.$$

4E

$$\varepsilon = -\frac{d\Phi_B}{dt} = -A\frac{dB}{dt} = -\pi r^2 \frac{d}{dt}(B_0 e^{-t/\tau}) = \frac{\pi r^2 B_0 e^{-t/\tau}}{\tau}.$$

5E
(a)

$$|\varepsilon| = \left|\frac{d\Phi_B}{dt}\right| = \frac{d}{dt}(6.0t^2 + 7.0t) = 12t + 7.0$$
$$= 12(2.0) + 7.0 = 31\,\text{mV}.$$

From right to left.

6E

Use $\varepsilon = -d\Phi_B/dt = -\pi r^2 dB/dt$

(a) For $0 < t < 2.0\,\text{s}$:

$$\varepsilon = -\pi r^2 \frac{dB}{dt} = -\pi(0.12\,\text{m})^2 \left(\frac{0.5\,\text{T}}{2.0\,\text{s}}\right) = -1.1 \times 10^{-2}\,\text{V}.$$

(b) $2.0\,\text{s} < t < 4.0\,\text{s} : \varepsilon \propto dB/dt = 0$.

(c) $4.0\,\text{s} < t < 6.0\,\text{s}$:

$$\varepsilon = -\pi r^2 \frac{dB}{dt} = -\pi(0.12\,\text{m})^2 \left(\frac{-0.5\,\text{T}}{6.0\,\text{s} - 4.0\,\text{s}}\right) = 1.1 \times 10^{-2}\,\text{V}.$$

7E

$$U_{\text{thermal}} = P_{\text{thermal}}\Delta t = \frac{\varepsilon^2 \Delta t}{R} = \frac{1}{R}\left(-\frac{d\Phi_B}{dt}\right)^2 \Delta t = \frac{1}{R}\left(-A\frac{\Delta B}{\Delta t}\right)^2 \Delta t = \frac{A^2 B^2}{R\Delta t}.$$

8E

(a)

$$R = \rho\frac{L}{A} = (1.68 \times 10^{-8}\,\Omega \cdot \text{m})\left[\frac{\pi(0.10\,\text{m})}{\pi(2.5 \times 10^{-3})^2/4}\right]$$

$$= 1.1 \times 10^{-3}\,\Omega.$$

(b) Use $i = |\varepsilon|/R = |d\Phi_B/dt|/R = (\pi r^2/R)|dB/dt|$. Thus

$$\left|\frac{dB}{dt}\right| = \frac{iR}{\pi r^2} = \frac{(10\,\text{A})(1.1 \times 10^{-3}\,\Omega)}{\pi(0.10\,\text{m})^2/4} = 1.4\,\text{T/s}.$$

9P

(a)

$$\varepsilon = N\frac{d\Phi_B}{dt} = N\frac{d(BA)}{dt}$$

$$= NA\frac{d}{dt}(\mu_0 ni) = N\left(\frac{\pi d^2}{4}\right)\mu_0 n\frac{di}{dt}$$

$$= N\left(\frac{\pi d^2}{4}\right)\mu_0 n\frac{d}{dt}(3.0t + 1.0t^2)$$

$$= \frac{\pi d^2 N\mu_0 n(3.0 + 2.0t)}{4}.$$

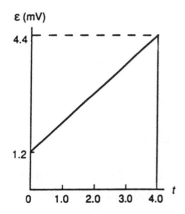

831

(b)

$$i|_{t=2.0\,\text{s}} = \frac{\varepsilon|_{t=2.0\,\text{s}}}{R} = \frac{\pi d^2 N \mu_0 n(3.0 + 2.0t)}{4R}$$

$$= \frac{\pi(2.1 \times 10^{-2}\,\text{m})^2(130)(1.26 \times 10^{-6}\,\text{T} \cdot \text{m/A})(2.2\,\text{turns/m})[3.0 + (2.0)(2.0)](\text{A/s})}{4(0.15\,\Omega)}$$

$$= 5.8 \times 10^{-2}\,\text{A}.$$

10P

(a) The magnitude of the magnetic field inside the solenoid is $B = \mu_0 n i_s$, where n is the number of turns per unit length and i_s is the current. The field is parallel to the solenoid axis, so the flux through a cross section of the solenoid is $\Phi_B = A_s B = \mu_0 \pi r_s^2 n i_s$, where A_s ($= \pi r_s^2$) is the cross-sectional area of the solenoid. Since the magnetic field is zero outside the solenoid this is also the flux through the coil. The emf in the coil has magnitude

$$\varepsilon = \frac{N d\Phi}{dt} = \mu_0 \pi r_s^2 N n \frac{di_s}{dt}$$

and the current in the coil is

$$i_c = \frac{\varepsilon}{R} = \frac{\mu_0 \pi r_s^2 N n}{R} \frac{di_s}{dt},$$

where N is the number of turns in the coil and R is the resistance of the coil. According to Sample Problem 32–1 the current changes linearly by 3.0 A in 50 ms, so $di_s/dt = (3.0\,\text{A})/(50 \times 10^{-3}\,\text{s}) = 60\,\text{A/s}$. Thus

$$i_c = \frac{(4\pi \times 10^{-7}\,\text{T} \cdot \text{m/A})\pi(0.016\,\text{m})^2(120)(220 \times 10^2\,\text{m}^{-1})}{5.3\,\Omega} = 30 \times 10^{-2}\,\text{A}.$$

(b) As the magnetic field changes, an electric field appears and affects the motions of the conduction electrons in the coil. See Chapter 32.

11P

$$\varepsilon = -\frac{d\Phi_B}{dt} = -\frac{d(BA)}{dt} = -A\frac{d}{dt}(\mu_0 n i) = -\mu_0 n \pi r^2 \frac{di}{dt}$$

$$= -(1.26 \times 10^{-6}\,\text{T} \cdot \text{m/A})(1.00\,\text{turns/m})(\pi)(25 \times 10^{-3}\,\text{m})^2\left(\frac{0.50\,\text{A} - 1.0\,\text{A}}{10 \times 10^{-3}\,\text{s}}\right)$$

$$= 1.2 \times 10^{-3}\,\text{V}.$$

Note that since **B** only apperas inside the solenoid the area A should be the cross-sectional area of the solenoid, not the (large) loops.

12P

Consider the cross-section of the toroid. The magnetic flux through the shaded area as shown is $d\Phi_B = B(r)dA = B(r)hdr$. Thus from Eq. 31-22

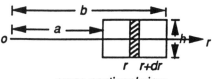

cross-sectional view

$$\Phi_B = \int_a^b B(r)hdr = \int_a^b \frac{\mu_0 i_0 Nh}{2\pi} \frac{1}{r}dr = \frac{\mu_0 iNh}{2\pi}\ln\frac{b}{a}.$$

13P

$$\Phi_B = BA = \left(\frac{\mu_0 i_0 N}{2\pi r}\right)A$$

$$= \frac{(1.26 \times 10^{-6}\,\text{T}\cdot\text{m/A})(0.800\,\text{A})(500)(5.00 \times 10^{-2}\,\text{m})^2}{2\pi(0.150\,\text{m} + 0.0500\,\text{m/2})} = 1.16 \times 10^{-6}\,\text{Wb}.$$

14P

Thermal energy is generated at the rate ε^2/R, where ε is the emf in the wire and R is the resistance of the wire. The resistance is given by $R = \rho L/A$, where ρ is the resistivity of copper, L is the length of the wire, and A is the cross-sectional area of the wire. The resistivity can be found in Table 28–1. Thus

$$R = \frac{(1.69 \times 10^{-8}\,\Omega\cdot\text{m})(0.500\,\text{m})}{\pi(0.500 \times 10^{-3}\,\text{m})^2} = 1.076 \times 10^{-2}\,\Omega.$$

Faraday's law is used to find the emf. If B is the magnitude of the magnetic field through the loop, then $\varepsilon = A\,dB/dt$, where A is the area of the loop. The radius r of the loop is $r = L/2\pi$ and its area is $\pi r^2 = \pi L^2/4\pi^2 = L^2/4\pi$. Thus

$$\varepsilon = \frac{L^2}{4\pi}\frac{dB}{dt} = \frac{(0.500\,\text{m})^2}{4\pi}(10.0 \times 10^{-3}\,\text{T/s}) = 1.989 \times 10^{-4}\,\text{V}.$$

The rate of thermal energy generation is

$$P = \frac{\varepsilon^2}{R} = \frac{(1.989 \times 10^{-4}\,\text{V})^2}{1.076 \times 10^{-2}\,\Omega} = 3.68 \times 10^{-6}\,\text{W}.$$

15P

The magnetic flus Φ_B through the loop is given by $\Phi_B = 2B(\pi r^2/2)(\cos 45°) = \pi r^2 B/\sqrt{2}$. Thus

$$\varepsilon = -\frac{d\Phi_B}{dt} = -\frac{d}{dt}\left(\frac{\pi r^2 B}{\sqrt{2}}\right) = -\frac{\pi r^2}{\sqrt{2}}\left(\frac{\Delta B}{\Delta t}\right)$$

$$= -\frac{\pi(3.7 \times 10^{-2}\,\mathrm{m})^2}{\sqrt{2}}\left(\frac{0 - 76 \times 10^{-3}\,\mathrm{T}}{4.5 \times 10^{-3}\,\mathrm{s}}\right) = 5.1 \times 10^{-2}\,\mathrm{V}.$$

The direction of the induced current is clockwise when viewed along the direction of **B**.

16P

(a) In the region of the smaller loop the magnetic field produced by the larger loop may be taken to be uniform and equal to its value at the center of the smaller loop, on the axis. Eq. 31–24, with $z = x$ and much greater than R, gives

$$B = \frac{\mu_0 i R^2}{2x^3}$$

for the magnitude. The field is upward in the diagram. The magnetic flux through the smaller loop is the product of this field and the area (πr^2) of the smaller loop:

$$\Phi_B = \frac{\pi \mu_0 i r^2 R^2}{2x^3}.$$

(b) The emf is given by Faraday's law:

$$\varepsilon = -\frac{d\Phi_B}{dt} = -\left(\frac{\pi \mu_0 i r^2 R^2}{2}\right)\frac{d}{dt}\left(\frac{1}{x^3}\right) = -\left(\frac{\pi \mu_0 i r^2 R^2}{2}\right)\left(-\frac{3}{x^4}\frac{dx}{dt}\right) = \frac{3\pi \mu_0 i r^2 R^2 v}{2x^4}.$$

(c) The field of the larger loop is upward and decreases with distance away from the loop. As the smaller loop moves away the flux through it decreases. The induced current will be directed so as to produce a magnetic field that is upward through the smaller loop, in the same direction as the field of the larger loop. It will be counterclockwise as viewed from above, in the same direction as the current in the larger loop.

17P

(a) The emf induced around the loop is given by Faraday's law: $\varepsilon = -d\Phi_B/dt$ and the current in the loop is given by $i = \varepsilon/R = -(1/R)(d\Phi_B/dt)$. The charge that passes through the resistor from time zero to time t is given by the integral

$$q = \int_0^t i\,dt = -\frac{1}{R}\int_0^t \frac{d\Phi_B}{dt}\,dt = -\frac{1}{R}\int_{\Phi_B(0)}^{\Phi_B(t)} d\Phi_B = \frac{1}{R}\left[\Phi_B(0) - \Phi_B(t)\right].$$

All that matters is the change in the flux, not how it was changed.

(b) If $\Phi_B(t) = \Phi_B(0)$ then $q = 0$. This does not mean that the current was zero for any extended time during the interval. If Φ_B increases and then decreases back to its original value there is current in the resistor while Φ_B is changing. It is in one direction at first, then in the opposite direction. When equal charge has passed through the resistor in opposite directions the net charge is zero.

18P

From the result of Problem 17

$$q = \frac{1}{R}[\Phi_B(0) - \Phi_B(t)] = \frac{A}{R}[B(0) - B(t)]$$

$$= \frac{1.20 \times 10^{-3}\,\text{m}^2}{13.0\,\Omega}[1.60\,\text{T} - (-1.60\,\text{T})] = 2.95 \times 10^{-2}\,\text{C}.$$

19P

(a) The area A of the loop exposed to the magnetic field is $A = a^2/2$ where $a = 2.00\,\text{m}$. Thus

$$\varepsilon_{\text{induced}} = -\frac{d\Phi_B}{dt} = -A\frac{dB}{dt} = -\frac{a^2}{2}\frac{d}{dt}(0.042 - 0.870t)$$

$$= \frac{(0.870)(2.00\,\text{m})^2}{2} = 1.70\,\text{V}.$$

From Lenz's law you can easily check that $\varepsilon_{\text{induced}}$ and the voltage drop V across the battery enhance each other. So

$$\varepsilon_{\text{total}} = \varepsilon_{\text{induced}} + V = 1.70\,\text{V} + 20.0\,\text{V} = 21.7\,\text{V}.$$

(b) The current is counterclockwise.

20P

(a) The magnetic flux Φ_B through the loop is

$$\Phi = \int \mathbf{B} \cdot d\mathbf{A} = \frac{1}{4}\pi r^2 B.$$

Thus

$$|\varepsilon| = \left|\frac{d\Phi_B}{dt}\right| = \left|\frac{d}{dt}\left(\frac{1}{4}\pi r^2 B\right)\right| = \frac{\pi r^2}{4}\left|\frac{dB}{dt}\right|$$

$$= \frac{\pi(0.10\,\text{m})^2(3.0 \times 10^{-3}\,\text{T}/\text{s})}{4} = 2.4 \times 10^{-5}\,\text{V}.$$

(b) From c to b (due to Lenz's law).

21P*

(a) Suppose each wire has radius R and the distance between their axes is a. Consider a single wire and calculate the flux through a rectangular area with the axis of the wire along one side. Take this side to have length L and the other dimension of the rectangle to be a. The magnetic field is everywhere perpendicular to the rectangle. First consider the part of the rectangle that is inside the wire. The field a distance r from the axis is given by $B = \mu_0 ir/2\pi R^2$ and the flux through the strip of length L and width dr at that distance is $(\mu_0 ir/2\pi R^2)L\,dr$. Thus the flux through the area inside the wire is

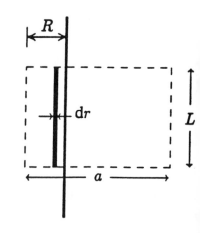

$$\Phi_{\text{in}} = \int_0^R \frac{\mu_0 iL}{2\pi R^2}\, r\,dr = \frac{\mu_0 iL}{4\pi}\,.$$

Now consider the region outside the wire. There the field is given by $B = \mu_0 i/2\pi r$ and the flux through an infinitesimally thin strip is $(\mu_0 i/2\pi r)L\,dr$. The flux through the whole region is

$$\Phi_{\text{out}} = \int_R^a \frac{\mu_0 iL}{2\pi}\,\frac{dr}{r} = \frac{\mu_0 iL}{2\pi}\ln\left(\frac{a}{R}\right)\,.$$

The total flux through the area bounded by the dotted lines is the sum of the two contributions:

$$\Phi = \frac{\mu_0 iL}{4\pi}\left[1 + 2\ln\left(\frac{a}{R}\right)\right]\,.$$

Now include the contribution of the other wire. Since the currents are in the same direction the two contributions have the same sign. They also have the same magnitude, so

$$\Phi_{\text{total}} = \frac{\mu_0 iL}{2\pi}\left[1 + 2\ln\left(\frac{a}{R}\right)\right]\,.$$

The total flux per unit length is

$$\frac{\Phi_{\text{total}}}{L} = \frac{\mu_0 i}{2\pi}\left[1 + 2\ln\left(\frac{a}{R}\right)\right] = \frac{(4\pi \times 10^{-7}\,\text{T}\cdot\text{m/A})(10\,\text{A})}{2\pi}\left[1 + 2\ln\left(\frac{20\,\text{mm}}{1.25\,\text{mm}}\right)\right]$$
$$= 1.31 \times 10^{-5}\,\text{Wb/m}\,.$$

(b) Again consider the flux of a single wire. The flux inside the wire itself is again $\Phi_{\text{in}} = \mu_0 iL/4\pi$. The flux inside the region of the other wire is

$$\Phi_{\text{out}} = \int_{a-R}^a \frac{\mu_0 iL}{2\pi}\,\frac{dr}{r} = \frac{\mu_0 iL}{2\pi}\ln\left(\frac{a}{a-R}\right)\,.$$

836

Double this to include the flux of the other wire (inside the first wire) and divide by L to obtain the flux per unit length. The total flux per unit length that is inside the wires is

$$\frac{\Phi_{\text{wires}}}{L} = \frac{\mu_0 i}{2\pi}\left[1 + 2\ln\left(\frac{a}{a-R}\right)\right]$$
$$= \frac{(4\pi \times 10^{-7}\,\text{T}\cdot\text{m/A})(10\,\text{A})}{2\pi}\left[1 + 2\ln\left(\frac{20\,\text{mm}}{20\,\text{mm} - 1.25\,\text{mm}}\right)\right]$$
$$= 2.26 \times 10^{-6}\,\text{Wb/m}.$$

The fraction of the total flux that is inside the wires is

$$\frac{2.26 \times 10^{-6}\,\text{Wb/m}}{1.31 \times 10^{-5}\,\text{Wb/m}} = 0.17.$$

(c) The contributions of the two wires to the total flux have the same magnitudes but now the currents are in opposite directions, so the contributions have opposite signs. This means $\Phi_{\text{total}} = 0$.

22E
Since Φ_B does not charge, $\varepsilon = -d\Phi_B/dt = 0$.

23E
(a) The flux changes because the area bounded by the rod and rails increases as the rod moves. Suppose that at some instant the rod is a distance x from the right-hand end of the rails and has speed v. Then the flux through the area is $\Phi_B = BA = BLx$, where L is the distance between the rails. According to Faraday's law the magnitude of the emf induced is $\varepsilon = d\Phi_B/dt = BL(dx/dt) = BLv = (0.350\,\text{T})(0.250\,\text{m})(0.550\,\text{m/s}) = 4.81 \times 10^{-2}\,\text{V}$.

(b) Use Ohm's law. If R is the resistance of the rod then the current in the rod is $i = \varepsilon/R = (4.81 \times 10^{-2}\,\text{V})/(18.0\,\Omega) = 2.67 \times 10^{-3}\,\text{A}$.

24E
(a) Let x be the distance from the right end of the rails to the rod. The area enclosed by the rod and rails is Lx and the magnetic flux through the area is $\Phi_B = BLx$. The emf induced is $\varepsilon = d\Phi_B/dt = BL\,dx/dt = BLv$, where v is the speed of the rod. Thus $\varepsilon = (1.2\,\text{T})(0.10\,\text{m})(5.0\,\text{m/s}) = 0.60\,\text{V}$.

(b) If R is the resistance of the rod, the current in the loop is $i = \varepsilon/R = (0.60\,\text{V})/(0.40\,\Omega) = 1.5\,\text{A}$. Since the rod moves to the left in the diagram, the flux increases. The induced current must produce a magnetic field that is into the page in the region bounded by the rod and rails. To do this the current must be clockwise.

(c) The rate of generation of thermal energy by the resistance of the rod is $P = \varepsilon^2/R = (0.60\,\text{V})^2/(0.40\,\Omega) = 0.90\,\text{W}$.

(*d*) Since the rod moves with constant velocity the net force on it must be zero. This means the force of the external agent has the same magnitude as the magnetic force but is in the opposite direction. The magnitude of the magnetic force is $F_B = iLB = (1.5\,\text{A})(0.10\,\text{m})(1.2\,\text{T}) = 0.18\,\text{N}$. Since the field is out of the page and the current is upward through the rod the magnetic force is to the right. The force of the external agent must be $0.18\,\text{N}$, to the left.

(*e*) As the rod moves an infinitesimal distance dx the external agent does work $dW = F\,dx$, where F is the force of the agent. The force is in the direction of motion, so the work done by the agent is positive. The rate at which the agent does work is $dW/dt = F\,dx/dt = Fv = (0.18\,\text{N})(5.0\,\text{m/s}) = 0.90\,\text{W}$, the same as the rate at which thermal energy is generated. The energy supplied by the external agent is converted completely to thermal energy.

25E
Apply Newton's second law to the rod:

$$m\frac{dv}{dt} = iBL.$$

Integrate to get

$$v = \frac{iBLt}{m}.$$

v points away form the generator, G.

26P

$$\varepsilon = -\frac{d\Phi_B}{dt} = -\frac{d(BA)}{dt} = -B\frac{dA}{dt} = -B\frac{d(\pi r^2)}{dt} = -2\pi r B\frac{dr}{dt}$$
$$= -2\pi(0.120\,\text{m})(0.800\,\text{T})(-0.750\,\text{m/s}) = 0.452\,\text{V}.$$

27P
(a) At time t the area of the closed triangular loop is $A(t) = \frac{1}{2}(vt)(2vt) = v^2 t^2$. Thus

$$\Phi_B|_{t=3.00\,\text{s}} = BA(t) = (0.350\,\text{T})[(5.20\,\text{m/s})(3.00\,\text{s})]^2 = 85.2\,\text{T}\cdot\text{m}^2.$$

(b)

$$\varepsilon = -\frac{d\Phi_B}{dt} = -\frac{d(BA)}{dt} = -B\frac{dA}{dt} = -B\frac{d(v^2 t^2)}{dt} = -2Bv^2 t$$
$$= -2(0.350\,\text{T})(5.20\,\text{m/s})^2(3.00\,\text{s}) = -56.8\,\text{V}.$$

(c) From (b) above we see that the magnitude of ε increases linearly with time.

28P

(a) and (b) Let $A = \pi r^2$. The emf as a function of time is given by

$$\varepsilon = -\frac{d\Phi_B}{dt} = -\frac{d}{dt}(\mathbf{B} \cdot \mathbf{A}) = -BA\frac{d}{dt}\cos(\mathbf{B}, \mathbf{A}) = -BA\frac{d}{dt}\cos(2\pi ft + \phi_0)$$
$$= -BA\omega\sin(2\pi ft + \phi_0).$$

Thus the frequency of ε is f and the amplitude is $\varepsilon_m = BA\omega = B(\pi r^2/2)(2\pi f) = \pi^2 r^2 Bf$.

29P

(a) The area of the loop is $A = ab$. Suppose that at some instant of time the normal to the loop makes the angle θ with the magnetic field. The magnetic flux through the loop is then $\Phi_B = NabB\cos\theta$ and the emf induced around the loop is

$$\varepsilon = -\frac{d\Phi_B}{dt} = -\frac{d}{dt}[NabB\cos\theta] = [NabB\sin\theta]\frac{d\theta}{dt}.$$

In terms of the frequency of rotation f and the time t, θ is given by $\theta = 2\pi ft$ and $d\theta/dt = 2\pi f$. The emf is therefore

$$\varepsilon = 2\pi fNabB\sin(2\pi ft).$$

This can be written $\varepsilon = \varepsilon_0\sin(2\pi ft)$, where $\varepsilon_0 = 2\pi fNabB$.

(b) You want $2\pi fNabB = 150\,\text{V}$. This means

$$Nab = \frac{\varepsilon_0}{2\pi fB} = \frac{150\,\text{V}}{2\pi(60.0\,rev/s)(0.500\,\text{T})} = 0.796\,\text{m}^2.$$

Any loop for which $Nab = 0.796\,\text{m}^2$ will do the job. An example is $N = 100\,\text{turns}$, $a = b = 8.92\,\text{cm}$.

30P

Use the result obtained in Problem 28, part (b):

$$\varepsilon = NBA\omega = 2\pi fBAN$$
$$= 2\pi(1000/60\,\text{s})(3.50\,\text{T})(0.500\,\text{m})(0.300\,\text{m})(100) = 5.50 \times 10^3\,\text{V}.$$

$$P_{\mathrm{av}} = \frac{\varepsilon_{\mathrm{av}}^2}{R} = \frac{\varepsilon_0^2 [\sin^2(2\pi f t)]_{\mathrm{av}}}{R} = \frac{\varepsilon_0^2}{2R}$$
$$= \frac{(150\,\mathrm{v})^2}{2(42.0\,\Omega)} = 268\,\mathrm{W},$$

where we used

$$[\sin^2(2\pi f t)]_{\mathrm{av}} = \frac{1}{T}\int_0^T \sin^2(2\pi f t)\,dt = \frac{1}{2}.$$

32P

(a) When the current i in the rod becomes zero, the rod will no longer be accelerated by a force $F = iBL$ and will therefore reach a constant terminal velocity. This happens when $|\varepsilon_{\mathrm{induced}}| = \varepsilon$, i.e.

$$|\varepsilon_{\mathrm{induced}}| = \left|\frac{d\Phi_B}{dt}\right| = \left|\frac{d(BA)}{dt}\right| = B\left|\frac{dA}{dt}\right| = BvL = \varepsilon,$$

or $v = \varepsilon/BL$, to the left.

(b) In Exercise 25, electric energy is supplied by the generator, and it is transferred into the kinetic energy of rod. In the current case the battery initially supplies electric energy to the rod, causing its kinetic energy to increase to a maximum value of $\frac{1}{2}mv^2 = \frac{1}{2}(\varepsilon/BL)^2$. Afterwards, no energy transfer from the battery to the rod takes place anymore, and the kinetic energy of the rod remains a constant value.

33P

$$q(t) = \frac{N}{R}\Delta\Phi_B = \frac{N}{R}[BA\cos 70° - (-BA\cos 70°)] = \frac{2WBA\cos 30°}{R}$$
$$= \frac{2(1000)(0.590 \times 10^{-4}\,\mathrm{T})\pi(0.100\,\mathrm{m})^2(\cos 30°)}{85.0\,\Omega + 140\,\Omega} = 1.55 \times 10^{-5}\,\mathrm{C}.$$

Note that the axis of the coil is at 30°, not 70°, from the magnetic field of the Earth.

34P

(a) Let x be the distance from the right end of the rails to the rod and find an expression for the magnetic flux through the area enclosed by the rod and rails. The magnetic field is not uniform but varies with distance from the long straight wire. The field is normal to the area and has magnitude $B = \mu_0 i/2\pi r$, where r is the distance from the wire and i is the current in the wire. Consider an infinitesimal strip of length x and width dr, parallel to the wire and a distance r from it. The area of this strip is $A = x\,dr$ and the flux through it is $d\Phi_B = (\mu_0 ix/2\pi r)\,dr$. The total flux through the areà enclosed by the rod and rails is

$$\Phi_B = \frac{\mu_0 ix}{2\pi} \int_a^{a+L} \frac{dr}{r} = \frac{\mu_0 ix}{2\pi} \ln\left(\frac{a+L}{a}\right).$$

According to Faraday's law the emf induced in the loop is

$$\varepsilon = \frac{d\Phi}{dt} = \frac{\mu_0 i}{2\pi} \frac{dx}{dt} \ln\left(\frac{a+L}{a}\right) = \frac{\mu_0 iv}{2\pi} \ln\left(\frac{a+L}{a}\right)$$

$$= \frac{(4\pi \times 10^{-7}\,\text{T}\cdot\text{m/A})(100\,\text{A})(5.00\,\text{m/s})}{2\pi} \ln\left(\frac{1.00\,\text{cm} + 10.0\,\text{cm}}{1.00\,\text{cm}}\right)$$

$$= 2.40 \times 10^{-4}\,\text{V}.$$

(b) If R is the resistance of the rod then the current in the conducting loop is $i_\ell = \varepsilon/R = (2.40 \times 10^{-4}\,\text{V})/(0.400\,\Omega) = 6.00 \times 10^{-4}\,\text{A}$. Since the flux is increasing the magnetic field produced by the induced current must be into the page in the region enclosed by the rod and rails. This means the current is clockwise.

(c) Thermal energy is be generated at the rate $P = i_\ell^2 R = (6.00 \times 10^{-4}\,\text{A})^2(0.400\,\Omega) = 1.44 \times 10^{-7}\,\text{W}$.

(d) Since the rod moves with constant velocity the net force on it is zero. The force of the external agent must have the same magnitude as the magnetic force and must be in the opposite direction. The magnitude of the magnetic force on an infinitesimal segment of the rod, with length dr and a distance r from the long straight wire, is $dF_B = i_\ell B\,dr = (\mu_0 i_\ell i/2\pi r)\,dr$. The total magnetic force on the rod has magnitude

$$F_B = \frac{\mu_0 i_\ell i}{2\pi} \int_a^{a+L} \frac{dr}{r} = \frac{\mu_0 i_\ell i}{2\pi} \ln\left(\frac{a+L}{a}\right)$$

$$= \frac{(4\pi \times 10^{-7}\,\text{T}\cdot\text{m/A})(6.00 \times 10^{-4}\,\text{A})(100\,\text{A})}{2\pi} \ln\left(\frac{1.00\,\text{cm} + 10.0\,\text{cm}}{1.00\,cm}\right)$$

$$= 2.87 \times 10^{-8}\,\text{N}.$$

Since the field is out of the page and the current in the rod is upward in the diagram, this force is toward the right. The external agent must apply a force of 2.87×10^{-8} N, to the left.

(e) The external agent does work at the rate $P = Fv = (2.87 \times 10^{-8}\,\text{N})(5.00\,m/s) = 1.44 \times 10^{-7}$ W. This is the same as the rate at which thermal energy is generated in the rod. All the energy supplied by the agent is converted to thermal energy.

35P

(a) It is clear that the magnetic flux through areas 1 and 2 as shown cancel out. Thus

$$\Phi_B = \Phi_{B3} = \int_{b-a}^{a} B(r)(b\,dr)$$

$$= \int_{b-a}^{a} \left(\frac{\mu_0 i}{2\pi r}\right) b\,dr$$

$$= \frac{\mu_0 i b}{2\pi} \ln\left(\frac{a}{b-a}\right).$$

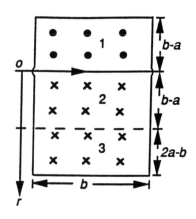

Thus

$$\varepsilon = -\frac{d\Phi_B}{dt} = -\frac{d}{dt}\left[\frac{\mu_0 i b}{2\pi} \ln\left(\frac{a}{b-a}\right)\right] = -\frac{\mu_0 b}{2\pi} \ln\left(\frac{a}{b-a}\right)\frac{di}{dt}$$

$$= -\frac{\mu_0 b}{2\pi} \ln\left(\frac{a}{b-a}\right)\frac{d}{dt}(4.50t^2 - 10.0t) = \frac{-4.50\mu_0 bt}{\pi} \ln\left(\frac{a}{b-a}\right)$$

$$= -\frac{(4.50)(1.26 \times 10^{-6}\,\text{T}\cdot\text{m/A})(0.160\,\text{m})(3.00\,\text{s})}{\pi} \ln\left(\frac{12.0\,\text{cm}}{16.0\,\text{cm} - 12.0\,\text{cm}}\right)$$

$$= -5.98 \times 10^{-7}\,\text{V}.$$

(b) From Lenz's law, the induced current in the loop is counterclockwise.

36P

Use Faraday's law to find an expression for the emf induced by the changing magnetic field. First find an expression for the magnetic flux through the loop. Since the field depends on y but not on x, divide the area into strips of length L and width dy, parallel to the x axis. Here L is the length of one side of the square. At time t the flux through a strip with coordinate y is $d\Phi_B = BL\,dy = 4.0Lt^2 y\,dy$ and the total flux through the square is

$$\Phi_B = \int_0^L 4.0Lt^2 y\,dy = 2.0L^3 t^2.$$

According to Faraday's law the magnitude of the emf around the square is

$$\varepsilon = \frac{d\Phi_B}{dt} = \frac{d}{dt}\left(2.0L^3 t^2\right) = 4.0L^3 t.$$

At $t = 2.5\,\text{s}$ this is $4.0(0.020\,\text{m})^3(2.5\,\text{s}) = 8.0 \times 10^{-5}\,\text{V}$.

The externally-produced magnetic field is out of the page and is increasing with time. The induced current produces a field that is into the page, so it must be clockwise. The induced emf is also clockwise.

37P

(a) Analogous to Prolem 35, part (a), we have

$$\Phi_B = \int_{\text{loop}} B(r)dA = \int_{r-\frac{b}{2}}^{r+\frac{b}{2}} B(r)adr$$

$$= \int_{r-\frac{b}{2}}^{r+\frac{b}{2}} \frac{\mu_0 ia}{2\pi r} dr = \frac{\mu_0 ia}{2\pi} \ln\left(\frac{2r+b}{2r-b}\right).$$

(b) Now

$$\varepsilon = -\frac{d\Phi_B}{dt} = -\left(\frac{\partial \Phi_B}{\partial r}\right)\left(\frac{dr}{dt}\right) = -v\frac{\partial}{\partial r}\left[\frac{\mu_0 ia}{2\pi} \ln\left(\frac{2r+b}{2r-b}\right)\right]$$

$$= -\frac{\mu_0 iav}{\pi}\left(\frac{1}{2r+b} - \frac{1}{2r-b}\right) = \frac{2\mu_0 iabv}{\pi(4r^2 - b^2)}.$$

Thus

$$i = \frac{\varepsilon}{R} = \frac{2\mu_0 iabv}{\pi R(4r^2 - b^2)}.$$

38P*

(a) Since the changing magnetic flux through the area enclosed by the rod and rails induces a current, the magnetic field exerts a force on the rod. The magnetic force is horizontal and to the left. It tends to slow the rod, while the gravitational force on the rod tends to speed it up. Since the magnetic force is zero when the rod is at rest and increases with the speed of the rod, a terminal speed is reached when the net force acting on the rod is zero.

First assume the rod has speed v and calculate the magnetic force on it. Let x represent the distance from the rod to the fixed cross rail at the bottom of the incline. The area of the loop formed by the rod and rails is $A = \ell x$ and, since the normal to the area makes the angle θ with the magnetic field, the magnetic flux through the loop is $\Phi = B\ell x \cos\theta$. According to Faraday's law the emf induced around the loop is $\varepsilon = B\ell v \cos\theta$. If R is the resistance in the rod then the induced current is $i = \varepsilon/R = (B\ell v/R)\cos\theta$ and the magnitude of the magnetic force is $F_B = i\ell B = (B^2\ell^2 v/R)\cos\theta$. This force is perpendicular to both the field and the current. It is horizontal and to the left.

The diagram shows the forces on the rod: mg is the force of gravity, F_B is the magnetic force, and N is the normal force of the incline. Take the x axis to be down the incline. The magnetic force makes the angle θ with the incline and the force of gravity makes the angle θ with the normal to the incline. The x component of Newton's second law yields $mg\sin\theta - F_B\cos\theta = ma$, where a is the acceleration of the rod. At terminal velocity $a = 0$ and $F_B\cos\theta = mg\sin\theta$.

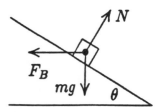

Substitute the expression for F_B found above and solve for v. You should get

$$v = \frac{mgR\sin\theta}{B^2\ell^2\cos^2\theta}.$$

(b) Thermal energy is generated in the rod at the rate $P_T = i^2 R$ and since $i = (B\ell v/R)\cos\theta$, this is $P_T = (B^2\ell^2 v^2/R)\cos^2\theta$. At terminal velocity $v = (mgR\sin\theta)/(B^2\ell^2\cos^2\theta)$, so

$$P_T = \frac{m^2 g^2 R\sin^2\theta}{B^2\ell^2\cos^2\theta}.$$

Suppose the rod is a vertical distance h above the base of the incline. Its potential energy is then $U = mgh = mgx\sin\theta$ where $h\sin\theta$ was substituted for x. The rate at which gravitational potential energy is lost is given by $P_g = dU/dt = mg(dx/dt)\sin\theta = mgv\sin\theta$. Substitute the expression for the terminal velocity for v to obtain

$$P_g = \frac{m^2 g^2 R\sin^2\theta}{B^2\ell^2\cos^2\theta},$$

the same as the expression for the rate of thermal energy generation. Note that the expression for the terminal velocity must be used. Until terminal velocity is reached some gravitational potential energy is converted to kinetic energy as the rod goes faster.

(c) If the magnetic field is downward the direction of the current will be reversed but the magnetic force will be in the same direction and the motion of the rod will be unaffected.

39P*
(a)

$$R(\theta) = \frac{\rho L(\theta)}{A_{\text{wire}}} = \frac{\rho(2r + r\theta)}{A_{\text{wire}}}$$

$$= \frac{(1.7 \times 10^{-8}\,\Omega\cdot\text{m})(0.24\,\text{m})(2 + \theta)}{1.2 \times 10^{-6}\,\text{m}^2} = (2 + \theta)(3.4 \times 10^{-3}\,\Omega).$$

(b)

$$\Phi_B(\theta) = BA(\theta) = B\left(\frac{1}{2}r^2\theta\right)$$

$$= \frac{1}{2}(0.15\,\text{T})(0.24\,\text{m})^2\theta = (4.3 \times 10^{-3}\theta)\,\text{Wb}.$$

(c)

$$|i| = \frac{1}{R}\left|\frac{d\Phi_B}{dt}\right| = \frac{1}{R}\left|\frac{\partial\Phi_B}{\partial\theta}\frac{d\theta}{dt}\right| = \frac{\sqrt{2\alpha\theta}}{R}\left|\frac{\partial\Phi_B}{\partial\theta}\right|$$

$$= \frac{\sqrt{2(12\,\text{rad/s}^2)\theta}}{(2 + \theta)(3.4 \times 10^{-3}\,\Omega)}\left|\frac{\partial}{\partial\theta}(4.3 \times 10^{-3}\theta)\,\text{Wb}\right| = \left(\frac{6.19\sqrt{\theta}}{\theta + 2}\right)A,$$

where we used $\omega^2 = 2\alpha\theta$. To maximize θ, set

$$\frac{d}{d\theta}\left(\frac{\sqrt{\theta}}{\theta + 2}\right) = \frac{(\theta + 2)/2\sqrt{\theta} - \sqrt{\theta}}{\theta + 2} = 0,$$

which yields $\theta = 2.0$ rad.

(d) Substitute $\theta = 2.0$ rad into the expression for $|i|$ obtained in (c) above:

$$|i|_{max} = \left(\frac{6.19\sqrt{2.0}}{2.0 + 2}\right) A = 2.2\,A.$$

40E

(a) The field point is inside the solenoid, so Eq. 32–24 applies. The magnitude of the induced electric field is

$$E = \frac{1}{2}\frac{dB}{dt}\,r = \frac{1}{2}(6.5 \times 10^{-3}\,T/s)(0.0220\,m) = 7.15 \times 10^{-5}\,V/m.$$

(b) Now the field point is outside the solenoid and Eq. 32–25 applies. The magnitude of the induced field is

$$E = \frac{1}{2}\frac{dB}{dt}\frac{R^2}{r} = \frac{1}{2}(6.5 \times 10^{-3}\,T/s)\frac{(0.0600\,m)^2}{(0.0820\,m)} = 1.43 \times 10^{-4}\,V/m.$$

41E

$$\oint_1 \mathbf{E} \cdot d\mathbf{s} = -\frac{d\Phi_{B1}}{dt} = \frac{d}{dt}(B_1 A_1) = A_1\frac{dB_1}{dt} = \pi r_1^2\frac{dB_1}{dt}$$
$$= \pi(0.200\,m)^2(-8.50 \times 10^{-3}\,T/s) = -1.07 \times 10^{-3}\,V,$$

$$\oint_2 \mathbf{E} \cdot d\mathbf{s} = -\frac{d\Phi_{B2}}{dt} = \pi r_2^2\frac{dB_2}{dt}$$
$$= \pi(0.300\,m)^2(-8.50 \times 10^{-3}\,T/s) = -2.40 \times 10^{-3}\,V,$$

and

$$\oint_3 \mathbf{E} \cdot d\mathbf{s} = \oint_1 \mathbf{E} \cdot d\mathbf{s} - \oint_2 \mathbf{E} \cdot d\mathbf{s} = -1.07 \times 10^{-3}\,V - (-2.4 \times 10^{-3}\,V) = 1.33 \times 10^{-3}\,V.$$

42P

The magnetic field B can be expressed as

$$B(t) = B_0 + B_1 \sin(\omega t + \phi_0),$$

where $B_0 = (30.0\,\text{T} + 29.6\,\text{T})/2 = 29.8\,\text{T}$ and $B_1 = (30.0\,\text{T} - 29.6\,\text{T})/2 = 0.200\,\text{T}$. Thus from Eq. 32-24:

$$E = \frac{1}{2}\left(\frac{dB}{dt}\right)r = \frac{r}{2}\frac{d}{dt}[B_0 + B_1 \sin(\omega t + \phi_0)] = \frac{B_1 \omega r}{2}\cos(\omega t + \phi_0).$$

Thus

$$E_{\max} = \frac{B_1(2\pi f)r}{2} = \frac{(0.200\,\text{T})(2\pi)(15\,\text{Hz})(1.6 \times 10^{-2}\,\text{m})}{2} = 0.15\,\text{V/m}.$$

43P

The induced electric field E as a function of r is given by $E(r) = (r/2)(dB/dt)$ so

$$a_c = a_a = \frac{eE}{m} = \frac{er}{2m}\left(\frac{dB}{dt}\right)$$
$$= \frac{(1.60 \times 10^{-19}\,\text{C})(5.0 \times 10^{-2}\,\text{m})(10 \times 10^{-3}\,\text{T/s})}{2(9.11 \times 10^{-27}\,\text{kg})} = 4.4 \times 10^{7}\,\text{m/s}^2.$$

$\mathbf{a}_a$ points to the right and $\mathbf{a}_c$ points to the left. At point b we have $a_b \propto r_b = 0$.

44P

Use Faraday's law in the form $\oint \mathbf{E} \cdot d\mathbf{s} = -(d\Phi_B/dt)$. Integrate around the dotted path shown in Fig. 32–53. At all points on the upper and lower sides the electric field is either perpendicular to the side or else it vanishes. Assume it vanishes at all points on the right side (outside the capacitor). On the left side it is parallel to the side and has constant magnitude. Thus direct integration yields $\oint \mathbf{E} \cdot d\mathbf{s} = EL$, where L is the length of the left side of the rectangle. The magnetic field is zero and remains zero, so $d\Phi_B/dt = 0$. Faraday's law leads to a contradiction: $EL = 0$, but neither E nor L is zero. There must be an electric field along the right side of the rectangle.

45E

(a) The Lorentz force exerted on the electron moving at velocity $\mathbf{v}$ is $\mathbf{F} = -e(\mathbf{E} + \mathbf{v} \times \mathbf{B})$. The magnetic force $\mathbf{F}_B = -e\mathbf{v} \times \mathbf{B}$ must point at the center of the circular path (i.e. serve as the centripetal force). $\mathbf{B}$ must then point out of the page. So the quarter cycles 1, 2, 5 and 6 is suitable for (i).

(b) Since $q_e = -e$ the electric field induced must be clockwise. So dB/dt must be greater than zero, which leads us to the quarter cycles 1, 4, 5 and 8 for purpose (ii).

(c) Only the quarter cycles 1 and 5 are suitable for both (i) and (ii) so they are suitable for operation of the betatron.

46E
(a)

$$E = \frac{r}{2}\left(\frac{dB_{av}}{dt}\right) = r\left(\frac{dB_{orb}}{dt}\right) = r\frac{d}{dt}[(0.280)\sin(120\pi t)]$$
$$= (0.320\,\text{m})(0.280)(120\pi)\cos[(120\pi)(0)]$$
$$= 33.8\,\text{V/m},$$

where we used $B_{av} = 2B_{orb}$.
(b) At $t = 0$ we have $B = 0$, so

$$a = \frac{F}{m} = \frac{eE}{m} = \frac{(1.60 \times 10^{-19}\,\text{C})(33.8\,\text{V/m})}{9.11 \times 10^{-11}\,\text{kg}} = 5.93 \times 10^{12}\,\text{m/s}^2.$$

47P
You need to evaluate numerically the integral

$$B_{av} = \frac{1}{\pi R^2}\int_0^R B(r)2\pi r\,dr$$

and compare this with $2B_{orb} \approx 2(0.400\,\text{T}) = 0.800\,\text{T}$. A crude estimate for $\bar{B}$ is as follows (you can do better than this if you want):

$$B_{av} \approx \frac{2}{R^2}\sum_{i=1}^7 B(\bar{r}_i)\bar{r}_i(r_{i+1} - r_i),$$

where $\bar{r}_i = (r_i + r_{i+1})/2$ and $R = 84\,\text{cm}$.

48
Let $F_{net} = BiL - mg = 0$, we find

$$i = \frac{mg}{BL} = \frac{1}{R}\left|\frac{d\Phi_B}{dt}\right| = \frac{B}{R}\left|\frac{dA}{dt}\right| = \frac{B(v_t L)}{R}$$

or

$$v_t = \frac{mgR}{B^2 L^2}.$$

49

(a) Use $B \simeq \mu_0 i/2R$ where R is the radius of the large loop. Here $i(t) = i_0 + kt$, where $i_0 = 200\,\text{A}$ and $k = (-200\,\text{A} - 200\,\text{A})/1.00\,\text{s} = -400\,\text{A/s}$. Thus

$$B|_{t=0} = \frac{\mu_0 i_0}{2R} = \frac{(1.26 \times 10^{-6}\,\text{T} \cdot \text{m/A})(200\,\text{A})}{2(1.00\,\text{m})} = 1.26 \times 10^{-4}\,\text{T};$$

$$B|_{t=0.500\,\text{s}} = \frac{\mu_0(i_0 + kt)}{2R} = \frac{(1.26 \times 10^{-6}\,\text{T} \cdot \text{m/A})[200\,\text{A} - (400\,\text{A/s})(0.500\,\text{s})]}{2(1.00\,\text{m})} = 0;$$

and

$$B|_{t=1.00\,\text{s}} = \frac{\mu_0(i_0 + kt)}{2R} = \frac{(1.26 \times 10^{-6}\,\text{T} \cdot \text{m/A})[200\,\text{A} - (400\,\text{A/s})(1.00\,\text{s})]}{2(1.00\,\text{m})}$$

$$= -1.26 \times 10^{-4}\,\text{T}.$$

(b) Let the area of the small loop be a. Then

$$\varepsilon(t) = a\frac{dB}{dt} = a\left(\frac{\Delta B}{\Delta t}\right)$$

$$= (2.00 \times 10^{-4}\,\text{m}^2)\left(\frac{-1.26 \times 10^{-4}\,\text{T} - 1.26 \times 10^{-4}\,\text{T}}{1.00\,\text{s}}\right) = -5.04 \times 10^{-8}\,\text{V}.$$

The minus sign here may be dropped.

50

The magnetic flux Φ_B through the loop is given by

$$\Phi_B = \int_{\text{loop}} d\Phi_B = \int_0^L B\sin\theta(W\,dx)$$

$$= \int_0^L \left(\frac{\mu_0 i}{2\pi r}\right)\sin\theta\,W\,dx$$

$$= \int_0^L \frac{\mu_0 i x W}{2\pi(x^2 + y^2)}\,dx$$

$$= \frac{\mu_0 i W}{4\pi}\ln\left(1 + \frac{L^2}{y^2}\right)$$

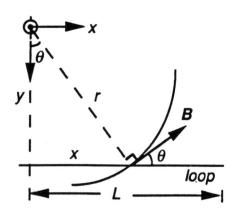

Thus

$$\varepsilon = -\frac{d\Phi_B}{dt} = \frac{\mu_0 W}{4\pi}\ln\left(1 + \frac{L^2}{y^2}\right)\frac{di}{dt} = \frac{\mu_0 I_0 W\omega}{4\pi}\ln\left(1 + \frac{L^2}{y^2}\right)\cos\omega t.$$

51

(a)

$$\varepsilon_{av} = -\left(\frac{d\Phi_B}{dt}\right)_{av} = -\frac{\Delta\Phi_B}{\Delta t} = -\frac{B A_i}{\Delta t}$$

$$= -\frac{(2.0\,\text{T})(0.20\,\text{m})^2}{0.20\,\text{s}} = -0.40\,\text{V}.$$

(b)

$$i_{av} = \frac{\varepsilon_{av}}{R} = \frac{-0.40\,\text{V}}{20 \times 10^{-3}\,\Omega} = -20\,\text{A}.$$

CHAPTER 33

1E

Since $N\Phi = Li$, where N is the number of turns, L is the inductance, and i is the current,

$$\Phi = \frac{Li}{N} = \frac{(8.0 \times 10^{-3}\,\text{H})(5.0 \times 10^{-3}\,\text{A})}{400} = 1.0 \times 10^{-7}\,\text{Wb}.$$

2E

(a)

$$\Phi_B = NBA = NB(\pi r^2)$$
$$= (30.0)(2.60 \times 10^{-3}\,\text{T})(\pi)(0.100\,\text{m})^2 = 2.45 \times 10^{-3}\,\text{Wb}.$$

(b)

$$L = \frac{\Phi_B}{i} = \frac{2.45 \times 10^{-3}\,\text{Wb}}{3.80\,\text{A}} = 6.45 \times 10^{-4}\,\text{H}.$$

3E

(a) $N = 2.0\,\text{m}/2.5\,\text{mm} = 800$.

(b) $L/l = \mu_0 n^2 A = (1.26 \times 10^{-6}\,\text{T} \cdot \text{m/A})(800/2.0\,\text{m})^2(\pi)(0.040\,\text{m})^2/4 = 2.5 \times 10^{-4}\,\text{H}$.

4P

If the solenoid is long and thin, then when it is bent into a toroid $(b - a)/a \ll 1$. Thus

$$L_{\text{toroid}} = \frac{\mu_0 N^2 h}{2\pi} \ln \frac{b}{a} = \frac{\mu_0 N^2 h}{2\pi} \ln\left(1 + \frac{b - a}{b}\right) \approx \frac{\mu_0 N^2 h(b - a)}{2\pi b}.$$

Since $A = h(b - a)$ is the cross-sectional area and $l = 2\pi b$ is the length of the toroid, we may rewrite the expression for L toroid above as

$$\frac{L_{\text{toroid}}}{l} \approx \frac{\mu_0 N^2 A}{l^2} = \mu_0 n^2 A,$$

which indeed reduces to that of a long solenoid.

5P

(a)

$$L_{eq} = \frac{\Phi_{total}}{i} = \frac{\Phi_1 + \Phi_2}{i} = \frac{\Phi_1}{i} + \frac{\Phi_2}{i} = L_1 + L_2.$$

(b) If the separation is not large enough then the magnetic field in one of the inductors may produce a flux in the other, which would render the expression $\Phi = Li$ invalid.

(c) For N inductors in series

$$L_{eq} = \frac{\Phi_{total}}{i} = \frac{\sum_{n=1}^{N} \Phi_n}{i} = \sum_{n=1}^{N} \frac{\Phi_n}{i} = \sum_{n=1}^{N} L_n.$$

6P

(a) In this case $i_{total} = i_1 + i_2$. But $V_{total} = \Phi/L_{eq}$ and $i_{1,2} = \Phi/L_{1,2}$ so $\Phi/L_{eq} = \Phi/L_1 + \Phi/L_2$, or

$$\frac{1}{L_{eq}} = \frac{1}{L_1} + \frac{1}{L_2}.$$

(b) The reason is the same as in part (b) of the previous problem.

(c) For N inductors in parallel, you can easily generize the expression above to

$$\frac{1}{L_{eq}} = \sum_{n=1}^{N} \frac{1}{L_n}.$$

7P

(a) Suppose we divide the one-turn solenoid into N small circular loops placed along the width w of the copper strip. Each loop carreis a current of $\Delta i = i/N$. Then the magnetic field inside the solenoid is $B = \mu_0 n \Delta i = \mu_0 (N/w)(i/N) = \mu_0 i/w$,

(b)

$$L = \frac{\Phi_B}{i} = \frac{\pi R^2 B}{i} = \frac{\pi R^2 (\mu_0 i/w)}{i} = \frac{\pi \mu_0 R^2}{w}.$$

8P

The area of integartion for the calculation of th magnetic flux is bounded by the two dotted lines and the boundaries of the wires. If the origin is taken to be on the axis of the right-hand wire and r measures distance from that axis, it extends from $r = a$ to $r = d - a$. Consider the right-hand wire first. In the region of integation the field it produces is into

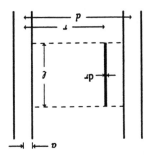

851

the page and has magnitude $B = \mu_0 i/2\pi r$. Divide the region into strips of length l and width dr, as shown. The flux through the strips a distnace r from the axis of the wire is $d\Phi = Bl\,dr$ adn the flux through the entire region is

$$\Phi = \frac{\mu_0 il}{2\pi} \int_a^{d-a} \frac{dr}{r} = \frac{\mu_0 il}{2\pi} \ln\left(\frac{d-a}{a}\right).$$

The other wire produces the same result, so the total flux through the dotted rectangle is

$$\Phi_{\text{total}} = \frac{\mu_0 il}{\pi} \ln\left(\frac{d-a}{a}\right).$$

The inductance is Φ_{total} diveded by i:

$$L = \frac{\Phi_{\text{total}}}{i} = \frac{\mu_0 l}{\pi} \ln\left(\frac{d-a}{a}\right).$$

9E
(a) Since ε enhances i, i must be decreasing.

(b) From $\varepsilon = L\,di/dt$ we get

$$L = \frac{\varepsilon}{di/dt} = \frac{17\,\text{V}}{2.5\,\text{kA/s}} = 6.8 \times 10^{-4}\,\text{H}.$$

10E
Since $\epsilon = -L(di/dt)$, cause the current to change at the rate

$$\frac{di}{dt} = \frac{\epsilon}{L} = \frac{60\,\text{V}}{12\,\text{H}} = 5.0\,\text{A/s}.$$

You might, for example, uniformly reduce the current to zero in $33\,\text{ms}$.

11E
(a)

$$\frac{L}{l} = \mu_0 n^2 A = (1.26 \times 10^{-6}\,\text{T} \cdot \text{m/A})(100\,\text{turns/cm})^2(\pi)(1.6\,\text{cm})^2 = 0.10\,\text{H}.$$

(b)

$$\varepsilon = L\frac{di}{dt} = (0.10\,\text{H})(13\,\text{A/s}) = 1.3\,\text{V}.$$

12E
(a)
$$L = \frac{\varepsilon}{di/dt} = \frac{3.0 \times 10^{-3} \text{ V}}{5.0 \text{ A/s}} = 6.0 \times 10^{-4} \text{ H}.$$

(b) From $L = N\Phi/i$ we get

$$N = \frac{iL}{\Phi} = \frac{(8.0 \text{ A})(6.0 \times 10^{-4} \text{ H})}{40 \times 10^{-6} \text{ Wb}} = 120.$$

13P
Use $\varepsilon = L \, di/dt$.
(a) For $0 < t < 2 \text{ ms}$,

$$\varepsilon = L\frac{\Delta i}{\Delta t} = \frac{(4.6 \text{ H})(7.0 \text{ A} - 0)}{2.0 \times 10^{-3} \text{ s}} = 1.6 \times 10^4 \text{ V}.$$

(b) For $2 \text{ ms} < t < 5 \text{ ms}$,

$$\varepsilon = L\frac{\Delta i}{\Delta t} = \frac{(4.6 \text{ H})(5.0 \text{ A} - 7.0 \text{ A})}{(5.0 - 2.0)10^{-3} \text{ s}} = 3.1 \times 10^3 \text{ V}.$$

(c) For $5 \text{ ms} < t < 6 \text{ ms}$,

$$\varepsilon = L\frac{\Delta i}{\Delta t} = \frac{(4.6 \text{ H})(0 - 5.0 \text{ A})}{(6.0 - 5.0)10^{-3} \text{ s}} = 2.3 \times 10^4 \text{ V}.$$

14E
Suppose that $i(t_0) = i_0/3$ at $t = t_0$. Write $i(t_0) = i_0(1 - e^{-t_0/\tau_L})$ or

$$\tau_L = -\frac{t_0}{\ln(1 - i/i_0)} = -\frac{5.00 \text{ s}}{\ln(1 - 1/3)} = 12.3 \text{ s}.$$

15E
Starting with zero current at time $t = 0$, when the switch is closed, the current in an RL series circuit at a later time t is given by

$$i = \frac{\epsilon}{R}\left(1 - e^{-t/\tau_L}\right),$$

where τ_L is the inductive time constant, ϵ is the emf, and R is the resistance. You want to calculate the time t for which $i = 0.9990\epsilon/R$. This means

$$0.9990\frac{\epsilon}{R} = \frac{\epsilon}{R}\left(1 - e^{-t/\tau_L}\right),$$

so

$$0.9990 = 1 - e^{-t/\tau_L}$$

or

$$e^{-t/\tau_L} = 0.0010.$$

Take the natural logarithm of both sides to obtain $-(t/\tau) = \ln(0.0010) = -6.91$. Thus $t = 6.91\tau_L$. That is, 6.91 inductive time constants must elapse.

16E
The current in the circuit is given by

$$i = i_0 e^{-t/\tau_L},$$

where i_0 is the initial current (at time $t = 0$) and τ_L $(= L/R)$ is the inductive time constant. Solve for τ_L. Divide by i_0 and take the natural logarithm of both sides of the resulting equation to obtain

$$\ln\left(\frac{i}{i_0}\right) = -\frac{t}{\tau_L}.$$

This yields

$$\tau_L = -\frac{t}{\ln[i/i_0]} = -\frac{1.0\,\text{s}}{\ln[(10 \times 10^{-3}\,\text{A})/(1.0\,\text{A})]} = 0.217\,\text{s}.$$

Thus $R = L/\tau_L = (10\,\text{H})/(0.217\,\text{s}) = 46\,\Omega$.

17E
Write $i = i_0 e^{-t/\tau_L}$ and note that $i = i_0/10$. Solve for t:

$$t = \tau_L \ln\frac{i_0}{i} = \frac{L}{R}\ln\frac{i_0}{i} = \frac{2.00\,\text{H}}{3.00\,\Omega}\ln\left(\frac{i_0}{10.0\%i_0}\right) = 1.54\,\text{s}.$$

18E
(a) After the switch is closed on a $\varepsilon - \varepsilon_L = iR$. But $i = 0$ at this instant so $\varepsilon_L = \varepsilon$.
(b) $\varepsilon_L(t) = \varepsilon e^{-t/\tau_L} = \varepsilon e^{-2.0\tau_L/\tau_L} = \varepsilon e^{-2.0} = 0.135\varepsilon$.
(c) Solve $\varepsilon_L(t) = \varepsilon e^{-t/\tau_L}$ for t/τ_L: $t/\tau_L = \ln(\varepsilon/\varepsilon_L) = \ln 2$. so $t = \tau_L \ln 2 = 0.693\tau_L$.

19E
(a) If the battery is switched into the circuit at time $t = 0$, then the current at a later time t is given by

$$i = \frac{\epsilon}{R}\left(1 - e^{-t/\tau_L}\right),$$

where $\tau_L = L/R$. You want to find the time for which $i = 0.800\epsilon/R$. This means

$$0.800 = 1 - e^{-t/\tau_L}$$

or

$$e^{-t/\tau_L} = 0.200.$$

Take the natural logarithm of both sides to obtain $-(t/\tau_L) = \ln(0.200) = -1.609$. Thus

$$t = 1.609\tau_L = \frac{1.609L}{R} = \frac{1.609(6.30 \times 10^{-6}\,\text{H})}{1.20 \times 10^3\,\Omega} = 8.45 \times 10^{-9}\,\text{s}.$$

(b) At $t = 1.0\tau_L$ the current in the circuit is

$$i = \frac{\epsilon}{R}\left(1 - e^{-1.0}\right) = \left(\frac{14.0\,\text{V}}{1.20 \times 10^3\,\Omega}\right)\left(1 - e^{-1.0}\right) = 7.37 \times 10^{-3}\,\text{A}.$$

20E
(a) $L = \Phi/i = 26 \times 10^{-3}\,\text{Wb}/5.5\,\text{A} = 4.7 \times 10^{-3}\,\text{H}$.
(b) Use Eq. 33-18 to solve for t:

$$t = -\tau_L \ln\left(1 - \frac{iR}{\varepsilon}\right) = -\frac{L}{R}\ln\left(1 - \frac{iR}{\varepsilon}\right)$$

$$= -\frac{4.7 \times 10^{-3}\,\text{H}}{0.75\,\Omega}\ln\left[1 - \frac{(2.5\,\text{A})(0.75\,\Omega)}{6.0\,\text{V}}\right] = 2.4 \times 10^{-3}\,\text{s}.$$

21P
Apply the loop theorem:

$$\varepsilon(t) - L\frac{di}{dt} = iR$$

and solve for $\varepsilon(t)$:

$$\varepsilon(t) = L\frac{di}{dt} + iR = L\frac{d}{dt}(3.0 + 5.0t) + (3.0 + 5.0t)R$$
$$= (6.0\,\text{H})(5.0\,\text{A/s}) + (3.0\,\text{A} + 5.0t)(4.0\,\Omega)$$
$$= (42 + 20t)\,\text{V},$$

where t is seconds.

22P

(a) and (b) Write $V_L(t) = \varepsilon e^{-t/\tau_l}$. Consider the first two data points, (V_{L1}, t_1) and (V_{L2}, t_2), satisfying $V_{Li} = \varepsilon e^{-t_i/\tau_L}$ $(i = 1.2)$. We have $V_{L1}/V_{L2} = \varepsilon e^{-(t_1-t_2)/\tau_L}$, which gives

$$\tau_L = \frac{t_1 - t_2}{\ln(V_2/V_1)} = \frac{1.0\,\text{ms} - 2.0\,\text{ms}}{\ln(13.8/18.2)}$$
$$= 3.6\,\text{ms}.$$

So $\varepsilon = V_{L1}e^{t_1/\tau_L} = (18.2\,\text{V})e^{1.0\,\text{ms}/3.6\,\text{ms}} = 24\,\text{V}$. You can easily check that these values of τ_L and ε are consistent with the rest of the date points.

23P

Use Eq. 33-17:

$$\frac{di}{dt} = \frac{\varepsilon}{L}e^{-RT/L} = \frac{45.0\,\text{V}}{50.0 \times 10^{-3}\,\text{H}}e^{-(180\,\Omega)(1.20\times10^{-3}\,\text{s})/(50.0\times10^{-3}\,\text{H})}$$
$$= 12.0\,\text{A/s}.$$

24P

(a) Since the inner circumference of the toroid is $l = 2\pi a = 2\pi(10\,\text{cm}) = 62.8\,\text{cm}$, the number fo turns of the toroid is roughly $N = 62.8\,\text{cm}/1.0\,\text{mm} = 628$. Thus

$$L = \frac{\mu_0 N^2 H}{2\pi}\ln\frac{b}{a} \approx \frac{(1.26 \times 10^{-6}\,\text{T}\cdot\text{m/A})(628)^2(0.12\,\text{m} - 0.10\,\text{m})}{2\pi}\ln\left(\frac{12\,\text{cm}}{10\,\text{cm}}\right)$$
$$= 2.9 \times 10^{-4}\,\text{H}.$$

(b) Since the total length l of the wire is $l = (628)4(2.0\,\text{cm}) = 50\,\text{m}$, the resistance of the wire is $R = (50\,\text{m})(0.02\,\Omega/\text{m}) = 1.0\,\Omega$. Thus

$$\tau_L = \frac{L}{R} = \frac{2.9 \times 10^{-4}\,\text{H}}{1.0\,\Omega} = 2.9 \times 10^{-4}\,\text{s}.$$

25P

(a) The inductor prevents a fast build-up of the current through it, so immediately after the switch is closed the current in the inductor is zero. This means

$$i_1 = i_2 = \frac{\epsilon}{R_1 + R_2} = \frac{100\,\text{V})}{10.0\,\Omega + 20.0\,\Omega} = 3.33\,\text{A}.$$

(*b*) A long time later the current reaches steady state and no longer changes. The emf across the inductor is zero and the circuit behaves as if it were replaced by a wire. The current in R_3 is $i_1 - i_2$. Kirchhoff's loop rule gives

$$\epsilon - i_1 R_1 - i_2 R_2 = 0$$

and

$$\epsilon - i_1 R_1 - (i_1 - i_2) R_3 = 0.$$

Solve these simultaneously for i_1 and i_2. The results are

$$i_1 = \frac{\epsilon(R_2 + R_3)}{R_1 R_2 + R_1 R_3 + R_2 R_3}$$
$$= \frac{(100\,\text{V})(20.0\,\Omega + 30.0\,\Omega)}{(10.0\,\Omega)(20.0\,\Omega) + (10.0\,\Omega)(30.0\,\Omega) + (20.0\,\Omega)(30.0\,\Omega)}$$
$$= 4.55\,\text{A}$$

and

$$i_2 = \frac{\epsilon R_3}{R_1 R_2 + R_1 R_3 + R_2 R_3}$$
$$= \frac{(100\,\text{V})(30.0\,\Omega)}{(10.0\,\Omega)(20.0\,\Omega) + (10.0\,\Omega)(30.0\,\Omega) + (20.0\,\Omega)(30.0\,\Omega)}$$
$$= 2.73\,\text{A}.$$

(*c*) The left-hand branch is now broken. If its inductance is zero the current immediately drops to zero when the switch is opened. That is, $i_1 = 0$. The current in R_3 changes only slowly because there is an inductor in its branch. Immediately after the switch is opened it has the same value as it had just before the switch was opened. That value is $4.55\,\text{A} - 2.73\,\text{A} = 1.82\,\text{A}$. The current in R_2 is the same as that in R_3, $1.82\,\text{A}$.

(*d*) There are no longer any sources of emf in the circuit, so all currents eventually drop to zero.

26P
(a) When swith S is just closed (case I) we have $V_1 = \varepsilon$ and $i_1 = \varepsilon/R_1 = 10\,\text{V}/5.0\,\Omega = 2.0\,\text{A}$.
After a long time (case II) we still have $V_1 = \varepsilon$ so $i_1 = 2.0\,\text{A}$.
(b) Case I: Since now $\varepsilon_L = \varepsilon$ we have $i_2 = 0$.
Case II: Since now $\varepsilon_L = 0$ we have $i_2 = \varepsilon/R_2 = 10\,\text{V}/10\,\Omega = 1.0\,\text{A}$.
(c) Case I: $i = i_1 + i_2 = 2.0\,\text{A} + 0 = 2.0\,\text{A}$.
Case II: $i = i_1 + i_2 = 2.0\,\text{A} + 1.0\,\text{A} = 3.0\,\text{A}$.
(d) Case I: Since $\varepsilon_L = \varepsilon$, $V_2 = \varepsilon - \varepsilon_L = 0$.
Case II: Since $\varepsilon_L = 0$, $V_2 = \varepsilon - \varepsilon_L = \varepsilon = 10\,\text{V}$.
(e) Case I: $\varepsilon_L = \varepsilon = 10\,\text{V}$
Case I: $\varepsilon_L = 0$.

(f) Case I: $di_2/dt = \varepsilon_L/L = \varepsilon/L = 10\,\text{V}/5.0\,\text{H} = 2.0\,\text{A/s}$.
Case II: $di_2/dt = \varepsilon_L/L = 0$.

27P

(a) Before the fuse blows, the current through the resistor remains zero. Apply the loop theorem to the battery-fuse-inductor loop: $\varepsilon - L\,di/dt = 0$. So $i = \varepsilon t/L$. As the fuse blows at $t = t_0$, $i = i_0 = 3.0\,\text{A}$. Thus

$$t_0 = \frac{i_0 L}{\varepsilon} = \frac{(3.0\,\text{A})(5.0\,\text{H})}{10\,\text{V}} = 1.5\,\text{s}.$$

(b)

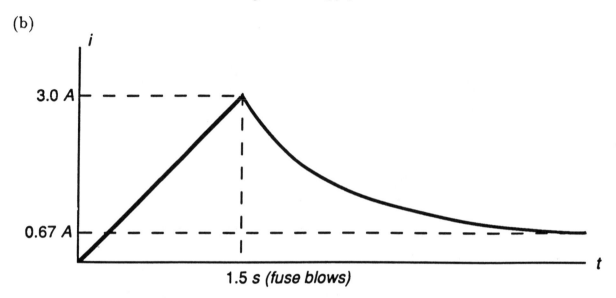

3.0 A

0.67 A

1.5 s (fuse blows)

28P*

(a) Assume i is from left to right through the closed switch. Let i_1 be the current in the resistor and take it to be downward. Let i_2 be the current in the inductor and also take it to be downward. The junction rule gives $i = i_1 + i_2$ and the loop rule gives $i_1 R - L(di_2/dt) = 0$. According to the junction rule, $(di_1/dt) = -(di_2/dt)$. Substitute into the loop equation to obtain

$$L\frac{di_1}{dt} + i_1 R = 0.$$

This equation is similar to the one given in Section 33-4, just before Eq. 33-20, and its solution is the function given as Eq. 33-20:

$$i_1 = i_0 e^{-Rt/L},$$

where i_0 is the current through the resistor at $t = 0$, just after the switch is closed. Now just after the switch is closed the inductor prevents the rapid build-up of current in its branch, so at that time $i_2 = 0$ and $i_1 = i$. Thus $i_0 = i$, so

$$i_1 = i e^{-Rt/L}$$

858

and

$$i_2 = i - i_1 = i\left[1 - e^{-Rt/L}\right].$$

(b) When $i_2 = i_1$,

$$e^{-Rt/L} = 1 - e^{-Rt/L},$$

so

$$e^{-Rt/L} = \frac{1}{2}.$$

Take the natural logarithm of both sides and use $\ln(1/2) = -\ln 2$ to obtain $(Rt/L) = \ln 2$ or

$$t = \frac{L}{R}\ln 2.$$

29P

(a) Use $U_B = \frac{1}{2}Li^2$:

$$L = \frac{2U_B}{i^2} = \frac{2(25.0 \times 10^{-3}\,\text{J})}{(60.0 \times 10^{-3}\,\text{A})^2} = 13.9\,\text{H}.$$

(b) Since $U_B \propto i^2$, for U_B to increase by a factor of 4, i must increase by a factor of 2, i.e. i should be $2(60.0\,\text{mA}) = 120\,\text{mA}$.

30E

Let $U_B(t) = \frac{1}{2}Li^2(t) = \frac{1}{2}U_B(t \to \infty) = \frac{1}{4}Li_0^2$. This gives $i(t) = i_0/\sqrt{2}$. But $i(t) = i_0(1 - e^{-t/\tau_L})$, so $1 - e^{-t/\tau_L} = 1/\sqrt{2}$. Solve for t:

$$t = -\tau_L \ln\left(1 - \frac{1}{\sqrt{2}}\right) = 1.23\tau_L.$$

31E

(a) $i_0 = \varepsilon/R = 100\,\text{V}/10\,\Omega = 10\,\text{A}$.
(b) $U_B = \frac{1}{2}Li_0^2 = \frac{1}{2}(2.0\,\text{H})(10\,\text{A})^2 = 100\,\text{J}$.

32E

(a)

$$\frac{dU_B}{dt} = \frac{d}{dt}\left(\frac{1}{2}Li^2\right) = Li\frac{di}{dt} = Li_0(1 - e^{-t/\tau_L})\frac{d}{dt}[i_0(1 - e^{-t/\tau_L})]$$

$$= \frac{Li_0^2}{\tau_L}e^{-t/\tau_L}(1 - e^{-t/\tau_L}) = \frac{L\varepsilon^2}{(L/R)R^2}e^{-Rt/L}(1 - e^{-t/\tau_L})$$

$$= \frac{(100\,\text{V})^2}{10\,\Omega}e^{-(10\,\Omega)(0.10\,\text{s})/2.0\,\text{H}}[1 - e^{-(10\,\Omega)(0.10\,\text{s})/2.0\,\text{H}}]$$

$$= 2.4 \times 10^2\,\text{W}.$$

859

(b)

$$P_{\text{thermal}} = i^2 R = i_0^2 (1 - e^{-t/\tau_L})^2 R = \frac{\varepsilon^2}{R}(1 - e^{-Rt/L})^2$$

$$= \frac{(100\,\text{V})^2}{10\,\Omega}[1 - e^{-(10\,\Omega)(0.10\,\text{s})/2.0\,\text{H}}]^2$$

$$= 1.5 \times 10^2\,\text{W}.$$

(c)

$$P_{\text{battery}} = i\varepsilon = \varepsilon i_0 (1 - e^{-t/\tau_L}) = \frac{\varepsilon^2}{R}(1 - e^{-Rt/L})$$

$$= \frac{(100\,\text{V})^2}{10\,\Omega}[1 - e^{-(10\,\Omega)(0.10\,\text{s})/2.0\,\text{H}}]$$

$$= 3.9 \times 10^2\,\text{W}.$$

Note that the law of conservation of energy requirement $P_{\text{battery}} = dU_B/dt + P_{\text{thermal}}$ is satisfied.

33P
Use the results of the last problem. Let $P_{\text{thermal}} = dU_B/dt$, or

$$\frac{\varepsilon^2}{R}(1 - e^{-Rt/L})^2 = \frac{\varepsilon^2}{R}e^{-Rt/L}(1 - e^{-Rt/L})$$

and solve for t:

$$t = \frac{L}{R}\ln 2 = \tau_L \ln 2 = (37.0\,\text{ms})\ln 2 = 25.6\,\text{ms}.$$

34P
(a) If the battery is applied at time $t = 0$ the current is given by

$$i = \frac{\epsilon}{R}\left(1 - e^{-t/\tau_L}\right),$$

where ϵ is the emf of the battery, R is the resistance, and τ_L is the inductive time constant. In terms of R and the inductance L, $\tau_L = L/R$. Solve the current equation for the time constant. First obtain

$$e^{-t/\tau_L} = 1 - \frac{iR}{\epsilon},$$

then take the natural logarithm of both sides to obtain

$$-\frac{t}{\tau_L} = \ln\left[1 - \frac{iR}{\epsilon}\right].$$

Since
$$\ln\left[1 - \frac{iR}{\epsilon}\right] = \ln\left[1 - \frac{(2.00 \times 10^{-3}\,\mathrm{A})(10.0 \times 10^3\,\Omega)}{50.0\,\mathrm{V}}\right] = -.5108 ,$$

the inductive time constant is $\tau_L = t/0.5108 = (5.00 \times 10^{-3}\,\mathrm{s})/(0.5108) = 9.79 \times 10^{-3}\,\mathrm{s}$ and the inductance is

$$L = \tau_L R = (9.79 \times 10^{-3}\,\mathrm{s})(10.0 \times 10^3\,\Omega) = 97.9\,\mathrm{H} .$$

(b) The energy stored in the coil is

$$U_B = \frac{1}{2}Li^2 = \frac{1}{2}(97.9\,\mathrm{H})(2.00 \times 10^{-3}\,\mathrm{A})^2 = 1.96 \times 10^{-4}\,\mathrm{J} .$$

35P
(a)

$$E_{\text{battery}} = \int_0^t P_{\text{battery}}\,dt = \int_0^t \frac{\epsilon^2}{R}(1 - e^{-Rt/L})\,dt = \frac{\epsilon^2}{R}\left[t + \frac{L}{R}(e^{-Rt/L} - 1)\right]$$

$$= \frac{(10.0\,\mathrm{V})^2}{6.70\,\Omega}\left[2.00\,\mathrm{s} + \frac{(5.50\,\mathrm{H})[e^{-(6.70\,\Omega)(2.00\,\mathrm{s})/5.50\,\mathrm{H}} - 1]}{6.70\,\Omega}\right]$$

$$= 18.7\,\mathrm{J} .$$

(b)

$$E_{\text{inductor}} = U_B(t) = \frac{1}{2}Li^2(t) = \frac{1}{2}L\left(\frac{\epsilon}{R}\right)^2(1 - e^{-Rt/L})^2$$

$$= \frac{(5.50\,\mathrm{H})}{2}\left(\frac{10.0\,\mathrm{V}}{6.70\,\Omega}\right)^2\left[1 - e^{-(6.70\,\Omega)(2.00\,\mathrm{s})/5.50\,\mathrm{H}}\right]^2$$

$$= 5.10\,\mathrm{J} .$$

(c) $E_{\text{dissipated}} = E_{\text{battery}} - E_{\text{inductor}} = 18.7\,\mathrm{J} - 5.10\,\mathrm{J} = 13.6\,\mathrm{J} .$

36P
(a) The inductance of the solenoid is

$$L = \mu_0 n^2 A l = (1.26 \times 10^{-6}\,\mathrm{T \cdot m/A})(3000\,\text{turns}/0.800\,\mathrm{m})^2(\pi)(5.00 \times 10^{-2}\,\mathrm{m})^2(0.800\,\mathrm{m})$$
$$= 0.111\,\mathrm{H} .$$

Thus

$$U_B(t) = \frac{1}{2}Li^2(t) = \frac{1}{2}L\left(\frac{\epsilon}{R}\right)^2(1 - e^{-Rt/L})^2$$

$$= \frac{(0.111\,\mathrm{H})}{2}\left(\frac{12.0\,\mathrm{V}}{10.0\,\Omega}\right)^2[1 - e^{-(10.0\,\Omega)(5.00 \times 10^{-3}\,\mathrm{s})/0.111\,\mathrm{H}}]^2$$

$$= 1.05 \times 10^{-2}\,\mathrm{J} .$$

(b)

$$E_{\text{battery}} = \frac{\varepsilon^2}{R}\left[t + \frac{L}{R}(e^{-Rt/L} - 1)\right]$$

$$= \frac{(12.0\,\text{V})^2}{10.0\,\Omega}\left(5.00 \times 10^{-3}\,\text{s} + \left(\frac{0.111\,\text{H}}{10.0\,\Omega}\right)[e^{-(10.0\,\Omega)(5.00\times10^{-3}\,\text{s})/0.111\,\text{H}} - 1]\right)$$

$$= 1.41 \times 10^{-2}\,\text{J}.$$

37P

Suppose that the switch has been in position a for a long time, so the current has reached the steady-state value i_0. The energy stored in the inductor is $U_B = \frac{1}{2}Li_0^2$. Now the switch is thrown to position b at time $t = 0$. Thereafter the current is given by

$$i = i_0 e^{-t/\tau_L},$$

where τ_L is the inductive time constant, given by $\tau = L/R$. The rate at which thermal energy is generated in the resistor is given by

$$P = i^2 R = i_0^2 R e^{-2t/\tau_L}.$$

Over a long time period the energy dissipated is

$$E = \int_0^\infty P\,dt = i_0^2 R \int_0^\infty e^{-2t/\tau_L}\,dt = -\frac{1}{2}i_0^2 R\tau_L e^{-2t/\tau_L}\bigg|_0^\infty = \frac{1}{2}i_0^2 R\tau_L.$$

Substitute $\tau_L = L/R$ to obtain

$$E = \frac{1}{2}Li_0^2,$$

the same as the total energy originally stored in the inductor.

38E

(a) At any point the magnetic energy density is given by $u_B = B^2/2\mu_0$, where B is the magnitude of the magnetic field at that point. Inside a solenoid $B = \mu_0 ni$, where n is the number of turns per unit length and i is the current. For the solenoid of this problem $n = (950)/(0.850\,\text{m}) = 1.118 \times 10^3\,\text{m}^{-1}$. The magnetic energy density is

$$u_B = \frac{1}{2}\mu_0 n^2 i^2 = \frac{1}{2}(4\pi \times 10^{-7}\,\text{T}\cdot\text{m/A})(1.118 \times 10^3\,\text{m}^{-1})^2(6.60\,\text{A})^2 = 34.2\,\text{J/m}^3.$$

(b) Since the magnetic field is uniform inside an ideal solenoid, the total energy stored in the field is $U_B = u_B V$, where V is the volume of the solenoid. V is calculated as the product of the cross-sectional area and the length. Thus

$$U_B = (34.2\,\text{J/m}^3)(17.0 \times 10^{-4}\,\text{m}^2)(0.850\,\text{m}) = 4.94 \times 10^{-2}\,\text{J}.$$

39E

The magnetic energy stored in the toroid is given by $U_B = \frac{1}{2}Li^2$, where L is its inductance and i is the current. The energy is also given by $U_B = u_B V$, where u_B is the average energy density and V is the volume. Thus

$$i = \sqrt{\frac{2u_B V}{L}} = \sqrt{\frac{2(70.0\,\text{J/m}^3)(0.0200\,\text{m}^3)}{90.0 \times 10^{-3}\,\text{H}}} = 5.58\,\text{A}\,.$$

40E

Let $u_E = \frac{1}{2}\epsilon_0 E^2 = u_B = \frac{1}{2}B^2/\mu_0$ and solve for E:

$$E = \frac{B}{\sqrt{\epsilon_0 \mu_0}} = \frac{0.50\,\text{T}}{\sqrt{(8.85 \times 10^{-12}\,\text{F/m})(1.26 \times 10^{-6}\,\text{T}\cdot\text{m/A})}} = 1.5 \times 10^8\,\text{V/m}.$$

41E

Use $1\,\text{ly} = 9.46 \times 10^{15}\,\text{m}$.

$$U_B = V u_B = \frac{VB^2}{2\mu_0}$$

$$= \frac{(9.46 \times 10^{15})^3 (10^{-10}\,\text{T})^2}{2(1.26 \times 10^{-6}\,\text{T}\cdot\text{m/A})} = 3 \times 10^{36}\,\text{J}.$$

42E

Use Eq. 33-28:

$$L = \frac{2U}{i^2} = \frac{2}{i^2}\frac{\mu_0 i^2 l}{4\pi}\ln\frac{b}{a} = \frac{\mu_0 l}{2\pi}\ln\frac{b}{a}.$$

43E

(a)

$$B = \frac{\mu_0 i}{2R} = \frac{(1.26 \times 10^{-6}\,\text{T}\cdot\text{m/A})(100\,\text{A})}{2(50 \times 10^{-3}\,\text{m})} = 1.3 \times 10^{-3}\,\text{T}.$$

(b)

$$u_B = \frac{B^2}{2\mu_0} = \frac{(1.3 \times 10^{-3}\,\text{T})^2}{2(1.26 \times 10^{-6}\,\text{T}\cdot\text{m/A})} = 0.63\,\text{J/m}^3.$$

44P

(a) The energy density at any point is given by $u_B = B^2/2\mu_0$, where B is the magnitude of the magnetic field. The magnitude of the field inside a toroid, a distance r from the center, is given by Eq. 31–22: $B = \mu_0 i N/2\pi r$, where N is the number of turns and i is the current. Thus

$$u_B = \frac{1}{2\mu_0} \left(\frac{\mu_0 i N}{2\pi r} \right)^2 = \frac{\mu_0 i^2 N^2}{8\pi^2 r^2}.$$

(b) Evaluate the integral $U_B = \int u_B \, dV$ over the volume of the toroid. A circular strip with radius r, height h, and thickness dr has volume $dV = 2\pi r h \, dr$, so

$$U_B = \frac{\mu_0 i^2 N^2}{8\pi^2} 2\pi h \int_a^b \frac{dr}{r} = \frac{\mu_0 i^2 N^2 h}{4\pi} \ln\left(\frac{b}{a} \right).$$

Numerically,

$$U_B = \frac{(4\pi \times 10^{-7}\,\text{T} \cdot \text{m/A})(0.500\,\text{A})^2 (1250)^2 (13 \times 10^{-3}\,\text{m})}{4\pi} \ln\left(\frac{95\,\text{mm}}{52\,\text{mm}} \right)$$

$$= 3.06 \times 10^{-4}\,\text{J}.$$

(c) The inductance is given by Eq. 33–7:

$$L = \frac{\mu_0 N^2 h}{2\pi} \ln\left(\frac{b}{a} \right)$$

so the energy is given by

$$U_B = \frac{1}{2} L i^2 = \frac{\mu_0 N^2 i^2 h}{4\pi} \ln\left(\frac{b}{a} \right).$$

This the exactly the same as the expression found in part (b) and yields the same numerical result.

45P

(a)

$$u_B = \frac{B^2}{2\mu_0} = \frac{1}{2\mu_0} \left(\frac{\mu_0 i}{2R} \right)^2 = \frac{\mu_0 i^2}{R^2}$$

$$= \frac{(1.26 \times 10^{-6}\,\text{T} \cdot \text{m/A})(10\,\text{A})^2}{8(2.5 \times 10^{-3}\,\text{m/2})^2} = 1.0\,\text{J/m}^3.$$

(b)

$$u_E = \frac{\epsilon_0 E^2}{2} = \frac{\epsilon_0}{2} \left(\frac{J}{\sigma} \right)^2 = \frac{\epsilon_0}{2} \left(\frac{iR}{l} \right)^2$$

$$= \frac{(8.85 \times 10^{-12}\,\text{F/m})}{2} [(10\,\text{A})(3.3\,\Omega/10^3\,\text{m})]^2$$

$$= 4.8 \times 10^{-15}\,\text{J/m}^3.$$

Here we used $j/\sigma = i/\sigma A$ and $R/l = \rho/A = 1/\sigma A$ to obtain $J/\sigma = iR/l$.

46P
(a)

$$u_B = \frac{B_E^2}{2\mu_0} = \frac{(50 \times 10^{-6}\,\text{T})^2}{2(1.26 \times 10^{-6}\,\text{T}\cdot\text{m/A})} = 1.0 \times 10^{-3}\,\text{J/m}^3.$$

(b) The volume of the shell of thickness h is $V \approx 4\pi R_E^2 h$, where R_E is the radius of the Earth. So

$$U_B \approx VU_B \approx 4\pi(6.4 \times 10^6\ m)^2(16 \times 10^3\,\text{m})(1.0 \times 10^{-3}\,\text{J/m}^3)$$
$$= 8.4 \times 10^{15}\,\text{J}.$$

47E
(a)

$$M = \frac{\varepsilon_1}{|di_1/dt|} = \frac{25.0\,\text{mV}}{15.0\,\text{A/s}} = 1.67\,\text{mH}.$$

(b)

$$\Phi_{B2} = Mi_1 = (1.67\,\text{mH})(3.60\,\text{A}) = 6.00\,\text{mWb}.$$

48E
(a)

$$\Phi_{12} = \frac{L_1 i_1}{N_1} = \frac{(25\,\text{mH})(6.0\,\text{mA})}{100} = 1.5\,\mu\text{Wb}.$$

$$\varepsilon_1 = L_1 \frac{di_1}{dt} = (25\,\text{mH})(4.0\,\text{A/s}) = 100\,\text{mV}.$$

(b)

$$\Phi_{21} = \frac{Mi_1}{N_2} = \frac{(3.0\,\text{mH})(6.0\,\text{mA})}{200} = 90\,\text{nWb}.$$

$$\varepsilon_{21} = M\frac{di_1}{dt} = (3.0\,\text{mH})(4.0\,\text{A/s}) = 12\,\text{mV}.$$

49P
(a) Assume the current is changing at the rate di/dt and calculate the total emf across both coils. First consider the left-hand coil. The magnetic field due to the current in that coil points to the left. So does the magnetic field due to the current in coil 2. When the

current increases both fields increase and both changes in flux contribute emf's in the same direction. Thus the emf in coil 1 is

$$\epsilon_1 = -(L_1 + M)\frac{di}{dt}.$$

The magnetic field in coil 2 due to the current in that coil points to the left, as does the field in coil 2 due to the current in coil 1. The two sources of emf are again in the same direction and the emf in coil 2 is

$$\epsilon_2 = -(L_2 + M)\frac{di}{dt}.$$

The total emf across both coils is

$$\epsilon = \epsilon_1 + \epsilon_2 = -(L_1 + L_2 + 2M)\frac{di}{dt}.$$

This is exactly the emf that would be produced if the coils were replaced by a single coil with inductance $L_{eq} = L_1 + L_2 + 2M$.

(b) Reverse the leads of coil 2 so the current enters at the back of coil rather than the front as pictured in the diagram. Then the field produced by coil 2 at the site of coil 1 is opposite the field produced by coil 1 itself. The fluxes have opposite signs. An increasing current in coil 1 tends to increase the flux in that coil but an increasing current in coil 2 tends to decrease it. The emf across coil 1 is

$$\epsilon_1 = -(L_1 - M)\frac{di}{dt}.$$

Similarly the emf across coil 2 is

$$\epsilon_2 = -(L_2 - M)\frac{di}{dt}.$$

The total emf across both coils is

$$\epsilon = -(L_1 + L_2 - 2M)\frac{di}{dt}.$$

This the same as the emf that would be produced by a single coil with inductance $L_{eq} = L_1 + L_2 - 2M$.

50P

$$M = M_{cs} = \frac{N\Phi_{cs}}{i_s} = \frac{N(\mu_0 i_s n\pi R^2)}{i_s} = \mu_0 \pi R^2 nN.$$

As long as the magnetic field of the solenoid is entirely contained within the cross-section of the coil we always have $\Phi_{sc} = B_s A_s = B_s \pi R^2$, regardless of the shape, size, or possible lack of close-packing of the coil.

51P

Using the result for the flux Φ over the toroid cross section derived on page 901 of the text, we have

$$M = M_{ct} = \frac{N_c \Phi_{ct}}{i_t} = \frac{N_c}{i_t} \frac{\mu_0 i_t N_t h}{2\pi} \ln \frac{b}{a} = \frac{\mu_0 N_1 N_2 h}{2\pi} \ln \frac{b}{a},$$

where $N_t = N_1$ and $N_c = N_2$.

52P

Assume the current in solenoid 1 is i and calculate the flux linkage in solenoid 2. The mutual inductance is this flux linkage divided by i. The magnetic field inside solenoid 1 is parallel to the axis and has uniform magnitude $B = \mu_0 i n_1$, where n_1 is the number of turns per unit length of the solenoid. The cross-sectional area of the solenoid is πR_1^2 and since the field is normal to a cross section the flux through a cross section is

$$\Phi = AB = \pi R_1^2 \mu_0 n_1 i.$$

Since the magnetic field is zero outside the solenoid, this is also the flux through a cross section of solenoid 2. The number of turns in a length ℓ of solenoid 2 is $N_2 = n_2 \ell$ and the flux linkage is

$$N_2 \Phi = n_2 \ell \pi R_1^2 \mu_0 n_1 i.$$

The mutual inductance is

$$M = \frac{N_2 \Phi}{i} = \pi R_1^2 \ell \mu_0 n_1 n_2.$$

M does not depend on R_2 because there is no magnetic field in the region between the solenoids. Changing R_2 does not change the flux through solenoid 2, but changing R_1 does.

53P

(a) The flux over the loop cross section due to the current i in the wire is given by

$$\Phi_{1w} = \int_a^{a+b} B_{\text{wire}}(r) l \, dr = \int_a^{a+b} \frac{\mu_0 i l}{2\pi r} dr = \frac{\mu_0 i l}{2\pi} \ln\left(1 + \frac{b}{a}\right)$$

Thus

$$M = \frac{N \Phi_{1w}}{i} = \frac{N \mu_0 l}{2\pi} \ln\left(1 + \frac{b}{a}\right).$$

(b)

$$N = \frac{(100)(1.26 \times 10^{-6}\,\text{T} \cdot \text{m/A})(0.30\,\text{m})}{2\pi} \ln\left(1 + \frac{8.0}{1.0}\right) = 1.3 \times 10^{-5}\,\text{H}.$$

The emf ε_2 for coil 2 is given by $\varepsilon_2 = M\, di_1/dt$, so the current i_2 that passes through G is

$$i_2 = \frac{\varepsilon_2}{R} = \frac{M}{R}\frac{di_1}{dt}.$$

Integrating over t, we get

$$Q = \int_0^\infty i_2\,dt = \int_o^{i_f} \frac{M}{R}\,di_1 = \frac{Mi_f}{R}.$$

Thus $M = QR/i_f$.

Use $\varepsilon_2 = M\, di_1/dt$ to find M:

$$M = \frac{\varepsilon}{di_1/dt} = \frac{30 \times 10^3\,\text{V}}{6.0\,\text{A}/(2.5 \times 10^{-3}\,\text{s})} = 13\,\text{H}.$$

The flux over the triangular loop due to the current i in the straight wire is given by

$$\Phi = \int_d^{d+S\cos\theta} B(r)y\,dr$$

$$= \int_d^{d+S\cos\theta} \left(\frac{\mu_0 i}{2\pi r}\right)2(r-d)\tan\theta\,dr$$

$$= \frac{\mu_0 i\tan\theta}{\pi}\left[S\cos\theta - d\ln\left(1 + \frac{S\cos\theta}{d}\right)\right]$$

$$= \frac{\mu_0 i}{\pi\sqrt{3}}\left[\frac{\sqrt{3}S}{2} - d\ln\left(1 + \frac{\sqrt{3}S}{2d}\right)\right]$$

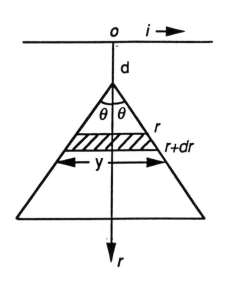

Thus

$$M = \frac{\Phi}{i} = \frac{\mu_0}{2\pi}\left[S - \frac{2d}{\sqrt{3}}\ln\left(1 + \frac{\sqrt{3}S}{2d}\right)\right].$$

57

At this instant $iR_1 + L_1\, di_1/dt = 0$ so the loop theorem reads

$$\epsilon = -L_2\frac{di}{dt} + iR_2 = L_2\left(\frac{iR_1}{L_1}\right) + iR_2 = i\left(\frac{L_2 R_1}{L_1} + R_2\right),$$

or

$$i = \frac{\epsilon L_1}{L_2 R_1 + L_1 R_2} = \frac{L_1}{L_1 + L_2}\frac{\epsilon}{R},$$

where in the last step we assumed $R_1 = R_2 = R$.

CHAPTER 34

1E
From Table 34-1,

$$\frac{e}{m}S = \left(\frac{1.6022 \times 10^{-19} \text{ C}}{9.1094 \times 10^{-31} \text{ kg}}\right)(5.2729 \times 10^{-35} \text{ J} \cdot \text{s}) = 9.2742 \times 10^{-24} \text{ J}/\text{T}$$
$$\approx \mu_s.$$

2P
Case (a): Stable; case (b): unstable; case (c): stable; and case (d): unstable. For exapmple, in case (a) if the compass to the left rotates slightly clockwise then from $\vec{\tau} = \vec{\mu} \times \mathbf{B}$ the torque $\vec{\tau}$ it is subject to is counterclockwise, pushing it back to the original position. Here $\mathbf{B}$ is the magnetic field provided by the compass to the right.

3P

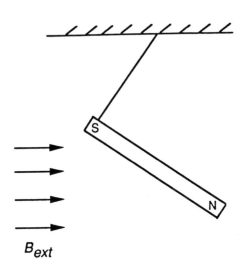

4E
(a)

$$E = \frac{e}{4\pi\epsilon_0 r^2} = \frac{(1.60 \times 10^{-19} \text{ C})(8.99 \times 10^9 \text{ N} \cdot \text{m}^2/\text{C}^2)}{(5.2 \times 10^{-11} \text{ m})^2} = 5.3 \times 10^{11} \text{ N/C}.$$

(b) Use Eq. 31-25:

$$B = \frac{\mu_0}{2\pi} \frac{\mu_p}{r^3} = \frac{(1.26 \times 10^{-6} \text{ T} \cdot \text{m/A})(1.4 \times 10^{-26} \text{ J/T})}{2\pi(5.2 \times 10^{-11} \text{ m})^3} = 1.9 \times 10^{-2} \text{ T}.$$

(c) From Eq. 34-12,

$$\frac{\mu_{\text{orb}}}{\mu_p} = \frac{eh/4\pi m}{\mu_p} = \frac{\mu_B}{\mu_p} = \frac{9.27 \times 10^{-24} \text{ J/T}}{1.4 \times 10^{-26} \text{ J/T}} = 6.6 \times 10^2.$$

5P

(a) The period of rotation is $T = 2\pi/\omega$ and in this time all the charge passes any fixed point near the ring. The average current is $i = q/T = q\omega/2\pi$ and the magnitude of the magnetic dipole moment is

$$\mu = iA = \frac{q\omega}{2\pi} \pi r^2 = \frac{1}{2} q\omega r^2.$$

(b) Curl the fingers of your right hand in the direction of rotation. Since the charge is positive your thumb points in the direction of the dipole moment. It is the same as the direction of the angular momentum of the ring.

6E

(a)

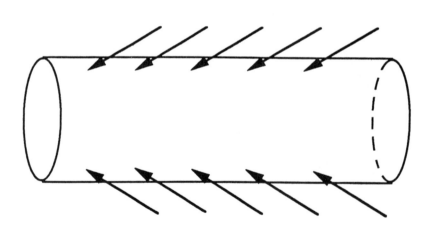

(b) The sign of $\mathbf{B} \cdot d\mathbf{A}$ for every $d\mathbf{A}$ of the side of the paper cylinder is negative.

(c) No, because Gauss's law for magnetism applies to an *enclosed* surface. In fact if we include the top and bottom of the cylinder to form an enclosed surface S then $\oint_s \mathbf{B} \cdot d\mathbf{A} = 0$ will be valid, as the flux through the open end of the cylinder near the magnet is positive.

7E

Use $\sum_{n=1}^{6} \Phi_{Bn} = 0$ to obtain

$$\Phi_{B6} = -\sum_{n=1}^{5} \Phi_{Bn} = -(-1\,\text{Wb} + 2\,\text{Wb} - 3\,\text{Wb} + 4\,\text{Wb} - 5\,\text{Wb})$$
$$= +3\,\text{Wb}.$$

8P

Use Gauss' law for magnetism: $\oint \mathbf{B} \cdot d\mathbf{A} = 0$. Write $\oint \mathbf{B} \cdot d\mathbf{A} = \Phi_1 + \Phi_2 + \Phi_C$, where Φ_1 is the magnetic flux through the first end mentioned, Φ_2 is the magnetic flux through the second end mentioned, and Φ_C is the magnetic flux through the curved surface. Over the first end the magnetic field is inward, so the flux is $\Phi_1 = -25.0\,\mu\text{Wb}$. Over the second end the magnetic field is uniform, normal to the surface, and outward, so the flux is $\Phi_2 = AB = \pi r^2 B$, where A is the area of the end and r is the radius of the cylinder. It value is

$$\Phi_2 = \pi(0.120\,\text{m})^2(1.60 \times 10^{-3}\,\text{T}) = +7.24 \times 10^{-5}\,\text{Wb} = +72.4\,\mu\text{Wb}.$$

Since the three fluxes must sum to zero,

$$\Phi_C = -\Phi_1 - \Phi_2 = 25.0\,\mu\text{Wb} - 72.4\,\mu\text{Wb} = -47.4\,\mu\text{Wb}.$$

The minus sign indicates that the flux is inward through the curved surface.

9P*

From Gauss's Law the flux through S_1 is equal to that through S_2, the portion of the xz plane that is within the cylinder. Here the normal direction of S_2 is in the positive y-axis. So

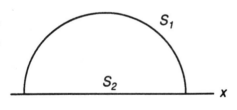

$$\Phi_B(S_1) = \Phi_B(S_2) = \int_{-r}^{r} B(x)L\,dx = 2\int_{-r}^{r} B_{\text{left}}(x)L\,dx$$
$$= 2\int_{-r}^{r} \frac{\mu_0 i}{2\pi} \frac{1}{2r-x} L\,dx = \frac{\mu_0 i L}{\pi}\ln 3.$$

10E

The horizontal component of the Earth's magnetic field is given by $B_h = B\cos\phi_i$, where B is the magnitude of the field and ϕ_i is the inclination angle. Thus

$$B = \frac{B_h}{\cos\phi_i} = \frac{16\,\mu\text{T}}{\cos 73°} = 55\,\mu\text{T}.$$

11E

The flux through Arizona is

$$\Phi = -B_r A = -(43 \times 10^{-6}\,\text{T})(295,000\,\text{km}^2)(10^3\,\text{m/km})^2 = -1.3 \times 10^7\,\text{Wb},$$

inward. By Gauss's Law this is equal to the negative value of the flux Φ' through the rest of sruface of the Earth. So $\Phi' = 1.3 \times 10^7\,\text{Wb}$, outward.

12E

(a) From $\mu = iA = i\pi R_E^2$ we get

$$i = \frac{\mu}{\pi R_E^2} = \frac{8.0 \times 10^{22}\,\text{J/T}}{\pi(6.37 \times 10^6\,\text{m})^2} = 6.3 \times 10^8\,\text{A}.$$

(b) Yes, because far away from the Earth the fields of both the Earth itself and the current loop are dipole fields. If these two dipoles cancel out then the net field will be zero.

(c) No, because the field of the current loop is not that of a magnetic dipole in the region close to the loop.

13P

(a)

$$B = \sqrt{B_h^2 + B_v^2} = \sqrt{\left(\frac{\mu_0\mu}{4\pi r^3}\cos\lambda_m\right)^2 + \left(\frac{\mu_0\mu}{2\pi r^3}\sin\lambda_m\right)^2}$$

$$= \frac{\mu_0\mu}{4\pi r^3}\sqrt{\cos^2\lambda_m + 4\sin^2\lambda_m} = \frac{\mu_0\mu}{4\pi r^3}\sqrt{1 + 3\sin^2\lambda_m},$$

where $\cos^2\lambda_m + \sin^2\lambda_m = 1$ was used.

(b)

$$\tan\phi_i = \frac{B_v}{B_h} = \frac{(\mu_0\mu/2\pi r^3)\sin\lambda_m}{(\mu_0\mu/4\pi r^3)\cos\lambda_m} = 2\tan\lambda_m.$$

14P

(a) At the magnetic equator $\lambda_m = 0$, so

$$B = \frac{\mu_0\mu}{4\pi r^3} = \frac{(1.26 \times 10^{-6}\,\text{T}\cdot\text{m/A})(8.00 \times 10^{22}\,\text{A}\cdot\text{m}^2)}{4\pi(6.37 \times 10^6\,\text{m})^3} = 3.1 \times 10^{-5}\,\text{T},$$

and $\phi_i = \tan^{-1}(2\tan\lambda_m) = \tan^{-1}(0) = 0$.

(b) At $\lambda_m = 60°$:

$$B = \frac{\mu_0 \mu}{4\pi r^3}\sqrt{1 + 3\sin^2 \lambda_m} = (3.1 \times 10^{-5})\sqrt{1 + 3\sin^2 60°}$$
$$= 5.6 \times 10^{-5}\,\text{T},$$

and $\phi_i = \tan^{-1}(2\tan 60°) = 74°$.

(c) At the north magnetic pole $\lambda_m = 90°$, so

$$B = \frac{\mu_0 \mu}{4\pi r^3}\sqrt{1 + 3\sin^2 \lambda_m} = (3.1 \times 10^{-5})\sqrt{1 + 3(1)^2}$$
$$= 6.2 \times 10^{-5}\,\text{T},$$

and $\phi_i = \tan^{-1}(2\tan 90°) = 90°$.

15P

At a distance r from the center of the Earth, the magnitude of the magnetic field is given by

$$B = \frac{\mu_0 \mu}{4\pi r^3}\sqrt{1 + 3\sin^2 \lambda_m},$$

where μ is the Earth's dipole moment and λ_m is the magnetic latitude. The ratio of the field magnitudes for two different distances at the same latitude is

$$\frac{B_2}{B_1} = \frac{r_1^3}{r_2^3}.$$

Take B_1 to be at the surface and B_2 to be half of B_1. Set r_1 equal to the radius r_e of the Earth and r_2 equal to $r_e + h$, where h is altitude at which B is half its value at the surface. Thus

$$\frac{1}{2} = \frac{r_e^3}{(r_e + h)^3}.$$

Take the cube root of both sides and solve for h. You should get

$$h = \left(2^{1/3} - 1\right) r_e = \left(2^{1/3} - 1\right)(6370\,\text{km}) = 1660\,\text{km}.$$

16P

In this case $r = 6370\,\text{km} - 2900\,\text{km} = 3470\,\text{km}$, so

$$B = \frac{\mu_0 \mu}{4\pi r^3}\left(\sqrt{1 + 3\sin^2 \lambda_m}\right)_{\text{max}} = \frac{\mu_0 \mu}{4\pi r^3}\sqrt{1 + 3(1)^2}$$
$$= \frac{(1.26 \times 10^{-6}\,\text{T} \cdot \text{m/A})(8.0 \times 10^{22}\,\text{J/T})\sqrt{4}}{4\pi(3.47 \times 10^6\,\text{m})^3} = 3.8 \times 10^{-4}\,\text{T}.$$

873

17P
In this case $\lambda_m = 90.0° - 11.5° = 78.5°$ and $r = R_E$. So

$$B = \frac{\mu_0 \mu}{4\pi R_E^3}\sqrt{1 + 3\sin^2 \lambda_m}$$

$$= \frac{(1.26 \times 10^{-6}\,\text{T} \cdot \text{m/A})(8.0 \times 10^{22}\,\text{J/T})\sqrt{1 + 3\sin^2 78.5°}}{4\pi(6.37 \times 10^6\,\text{m})^3} = 6.1 \times 10^{-5}\,\text{T},$$

and $\phi_i = \tan^{-1}(2\tan 78.5°) = 84.2°$.

18E
Let $E = \frac{3}{2}kt = |\vec{\mu} \cdot \mathbf{B} - (-\vec{\mu} \cdot \mathbf{B})| = 2\mu B$ to obtain

$$T = \frac{4\mu B}{3k} = \frac{4(1.0 \times 10^{-23}\,\text{J/T})(0.50\,\text{T})}{3(1.38 \times 10^{-23}\,\text{J/K})} = 0.48\,\text{K}.$$

19E
The magnetization is the dipole moment per unit volume, so the dipole moment is given by $\mu = MV$, where M is the magnetization and V is the volume of the cylinder. Use $V = \pi r^2 L$, where r is the radius of the cylinder and L is its length. Thus

$$\mu = M\pi r^2 L = (5.30 \times 10^3\,\text{A/m})\pi(0.500 \times 10^{-2}\,\text{m})^2(5.00 \times 10^{-2}\,\text{m}) = 2.08 \times 10^{-2}\,\text{J/T}.$$

20E
(a)

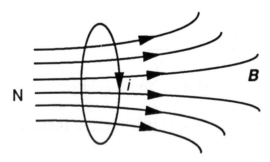

(b) The current is clockwise when the loop is viewed along the direction of the magnetic field of teh bar magnet.
(c) From this side view we see that $d\mathbf{F} = i\,d\mathbf{s} \times \mathbf{B}$ indeed has a component pointing toward the bar magnet.

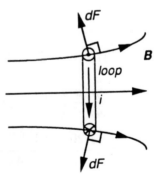

21P

For the measurements carried out the largest ratio of the magnetic field to the temperature is $(0.50\,\text{T})/(10\,\text{K}) = 0.050\,\text{T/K}$. Look at Fig. 34-11 to see if this is in the region where the magnetization is a linear function of the ratio. It is quite close to the origin, so we conclude that the magnetization obeys Curie's law.

22P

(a) From Fig. 34-11 we see that $B/T = 0.50$ when $M/M_{\text{max}} = 50\%$. So $B = 0.50\,\text{T} = (0.50)(300\,\text{K}) = 150\,\text{K}$.
(b) Similarly, now $B/T = 2.0$ so $B = (2.0)(300) = 600\,\text{T}$.
(c) Not yet.

23P

(a) Again from Fig. 34-11, for $M/M_{\text{max}} = 50\%$ we have $B/T = 0.50$. So $T = B/0.50 = 2/0.50 = 4\,\text{K}$.
Now $B/T = 2.0$ so $T = 2/2.0 = 1\,\text{K}$.

24P

(a) A charge e traveling with uniform speed v around a circular path of radius r takes time $T = 2\pi r/v$ to complete one orbit, so the average current is

$$i = \frac{e}{T} = \frac{ev}{2\pi r}\,.$$

The magnitude of the dipole moment is this times the area of the orbit:

$$\mu = \frac{ev}{2\pi r}\,\pi r^2 = \frac{evr}{2}\,.$$

Since the magnetic force, with magnitude evB, is centripetal, Newton's law yields $evB = mv^2/r$, so

$$r = \frac{mv}{eB}\,.$$

Thus

$$\mu = \frac{1}{2}(ev)\left(\frac{mv}{eB}\right) = \left(\frac{1}{B}\right)\left(\frac{1}{2}mv^2\right) = \frac{K_e}{B}\,.$$

The magnetic force $-e\mathbf{v} \times \mathbf{B}$ must point toward the center of the circular path. If the magnetic field is into the page, for example, the electron will travel clockwise around the circle. Since the electron is negative, the current is in the opposite direction, counterclockwise and, by the right-hand rule for dipole moments, the dipole moment is out of the page. That is, the dipole moment is directed opposite to the magnetic field vector.

(b) Notice that the charge canceled in the derivation of $\mu = K_e/B$. Thus the relation $\mu = K_i/B$ holds for a positive ion. If the magnetic field is into the page, the ion travels counterclockwise around a circular orbit and the current is in the same direction. Thus the dipole moment is again out of the page, opposite to the magnetic field.

(c) The magnetization is given by $M = \mu_e n_e + \mu_i n_i$, where μ_e is the dipole moment of an electron, n_e is the electron concentration, μ_i is the dipole moment of an ion, and n_i is the ion concentration. Since $n_e = n_i$, we may write n for both concentrations. Substitute $\mu_e = K_e/B$ and $\mu_i = K_i/B$ to obtain

$$M = \frac{n}{B}\left[K_e + K_i\right] = \frac{5.3 \times 10^{21}\,\mathrm{m}^{-3}}{1.2\,\mathrm{T}}\left[6.2 \times 10^{-20}\,\mathrm{J} + 7.6 \times 10^{-21}\,\mathrm{J}\right] = 310\,\mathrm{A/m}.$$

25P

$$M = \frac{N\mu P(\mu) - N\mu P(-\mu)}{P(\mu) + P(-\mu)}$$
$$= \frac{N\mu(e^{\mu B/KT} - e^{-\mu B/KT})}{e^{\mu B/KT} + e^{-\mu B/KT}} = N\mu\tanh\left(\frac{\mu B}{kT}\right).$$

(b) $\mu B \ll kT$, $e^{\pm \mu B/kT} \approx 1 \pm \mu B/kT$, so

$$M = N\mu\tanh\left(\frac{\mu B}{kT}\right) \approx \frac{N\mu[(1 + \mu B/kT) - (1 - \mu B/kT)]}{(1 + \mu B/kT) + (1 - \mu B/kT)}$$
$$= \frac{N\mu^2 B}{kT}.$$

(c) The following is a plot of $\tanh(\alpha x)$ as a function of x for $\alpha = 1$. Notice the resemblence between this plot and Fig. 34-11. By adjusting α properly you can fit the curve in Fig. 34-11 with a tanh function.

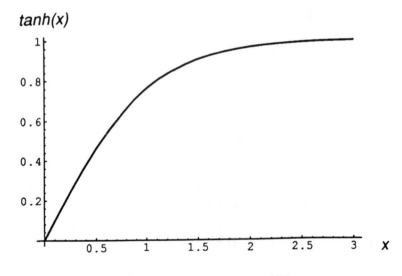

876

26P

This exercise is analogous to Exercise 20. All you need to change is the direction of i (since the direction of $\vec{\mu}$ of the loop has been reversed). This also result in the revision of direction for $d\mathbf{F}$ in part (c) of Exercise 20, which then gives a weakly repulsive force from the bar magnet.

27P

An electric field with circular field lines is induced as the magnetic field is turned on. Suppose the magnetic field increases linearly from zero to B in time t. According to Eq. 32–24 the magnitude of the electric field at the orbit is given by

$$E = \left(\frac{r}{2}\right)\frac{dB}{dt} = \left(\frac{r}{2}\right)\frac{B}{t},$$

where r is the radius of the orbit. The induced electric field is tangent to the orbit and changes the speed of the electron, the change in speed being given by

$$\Delta v = at = \frac{eE}{m}t = \left(\frac{e}{m}\right)\left(\frac{r}{2}\right)\left(\frac{B}{t}\right)t = \frac{erB}{2m}.$$

The average current associated with the circulating electron is $i = ev/2\pi r$ and the dipole moment is

$$\mu = Ai = \left(\pi r^2\right)\left(\frac{ev}{2\pi r}\right) = \frac{1}{2}evr.$$

The change in the dipole moment is

$$\Delta\mu = \frac{1}{2}er\,\Delta v = \frac{1}{2}er\frac{erB}{2m} = \frac{e^2 r^2 B}{4m}.$$

28E

The Curie temperature for iron is $770°$ C. If x is the depth at which the temperature has this value, then $10°$ C $+ (30°$ C$/km)x = 770°$ C or

$$x = \frac{770°\text{ C} - 10°\text{ C}}{30°\text{ C/km}} = 25\,\text{km}.$$

29E

(a) The field of a dipole along its axis is given by Eq. 31–25:

$$B = \frac{\mu_0}{2\pi}\frac{\mu}{z^3},$$

877

where μ is the dipole moment and z is the distance from the dipole. Thus

$$B = \frac{(4\pi \times 10^{-7} \text{ T} \cdot \text{m}/A)(1.5 \times 10^{-23} \text{ J/T})}{2\pi(10 \times 10^{-9} \text{ m})} = 3.0 \times 10^{-6} \text{ T}.$$

(b) The energy of a magnetic dipole $\vec{\mu}$ in a magnetic field $\mathbf{B}$ is given by $U = \vec{\mu} \cdot \mathbf{B} = \mu B \cos \phi$, where ϕ is the angle between the dipole moment and the field. The energy required to turn it end-for-end (from $\phi = 0°$ to $\phi = 180°$) is

$$\Delta U = 2\mu B = 2(1.5 \times 10^{-23} \text{ J/T})(3.0 \times 10^{-6} \text{ T}) = 9.0 \times 10^{-29} \text{ J} = 5.6 \times 10^{-10} \text{ eV}.$$

The mean kinetic energy of translation at room temperature is about 0.04 eV (see Sample Problem 34–4). Thus if dipole-dipole interactions were responsible for aligning dipoles, collisions would easily randomize the directions of the moments and they would not remain aligned.

30E

The saturation magnetization corresponds to complete alignment of all atomic dipoles and is given by $M_{\text{sat}} = \mu n$, where n is the number of atoms per unit volume and μ is the magnetic dipole moment of an atom. The number of nickel atoms per unit volume is $n = \rho/m$, where ρ is the density of nickel and m is the mass of a single nickel atom, calculated using $m = M/N_A$, where M is the atomic mass of nickel and N_A is the Avogadro constant. Thus

$$n = \frac{\rho N_A}{M} = \frac{(8.90 \text{ g}/cm^3)(6.02 \times 10^{23} \text{ atoms/mol})}{58.71 \text{ g}/mol}$$
$$= 9.126 \times 10^{22} \text{ atoms/cm}^3 = 9.126 \times 10^{28} \text{ atoms}/m^3.$$

The dipole moment of a single atom of nickel is

$$\mu = \frac{M_{\text{sat}}}{n} = \frac{4.70 \times 10^5 \text{ A/m}}{9.126 \times 10^{28} \text{ m}^3} = 5.15 \times 10^{-24} \text{ A} \cdot \text{m}^2.$$

31E

(a) The number of iron atoms in the bar is

$$N = \frac{(7.9 \text{ g}/cm^3)(5.0 \text{ cm})(1.0 \text{ cm}^2)}{(55.847 \text{ g/mol})/(6.022 \times 10^{23}/ \text{mol})} = 4.3 \times 10^{23}.$$

Thus the dipole moment of the bar is

$$\mu = (2.1 \times 10^{-23} \text{ J/T})(4.3 \times 10^{23}) = 8.9 \text{ A} \cdot \text{m}^2.$$

(b) $\tau = \mu B \sin 90° = (8.9\,\mathrm{A \cdot m^2})(1.57\,\mathrm{T}) = 13\,\mathrm{N \cdot m}$.

32P
(a) If the magnetization of the sphere is saturated the total dipole moment is $\mu_{total} = N\mu$, where N is the number of iron atoms in the sphere and μ is the dipole moment of an iron atom. We wish to find the radius of an iron sphere with N iron atoms. The mass of such a sphere is Nm, where m is the mass of an iron atom. It is also given by $4\pi\rho R^3/3$, where ρ is the density of iron and R is the radius of the sphere. Thus $Nm = 4\pi\rho R^3/3$ and

$$N = \frac{4\pi\rho R^3}{3m}.$$

Substitute this into $\mu_{total} = N\mu$ to obtain

$$\mu_{total} = \frac{4\pi\rho R^3\mu}{3m}.$$

Solve for R and obtain

$$R = \left[\frac{3m\mu_{total}}{4\pi\rho\mu}\right]^{1/3}.$$

The mass of an iron atom is

$$m = 56\,\mathrm{u} = (56\,\mathrm{u})(1.66 \times 10^{-27}\,\mathrm{kg/u}) = 9.30 \times 10^{-26}\,\mathrm{kg}.$$

So

$$R = \left[\frac{3(9.30 \times 10^{-26}\,\mathrm{kg})(8.0 \times 10^{22}\,\mathrm{J/T})}{4\pi(14 \times 10^3\,\mathrm{kg/m^3})(2.1 \times 10^{-23}\,\mathrm{J/T})}\right]^{1/3} = 1.8 \times 10^5\,\mathrm{m}.$$

(b) The volume of the sphere is

$$V_s = \frac{4\pi}{3}R^3 = \frac{4\pi}{3}(1.82 \times 10^5\,\mathrm{m})^3 = 2.53 \times 10^{16}\,\mathrm{m^3}$$

and the volume of the Earth is

$$V_e = \frac{4\pi}{3}(6.37 \times 10^6\,\mathrm{m})^3 = 1.08 \times 10^{21}\,\mathrm{m^3},$$

so the fraction of the Earth's volume that is occupied by the sphere is

$$\frac{2.53 \times 10^{16}\,\mathrm{m^3}}{1.08 \times 10^{21}\,\mathrm{m^3}} = 2.3 \times 10^{-5}.$$

33P

Due to the way the wire is wound it is clear that P_2 is the magnetic north pole while P_1 is the south pole.

(a) From Exercise 26 we know that the deflection will be toward P_1 (away from the magnetic north pole).

(b) As the electromagnet is turned on the magnetic flus Φ through the aluminum changes abruptly, causing a strong induced current which produces a magnetic field opposite to that of the electromagnet. As a result the aluminum sample will be pushed toward P_1, away from the magnetic north pole of the bar magnet. As Φ reaches a constant value, however, the induced current disappears and the aluminum sample, being paramagnetic, will move slightly toward P_2, the magnetic north pole of the electromagnet. This is explained in Exercise 20.

(c) A magnetic north pole will now be induced on the side of the sample closer to P_1, and a magnetic south pole will appear on the other side. If the field of the electromagnet is stonger near P_1 then the sample will move toward P_1.

34P

(a) Use Eq. 34–16 for the magnitude of the toroidal field: $B_0 = \mu_0 n i_p$, where n is the number of turns per unit length of toroid and i_p is the current required to produce the field (in the absence of the ferromagnetic material). Use the average radius ($\bar{r} = 5.5\,\text{cm}$) to calculate n:

$$n = \frac{N}{2\pi\bar{r}} = \frac{400\,turns}{2\pi(5.5 \times 10^{-2}\,\text{m})} = 1.16 \times 10^3\,\text{turns/m}.$$

Thus

$$i_p = \frac{B_0}{\mu_0 n} = \frac{0.20 \times 10^{-3}\,\text{T}}{(4\pi \times 10^{-7}\,\text{T}\cdot\text{m/A})(1.16 \times 10^3\,\text{m}^{-1})} = 0.14\,\text{A}.$$

(b) If Φ is the magnetic flux through the secondary coil then the magnitude of the emf induced in that coil is $\varepsilon = N(d\Phi/dt)$ and the current in the secondary is $i_s = \varepsilon/R$, where R is the resistance of the coil. Thus

$$i_s = \left(\frac{N}{R}\right)\frac{d\Phi}{dt}.$$

The charge that passes through the secondary when the primary current is turned on is

$$q = \int i_s\,dt = \frac{N}{R}\int \frac{d\Phi}{dt}\,dt = \frac{N}{R}\int_0^{\Phi} d\Phi = \frac{N\Phi}{R}.$$

The magnetic field through the secondary coil has magnitude $B = B_0 + B_M = 801 B_0$, where B_M is the field of the magnetic dipoles in the magnetic material. The total field is perpendicular to the plane of the secondary coil, so the magnetic flux is $\Phi = AB$, where A is the area of the Rowland ring (the field is inside the ring, not in the region between the ring and coil). If r is the radius of the ring's cross section then $A = \pi r^2$. Thus

$$\Phi = 801\pi r^2 B_0.$$

The radius r is $(6.0\,\text{cm} - 5.0\,\text{cm})/2 = 0.50\,cm$ and

$$\Phi = 801\pi(0.50 \times 10^{-2}\,\text{m})^2(0.20 \times 10^{-3}\,\text{T}) = 1.26 \times 10^{-5}\,\text{Wb}.$$

Thus

$$q = \frac{50(1.26 \times 10^{-5}\,\text{Wb})}{8.0\,\Omega} = 7.9 \times 10^{-5}\,\text{C}.$$

35

The interacting potenial energy between the magnetic dipole of the compass and the Earth's magnetic field is $U = -\vec{\mu} \cdot \mathbf{B}_E = -\mu B_E \cos\theta$, where θ is the angle between $\vec{\mu}$ and $\mathbf{B}_E$. For small angle θ we have

$$U(\theta) = -\mu B_E \cos\theta \approx -\mu B_E\left(1 - \frac{\theta^2}{2}\right) = \frac{1}{2}k\theta^2 - \mu B_E,$$

where $k = \mu B_E$. Conservation of energy for the compass then gives

$$\frac{1}{2}I\left(\frac{d\theta}{dt}\right)^2 + \frac{1}{2}k\theta^2 = \text{const.}$$

This is to be compared with the mechanical energy of a spring-mass system:

$$\frac{1}{2}m\left(\frac{dx}{dt}\right)^2 + \frac{1}{2}kx^2 = \text{const.},$$

which in turn yields $\omega = \sqrt{k/m}$. So by analogy, in our case

$$\omega = \sqrt{\frac{k}{I}} = \sqrt{\frac{\mu B_E}{I}} = \sqrt{\frac{\mu B_E}{ml^2/12}},$$

which gives

$$\mu = \frac{ml^2\omega^2}{12B_E} = \frac{(0.050\,\text{kg})(4.0 \times 10^{-2}\,\text{m})^2(45\,\text{rad/s})^2}{12(16 \times 10^{-6}\,\text{T})} = 8.4 \times 10^2\,\text{J/T}.$$

36

(a) Since the magnetic field $\mathbf{B}$ exerts a force $\mathbf{F}_B = q\mathbf{v} \times \mathbf{B}$ on the particle, $\mathbf{B}$ does not do any work on the particle ($\mathbf{F}_B \perp \mathbf{v}$). So the speed v of the particle is unchanged as a result of the $\mathbf{B}$-field. However since $\mathbf{F}_B$ does change the net centripetal force, $F_{\text{cen}} = mv^2/r$ must change, i.e. r must change. Thus $\mu_{\text{orb}} = qvr/2$ must also change.

(b) Since the original centripetal force is large, the relative change in orbital radius for the particle is small: $|\Delta r/r| \ll 1$. Thus

$$\Delta F_{\text{cen}} = \pm F_B = \pm qvB = \Delta\left(\frac{mv^2}{r}\right) = -\frac{mv^2\Delta r}{r^2},$$

so $\Delta r = \mp qBr^2/mv$. Thus

$$\Delta\mu_{\text{orb}} = \mp\frac{1}{2}qv\Delta r = \mp\frac{1}{2}qv\left(\frac{qBr^2}{mv}\right) = \mp\frac{Bq^2r^2}{2m}.$$

37

Apply Eq. 34-13 to all the six surfaces of the parallelepiped: $\sum_{i=1}^{6}\mathbf{B}_i \cdot \mathbf{A}_i = 0$. Note that

$$\mathbf{B}_1 \cdot \mathbf{A}_1 + \mathbf{B}_2 \cdot \mathbf{A}_2 = \left[B_x + \left(\frac{dB_x}{dx}\right)a\right]bc - B_xbc = \left(\frac{dB_x}{dx}\right)abc,$$

and similarly

$$\mathbf{B}_3 \cdot \mathbf{A}_3 + \mathbf{B}_4 \cdot \mathbf{A}_4 = \left(\frac{dB_y}{dy}\right)abc,$$

$$\mathbf{B}_5 \cdot \mathbf{A}_5 + \mathbf{B}_6 \cdot \mathbf{A}_6 = \left(\frac{dB_z}{dz}\right)abc.$$

Thus

$$\sum_{i=1}^{6}\mathbf{B}_i \cdot \mathbf{A}_i = \left(\frac{dB_x}{dx} + \frac{dB_y}{dy} + \frac{dB_z}{dz}\right)abc = 0,$$

which yields

$$\frac{dB_x}{dx} + \frac{dB_y}{dy} + \frac{dB_z}{dz} = 0.$$

38

Consider the current loop of length a and width b, as shown. The magnetic forces on side 1 and 3 of the loop is

$$\mathbf{F}_1 + \mathbf{F}_3 \approx ib\mathbf{B}(0,\,0,\,0) \times (-\mathbf{j})$$
$$+ ib\mathbf{B}(a,\,0,\,0) \times \mathbf{j}$$
$$= ib[\mathbf{B}(a,\,0,\,0) - \mathbf{B}(0,\,0,\,0)] \times \mathbf{j}$$
$$\approx i\left(\frac{dB_x}{dx}\right)ab\mathbf{i} \times \mathbf{j}$$
$$= i\left(\frac{dB_x}{dx}\right)ab\mathbf{k}.$$

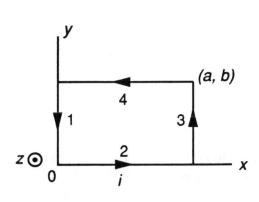

Similarly the magnetic forces on sides 2 and 4 is

$$\mathbf{F}_1 + \mathbf{F}_4 \approx i \left(\frac{dB_y}{dy} \right) ab\mathbf{k}.$$

Thus the net force on the loop is

$$\mathbf{F}_{\text{net}} = \mathbf{F}_1 + \mathbf{F}_2 + \mathbf{F}_3 + \mathbf{F}_4 \approx iab\mathbf{k} \left[\left(\frac{dB_x}{dx} \right) + \left(\frac{dB_y}{dy} \right) \right]$$

$$= - \left(\frac{dB_z}{dz} \right) \vec{\mu},$$

where in the last step we used $\vec{\mu} = iab\mathbf{k}$ and the Gauss's law of magnetism.

CHAPTER 35

1E
Solve C from $U = q_{max}^2/2C$:

$$C = \frac{q_{max}^2}{2U} = \frac{(1.60 \times 10^{-6} \text{ C})^2}{2(140 \times 10^{-6} \text{ J})} = 9.14 \times 10^{-9} \text{ F}.$$

2E
Solve i_{max} from $U = Li_{max}^2/2$:

$$i_{max} = \sqrt{\frac{2U}{L}} = \sqrt{\frac{2(10.0 \times 10^{-6} \text{ J})}{1.50 \times 10^{-3}}} = 0.115 \text{ A}.$$

3E
From $U = \frac{1}{2}Li_{max}^2 = \frac{1}{2}q_{max}^2/C$ we find

$$i_{max} = \frac{q_{max}}{\sqrt{LC}} = \frac{3.00 \times 10^{-6} \text{ C}}{\sqrt{(1.10 \times 10^{-3} \text{ H})(4.00 \times 10^{-6} \text{ F})}} = 4.52 \times 10^{-2} \text{ A}.$$

4E
(*a*) All the energy in the circuit resides in the capacitor when it has its maximum charge. The current is then zero. If C is the capacitance and Q is the maximum charge on the capacitor then the total energy is

$$U = \frac{Q^2}{2C} = \frac{(2.90 \times 10^{-6} \text{ C})^2}{2(3.60 \times 10^{-6} \text{ F})} = 1.17 \times 10^{-6} \text{ J}.$$

(*b*) When the capacitor is fully discharged the current is a maximum and all the energy resides in the inductor. If I is the maximum current, then $U = LI^2/2$ and

$$I = \sqrt{\frac{2U}{L}} = \sqrt{\frac{2(1.17 \times 10^{-6} \text{ J})}{75 \times 10^{-3} \text{ H}}} = 5.59 \times 10^{-3} \text{ A}.$$

5E
(a) $T = 4(1.50\mu\text{s}) = 6.00\mu\text{s}.$

(b) $f = T^{-1} = (6.00 \mu \text{s})^{-1} = 1.67 \times 10^5$ Hz.

(c) Half a period, or 3.00μ s.

6P
Refer to Fig. 35-1.

(a)
$$t_a = nT = \frac{n}{T} = \frac{n}{2.00 \times 10^3 \text{ Hz}} = n(5.00 \mu \text{s}),$$

where $n = 1, 2, 3, 4, \cdots$.

(b) First, it takes $T/2$ for the other plate to have maximum positive charge for the first time. Then every later this will repeat once every period. So

$$t_b = \frac{T}{2} + nT = (2n+1)\frac{T}{2} = \frac{(2n+1)}{2f} = \frac{(2n+1)}{2(2 \times 10^3 \text{ Hz})}$$
$$= (2n+1)(2.50 \mu \text{s}),$$

where $n = 0, 1, 2, 3, 4, \cdots$.

(c) First, it takes $T/4$ for the inductor to have maximum magnetic field for the first time. Then this will repeat every half a period. So

$$t_c = \frac{T}{4} + \frac{nT}{2} = \frac{1}{2} t_b = (2n+1)(1.25 \mu \text{s}),$$

where $n = 0, 1, 2, 3, 4, \cdots$.

7E
(a)
$$\omega = \sqrt{\frac{k}{m}} = \sqrt{\frac{F/x}{m}} = \sqrt{\frac{8.0 \text{ N}}{(2.0 \times 10^{-3} \text{ m})(0.50 \text{ kg})}} = 89 \text{ rad/s}.$$

(b)
$$T = \frac{2\pi}{\omega} = \frac{2\pi}{89 \text{ rad/s}} = 7.0 \times 10^{-2} \text{ s}.$$

(c) Let $\omega = (LC)^{-1/2}$ and solve for C:

$$C = \frac{1}{\omega^2 L} = \frac{1}{(89 \text{ rad/s})^2 (5.0 \text{ H})} = 2.5 \times 10^{-5} \text{ F}.$$

8P
(a) The mass m corresponds to the inductance, so $m = 1.25$ kg.

(*b*) The spring constant k corresponds to the reciprocal of the capacitance. Since the total energy is given by $U = Q^2/2C$, where Q is the maximum charge on the capacitor and C is the capacitance,

$$C = \frac{Q^2}{2U} = \frac{(175 \times 10^{-6}\,\text{C})^2}{2(5.70 \times 10^{-6}\,\text{J})} = 2.69 \times 10^{-3}\,\text{F}$$

and

$$k = \frac{1}{2.69 \times 10^{-3}\,\text{m/N}} = 372\,\text{N/m}.$$

(*c*) The maximum displacement x_m corresponds to the maximum charge, so

$$x_m = 175 \times 10^{-6}\,\text{m}.$$

(*d*) The maximum speed v_m corresponds to the maximum current. The maximum current is

$$I = Q\omega = \frac{Q}{\sqrt{LC}} = \frac{175 \times 10^{-6}\,\text{C}}{\sqrt{(1.25\,\text{H})(2.69 \times 10^{-3}\,\text{F})}} = 3.02 \times 10^{-3}\,\text{A}.$$

Thus $v_m = 3.02 \times 10^{-3}\,\text{m/s}$.

9E
Solve L from $f = (2\pi\sqrt{LC})^{-1}$:

$$L = \frac{1}{4\pi^2 f^2 C} = \frac{1}{4\pi^2 (10 \times 10^3\,\text{Hz})^2 (6.7 \times 10^{-6}\,\text{F})} = 3.8 \times 10^{-5}\,\text{H}.$$

10E
Solve C from $f = (2\pi\sqrt{LC})^{-1}$:

$$C = \frac{1}{4\pi^2 f^2 L} = \frac{1}{4\pi^2 (3.50 \times 10^3\,\text{Hz})^2 (1.30 \times 10^{-3}\,\text{H})} = 1.59 \times 10^{-6}\,\text{F}.$$

11E
If T is the period of oscillation, the time required is $t = T/4$. The period is given by $T = 2\pi/\omega = 2\pi\sqrt{LC}$, where ω is the angular frequency of oscillation, L is the inductance, and C is the capacitance. Hence

$$t = \frac{T}{4} = \frac{2\pi\sqrt{LC}}{4} = \frac{2\pi\sqrt{(0.050\,\text{H})(4.0 \times 10^{-6}\,\text{F})}}{4} = 7.0 \times 10^{-4}\,\text{s}.$$

12E

When switch S_1 is closed and the others are open, the inductor is essentially out of the circuit and what remains is an RC circuit. The time constant is $\tau_C = RC$. When switch S_2 is closed and the others are open the capacitor is essentially out of the circuit and what remains is an LR circuit with time constant $\tau_L = L/R$. When switch S_3 is closed and the others are open the resistor is essentially out of the circuit and what remains is an LC circuit that oscillates with period $T = 2\pi\sqrt{LC}$. Substitute $L = R\tau_L$ and $C = \tau_C/R$ to obtain $T = 2\pi\sqrt{\tau_C\tau_L}$.

13E

Apply the loop rule to the LC circuit:

$$\varepsilon_{\text{total}} = \varepsilon_L + \varepsilon_C = L\frac{di}{dt} + \frac{q}{C} = 0.$$

Since $i = dq/dt$, $di/dt = d^2q/dt^2$. Thus

$$L\frac{d^2q}{dt^2} + \frac{q}{C} = 0.$$

14E

Apply the loop rule to the whole circuit:

$$\varepsilon_{\text{total}} = \varepsilon_{L1} + \varepsilon_{C1} + \varepsilon_{R1} + \cdots = \sum_i \varepsilon_{Li} + \sum_j \varepsilon_{Cj} + \sum_k \varepsilon_{Rk}$$

$$= \sum_i L_i\frac{di}{dt} + \sum_j \frac{q}{C_j} + \sum_k iR_k$$

$$= L\frac{di}{dt} + \frac{q}{C} + iR = 0,$$

where $L = \sum_i L_i$, $C^{-1} = (\sum_j C_j^{-1})^{-1}$, and $R = \sum_k R_k$. This is equivalent to the simple LRC circuit shown in Fig 35-11(b).

15P

(a) $q_{\text{max}} = CV_{\text{max}} = (1.0 \times 10^{-9}\,\text{F})(3.0\,\text{V}) = 3.0 \times 10^{-9}\,\text{C}.$

(b) From $U = \frac{1}{2}Li_{\text{max}}^2 = \frac{1}{2}q_{\text{max}}^2/C$ we get

$$i_{\text{max}} = \frac{q_{\text{max}}}{\sqrt{LC}} = \frac{3.0 \times 10^{-9}\,\text{C}}{\sqrt{(3.0 \times 10^{-3}\,\text{H})(1.0 \times 10^{-9}\,\text{F})}} = 1.7 \times 10^{-3}\,\text{A}.$$

(c) $U_{B,\,max} = \frac{1}{2}Li^2_{max} = \frac{1}{2}(3.0 \times 10^{-3}\text{ H})(1.7 \times 10^{-3}A)^2 = 4.5 \times 10^{-9}\text{ J.}$

16P

(a)
$$\omega = \frac{1}{\sqrt{LC}} = \frac{1}{\sqrt{(3.00 \times 10^{-3}\text{ H})(10.0 \times 10^{-6}\text{ F})}} = 5.77 \times 10^3\text{ rad/s.}$$

(b)
$$T = \frac{2\pi}{\omega} = \frac{2\pi}{5.77 \times 10^3\text{ rad/s}} = 1.09 \times 10^{-3}\text{ s.}$$

(c) Use $q(t) = q_{max}\cos(\omega t)$. The sketch is shown below. Here $q_{max} = 220\mu\text{ C}$ and $T = 1.09 \times 10^{-3}$ s.

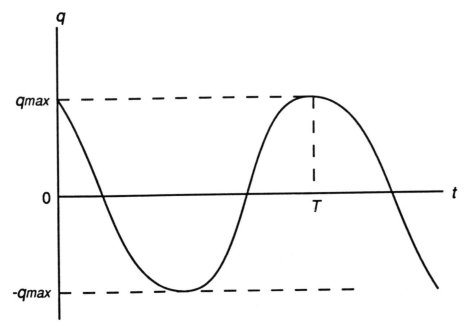

17P

(a) $U = \frac{1}{2}Li^2_{max} = \frac{1}{2}q^2_{max}/C$ and solve for L:

$$L = \frac{1}{C}\left(\frac{q_{max}}{i_{max}}\right)^2 = \frac{1}{C}\left(\frac{CV_{max}}{i_{max}}\right)^2 = C\left(\frac{V_{max}}{i_{max}}\right)^2$$

$$= (4.00 \times 10^{-6}\text{ F})\left(\frac{1.50\text{ V}}{50.0 \times 10^{-3}\text{ A}}\right)^2 = 3.60 \times 10^{-3}\text{ H.}$$

(b)
$$f = \frac{1}{2\pi\sqrt{LC}} = \frac{1}{2\pi\sqrt{(3.60 \times 10^{-3}\text{ H})(4.00 \times 10^{-6}\text{ F})}} = 1.33 \times 10^3\text{ Hz.}$$

(c) Refer to Fig. 35-1.

$$t = \frac{T}{4} = \frac{1}{4f} = \frac{1}{4(1.33 \times 10^3 \text{ Hz})} = 1.88 \times 10^{-4} \text{ s}.$$

18P

(a) After the switch is thrown to position b the circuit is an LC circuit. The angular frequency of oscillation is $\omega = 1/\sqrt{LC}$ and the frequency is

$$f = \frac{\omega}{2\pi} = \frac{1}{2\pi\sqrt{LC}} = \frac{1}{2\pi\sqrt{(54.0 \times 10^{-3} \text{ H})(6.20 \times 10^{-6} \text{ F})}} = 275 \text{ Hz}.$$

(b) When the switch is thrown, the capacitor is charged to $V = 34.0$ V and the current is zero. Thus the maximum charge on the capacitor is $Q = VC = (34.0 \text{ V})(6.20 \times 10^{-6} \text{ F}) = 2.11 \times 10^{-4}$ C. The current amplitude is

$$I = \omega Q = 2\pi f Q = 2\pi(275 \text{ Hz})(2.11 \times 10^{-4} \text{ C}) = 0.365 \text{ A}.$$

19P

The capacitors C_1 and C_2 can be used in four different ways: (1) C_1 only; (2) C_2 only; (3) C_1 and C_2 in parallel; and (4) C_1 and C_2 in series. Then corresponding oscillation frequencies are:

$$f_1 = \frac{1}{2\pi\sqrt{LC_1}} = \frac{1}{2\pi\sqrt{(1.0 \times 10^{-2} \text{ H})(5.0 \times 10^{-6} \text{ F})}} = 7.1 \times 10^2 \text{ Hz};$$

$$f_2 = \frac{1}{2\pi\sqrt{LC_2}} = \frac{1}{2\pi\sqrt{(1.0 \times 10^{-2} \text{ H})(2.0 \times 10^{-6} \text{ F})}} = 1.1 \times 10^3 \text{ Hz};$$

$$f_3 = \frac{1}{2\pi\sqrt{L(C_1 + C_2)}} = \frac{1}{2\pi\sqrt{(1.0 \times 10^{-2} \text{ H})(2.0 + 5.0)10^{-6} \text{ F}}} = 6.0 \times 10^2 \text{ Hz};$$

and

$$f_4 = \frac{1}{2\pi\sqrt{LC_1C_2/(C_1 + C_2)}} = \frac{1}{2\pi}\sqrt{\frac{(2.0 + 5.0)10^{-6} \text{ F}}{(1.0 \times 10^{-2} \text{ H})(2.0 \times 10^{-6} \text{ F})(5.0 \times 10^{-6} \text{ F})}}$$
$$= 1.3 \times 10^3 \text{ Hz}.$$

20P

(a) Solve L from $2\pi f = (LC)^{-1/2}$:

$$L = \frac{1}{4\pi^2 f^2 C} = \frac{1}{4\pi^2(10.4 \times 10^3 \text{ Hz})^2(340 \times 10^{-6} \text{ F})} = 6.89 \times 10^{-7} \text{ H}.$$

(b) $U = \frac{1}{2}Li_{max}^2 = \frac{1}{2}(6.89 \times 10^{-7} \text{ H})(7.20 \times 10^{-3} \text{ A})^2 = 1.79 \times 10^{-11} \text{ J}.$

(c) Solve for q_{max} from $U = q_{max}^2/(2C)$:

$$q_{max} = \sqrt{2CU} = \sqrt{2(340 \times 10^{-6} \text{ F})(1.79 \times 10^{-11} \text{ J})} = 1.10 \times 10^{-7} \text{ C}.$$

21P

(a) At any time the total energy U in the circuit is the sum of the energy U_E in the electric field of the capacitor and the energy U_B in the magnetic field of the inductor. When $U_E = 0.500U_B$, then $U_B = 2.00U_E$ and $U = U_E + U_B = 3.00U_E$. U_E is given by $q^2/2C$, where q is the charge on the capacitor and C is the capacitance. The total energy U is given by $Q^2/2C$, where Q is the maximum charge on the capacitor, so $Q^2/2C = 3.00q^2/2C$ or $q = Q/\sqrt{3.00} = 0.577Q$.

(b) If the capacitor is fully charged at time $t = 0$ then the charge on the capacitor is given by $q(t) = Q\cos\omega t$, where ω is the angular frequency of oscillation. The condition $q = 0.577Q$ is satisfied when $\cos\omega t = 0.557$ or $\omega t = 0.955\text{ rad}$. Since $\omega = 2\pi/T$, where T is the period of oscillation, $t = 0.955T/2\pi = 0.152T$.

22P

(a) Since the percentage of energy stored in the electric field of the capacitor is $(1 - 75.0\%) = 25.0\%$, we have

$$\frac{U_E}{U} = \frac{q^2/2C}{q_{max}^2/2C} = 25.0\%,$$

which gives $q = \sqrt{25.0\%}\, q_{max} = 0.500q_{max}$.

(b) From

$$\frac{U_B}{U} = \frac{Li^2/2}{Li_{max}^2/2} = 75.0\%$$

we get $i = \sqrt{75.0\%}\, i_{max} = 0.866i_{max}$.

23P

The frequency f as a function of θ, the angle of rotation of the knob, is given by $f(\theta) = f_0 + k\theta$, when $f_0 = 2 \times 10^5$ Hz and $k = [f(180°) - f_0]/\pi = (4 \times 10^5 \text{ Hz} - 2 \times 10^5 \text{ Hz})/\pi = 6.4 \times 10^4$ Hz/rad. Thus from $2\pi f(\theta) = [LC(\theta)]^{-1/2}$ we get

$$C(\theta) = \frac{1}{4\pi^2 L f^2(\theta)} = \frac{1}{4\pi^2(f_0 + k\theta)^2 L}.$$

The plot of $C(\theta)$ vs θ is as follows.

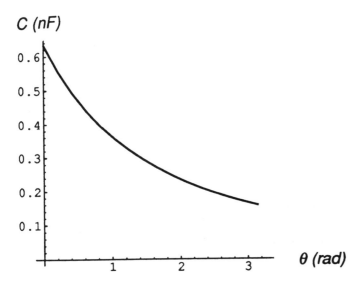

24P

(a) Since the frequency of oscillation f is related to the inductance L and capacitance C by $f = 1/2\pi\sqrt{LC}$, the smaller value of C gives the larger value of f. Hence, $f_{\max} = 1/2\pi\sqrt{LC_{\min}}$, $f_{\min} = 1/2\pi\sqrt{LC_{\max}}$, and

$$\frac{f_{\max}}{f_{\min}} = \frac{\sqrt{C_{\max}}}{\sqrt{C_{\min}}} = \frac{\sqrt{365\,\mathrm{pF}}}{\sqrt{10\,\mathrm{pF}}} = 6.0 \,.$$

(b) You want to choose the additional capacitance C so the ratio of the frequencies is

$$r = \frac{1.60\,\mathrm{MHz}}{0.54\,\mathrm{MHz}} = 2.96 \,.$$

Since the additional capacitor is in parallel with the tuning capacitor, its capacitance adds to that of the tuning capacitor. If C is in picofarads, then

$$\frac{\sqrt{C + 365\,\mathrm{pF}}}{\sqrt{C + 10\,\mathrm{pF}}} = 2.96 \,.$$

The solution for C is

$$C = \frac{(365\,\mathrm{pF}) - (2.96)^2(10\,\mathrm{pF})}{(2.96)^2 - 1} = 36\,\mathrm{pF} \,.$$

Solve $f = 1/2\pi\sqrt{LC}$ for L. For the minimum frequency $C = 365\,\mathrm{pF} + 36\,\mathrm{pF} = 401\,\mathrm{pF}$ and $f = 0.54\,\mathrm{MHz}$. Thus

$$L = \frac{1}{(2\pi)^2 C f^2} = \frac{1}{(2\pi)^2(401 \times 10^{-12}\,\mathrm{F})(0.54 \times 10^6\,\mathrm{Hz})^2} = 2.2 \times 10^{-4}\,\mathrm{H} \,.$$

25P

(a) The total energy U is the sum of the energies in the inductor and capacitor. If q is the charge on the capacitor, C is the capacitance, i is the current, and L is the inductance, then

$$U = U_E + U_B = \frac{q^2}{2C} + \frac{i^2 L}{2}$$
$$= \frac{(3.80 \times 10^{-6}\,\text{C})^2}{2(7.80 \times 10^{-6}\,\text{F})} + \frac{(9.20 \times 10^{-3}\,\text{A})^2(25.0 \times 10^{-3}\,\text{H})}{2} = 1.98 \times 10^{-6}\,\text{J}.$$

(b)
Solve $U = Q^2/2C$ for the maximum charge Q:

$$Q = \sqrt{2CU} = \sqrt{2(7.80 \times 10^{-6}\,\text{F})(1.98 \times 10^{-6}\,\text{J})} = 5.56 \times 10^{-6}\,\text{C}.$$

(c) Solve $U = I^2 L/2$ for the maximum current I:

$$I = \sqrt{\frac{2U}{L}} = \sqrt{\frac{2(1.98 \times 10^{-6}\,\text{J})}{25.0 \times 10^{-3}\,\text{H}}} = 1.26 \times 10^{-2}\,\text{A}.$$

(d) If q_0 is the charge on the capacitor at time $t = 0$, then $q_0 = Q \cos \phi$ and

$$\phi = \cos^{-1}\left(\frac{q}{Q}\right) = \cos^{-1}\left(\frac{3.80 \times 10^{-6}\,\text{C}}{5.56 \times 10^{-6}\,\text{C}}\right) = \pm 46.9°.$$

For $\phi = +46.9°$ the charge on the capacitor is decreasing, for $\phi = -46.9°$ it is increasing. To check this calculate the derivative of q with respect to time, evaluated for $t = 0$. You should get $-\omega Q \sin \phi$. You want this to be positive. Since $\sin(+46.9°)$ is positive and $\sin(-46.9°)$ is negative the correct value for increasing charge is $\phi = -46.9°$.

(e) Now you want the derivative to be negative and $\sin \phi$ to be positive. Take $\phi = +46.9°$.

26P

(a) The charge is given by $q(t) = Q \sin \omega t$, where Q is the maximum charge on the capacitor and ω is the angular frequency of oscillation. A sine function was chosen so that $q = 0$ at time $t = 0$. The current is

$$i(t) = \frac{dq}{dt} = \omega Q \cos \omega t$$

and at $t = 0$ it is $I = \omega Q$. Since $\omega = 1/\sqrt{LC}$,

$$Q = I\sqrt{LC} = (2.00\,\text{A})\sqrt{(3.00 \times 10^{-3}\,\text{H})(2.70 \times 10^{-6}\,\text{F})} = 1.80 \times 10^{-4}\,\text{C}.$$

(b) The energy stored in the capacitor is given by

$$U_E = \frac{q^2}{2C} = \frac{Q^2 \sin^2 \omega t}{2C}$$

and its rate of change is

$$\frac{dU_E}{dt} = \frac{Q^2\omega \sin\omega t \cos\omega t}{C}.$$

Use the trigonometric identity $\cos\omega t \sin\omega t = \frac{1}{2}\sin(2\omega t)$ to write this

$$\frac{dU_E}{dt} = \frac{\omega Q^2}{2C}\sin(2\omega t).$$

The greatest rate of change occurs when $\sin(2\omega t) = 1$ or $2\omega t = \pi/2\,\text{rad}$. This means

$$t = \frac{\pi}{4\omega} = \frac{\pi T}{4(2\pi)} = \frac{T}{8},$$

where T is the period of oscillation. The relationship $\omega = 2\pi/T$ was used.

(c) Substitute $\omega = 2\pi/T$ and $\sin(2\omega t) = 1$ into $dU_E/dt = (\omega Q^2/2C)\sin(2\omega t)$ to obtain

$$\left(\frac{dU_E}{dt}\right)_{\text{max}} = \frac{2\pi Q^2}{2TC} = \frac{\pi Q^2}{TC}.$$

Now $T = 2\pi\sqrt{LC} = 2\pi\sqrt{(3.00 \times 10^{-3}\,\text{H})(2.70 \times 10^{-6}\,\text{F})} = 5.655 \times 10^{-4}\,\text{s}$, so

$$\left(\frac{dU_E}{dt}\right)_{\text{max}} = \frac{\pi(1.80 \times 10^{-4}\,\text{C})^2}{(5.655 \times 10^{-4}\,\text{s})(2.70 \times 10^{-6}\,\text{F})} = 66.7\,\text{W}.$$

Notice that this is a positive result, indicating that the energy in the capacitor is indeed increasing at $t = T/8$.

27P

Compare the expression for i here with $i = i_{\text{max}}\sin(\omega t + \phi_0)$. Let $(\omega t + \phi) = 2500t + 0.680 = \pi/2$ to obtain $t = 3.56 \times 10^{-4}\,\text{s}$.
(b) Since $\omega = 2500 = (LC)^{-1/2}$,

$$L = \frac{1}{(2500)^2 C} = \frac{1}{(2500)^2(64.0 \times 10^{-6}\,\text{F})} = 2.50 \times 10^{-3}\,\text{H}.$$

(c)

$$U = \frac{1}{2}Li^2_{\text{max}} = \frac{1}{2}(2.50 \times 10^{-3}\,\text{H})(1.60\,\text{A})^2 = 3.20 \times 10^{-3}\,\text{J}.$$

28P

For the first circuit $\omega = (L_1 C_1)^{-1/2}$, and for the second one $\omega = (L_2 C_2)^{-1/2}$. When the two circuits are connected in series the new frequency is

$$\omega' = \frac{1}{\sqrt{L_{eq} C_{eq}}} = \frac{1}{\sqrt{(L_1 + L_2) C_1 C_2/(C_1 + C_2)}} = \frac{1}{\sqrt{(L_1 C_1 C_2 + L_2 C_2 C_1)/(C_1 + C_2)}}$$

$$= \frac{1}{\sqrt{L_1 C_1}\sqrt{(C_1 + C_2)/(C_1 + C_2)}} = \omega,$$

where we used $\omega^{-1} = \sqrt{L_1 C_1} = \sqrt{L_2 C_2}$.

29P

(a) Consider the joint point P. We have $i' = i - i = 0$. Since no current goes through the middle inductor the circuit is equivalent to two L's and C's in series. The loop equation is

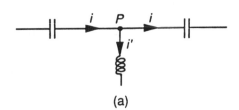

(a)

$$L \frac{di}{dt} + \frac{q}{C} + L \frac{di}{dt} + \frac{q}{C} = 0,$$

or

$$2L \frac{di}{dt} + \frac{q}{C/2} = 0.$$

This is equivalent with a single LC circuit with $L_{eq} = 2L$ and $C_{eq} = C/2$. Thus

$$\omega = \frac{1}{\sqrt{L_{eq} C_{eq}}} = \frac{1}{\sqrt{(2L)(C/2)}} = \frac{1}{\sqrt{LC}}.$$

(b) Now $i' = i + i = 2i$ (see the figure to the right). Apply the loop equation to the left half of the circuit containing the capacitor on the left and the inductors on the left and in the middle, we have

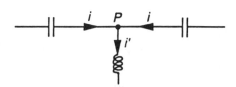

(b)

$$L \frac{di}{dt} + \frac{q}{C} + L \frac{di'}{dt} = L \frac{di}{dt} + \frac{q}{C} + 2L \frac{di}{dt} = 0,$$

or

$$L_{eq} \frac{di}{dt} + \frac{q}{C_{eq}} = 0,$$

where $L_{eq} = 3L$ and $C_{eq} = C$. The corresponding oscillation angular frequency is then

$$\omega = \frac{1}{\sqrt{L_{eq} C_{eq}}} = \frac{1}{\sqrt{3LC}}.$$

(c) In a single-loop LC circuit there is only one frequency, $\omega = (L_{eq} C_{eq})^{-1/2}$. This contradicts our case here so it is impossible to reduce our circuit to a single-loop one.

30P*

The energy needed to charge the $100\,\mu\text{F}$ capacitor to $300\,\text{V}$ is

$$\frac{1}{2}C_{100}V^2 = \frac{1}{2}(100 \times 10^{-6}\,\text{F})(300\,\text{V})^2 = 4.50\,\text{J}.$$

The energy originally in the $900\,\mu\text{F}$ capacitor is

$$\frac{1}{2}C_{900}V^2 = \frac{1}{2}(900 \times 10^{-6}\,\text{F})(100\,\text{V})^2 = 4.5\,\text{J}.$$

All the energy originally in the $900\,\mu\text{F}$ capacitor must be transferred to the $100\,\mu\text{F}$ capacitor. The plan is to store it temporarily in the inductor. To do this leave switch S_1 open and close switch S_2. Wait until the $900\,\mu\text{F}$ capacitor is completely discharged and the current in the right-hand loop is a maximum. This is one quarter of the period of oscillation. Since

$$T_{900} = 2\pi\sqrt{LC_{900}} = 2\pi\sqrt{(10.0\,\text{H})(900 \times 10^{-6}\,\text{F})} = 0.596\,\text{s},$$

you should wait $(0.596\,\text{s})/4 = 0.149\,\text{s}$. At that instant close switch S_1 and open switch S_2 so the current is in the left-hand loop. Now wait one quarter of the period of oscillation of the left-hand LC circuit and open switch S_1. The $100\,\mu\text{F}$ capacitor then has maximum charge and all the energy resides in it. The period of oscillation is

$$T_{100} = 2\pi\sqrt{LC_{100}} = 2\pi\sqrt{(10.0\,\text{H})(100 \times 10^{-6}\,\text{F})} = 0.199\,\text{s}$$

and you must keep S_1 closed for $(0.199\,\text{s})/4 = 0.0497\,\text{s}$ before opening it again.

31E

From Eq. 35-18, Let

$$\frac{q}{Q} = e^{-RnT/2L} = 99.0\%,$$

where $n = 50.0$ and $T \approx 2\pi\sqrt{LC}$, we get

$$R = \frac{-\ln(99.0\%)}{n\pi}\sqrt{\frac{L}{C}}$$

$$= \frac{-\ln(99.0\%)}{50.0\pi}\sqrt{\frac{220 \times 10^{-3}\,\text{H}}{12.0 \times 10^{-6}\,\text{F}}} = 8.66 \times 10^{-3}\,\Omega.$$

32E

(a) Since $T = 2\pi/\omega = 2\pi\sqrt{LC}$,

$$-\pi R\sqrt{\frac{C}{L}}\frac{t}{T} = -\pi R\sqrt{\frac{C}{L}}\frac{t}{2\pi\sqrt{LC}} = -\frac{Rt}{2L}.$$

Thus $e^{-Rt/2L} = e^{-\pi R\sqrt{C/L}(t/T)}$.

(b) Since $-\pi R\sqrt{C/L}(t/T)$ must be unitlss and so is t/T, $R\sqrt{C/L}$ must also be unitless. So the SI unit of $\sqrt{C/L}$ must be Ω^{-1}, i.e. $\sqrt{L/C}$ must have an SI unit of Ω.

(c) Since the amplitude of oscillation reduces by a factor of $e^{-\pi R\sqrt{C/L}(T/T)} = e^{-\pi R\sqrt{C/L}}$ after each cycle, the condition is equivalent to $\pi R\sqrt{C/L} \ll 1$, or $R \ll \sqrt{L/C}$.

33P

Since the maximum energy in the capacitor each cycle is given by $q_{max}^2/2C$, where q_{max} is the maximum charge and C is the capacitance, you want the time for which

$$\frac{q_{max}^2}{2C} = \frac{1}{2}\frac{Q^2}{2C}.$$

This means $q_{max} = Q/\sqrt{2}$. Now q_{max} is given by

$$q_{max} = Qe^{-Rt/2L},$$

where R is the resistance and L is the inductance in the circuit. Divide by Q and take the natural logarithm of both sides to obtain

$$\ln\left(\frac{q_{max}}{Q}\right) = -\frac{Rt}{2L}.$$

Solve for t:

$$t = -\frac{2L}{R}\ln\left(\frac{q_{max}}{Q}\right) = -\frac{2L}{R}\ln\left(\frac{1}{\sqrt{2}}\right) = \frac{L}{R}\ln 2.$$

The identities $\ln(1/\sqrt{2}) = -\ln\sqrt{2} = -\frac{1}{2}\ln 2$ were used to obtain the last form of the result.

34P

The charge q after N cycles is obtained by stbstituting $t = NT = 2\pi N/\omega'$ into Eq. 35-18:

$$q = Qe^{-Rt/2L}\cos(\omega't) = Qe^{-RNT/2L} = Qe^{-RN(2\pi\sqrt{L/C})/2L}$$
$$= Qe^{-\pi NR\sqrt{C/L}}.$$

So

$q|_{N=5} = (6.20\mu\,\text{C})e^{-5\pi(7.20\,\Omega)\sqrt{3.20\mu\,\text{F}/12.0\,\text{H}}} = 5.85\mu\,\text{C}$;

$q|_{N=10} = (6.20\mu\,\text{C})e^{-10\pi(7.20\,\Omega)\sqrt{3.20\mu\,\text{F}/12.0\,\text{H}}} = 5.52\mu\,\text{C}$;

and $q|_{N=100} = (6.20\mu\,\text{C})e^{-100\pi(7.20\,\Omega)\sqrt{3.20\mu\,\text{F}/12.0\,\text{H}}} = 1.93\mu\,\text{C}$.

35P
(a) From Eq. 35-18 we get

$$\frac{dq}{dt} = \frac{d}{dt}[Qe^{-Rt/2L}\cos(\omega't + \phi)]$$

$$= -\frac{RQ}{2L}e^{-Rt/2L}\cos(\omega't + \phi) - \omega'Qe^{-Rt/2L}\sin(\omega't + \phi)$$

and

$$\frac{d^2q}{dt^2} = \left(\frac{R}{2L}\right)e^{-Rt/2L}\left[\left(\frac{RQ}{2L}\right)\cos(\omega't + \phi) - \omega'Q\sin(\omega't + \phi)\right]$$

$$+ e^{-Rt/2L}\left[\frac{RQ\omega'}{2L}\sin(\omega't + \phi) - \omega'^2Q\cos(\omega't + \phi)\right].$$

Substituting these expressions and Eq. 35-18 into Eq. 350-17:

$$Qe^{-Rt/2L}\left[-\omega'^2L - \left(\frac{R}{2L}\right)^2 + \frac{1}{c}\right]\cos(\omega't + \phi) = 0.$$

Since this equation is valid at any time t, we must have

$$-\omega'^2L - \left(\frac{R}{2L}\right)^2 + \frac{1}{C} = 0,$$

or

$$\omega' = \sqrt{\frac{1}{LC} - \left(\frac{R}{2L}\right)^2} = \sqrt{\omega^2 - \left(\frac{R}{2L}\right)^2}.$$

(b) The fractional shift in frequency is

$$\frac{\Delta\omega}{\omega} = \frac{\omega - \omega'}{\omega} = 1 - \frac{\sqrt{(1/LC) - (R/2L)^2}}{\sqrt{1/LC}} = 1 - \sqrt{1 - \frac{R^2C}{4L}}$$

$$= 1 - \sqrt{1 - \frac{(100\,\Omega)^2(7.30 \times 10^{-6}\,\text{F})}{4(4.40\,\text{H})}} = 0.21\%.$$

36P*
Let t be a time at which the capacitor is fully charged in some cycle and let $q_{\text{max 1}}$ be the charge on the capacitor then. The energy in the capacitor at that time is

$$U(t) = \frac{q_{\text{max 1}}^2}{2C} = \frac{Q^2}{2C}e^{-Rt/L},$$

897

where

$$q_{max\ 1} = Q\,e^{-Rt/2L}$$

was used. Here Q is the charge at $t = 0$. One cycle later the maximum charge is

$$q_{max\ 2} = Q\,e^{-R(t+T)/2L}$$

and the energy is

$$U(t+T) = \frac{q_{max\ 2}^2}{2C} = \frac{Q^2}{2C}\,e^{-R(t+T)/L}\,,$$

where T is the period of oscillation. The fractional loss in energy is

$$\frac{\Delta U}{U} = \frac{U(t) - U(t+T)}{U(t)} = \frac{e^{-Rt/L} - e^{-R(t+T)/L}}{e^{-Rt/L}} = 1 - e^{-RT/L}\,.$$

Assume that RT/L is small compared to 1 (the resistance is small) and use the binomial theorem to expand the exponential. The first two terms are:

$$e^{-RT/L} \approx 1 - \frac{RT}{L}\,.$$

Replace T with $2\pi/\omega$, where ω is the angular frequency of oscillation. Thus

$$\frac{\Delta U}{U} \approx 1 - \left(1 - \frac{RT}{L}\right) = \frac{RT}{L} = \frac{2\pi R}{\omega L}\,.$$

37E

$$f = f_0 = \frac{1}{2\pi\sqrt{LC}} = \frac{1}{2\pi\sqrt{(2.50 \times 10^{-3}\,\text{H})(3.00 \times 10^{-6}\,\text{F})}} = 1.84 \times 10^3\,\text{Hz}.$$

38E

(a) The resonance frequency f_0 of the circuit is about $(1.50\,\text{KHz} - 1.30\,\text{KHz})/2 = 1.40\,\text{KHz}$. Thus from $2\pi f_0 = (LC)^{-1/2}$ we get

$$L = \frac{1}{4\pi^2 f_0^2 C} = \frac{1}{4\pi^2 (1.40 \times 10^3\,\text{Hz})^2 (5.50 \times 10^{-6}\,\text{F})} = 2.35 \times 10^{-3}\,\text{H}.$$

(b) From Fig. 35-16 we see that as R increases the resonance curve gets more spread out, so the two frequencies at which the amplitude is at half-maximum level will move away from each other.

39P

Four possibilties exist: (1) $C_1 = 4.00\mu\,\mathrm{F}$ is used alone; (2) $C_2 = 6.00\mu\,\mathrm{F}$ is used alone; (3) C_1 and C_2 are connected in series; and (4) C_1 and C_2 are connected in parallel. The corresponding resonant frequencies are

$$f_1 = \frac{1}{2\pi\sqrt{LC_1}} = \frac{1}{2\pi\sqrt{(2.00\times 10^{-3}\,\mathrm{H})(4.00\times 10^{-6}\,\mathrm{F})}} = 1.78\times 10^3\,\mathrm{Hz};$$

$$f_2 = \frac{1}{2\pi\sqrt{LC_2}} = \frac{1}{2\pi\sqrt{(2.00\times 10^{-3}\,\mathrm{H})(6.00\times 10^{-6}\,\mathrm{F})}} = 1.45\times 10^3\,\mathrm{Hz};$$

$$f_3 = \frac{1}{2\pi\sqrt{LC_1C_2/(C_1+C_2)}} = \frac{1}{2\pi\sqrt{(2.00\times 10^{-3}\,\mathrm{H})(4.00)(6.00)10^{-6}\,\mathrm{F}/(4.00+6.00)}}$$
$$= 2.30\times 10^3\,\mathrm{Hz};$$

and

$$f_4 = \frac{1}{2\pi\sqrt{L(C_1+C_2)}} = \frac{1}{2\pi\sqrt{(2.00\times 10^{-3}\,\mathrm{H})(4.00+6.00)10^{-6}\,\mathrm{F}}}$$
$$= 1.13\times 10^3\,\mathrm{Hz}.$$

40P

(a) Since $L_{eq} = L_1 + L_2$ and $C_{eq} = C_1 + C_2 + C_3$ for the circuit, the resonant frequency is

$$\omega = \frac{1}{2\pi\sqrt{L_{eq}C_{eq}}} = 2\pi\frac{1}{\sqrt{(L_1+L_2)(C_1+C_2+C_3)}}$$

$$= \frac{1}{2\pi(1.70+2.30)(10^{-3}\,\mathrm{H})(4.00+2.50+3.50)(10^{-6}\,\mathrm{F})} = 796\,\mathrm{Hz}.$$

(b) The resonant frequency does not depend on R so it will not change as R increases.

(c) Since $\omega \propto (L_1 + L_2)^{-1/2}$, it will decrease as L_1 is increased.

(d) Since $\omega \propto C_{eq}^{-1/2}$ and C_{eq} decreases as C_3 is removed, ω will increase.

41

(a) In Eq. 35-18, let $q = 0$ and $t = 0$, we get $0 = Q\cos\phi$. This gives $\phi = \pi/2$.

(b) First, since

$$i(t) = \frac{dq}{dt} = \frac{d}{dt}[Qe^{-Rt/2L}\cos(\omega't+\phi)]$$

$$= -\frac{QR}{2L}e^{-Rt/2L}\cos(\omega't+\phi) - \omega'Qe^{-Rt/2L}\sin(\omega't+\phi)$$

$$= -Q\sqrt{\omega'^2 + \left(\frac{R}{2L}\right)^2}\,e^{-Rt/2L}\sin(\omega't+\phi+\theta),$$

where $\tan\theta = R/2L\omega'$, the current amplitude is

$$I_{\max}(t) = Q\sqrt{\omega'^2 + (R/2L)^2}\,e^{-Rt/2L} = Q\omega e^{-Rt/2L} = Ie^{-Rt/2L}.$$

Thus

$$q(t) = Qe^{-Rt/2L}\cos(\omega't + \phi) = \frac{I}{\omega}e^{-Rt/2L}\cos\left(\omega't + \frac{\pi}{2}\right)$$

$$= \frac{I}{\omega}e^{-Rt/2L}\sin(\omega't).$$

42

The amplitude of oscillation of the LRC circuit charges by a factor of $e^{-RT/2L}$ per cycle. Thus $e^{-Rt/2L} = 1 - p\% = 1 - 0.01p$, or $-RT/2L = \ln(1 - 0.01p) \simeq -0.01p$, which gives

$$L \approx \frac{RT}{0.02p} = \frac{R(2\pi/\omega)}{0.02p} = \frac{100\pi R}{\omega p}.$$

Here we used $\ln(1 + x) \approx x$ for $|x| \ll 1$. Thus from $\omega^{-2} = LC$,

$$C = \frac{1}{\omega^2 L} = \frac{1}{\omega^2(100\pi R/\omega p)} = \frac{p}{100\pi R\omega}.$$

43

Let the current through L be i_1 and that through C be i_2. Then $i_1 + i_2 = i = \varepsilon/R$. Apply the loop theorem to the circuit:

$$\varepsilon = Ri_1 + L\frac{di_1}{dt} = \frac{q_2}{C} + Ri_2.$$

Differentiating with respect to t:

$$0 = R\frac{di_1}{dt} + L\frac{d^2i_1}{dt^2} = \frac{i_2}{C} + R\frac{di_2}{dt} = \frac{\varepsilon/R - i_1}{C} - R\frac{di_1}{dt},$$

where in the last step we used $i_1 + i_2 = \varepsilon/R$. The solution to the equation obtained above,

$$\frac{\varepsilon}{RC} - \frac{i_1}{C} - R\frac{dI_1}{dt} = 0,$$

has the form $i_1(t) = a + be^{-\alpha t}$, where a, b and α are all constants. Substituting this trial solution into the equation, we get

$$\left(\frac{\varepsilon}{RC} - \frac{a}{C}\right) + \left(\alpha R - \frac{1}{C}\right)e^{-\alpha t} = 0.$$

Since this is valid regardless of the value of t, we have $a = \varepsilon/R$ and $\alpha = (RC)^{-1}$. Now substitute the solution $i_1(t) = \varepsilon/R + be^{-t/RC}$ into the first equation we wrote down: $\varepsilon = Ri_1 + L\,di_1/dt$, we get

$$b\left(R - \frac{L}{RC}\right)e^{-t/RC} = 0.$$

Again, since this is valid at any time t, we must have $R - L/RC = 0$, or $L = R^2C$.

CHAPTER 36

1E
$\omega = 2\pi f = 2\pi(60\,\text{Hz}) = 377\,\text{rad/s}$. This frequency is established by turning the rotating shaft (see Fig. 36-1) at 60 rounds per second.

2E
Use $I = \varepsilon/X_c = \omega C\varepsilon$.
(a) $I = \omega C\varepsilon_m = 2\pi f C\varepsilon_m = (2\pi)(1.00 \times 10^3\,\text{Hz})(1.50 \times 10^{-6}\,\text{F})(30.0\,\text{V}) = 0.283\,\text{A}$.
(b) $I = (2\pi)(8.00 \times 10^3\,\text{Hz})(1.50 \times 10^{-6}\,\text{F})(30.0\,\text{V}) = 2.26\,\text{A}$.

3E
(a) The current amplitude I is given by $I = V_L/X_L$, where V_L is the voltage amplitude across the inductor and X_L is the inductive reactance. The reactance is given by $X_L = \omega L = 2\pi f L$, where ω is the angular frequency, f is the frequency, and L is the inductance. Since the circuit contains only the inductor and a sinusoidal generator, $V_L = \varepsilon_m$, where ε_m is the generator emf amplitude. Thus

$$I = \frac{V_L}{X_L} = \frac{\varepsilon_m}{2\pi f L} = \frac{30.0\,\text{V}}{2\pi(1.00 \times 10^3\,\text{Hz})(50.0 \times 10^{-3}\,\text{H})} = 0.0955\,\text{A}\,.$$

(b) The frequency is now eight times larger than in part (a), so the inductive reactance is eight times larger and the current is one-eighth as much, or $= (0.0955\,\text{A})/8 = 0.0119\,\text{A}$.

4E
(a) and (b) Regardless of the frequency of the emf,

$$I = \frac{\varepsilon_m}{R} = \frac{30.0\,\text{V}}{50\,\Omega} = 0.60\,\text{A}.$$

5E
(a) Solve L from $X_L = \omega L = 2\pi f L$:

$$f = \frac{X_L}{2\pi L} = \frac{1.30 \times 10^3\,\Omega}{(2\pi)(45.0 \times 10^{-3}\,\text{H})} = 4.60 \times 10^3\,\text{Hz}.$$

(b) Solve C from $X_c = (\omega C)^{-1} = (2\pi f C)^{-1}$:

$$C = \frac{1}{2\pi f X_c} = \frac{1}{2\pi(4.60 \times 10^3\,\text{Hz})(1.30 \times 10^3\,\Omega)} = 2.66 \times 10^{-8}\,\text{F}.$$

(c) Since $X_L \propto f$ and $X_C \propto f^{-1}$, when f is doubled $X_L = 2(1.30 \times 10^3\,\Omega) = 2.60 \times 10^3\,\Omega$ and $X_C = 1.30 \times 10^3\,\Omega/2 = 6.50 \times 10^2\,\Omega$.

6E
(a)
$$f = \frac{1}{2\pi C X_c} = \frac{1}{2\pi(1.50 \times 10^{-6}\,\text{F})(12.0\,\Omega)} = 8.84 \times 10^3\,\text{Hz}.$$

(b) Since $X_c \propto f^{-1}$, if the frequency is doubled then $X_c = 12.0\,\Omega/2 = 6.00\,\Omega$.

7E
(a) The inductive reactance for angular frequency ω is given by $X_L = \omega L$, where L is the inductance, and the capacitive reactance is given by $X_C = 1/\omega C$, where C is the capacitance. The two reactances are equal if $\omega L = 1/\omega C$, or $\omega = 1/\sqrt{LC}$. The frequency is
$$f = \frac{\omega}{2\pi} = \frac{1}{2\pi\sqrt{LC}} = \frac{1}{2\pi\sqrt{(6.0 \times 10^{-3}\,\text{H})(10 \times 10^{-6}\,\text{F})}} = 650\,\text{Hz}.$$

(b) The inductive reactance is $X_L = \omega L = 2\pi f L = 2\pi(650\,\text{Hz})(6.0 \times 10^{-3}\,\text{H}) = 24\,\Omega$. The capacitive reactance has the same value for this frequency.

(c) The natural frequency for free LC oscillations is $f = \omega/2\pi = 1/2\pi\sqrt{LC}$, the same as that for which the reactances are equal.

8P
(a)
$$I = \frac{\varepsilon_m}{X_L} = \frac{\varepsilon_m}{\omega L} = \frac{25.0\,\text{V}}{(377\,\text{rad/s})(12.7\,\text{H})} = 5.22 \times 10^{-3}\,\text{A}.$$

(b) Since $\varepsilon(t)$ and $i(t)$ has a 90°-phase difference, $\varepsilon(t)$ is zero when $i(t) = I$.
(c) In this case ωt must be $(2n\pi - \pi/6)$, (n is an integer), so $i = I\sin(2n\pi - \pi/6 + \pi/2) = I\sin(\pi/3) = (5.22 \times 10^{-3}\,\text{A})(\sqrt{3}/2) = 4.51 \times 10^{-3}\,\text{A}$.
(d) The power delivered by the generator at this instant is $D = \varepsilon(t)i(t) = \varepsilon_m\sin(2n\pi - \pi/6)I\sin(\pi/3) = -\varepsilon_m I\sin(\pi/6)\sin(\pi/3) < 0$, so it is taking energy from the rest of the circuit.

9P
(a)
$$I = \frac{\varepsilon_m}{X_c} = \omega c \varepsilon_m = (377\,\text{rad/s})(4.15 \times 10^{-6}\,\text{F})(25.0\,\text{V}) = 3.91 \times 10^{-2}\,\text{A}.$$

(b) Since $\varepsilon(t)$ and $i(t)$ again has a 90°-phase difference, $\varepsilon(t)$ is zero when $i(t) = I$.
(c) In this case ωt must again be $2n\pi - \pi/6$, so $i = I\sin(2n\pi - \pi/6 - pi/2) = -I\sin(2\pi/3) = -(3.91 \times 10^{-3}\,\text{A})(\sqrt{3}/2) = -3.38 \times 10^{-2}\,\text{A}$.

(d) The power delivered by the generator at this instant is $P = \varepsilon(t)i(t) = \varepsilon_m \sin(2n\pi - \pi/6)I \sin(-2\pi/3) = \varepsilon_m I \sin(\pi/6)\sin(2\pi/3) > 0$, so it is supplying energy to the rest of the system.

10P

(a) The generator emf is a maximum when $\sin(\omega t - \pi/4) = 1$ or $\omega t - \pi/4 = \pi/2 \pm 2n\pi$, where n is an integer, including zero. The first time this occurs after $t = 0$ is when $\omega t - \pi/4 = \pi/2$ or

$$t = \frac{3\pi}{4\omega} = \frac{3\pi}{4(350\,\mathrm{s}^{-1})} = 6.73 \times 10^{-3}\,\mathrm{s}\,.$$

(b) The current is a maximum when $\sin(\omega t - 3\pi/4) = 1$, or $\omega t - 3\pi/4 = \pi/2 \pm 2n\pi$. The first time this occurs after $t = 0$ is when

$$t = \frac{5\pi}{4\omega} = \frac{5\pi}{4(350\,\mathrm{s}^{-1})} = 1.12 \times 10^{-2}\,\mathrm{s}\,.$$

(c) The current lags the inductor by $\pi/2\,\mathrm{rad}$, so the circuit element must be an inductor.

(d) The current amplitude I is related to the voltage amplitude V_L by $V_L = I X_L$, where X_L is the inductive reactance, given by $X_L = \omega L$. Furthermore, since there is only one element in the circuit the amplitude of the potential difference across the element must be the same as the amplitude of the generator emf: $V_L = \varepsilon_m$. Thus $\varepsilon_m = I\omega L$ and

$$L = \frac{\varepsilon_m}{I\omega} = \frac{30.0\,\mathrm{V}}{(620 \times 10^{-3}\,\mathrm{A})(350\,\mathrm{rad/s})} = 0.138\,\mathrm{H}\,.$$

11P

(a) Let $\omega t - \pi/4 = \pi/2$ to obtain $t = 3\pi/4\omega = 3\pi/[4(350\,\mathrm{rad/s})] = 6.73 \times 10^{-3}$ s.
(b) Let $\omega t + \pi/4 = \pi/2$ to obtain $t = \pi/4\omega = \pi/[4(350\,\mathrm{rad/s})] = 2.24 \times 10^{-3}$ s.
(c) Since i leads ε in phase by $\pi/2$, the element must be a capacitor.
(d) Solve C from $X_c = (\omega C)^{-1} = \varepsilon_m/I$: $C = I/\varepsilon_m\omega = (6.20 \times 10^{-3}\,\mathrm{A})/[(30.0\,\mathrm{V})(350\,\mathrm{rad/s})] = 5.90 \times 10^{-5}$ F.

12P

(a) and (b) Consider the following combinations: $\Delta V_{12} = V_1 - V_2$, $\Delta V_{13} = V_1 - V_3$, and $\Delta V_{23} = V_2 - V_3$. For ΔV_{12} we have

$$\Delta V_{12} = A\sin(\omega t) - A\sin(\omega t - 120°) = 2A\sin\left(\frac{120°}{2}\right)\cos\left(\frac{2\omega t - 120°}{2}\right)$$

$$= \sqrt{3}\,A\cos(\omega t - 60°),$$

where we used $\sin\alpha - \sin\beta = 2\sin[(\alpha - \beta)/2]\cos[(\alpha + \beta)/2]$ and $\sin 60° = \sqrt{3}/2$. This expression indicates that ΔV_{12} oscillates sinusoidaly with angular frequency ω, and has an amplitude of $A\sqrt{3}$. Similarly,

$$\Delta V_{13} = A\sin(\omega t) - A\sin(\omega t - 240°) = 2A\sin\left(\frac{240°}{2}\right)\cos\left(\frac{2\omega t - 240°}{2}\right)$$

$$= \sqrt{3}\,A\cos(\omega t - 120°),$$

and

$$\Delta V_{23} = A\sin(\omega t - 120°) - A\sin(\omega t - 240°) = 2A\sin\left(\frac{120°}{2}\right)\cos\left(\frac{2\omega t - 360°}{2}\right)$$

$$= \sqrt{3}\,A\cos(\omega t - 180°),$$

both sinosoidal functions of t with an amplitude of $A\sqrt{3}$.

13E
(a) Now $X_C = 0$, R and X_L remain unchanged,

$$Z = \sqrt{R^2 + X_L^2} = \sqrt{(160\,\Omega)^2 + (86.7\,\Omega)^2} = 182\,\Omega,$$

$$I = \frac{\varepsilon_m}{Z} = \frac{36.0\,\text{V}}{182\,\Omega} = 0.198\,\text{A},$$

and

$$\phi = \tan^{-1}\left(\frac{X_L - X_C}{R}\right) = \tan^{-1}\left(\frac{86.7\,\Omega - 0}{160\,\Omega}\right) = 28.5°.$$

(b)

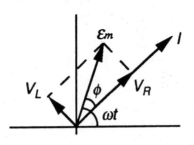

14E
(a) Now $X_L = 0$, R and X_C remain unchanged,

$$Z = \sqrt{R^2 + X_C^2} = \sqrt{(160\,\Omega)^2 + (177\,\Omega)^2} = 239\,\Omega,$$

$$I = \frac{\varepsilon_m}{Z} = \frac{36.0\,\text{V}}{239\,\Omega} = 0.151\,\text{A},$$

and

$$\phi = \tan^{-1}\left(\frac{X_L - X_C}{R}\right) = \tan^{-1}\left(\frac{0 - 177\,\Omega}{160\,\Omega}\right) = -47.9°.$$

(b)

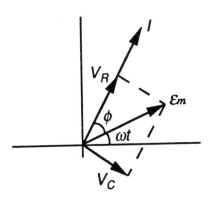

15E
(a) The capacitive reactance is

$$X_C = \frac{1}{\omega C} = \frac{1}{2\pi f C} = \frac{1}{2\pi(60.0\,\text{Hz})(70.0 \times 10^{-6}\,\text{F})} = 37.9\,\Omega.$$

The inductive reactance is unchanged, $86.7\,\Omega$. The new impedance is

$$Z = \sqrt{R^2 + (X_L - X_C)^2} = \sqrt{(160\,\Omega)^2 + (37.9\,\Omega - 86.7\,\Omega)^2} = 167\,\Omega.$$

The current amplitude is
$$I = \frac{\varepsilon_m}{Z} = \frac{36.0\,\text{V}}{167\,\Omega} = 0.216\,\text{A}.$$

The phase angle is

$$\phi = \tan^{-1}\left(\frac{X_L - X_C}{R}\right) = \tan^{-1}\left(\frac{86.7\,\Omega - 37.9\,\Omega}{160\,\Omega}\right) = 17.0°.$$

(b) The voltage amplitudes are

$$V_R = IR = (0.216\,\text{A})(160\,\Omega) = 34.6\,\text{V},$$

$$V_L = IX_L = (0.216\,\text{A})(86.7\,\Omega) = 18.7\,\text{V},$$

and

$$V_C = IX_C = (0.216\,\text{A})(37.9\,\Omega) = 8.19\,\text{V}.$$

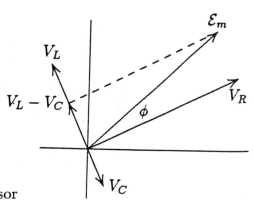

Note that $X_L > X_C$, so that ε_m leads I. The phasor diagram is drawn to scale on the right.

16E

(a) At the resonant frequency $\omega = \omega_0$, we have $X_L = \omega L = X_C = \dfrac{1}{\omega C}$, which results from $\omega_0 = (LC)^{-1/2}$. So for $\omega > \omega_0$ we have $X_L > X_C$, i.e. the circuit is predominantly inductive; for $\omega < \omega_0$ we have $X_C > X_L$, i.e. the circuit is predominatnly capacitive.

(b) At resonance we have $X = \sqrt{R^2 + (X_L - X_C)^2} = R$ so the circuit is purely resistive

(c)

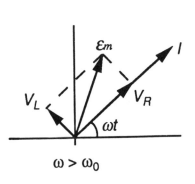

$\omega > \omega_0$

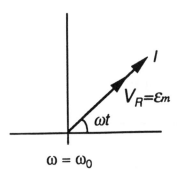

$\omega = \omega_0$

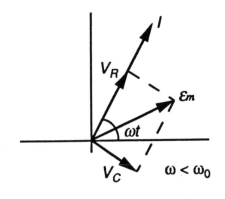

$\omega < \omega_0$

17P

From Fig. 36-11 we see that the x- and y-components of the Z-vector are $Z_x = R$ and $Z_y = X_C - X_L$. Thus

$$|Z| = \sqrt{Z_x^2 + Z_y^2} = \sqrt{R^2 + (X_C - X_L)^2},$$

and

$$\tan\phi = -\frac{Z_y}{Z_x} = \frac{X_L - X_C}{R},$$

which indeed are the same as Eqs. 36-23 and 36-26.

18P

The amplitude of the voltage across the inductor in an RLC series circuit is given by $V_L = IX_L$, where X_L $(= \omega L)$ is the inductive reactance. At resonance $\omega = 1/\sqrt{LC}$, where L is the inductance and C is the capacitance. For the given circuit

$$X_L = \frac{L}{\sqrt{LC}} = \frac{1.0\,\text{H}}{\sqrt{(1.0\,\text{H})(1.0 \times 10^{-6}\,\text{F})}} = 1000\,\Omega.$$

At resonance the capacitive reactance has the same value as the inductive reactance, so $X_C = 1000\,\Omega$. For $X_L = X_C$, Eq. 36–23 gives $Z = R$. Hence

$$I = \frac{\varepsilon_m}{R} = \frac{10\,\text{V}}{10\,\Omega} = 1.0\,\text{A}.$$

Thus

$$V_L = IX_L = (1.0\,\text{A})(1000\,\Omega) = 1000\,\text{V}.$$

This is much larger than the amplitude of the generator emf (10 V).

19P
The resistanc R of the coil satisfies

$$\frac{X_L - X_C}{R} = \frac{\omega L - 1/\omega C}{R} = \tan \phi,$$

which we solve for R:

$$R = \frac{1}{\tan \phi}\left(\omega L - \frac{1}{\omega C}\right)$$

$$= \frac{1}{\tan 75°}\left[(2\pi)(930\,\text{Hz})(8.8 \times 10^{-2}\,\text{H}) - \frac{1}{(2\pi)(930\,\text{Hz})(0.94 \times 10^{-6}\,\text{F})}\right]$$

$$= 89\,\Omega.$$

20P
(a) 36.0 V, by definition.

(b)

$$V_R = IR\cos|\phi| = (0.196\,\text{A})(160\,\Omega)\cos(29.4°) = 27.3\,\text{V}.$$

(c) Refer to the figure to the right.

$$V_C = IX_C \sin|\phi|$$
$$= (0.196\,\text{A})(177\,\Omega)\sin(29.4°)$$
$$= -17.0\,\text{V}.$$

(d)

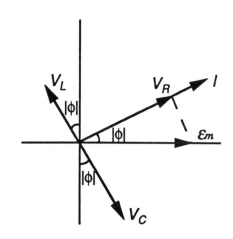

$$V_L = -IX_L\sin|\phi|$$
$$= -(0.196\,\text{A})(86.7\,\Omega)\sin(29.4°)$$
$$= -8.34\,\text{V}.$$

(e) Since $V_R + V_c + V_L = 27.3\,\text{V} + 17.0\,\text{V} - 8.34\,\text{V} = 36.0\,\text{V} = \varepsilon_m$, the loop theorem is satisfied.

21P
(a) For a given amplitude ε_m of the generator emf, the current amplitude is given by

$$I = \frac{\varepsilon_m}{Z} = \frac{\varepsilon_m}{\sqrt{R^2 + (\omega L - 1/\omega C)^2}},$$

where R is the resistance, L is the inductance, C is the capacitance, and ω is the angular frequency. To find the maximum set the derivative with respect to ω equal to zero and solve for ω. The derivative is

$$\frac{dI}{d\omega} = -\varepsilon_m \left[R^2 + (\omega L - 1/\omega C)^2\right]^{-3/2} \left[\omega L - \frac{1}{\omega C}\right]\left[L + \frac{1}{\omega^2 C}\right].$$

The only factor that can equal zero is $\omega L - (1/\omega C)$ and it does for $\omega = 1/\sqrt{LC}$. For the given circuit

$$\omega = \frac{1}{\sqrt{LC}} = \frac{1}{\sqrt{(1.00\,\text{H})(20.0 \times 10^{-6}\,\text{F})}} = 224\,\text{rad/s}.$$

(b) For this value of the angular frequency the impedance is $Z = R$ and the current amplitude is

$$I = \frac{\varepsilon_m}{R} = \frac{30.0\,\text{V}}{5.00\,\Omega} = 6.00\,\text{A}.$$

(c) You want to find the values of ω for which $I = \varepsilon_m/2R$. This means

$$\frac{\varepsilon_m}{\sqrt{R^2 + (\omega L - 1/\omega C)^2}} = \frac{\varepsilon_m}{2R}.$$

Cancel the factors ε_m that appear on both sides, square both sides, and set the reciprocals of the two sides equal to each other to obtain

$$R^2 + \left(\omega L - \frac{1}{\omega C}\right)^2 = 4R^2.$$

Thus

$$\left(\omega L - \frac{1}{\omega C}\right)^2 = 3R^2.$$

Now take the square root of both sides and multiply by ωC to obtain

$$\omega^2 (LC) \pm \omega \left(\sqrt{3}CR\right) - 1 = 0,$$

where the symbol $\pm$ indicates the two possible signs for the square root. The last equation is a quadratic equation for ω. Its solutions are

$$\omega = \frac{\pm\sqrt{3}CR \pm \sqrt{3C^2R^2 + 4LC}}{2LC}.$$

You want the two positive solutions. The smaller of these is

$$\omega_2 = \frac{-\sqrt{3}CR + \sqrt{3C^2R^2 + 4LC}}{2LC}$$

$$= \frac{-\sqrt{3}(20.0 \times 10^{-6}\,\text{F})(5.00\,\Omega)}{2(1.00\,\text{H})(20.0 \times 10^{-6}\,\text{F})}$$

$$+ \frac{\sqrt{3(20.0 \times 10^{-6}\,\text{F})^2(5.00\,\Omega)^2 + 4(1.00\,\text{H})(20.0 \times 10^{-6}\,\text{F})}}{2(1.00\,\text{H})(20.0 \times 10^{-6}\,\text{F})}$$

$$= 219\,\text{rad/s}$$

and the larger is

$$\begin{aligned}
\omega_1 &= \frac{+\sqrt{3}CR + \sqrt{3C^2R^2 + 4LC}}{2LC} \\
&= \frac{+\sqrt{3}(20.0 \times 10^{-6}\,\text{F})(5.00\,\Omega)}{2(1.00\,\text{H})(20.0 \times 10^{-6}\,\text{F})} \\
&\quad + \frac{\sqrt{3(20.0 \times 10^{-6}\,\text{F})^2(5.00\,\Omega)^2 + 4(1.00\,\text{H})(20.0 \times 10^{-6}\,\text{F})}}{2(1.00\,\text{H})(20.0 \times 10^{-6}\,\text{F})} \\
&= 228\,\text{rad/s}.
\end{aligned}$$

(d) The fractional width is

$$\frac{\omega_1 - \omega_2}{\omega_0} = \frac{228\,\text{rad/s} - 219\,\text{rad/s}}{224\,\text{rad/s}} = 0.04.$$

22P
(a)
$$Z = \frac{\epsilon_m}{I} = \frac{125\,\text{V}}{3.20\,\text{A}} = 39.1\,\Omega.$$

(b) from $V_R = IR = \varepsilon_m \cos\phi$ we get

$$R = \frac{\varepsilon_m \cos\phi}{I} = \frac{(125\,\text{V})\cos(0.982\,\text{rad})}{3.20\,\text{A}} = 21.7\,\Omega.$$

(c) Since $X_L - X_C \propto \sin\phi = \sin(-0.982\,\text{rad}) < 0$, i.e. $X_L < X_C$, the circuit is predominantly cpacitive.

23P
(a) The phase angle is given by

$$\phi = \tan^{-1}\left(\frac{V_L - V_c}{R}\right) = \tan^{-1}\left(\frac{V_L - V_L/2.00}{V_L/2.00}\right)$$
$$= \tan^{-1}(1.00) = 45.0°.$$

(b) Solve R from $\varepsilon_m \cos\phi = IR$:

$$R = \frac{\varepsilon_m \cos\phi}{I} = \frac{(30.0\,\text{V})(\cos 45°)}{300 \times 10^{-3}\,\text{A}} = 70.7\,\Omega.$$

24P

(a) The resonance frequency is $\omega_0 = 1/\sqrt{LC}$, at which $X_L = X_C$, which is not sqtisfied here.

(b) Let the additional capacitance by C'. Then the new impedance for the combined capacitors should satisfy

$$\frac{1}{\omega(C + C')} = \frac{1}{X_C^{-1} + \omega C'} = X_L,$$

which gives

$$C' = \frac{1}{\omega}\left(\frac{1}{X_L} - \frac{1}{X_C}\right)$$

$$= \frac{1}{2\pi(60.0\,\text{Hz})}\left(\frac{1}{86.7\,\Omega} - \frac{1}{177\,\Omega}\right) = 1.56 \times 10^{-5}\,\text{F}.$$

(c) At resonance $X_L - X_C = 0$ so $Z = R$. Thus

$$I = \frac{\varepsilon_m}{Z} = \frac{\varepsilon_m}{R} = \frac{36.0\,\text{V}}{160\,\Omega} = 0.255\,\text{A}.$$

25P

For the two circuits separately, we have $\omega_0 = (L_1 C_1)^{-1/2} = (L_2 C_2)^{-1/2}$. When combined, the resonance frequency is

$$\omega = \frac{1}{\sqrt{L_{eq}C_{eq}}} = \frac{1}{\sqrt{(L_1 + L_2)C_1 C_2/(C_1 + C_2)}} = \frac{1}{\sqrt{(L_1 C_1 C_2 + C_1 L_2 C_2)/(C_1 + C_2)}}$$

$$= \frac{1}{\sqrt{L_1 C_1}\sqrt{(C_2 + C_1)/(C_1 + C_2)}} = \omega_0,$$

where we used $\omega_0 = (L_1 C_1)^{-1/2} = (L_2 C_2)^{-1/2}$.

26P

Since the impedance of the voltmeter is large, it will not affect the impedance of the circuit when it is connected in parallel with the circuit. So the reading will be 100 V in all three cases.

27P

Use the results of Problem 21:

$$\omega_1 = \frac{+\sqrt{3}CR + \sqrt{3C^2 R^2 + 4LC}}{2LC}$$

and

$$\omega_2 = \frac{-\sqrt{3}CR + \sqrt{3C^2R^2 + 4LC}}{2LC}.$$

Also use

$$\omega_0 = \frac{1}{\sqrt{LC}}.$$

Thus

$$\frac{\Delta\omega}{\omega_0} = \frac{\omega_1 - \omega_2}{\omega_0} = \frac{2\sqrt{3}CR\sqrt{LC}}{2LC} = R\sqrt{\frac{3C}{L}}.$$

For the data of Problem 21

$$\frac{\Delta\omega}{\omega_0} = (5.00\,\Omega)\sqrt{\frac{3(20.0 \times 10^{-6}\,\text{F})}{1.00\,\text{H}}} = 3.87 \times 10^{-2}.$$

This is in agreement with the result of Problem 21. The method of Problem 21, however, gives only one significant figure since two numbers that are close in value (ω_1 and ω_2) are subtracted. Here the subtraction is done algebraically and 3 significant figures are obtained.

28P*

When the switch is open we have an LRC circuit with L, R, C in series, with

$$\frac{V_L - V_c}{R} = \frac{\omega L - 1/\omega C}{R} = \tan\phi_1 = \tan(-20°).$$

when the switch is in position 1 the equivalent capacitance of the LRC circuit becomes $2C$. So now

$$\frac{\omega L - 1/2\omega C}{R} = \tan\phi_2 = \tan 10.0°.$$

Finally, with the switch in position 2 the circuit is an LC circuit so

$$I = \frac{\varepsilon_m}{X} = \frac{\varepsilon_m}{\sqrt{(\omega L)^2 + (1/\omega C)^2}}.$$

Solve for L, R and C from these three equations:

$$R = \frac{\varepsilon_m}{2I\sqrt{(\tan\phi_2 - \tan\phi_1)^2 + (\tan\phi_2 - \frac{1}{2}\tan\phi_1)^2}}$$

$$= \frac{120\,\text{V}}{2(2.00\,\text{A})\sqrt{(-\tan 20.0° + \tan 10.0°)^2 + (\tan 10.0° + \frac{1}{2}\tan 20.0°)^2}}$$

$$= 1.65 \times 10^2\,\Omega,$$

$$L = \frac{2R}{\omega}\left(\tan \phi_2 - \frac{1}{2}\tan \phi_1\right)$$

$$= \frac{2(1.65 \times 10^2 \, \Omega)}{2\pi(60.0 \, \text{Hz})}\left(\tan 10.0° + \frac{1}{2}\tan 20.0°\right) = 0.313 \, \text{H},$$

and

$$C = \frac{1}{2\omega R(\tan \phi_2 - \tan \phi_1)}$$

$$= \frac{1}{2(2\pi)(60.0 \, \text{Hz})(1.65 \times 10^2 \, \Omega)(\tan 10.0° + \tan 20.0°)}$$

$$= 1.49 \times 10^{-5} \, \text{F}.$$

29E

$$V_{\text{max}} = \sqrt{2}V_{\text{rms}} = \sqrt{2}(100 \, \text{V}) = 141 \, \text{V}.$$

30E
The average power dissipated in resistance R when the current is alternating is given by $P_{\text{av}} = I_{\text{rms}}^2 R$, where I_{rms} is the root-mean-square current. Since $I_{\text{rms}} = I/\sqrt{2}$, where I is the current amplitude, this can be written $P_{\text{av}} = I^2 R/2$. The power dissipated in the same resistor when the current is direct is given by $P = i^2 R$, where i is the current. Set the two powers equal to each other and solve for i. You should get

$$i = \frac{I}{\sqrt{2}} = \frac{2.60 \, \text{A}}{\sqrt{2}} = 1.84 \, \text{A}.$$

31E
Use $P_{av} = I_{\text{rms}}^2 R = I^2 R/2$.
(a) $P_{av} = 0$ since $R = 0$.
(b) $P_{av} = I^2 R/2 = (0.600 \, \text{A})^2(50 \, \Omega)/2 = 9.0 \, \text{W}$.
(c) $P_{av} = I^2 R/2 = (0.198 \, \text{A})^2(160 \, \Omega)/2 = 3.14 \, \text{W}$.
(d) $P_{av} = I^2 R/2 = (0.151 \, \text{A})^2(160 \, \Omega)/2 = 1.82 \, \text{W}$.

32E

$$P_{av} = \varepsilon_{\text{rms}} I_{\text{rms}} \cos \phi = \varepsilon_{\text{rms}}\left(\frac{\varepsilon_{\text{rms}}}{Z}\right)\left(\frac{R}{Z}\right) = \frac{\varepsilon_{\text{rms}}^2 R}{Z^2}.$$

33E

The effective resistance R_{eff} satisfies $I_{rms}^2 R_{eff} = P_{mechanical}$, or

$$R_{eff} = \frac{P_{mechanical}}{I_{rms}^2} = \frac{(0.100\,\text{hp})(746\,\text{W/hp})}{(0.650\,\text{A})^2} = 177\,\Omega.$$

This will not be the same as the resistance R of its coils but just the effective resistance for power transfer from electrical to mechanical form. In fact $I_{rms}^2 R$ would not give you $P_{mechanical}$ but rather the rate of energy loss due to thermal dissipation.

34E

(a) The impedance is given by

$$Z = \sqrt{R^2 + (X_L - X_C)^2}\,,$$

where R is the resistance, X_L is the inductive reactance, and X_C is the capacitive reactance. Thus

$$Z = \sqrt{(12.0\,\Omega)^2 + (1.30\,\Omega - 0)^2} = 12.1\,\Omega\,.$$

(b) The average rate at which energy is supplied to the air conditioner is given by

$$P_{av} = \frac{\mathcal{E}_{rms}^2}{Z}\cos\phi\,,$$

where $\cos\phi$ is the power factor. Now

$$\cos\phi = \frac{R}{Z} = \frac{12\,\Omega}{12.1\,\Omega} = 0.992\,,$$

so

$$P_{av} = \left[\frac{(120\,\text{V})^2}{12.1\,\Omega}\right](0.992) = 1.18 \times 10^3\,\text{W}\,.$$

35E

$$
\begin{aligned}
I_{rms} &= \frac{\mathcal{E}_{rms}}{Z} = \frac{\mathcal{E}_{rms}}{\sqrt{R^2 + X_L^2}} \\
&= \frac{420\,\text{V}}{\sqrt{(45.0\,\Omega)^2 + (32.0\,\Omega)^2}} = 7.61\,\text{A}\,.
\end{aligned}
$$

$$[\sin^2(\omega t - \phi)]_{av} = \frac{1}{nT/2} \int_0^{\frac{nT}{2}} \sin^2(\omega t - \phi)\, dt$$

$$= \frac{2}{nT} \int_0^{\frac{nT}{2}} \frac{1 - \cos(2\omega t - 2\phi)}{2}\, dt$$

$$= \frac{2}{nT} \left[\frac{t}{2} - \frac{1}{4\omega} \sin(2\omega t - 2\phi) \right]\Big|^{\frac{nT}{2}}$$

$$= \frac{1}{2} - \frac{1}{4\omega} \left[\sin(n\omega T - 2\phi) + \sin 2\phi \right].$$

Since $n\omega T = n\omega(2\pi/\omega) = 2n\pi$, we have $\sin(n\omega T - 2\phi) = \sin(2n\pi - 2\phi) = -\sin 2\phi$ so $[\sin(n\omega T - 2\phi) + \sin 2\phi] = 0$. Thus

$$[\sin^2(\omega t - \phi)]_{av} = \frac{1}{2}.$$

37P
(a) The energy stored in the capacitor is given by $U_E = q^2/2C$. Since q is a periodic function of t with period T, so must be U_E. So U_E will not be changed over one complete cycle.

(b) Similarly, the energy stored in the inductor is $U_B = \frac{1}{2} i^2 L$. Since i is a periodic function of t with period T, so must be U_B.

(c) The energy supplied by the generator is

$$P_{av}T = (I_{rms}\varepsilon_{rms} \cos \phi)T = \left(\frac{1}{2}T\right)\varepsilon_m I \cos \phi,$$

where we used $I_{rms} = I/\sqrt{2}$ and $\varepsilon_{rms} = \varepsilon_m/\sqrt{2}$.

(d) The energy dissipated by the resistor is

$$P_{av,\,resistor}T = (I_{rms}V_R)T = I_{rms}(I_{rms}R)T = \left(\frac{1}{2}T\right)I^2 R,$$

where we used $I_{rms} = I/\sqrt{2}$.

(e) Since $\varepsilon_m I \cos \phi = \varepsilon_m I(V_R/\varepsilon_m) = \varepsilon_m I(IR/\varepsilon_m) = I^2 R$, the two quantities are indeed the same.

38P

The current in the circuit satisfies $i(t) = I\sin(\omega t - \phi)$, where

$$I = \frac{\varepsilon_m}{Z} = \frac{\varepsilon_m}{\sqrt{R^2 + (\omega L - 1/\omega C)^2}}$$

$$= \frac{45.0\,\text{V}}{\sqrt{(16.0\,\Omega)^2 + \{(3000\,\text{rad/s})(9.20\,\text{mH}) - 1/[(3000\,\text{rad/s})(31.2\,\mu\,\text{F})]\}^2}}$$

$$= 1.93\,\text{A},$$

and

$$\phi = \tan^{-1}\left(\frac{X_L - X_C}{R}\right) = \tan^{-1}\left(\frac{\omega L - 1/\omega C}{R}\right)$$

$$= \tan^{-1}\left[\frac{(3000\,\text{rad/s})(9.20\,\text{mH})}{16.0\,\Omega} - \frac{1}{(3000\,\text{rad/s})(16.0\,\Omega)(31.2\,\mu\,\text{F})}\right]$$

$$= 46.5°.$$

(a)

$$P_{\text{generator}} = i(t)\varepsilon(t) = I\sin(\omega t - \phi)\varepsilon_m\sin\omega t$$

$$= (1.93\,\text{A})(45.0\,\text{V})\sin[(3000\,\text{rad/s})(0.442\,\text{ms})]\sin[(3000\,\text{rad/s})(0.442\,\text{ms}) - 46.5°]$$

$$= 41.4\,\text{W}.$$

(b)

$$P_{\text{inductor}} = \frac{d}{dt}\left(\frac{1}{2}Li^2\right) = Li\frac{di}{dt} = LI\sin(\omega t - \phi)\frac{d}{dt}[I\sin(\omega t - \phi)]$$

$$= \frac{1}{2}\omega LI^2\sin[2(\omega t - \phi)]$$

$$= \frac{1}{2}(3000\,\text{rad/s})(1.93\,\text{A})^2(9.20\,\text{mH})\sin[2(3000\,\text{rad/s})(0.442\,\text{ms}) - 2(46.5°)]$$

$$= 44.0\,\text{W}.$$

(c)

$$P_{\text{capacitor}} = -\frac{d}{dt}\left(\frac{q^2}{2C}\right) = -i\frac{q}{C} = -iV_c$$

$$= -I\sin(\omega t - \phi)\left(\frac{I}{\omega C}\right)\cos(\omega t - \phi) = -\frac{I^2}{2\omega C}\sin[2(\omega t - \phi)]$$

$$= -\frac{(1.93\,\text{A})^2}{2(3000\,\text{rad/s})(31.2 \times 10^{-6}\,\text{F})}\sin[2(3000\,\text{rad/s})(0.442\,\text{ms}) - 2(46.5°)]$$

$$= -17.1\,\text{W}.$$

(d)

$$P_{\text{resistor}} = i^2 R = I^2 R \sin^2(\omega t - \phi)$$
$$= (1.93 \, \text{A})^2 (16.0 \, \Omega) \sin^2 [(3000 \, \text{rad/s})(0.442 \, \text{ms}) - 46.5°]$$
$$= 14.4 \, \text{W}.$$

(e) The negative result for P_{inductor} means that energy is being taken away from the inductor at this particular time.

(f) $P_{\text{inductor}} + P_{\text{resistor}} + P_{\text{capacitor}} = 44.0W - 17.1 \, \text{W} + 14.4 \, \text{W} = 41.3 \, \text{W} = P_{\text{generator}}$.

39P
Since

$$P_R = i^2 R = \left(\frac{\varepsilon_m}{r + R} \right)^2 R,$$

to maximize P_R we let

$$\frac{dP_R}{dR} = \frac{\varepsilon_m^2 [(r + R)^2 - 2(r + R)R]}{(r + R)^4} = \frac{\varepsilon_m^2 (r - R)}{(r + R)^3} = 0$$

and obtain $R = r$.

40P
(a) The power factor is $\cos \phi$, where ϕ is the phase angle when the current is written $i = I \sin(\omega t - \phi)$. Thus $\phi = -42.0°$ and $\cos \phi = \cos(-42.0°) = 0.743$.

(b) Since $\phi < 0$, $\omega t - \phi > \omega t$ and the current leads the emf.

(c) The phase angle is given by $\tan \phi = (X_L - X_C)/R$, where X_L is the inductive reactance, X_C is the capacitive reactance, and R is the resistance. Now $\tan \phi = \tan(-42.0°) = -0.900$, a negative number. This means $X_L - X_C$ is negative, or $X_C > X_L$. The circuit in the box is predominantly capacitive.

(d) If the circuit were in resonance X_L would be the same as X_C, $\tan \phi$ would be zero, and ϕ would be zero. Since ϕ is not zero, we conclude the circuit is not in resonance.

(e) Since $\tan \phi$ is negative and finite, neither the capacitive reactance nor the resistance are zero. This means the box must contain a capacitor and a resistor. The inductive reactance may be zero, so there need not be an inductor. If there is an inductor its reactance must be less than that of the capacitor at the operating frequency.

(f) The average power is

$$P_{\text{av}} = \frac{1}{2} \varepsilon_m I \cos \phi = \frac{1}{2}(75.0 \, \text{V})(1.20 \, \text{A})(0.743) = 33.4 \, \text{W}.$$

(g) The answers above depend on the frequency only through the phase angle ϕ, which is given. If values were given for R, L and C then the value of the frequency would also be needed to compute the power factor.

41P

(*a*) The average power is given by

$$P_{\text{av}} = \varepsilon_{\text{rms}} I_{\text{rms}} \cos\phi\,,$$

where ε_{rms} is the root-mean-square emf of the generator, I_{rms} is the root-mean-square current, and $\cos\phi$ is the power factor. Now

$$I_{\text{rms}} = \frac{I}{\sqrt{2}} = \frac{\varepsilon_m}{\sqrt{2}Z}\,,$$

where I is the current amplitude, ε_m is the maximum emf of the generator, and Z is the impedance of the circuit. $I = \varepsilon_m/Z$ was used. In addition, $\varepsilon_{\text{rms}} = \varepsilon_m/\sqrt{2}$ and $\cos\phi = R/Z$, where R is the resistance. Thus

$$P_{\text{av}} = \frac{\varepsilon_m^2 R}{2Z^2} = \frac{\varepsilon_m^2 R}{2\left[R^2 + (\omega L - 1/\omega C)^2\right]}\,.$$

Here the expression $Z = \sqrt{R^2 + (\omega L - 1/\omega C)^2}$ for the impedance in terms of the angular frequency was substituted.

Considered as a function of C, P_{av} has its largest value when the factor $R^2 + (\omega L - 1/\omega C)^2$ has the smallest possible value. This occurs for $\omega L = 1/\omega C$, or

$$C = \frac{1}{\omega^2 L} = \frac{1}{(2\pi)^2 (60.0\,\text{Hz})^2 (60.0 \times 10^{-3}\,\text{H})} = 1.17 \times 10^{-4}\,\text{F}\,.$$

The circuit is then at resonance.

(*b*) Now you want Z^2 to be as large as possible. Notice that it becomes large without bound as C becomes small. Thus the smallest average power occurs for $C = 0$.

(*c*) When $\omega L = 1/\omega C$ the expression for the average power becomes

$$P_{\text{av}} = \frac{\varepsilon_m^2}{2R}\,,$$

so the maximum average power is

$$P_{\text{av}} = \frac{(30.0\,\text{V})^2}{2(5.00\,\Omega)} = 90.0\,\text{W}\,.$$

The minimum average power is $P_{\text{av}} = 0$.

(*d*) At maximum power $X_L = X_C$, where X_L is the inductive reactance and X_C is the capacitive reactance. The phase angle ϕ is

$$\tan\phi = \frac{X_L - X_C}{R} = 0\,,$$

so $\phi = 0$. At minimum power X_C is infinite, so $\tan\phi = -\infty$ and $\phi = -90°$.

(e) At maximum power the power factor is $\cos\phi = \cos 0° = 1$ and at minimum power it is $\cos\phi = \cos(-90°) = 0$.

42P

The power consumed by the light bulb is $P = I^2R/2$. So we must let $P_{max}/P_{min} = (I_{max}/I_{min})^2 = 5$, or

$$\left(\frac{I_{max}}{I_{min}}\right)^2 = \left(\frac{\varepsilon_m/Z_{min}}{\varepsilon_m/Z_{max}}\right)^2 = \left(\frac{Z_{max}}{Z_{min}}\right)^2 = \left(\frac{\sqrt{R^2 + (\omega L_{max})^2}}{R}\right)^2 = 5.$$

Solve for L_{max}:

$$L_{max} = \frac{2R}{\omega} = \frac{2(120\,\text{V})^2/1000\,\text{W}}{2\pi(60.0\,\text{Hz})} = 7.64 \times 10^{-2}\,\text{H}.$$

(b) Now we must let

$$\left(\frac{R_{max} + R_{bulb}}{R_{bulb}}\right)^2 = 5,$$

or

$$R_{max} = (\sqrt{5} - 1)R_{bulb} = (\sqrt{5} - 1)\frac{(120\,\text{V})^2}{1000\,\text{W}} = 17.8\,\Omega.$$

43P

(a)

$$I_{rms} = \frac{\varepsilon_{rms}}{Z} = \frac{\varepsilon_{rms}}{\sqrt{R^2 + (2\pi fL - 1/2\pi fC)^2}}$$

$$= \frac{75.0\,\text{V}}{\sqrt{(15.0\,\Omega)^2 + \{2\pi(550\,\text{Hz})(25.0\,\text{mH}) - 1/[2\pi(550\,\text{Hz})(4.70\,\mu\text{F})]\}^2}}$$

$$= 2.59\,\text{A}.$$

(b) $V_{ab} = I_{rms}R = (2.59\,\text{A})(15.0\,\Omega) = 38.8\,\text{V}$,

$$V_{bc} = I_{rms}X_C = \frac{I_{rms}}{2\pi fC} = \frac{2.59\,\text{A}}{2\pi(550\,\text{Hz})(4.70\,\mu\text{F})} = 159\,\text{V},$$

$V_{cd} = I_{rms}X_L = 2\pi I_{rms}fL = 2\pi(2.59\,\text{A})(550\,\text{Hz})(25.0\,\text{mH}) = 224\,\text{V}$,
$V_{bd} = |V_{bc} - V_{cd}| = |159.5\,\text{V} - 223.7\,\text{V}| = 64.2\,\text{V}$,
$V_{ad} = \sqrt{V_{ab}^2 + V_{bd}^2} = \sqrt{(38.8\,\text{V})^2 + (64.2\,\text{V})^2} = 75.0\,\text{V}$.
(c) For L and C the rate is zero since they do not dissipate energy. For R

$$P_R = \frac{V_{ab}^2}{R} = \frac{(38.8\,\text{V})^2}{15.0\,\Omega} = 100\,\text{W}.$$

44E
Use $V_s N_p = V_p N_s$:

$$V_s = V_p \left(\frac{N_s}{N_p} \right) = (100 \text{ V}) \left(\frac{500}{50} \right) = 1.00 \times 10^3 \text{ V}.$$

45E
(a)

$$V_s = V_p \left(\frac{N_s}{N_p} \right) = (120 \text{ V}) \left(\frac{10}{500} \right) = 2.4 \text{ V}.$$

(b)

$$I_s = \frac{V_s}{R_s} = \frac{2.4 \text{ V}}{15 \, \Omega} = 0.16 \text{ A},$$

and

$$I_p = I_s \left(\frac{N_s}{N_p} \right) = (0.16 \text{ A}) \left(\frac{10}{500} \right) = 3.2 \times 10^{-3} \text{ A}.$$

46E
Step up: (i) Use $T_1 T_2$ as primary and $T_1 T_3$ as secondary coil: $V_{13}/V_{12} = (800 + 200)/200 = 5.00$. (ii) Use $T_1 T_2$ as primary and $T_2 T_3$ as secondary coil: $V_{23}/V_{13} = 800/200 = 4.00$. (iii) Use $T_2 T_3$ as primary and $T_1 T_3$ as secondary coil: $V_{13}/V_{23} = (800 + 200)/800 = 1.25$.
Step down: By exchanging the primary/secondary coils in each of the three cases above we get the following possible ratios: (i) $1/5.00 = 0.200$, (ii)$1/4.00 = 0.250$, and (iii)$1/1.25 = 0.800$.

47P
(a) The rms current in the cable is $I_{\text{rms}} = P/V_t = 250 \times 10^3 \text{ W}/(80 \times 10^3 \text{ V}) = 3.125 \text{ A}$. The rms voltage drop is then $\Delta V = I_{\text{rms}} R = (3.125 \text{ A})(2)(0.30 \, \Omega) = 1.9 \text{ V}$, and the rate of energy dissipation is $P_d = I_{\text{rms}}^2 R = (3.125 \text{ A})(2)(0.60 \, \Omega) = 5.9 \text{ W}$.
(b) Now $I_{\text{rms}} = 250 \times 10^3 \text{ W}/(8.0 \times 10^3 \text{ V}) = 31.25 \text{ A}$, so $\Delta V = (31.25 \text{ A})(0.60 \, \Omega) = 19 \text{ V}$, and $P_d = (3.125 \text{ A})^2(0.60 \, \Omega) = 5.9 \times 10^2 \text{ W}$.
(c) Now $I_{\text{rms}} = 250 \times 10^3 \text{ W}/(0.80 \times 10^3 \text{ V}) = 312.5 \text{ A}$, so $\Delta V = (312.5 \text{ A})(0.60 \, \Omega) = 1.9 \times 10^2 \text{ V}$, and $P_d = (312.5 \text{ A})^2(0.60 \, \Omega) = 5.9 \times 10^4 \text{ W}$.
Obviously, both the rate of energy dissipation and the voltage drop increase as V_t decreases. So to minimize these effects the best choice among the three V_t's above is $V_t = 80 \text{ kV}$.

48P
The amplifier is connected across the primary windings of a transformer and the resistor R is connected across the secondary windings. If I_s is the rms current in the secondary coil

then the average power delivered to R is $P_{av} = I_s^2 R$. Now $I_s = (N_p/N_s)I_p$, where N_p is the number of turns in the primary coil, N_s is the number of turns in the secondary coil, and I_p is the rms current in the primary coil. Thus

$$P_{av} = \left(\frac{I_p N_p}{N_s}\right)^2 R.$$

Now find the current in the primary circuit. It acts like a circuit consisting of a generator and two resistors in series. One resistance is the resistance r of the amplifier and the other is the equivalent resistance R_{eq} of the secondary circuit. Thus $I_p = \varepsilon/(r + R_{eq})$, where ε is the rms emf of the amplifier. According to Eq. 36–38 $R_{eq} = (N_p/N_s)^2 R$, so

$$I_p = \frac{\varepsilon}{r + (N_p/N_s)^2 R}$$

and

$$P_{av} = \frac{\varepsilon^2 (N_p/N_s)^2 R}{[r + (N_p/N_s)^2 R]^2}.$$

You wish to find the value of N_p/N_s so that P_{av} is a maximum.
Let $x = (N_p/N_s)^2$. Then

$$P_{av} = \frac{\varepsilon^2 R x}{(r + xR)^2}$$

and the derivative with respect to x is

$$\frac{dP_{av}}{dx} = \frac{\varepsilon^2 R(r - xR)}{(r + xR)^3}.$$

This is zero for $x = r/R = (1000\,\Omega)/(10\,\Omega) = 100$. Notice that for small x, P_{av} increases linearly with x and for large x it decreases in proportion to $1/x$. Thus $x = r/R$ is indeed a maximum, not a minimum.

Since $x = (N_p/N_s)^2$, maximum power is achieved for $(N_p/N_s)^2 = 100$, or $N_p/N_s = 10$.

49
(a)

$$X_C = \frac{1}{2\pi f C} = \frac{1}{2\pi (400\,\text{Hz})(24.0 \times 10^{-6}\,\text{F})} = 16.6\,\Omega.$$

(b)

$$Z = \sqrt{R^2 + (X_L - X_C)^2} = \sqrt{R^2 + (2\pi f L - X_C)^2}$$
$$= \sqrt{(220\,\Omega)^2 + [2\pi (400\,\text{Hz})(150 \times 10^{-3}\,\text{H}) - 16.6\,\Omega]^2} = 422\,\Omega.$$

(c)

$$I = \frac{\varepsilon_m}{Z} = \frac{220\,\text{V}}{422\,\Omega} = 0.521\,\text{A}.$$

(d) Now $X_C \propto C_{eq}^{-1}$ will increase since C_{eq} decreases.

(e) Now $C_{eq} = C/2$ and the new impedance is

$$Z' = \sqrt{(220\,\Omega)^2 + [2\pi(400\,\text{Hz})(150 \times 10^{-3}\,\text{H}) - 2(16.6\,\Omega)]^2} = 408\,\Omega,$$

i.e. $Z' > Z$, so the impedance increases.

(f) Since $I \propto Z^{-1}$, it decreases.

50

From the problem statement $2\pi f_0 = (LC)^{-1/2} = 6.00\,\text{kHz}$, $Z = \sqrt{R^2 + (2\pi f_1 L - 1/2\pi f_1 C)^2}$ $= 1.00\,\text{k}\omega$ where $f_1 = 8.00\,\text{kHz}$, and $\cos\phi = R/Z = \cos 45°$. Solve these equations for R, L and C:

(a) $R = Z\cos 45° = (1.00\,\text{k}\Omega)(\cos 45°) = 707\,\Omega.$

(b)

$$L = \frac{\sqrt{Z^2 - R^2}}{2\pi(f_1 - f_0^2/f_1)} = \frac{\sqrt{(1.00\,\text{k}\Omega)^2 - (707\,\Omega)^2}}{2\pi[8.00\,\text{kHZ} - (6.00\,\text{kHz})^2/8.00\,\text{kHz}]}$$

$$= 3.22 \times 10^{-2}\,\text{H}.$$

(c)

$$C = \frac{1}{4\pi^2 f_0^2 L} = \frac{1}{4\pi^2(6.00\,\text{kHz})^2(3.22 \times 10^{-2}\,\text{H})} = 2.19 \times 10^{-8}\,\text{F}.$$

51

From Problem 21 we know that $\Delta\Omega = \sqrt{3}RC\omega_0^2$. So

$$\frac{\Delta\omega}{\omega_0} = \frac{\sqrt{3}RC\omega_0^2}{\omega_0} = \frac{\sqrt{3}RC}{\sqrt{LC}} = \sqrt{3}R\sqrt{\frac{C}{L}} = \frac{\sqrt{3}}{Q},$$

where in the last step we used $Q = \sqrt{L/C}/R$.

52

The voltage across the capacitor is given by

$$V_c = IX_C = \frac{\varepsilon_m X_C}{Z} = \frac{\varepsilon_m}{\omega C\sqrt{R^2 + (\omega L - 1/\omega C)^2}}$$

$$= \frac{\varepsilon_m}{\sqrt{(R\omega C)^2 + (\omega^2 LC - 1)^2}} \equiv \frac{\varepsilon_m}{\sqrt{F(\omega)}}.$$

To maximize V_c, set $dF(\omega)/d\omega = 0$:

$$\frac{dF(\omega)}{d\omega} = 2\omega R^2 C^2 + 2(\omega^2 LC - 1)(2\omega LC) = 0,$$

which gives

$$\omega = \sqrt{\frac{1}{LC} - \frac{R^2}{2L^2}} = \sqrt{\frac{1}{LC}}\sqrt{1 - \frac{R^2 C}{2L}} = \omega_0\sqrt{1 - \frac{R^2}{2L}}.$$

CHAPTER 37

1E

Numerically,

$$C = \frac{1}{\sqrt{\epsilon_0 \mu_0}} = \frac{1}{\sqrt{(8.85 \times 10^{-12}\,\text{F/m})(1.26 \times 10^{-6}\,\text{H/m})}} = 2.99 \times 10^8\,\text{m/s}.$$

Dimensionally,

$$[(\text{F/m})(\text{H/m})]^{-1/2} = \text{m}[\text{FH}]^{-1/2} = \text{m}[(\text{C/V})(\text{T}\cdot\text{m}^2/\text{A})]$$

$$= \text{m}\left[\frac{\text{C}(\text{kg/s}^2)\,\text{m}^2}{(\text{kg}\,\text{m}^2/\text{s}^2)\,\text{A}}\right]^{-1/2} = \text{m}\left(\frac{\text{C}}{\text{A}}\right)^{-1/2} = \text{m/s}.$$

2E

(a)

$$\sqrt{\frac{\mu_0}{\epsilon_0}} = \sqrt{\frac{1.26 \times 10^{-6}\,\text{H/m}}{8.85 \times 10^{-12}\,\text{F/m}}} = 377\,\Omega.$$

(b) $\omega = 2\pi f = 2\pi(60\,\text{Hz}) = 377\,\text{rad/s}.$

3E

Let R be the radius of a capacitor plate and r be the distance from axis of the capacitor. For points with $r \leq R$ the magnitude of the magnetic field is given by

$$B = \frac{\mu_0 \epsilon_0 r}{2}\frac{dE}{dt}$$

and for $r \geq R$ it is

$$B = \frac{\mu_0 \epsilon_0 R^2}{2r}\frac{dE}{dt}.$$

The maximum magnetic field occurs at points for which $r = R$ and its value is given by either of the formulas above:

$$B_{\text{max}} = \frac{\mu_0 \epsilon_0 R}{2}\frac{dE}{dt}.$$

There are two values of r for which $B = B_{\text{max}}/2$: one less than R and one greater. To find the one that is less than R, solve

$$\frac{\mu_0 \epsilon_0 r}{2}\frac{dE}{dt} = \frac{\mu_0 \epsilon_0 R}{4}\frac{dE}{dt}$$

for r. The result is $r = R/2 = (55.0\,\text{mm})/2 = 27.5\,\text{mm}.$

To find the one that is greater than R, solve

$$\frac{\mu_0\epsilon_0 R^2}{2r}\frac{dE}{dt} = \frac{\mu_0\epsilon_0 R}{4}\frac{dE}{dt}$$

for r. The result is $r = 2R = 2(55.0\,\text{mm}) = 110\,\text{mm}$.

4E

Apply Eq. 37-6 to a circular loop of radius R centered at the center of the plates:

$$\oint \mathbf{B}\cdot d\mathbf{s} = 2\pi RB = \mu_0\epsilon_0\frac{d\Phi_E}{dt} = \mu_0\epsilon_0\frac{d}{dt}(\pi R^2 E) = \mu_0\epsilon_0\pi R^2\frac{dE}{dt}$$

$$= \frac{\mu_0\epsilon_0\pi R^2}{d}\frac{d}{dt}[V_m\cos(\omega t + \phi)] = \frac{\mu_0\epsilon_0\pi R^2 V_m\omega}{d}\sin(\omega t + \phi).$$

Thus

$$B_m = \frac{\mu_0\epsilon_0\pi R^2 V_m\omega}{2\pi Rd}[\sin(\omega t + \phi)]_{\text{max}} = \frac{\pi\mu_0\epsilon_0 RV_m f}{d} = \frac{RV_m f}{C^2 d}$$

$$= \frac{(30\times 10^{-3}\,\text{m})(150\,\text{V})(60\,\text{Hz})}{(3.0\times 10^8\,\text{m/s})^2(5.0\times 10^{-3}\,\text{m})} = 1.9\times 10^{-12}\,\text{T}.$$

5P

Use $B_m(r) = (V_m f/C^2 d)r = B_m(R)r/R$ for $r \ll R$ and $B_m(r) = B_m(R)(R/r)$ for $r \geqslant R$.

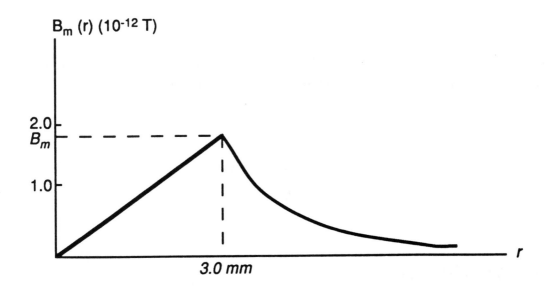

6E

The displacement current is given by

$$i_d = \epsilon_0 A \frac{dE}{dt},$$

where A is the area of a plate and E is the magnitude of the electric field between the plates. The field between the plates is uniform, so $E = V/d$, where V is the potential difference across the plates and d is the plate separation. Thus

$$i_d = \frac{\epsilon_0 A}{d} \frac{dV}{dt}.$$

Now $\epsilon_0 A/d$ is the capacitance C of a parallel-plate capacitor without a dielectric, so

$$i_d = C \frac{dV}{dt}.$$

7E

Let the area plate be A and the plate separation be d. Use Eq. 37-8:

$$i_d = \epsilon_0 \frac{d\Phi_E}{dt} = \epsilon_0 \frac{d}{dt}(AE) = \epsilon_0 A \frac{d}{dt}\left(\frac{V}{d}\right) = \frac{\epsilon_0 A}{d}\left(\frac{dV}{dt}\right),$$

or

$$\frac{dV}{dt} = \frac{i_d d}{\epsilon_0 A} = \frac{i_d}{C} = \frac{1.0\,\text{A}}{1.0 \times 10^{-6}\,\text{F}} = 1.0 \times 10^6 \,\text{V/s}.$$

So we need to change the voltage difference across the capacitor at the rate of 1.0×10^6 V/s.

8E

Consider an area A, normal to a uniform electric field $\mathbf{E}$. The displacement current density is uniform and normal to the area. Its magnitude is given by $J_d = i_d/A$. For this situation

$$i_d = \epsilon_0 A \frac{dE}{dt},$$

so

$$J_d = \frac{1}{A}\epsilon_0 A \frac{dE}{dt} = \epsilon_0 \frac{dE}{dt}.$$

9E

Apply Eq. 37-9 for each of the three circles:

$$\oint_{A1} \mathbf{B}_1 \cdot d\mathbf{s} = 2\pi r B_1 = \mu_0(i_d + i) = \mu_0 i,$$

or $B_1 = \mu_0 i/2\pi r$. Similarly for A_3 we have $B_3 = \mu_0 i/2\pi r$. For A_2,

$$\oint_{A2} \mathbf{B_2} \cdot d\mathbf{s} = 2\pi r B_2 = \mu_0(i_d + i) = \mu_0 i_d = \mu_0 \epsilon_0 \frac{d\Phi_E}{dt} = \mu_0 \epsilon_0 \frac{d}{dt}(\pi R^2 E)$$

$$= \mu_0 \epsilon_0 \frac{d}{dt}\left(\frac{\pi R^2 \sigma}{\epsilon_0}\right) = \mu_0 \frac{dq}{dt} = \mu_0 i,$$

or $B_2 = \mu_0 i/2\pi r$.

10P
Apply Eq. 37-9 to a circular loop of radius r centered at the center of the plates. Then

$$\oint \mathbf{B} \cdot d\mathbf{s} = 2\pi r E = \mu_0(i + i_d) = \mu_0 i_d = \mu_0 \frac{d\Phi_E(r)}{dt},$$

or

$$E(r) = \frac{\mu_0}{2\pi r}\frac{d\Phi_E(r)}{dt}.$$

Note that since $d\Phi_E(r)/dt = d(\pi r^2 E)/dt \propto r^2$ for $r < R$, we have

$$\frac{d\Phi_E(r)}{dt} = \frac{r^2}{R^2}\frac{d\Phi_E(R)}{dt} \quad (r \leqslant R).$$

So

$$E(r) = \frac{\mu_0}{2\pi r}\left(\frac{r}{R}\right)^2 \frac{d\Phi_E(R)}{dt} = \frac{\mu_0 r i_d}{2\pi R^2} \quad (r \leqslant R).$$

For $r > R$,

$$\frac{d\Phi_E(r)}{dt} = \frac{d\Phi_E(R)}{dt} = i_d.$$

So

$$E(r) = \frac{\mu_0 i_d}{2\pi r} \quad (r \geqslant R).$$

11P
(a) Use $\oint \mathbf{B} \cdot d\mathbf{s} = \mu_0 I_{\text{enclosed}}$ to find

$$B = \frac{\mu_0 I_{\text{enclosed}}}{2\pi r} = \frac{\mu_0(J_d \pi r^2)}{2\pi r} = \frac{1}{2}\mu_0 J_d r$$

$$= \frac{1}{2}(1.26 \times 10^{-6} \text{ H/m})(20 \text{ A/m}^2)(50 \times 10^{-3} \text{ m}) = 6.3 \times 10^{-7} \text{ T}.$$

(b) From

$$i_d = J_d \pi r^2 = \epsilon_0 \frac{d\Phi_E}{dt} = \epsilon_0 \pi r^2 \frac{dE}{dt}$$

925

we get

$$\frac{dE}{dt} = \frac{J_d}{\epsilon_0} = \frac{20 \, \text{A/m}^2}{8.85 \times 10^{-12} \, \text{F/m}} = 2.3 \times 10^{12} \, \text{V/m} \cdot \text{s}.$$

12P
(a)

$$i_d = \epsilon_0 \frac{d\Phi_E}{dt} = \epsilon_0 A \frac{dE}{dt}$$

$$= (8.85 \times 10^{-12} \, \text{F/m})(1.6 \, \text{m}^2) \left(\frac{4.5 \times 10^5 \, \text{N/C} - 6.0 \times 10^5 \, \text{N/C}}{4.0 \times 10^{-6} \, \text{s}} \right) = -0.71 \, \text{A}.$$

(b) $i_d \propto dE/dt = 0$.
(c)

$$i_d = \epsilon_0 A \frac{dE}{dt}$$

$$= (8.85 \times 10^{-12} \, \text{F/m})(1.6 \, \text{m}^2) \left(\frac{-4.0 \times 10^5 \, \text{N/C}}{15 \times 10^{-6} \, \text{s} - 10 \times 10^{-6} \, \text{s}} \right) = 1.1 \, \text{A}.$$

13P
(a) $i_d = i = 2.0 \, \text{A}$, as shown in Exercise 9.
(b)

$$\frac{dE}{dt} = \frac{1}{\epsilon_0 A} \left(\epsilon_0 \frac{d\Phi_E}{dt} \right) = \frac{i_d}{\epsilon_0 A} = \frac{2.0 \, \text{A}}{(8.85 \times 10^{-12} \, \text{F/m})(1.0 \, \text{m})^2} = 2.3 \times 10^{11} \, \text{V/m} \cdot \text{s}.$$

(c)

$$i_d' = i_d \left(\frac{\text{area enclosed by the path}}{\text{area of each plate}} \right) = (2.0 \, \text{A}) \left(\frac{0.50 \, \text{m}}{1.0 \, \text{m}} \right)^2 = 0.50 \, \text{A}.$$

(d)

$$\oint \mathbf{B} \cdot d\mathbf{s} = \mu_0 i_d' = (1.26 \times 10^{-6} \, \text{H/m})(0.50 \, \text{A}) = 0.63 \times 10^{-6} \, \text{T} \cdot \text{m}.$$

14P
(a) Use the results of Exercise 6, with $V = V_m \sin(2\pi f t)$. The derivative with respect to time is $dV/dt = 2\pi f V_m \cos(2\pi f t)$, so $i_d = 2\pi f C V_m \cos(2\pi f t)$ and the maximum displacement current is

$$i_{d \, \text{max}} = 2\pi f C V_m = 2\pi (50.0 \, \text{Hz})(100 \times 10^{-12} \, \text{F})(174 \times 10^3 \, \text{V}) = 5.47 \times 10^{-3} \, \text{A}.$$

(b) The maximum displacement current is directly proportional to the maximum potential difference applied. A large value of V_m produces a more easily measurable value of $i_{d\,max}$ than a smaller value of V_m.

15P

(a) At any instant the displacement current i_d in the gap between the plates equals the conduction current i in the wires. Thus $i_{max} = i_{d\,max} = 7.60\,\mu A$.

(b) Since $i_d = \epsilon_0\,(d\Phi_E/dt)$,

$$\left(\frac{d\Phi_E}{dt}\right)_{max} = \frac{i_{d\,max}}{\epsilon_0} = \frac{7.60 \times 10^{-6}\,A}{8.85 \times 10^{-12}\,F/m} = 8.59 \times 10^5\,V \cdot m/s\,.$$

(c) According to Exercise 6

$$i_d = \frac{\epsilon_0 A}{d}\frac{dV}{dt}\,.$$

Now the potential difference across the capacitor is the same in magnitude as the emf of the generator, so $V = \varepsilon_m \sin \omega t$ and $dV/dt = \omega \varepsilon_m \cos \omega t$. Thus

$$i_d = \frac{\epsilon_0 A \omega \varepsilon_m}{d} \cos \omega t$$

and

$$i_{d\,max} = \frac{\epsilon_0 A \omega \varepsilon_m}{d}\,.$$

This means

$$d = \frac{\epsilon_0 A \omega \varepsilon_m}{i_{d\,max}} = \frac{(8.85 \times 10^{-12}\,F/m)\pi(0.180\,m)^2(130\,rad/s)(220\,V)}{7.60 \times 10^{-6}\,A}$$

$$= 3.39 \times 10^{-3}\,m\,,$$

where $A = \pi R^2$ was used.

(d) Use the Ampere-Maxwell law in the form $\oint \mathbf{B} \cdot d\mathbf{s} = \mu_0 I_d$, where the path of integration is a circle of radius r between the plates and parallel to them. I_d is the displacement current through the area bounded by the path of integration. Since the displacement current density is uniform between the plates $I_d = (r^2/R^2)i_d$, where i_d is the total displacement current between the plates and R is the plate radius. The field lines are circles centered on the axis of the plates, so $\mathbf{B}$ is parallel to $d\mathbf{s}$. The field has constant magnitude around the circular path, so $\oint \mathbf{B} \cdot d\mathbf{s} = 2\pi r B$. Thus

$$2\pi r B = \mu_0 \left(\frac{r^2}{R^2}\right) i_d$$

and

$$B = \frac{\mu_0 i_d r}{2\pi R^2}\,.$$

The maximum magnetic field is given by

$$B_{\max} = \frac{\mu_0 i_{d\ \max} r}{2\pi R^2} = \frac{(4\pi \times 10^{-7}\ \text{T} \cdot \text{m/A})(7.6 \times 10^{-6}\ \text{A})(0.110\,\text{m})}{2\pi(0.180\,\text{m})^2} = 5.16 \times 10^{-12}\ \text{T}.$$

16E

Table 37-3 is not available in the book. Refer to Table 37-2 for the physical principle each of the Maxwell's Equations describe.

17P

(a) From

$$\oint_{abefa} \mathbf{E} \cdot d\mathbf{s} = -\left(\frac{d\Phi_B}{dt}\right)_{abefa}$$

and

$$\oint_{bedeb} \mathbf{E} \cdot d\mathbf{s} = -\left(\frac{d\Phi_B}{dt}\right)_{bcdeb},$$

we get

$$\oint_{abcdefa} \mathbf{E} \cdot d\mathbf{s} = \left(\oint_{abefa} + \oint_{bedeb}\right) \mathbf{E} \cdot d\mathbf{s} = -\left[\left(\frac{d\Phi_B}{dt}\right)_{abefa} + \left(\frac{d\Phi_B}{dt}\right)_{bcdeb}\right]$$

$$= -\left(\frac{d\Phi_B}{dt}\right)_{abcdefa}.$$

(b) Similarly, for Eq. IV

$$\oint_{abcdefa} \mathbf{B} \cdot d\mathbf{s} = \left(\oint_{abefa} + \oint_{bcdeb}\right) \mathbf{E} \cdot d\mathbf{s}$$

$$= \left(\mu_0 \epsilon_0 \frac{d\Phi_E}{dt} + \mu_0 i\right)_{abefa} + \left(\mu_0 \frac{\Phi_E}{dt} + \mu_0 i\right)_{bcdeb}$$

$$= \mu_0 \epsilon_0 \left[\left(\frac{d\Phi_E}{dt}\right)_{abefa} + \left(\frac{d\Phi_E}{dt}\right)_{bcdeb}\right] + \mu_0(i_{abefa} + i_{bcdeb})$$

$$= \mu_0 \epsilon_0 \left(\frac{d\Phi_E}{dt}\right)_{abcdefa} + \mu_0 i_{abcdefa}.$$

18P

(a) Lable the surface on the left as 1, the one on the right as 2, and the composite surface as 3. Then

$$\oint_3 \mathbf{E} \cdot d\mathbf{A} = \oint_1 \mathbf{E} \cdot d\mathbf{A} + \oint_2 \mathbf{E} \cdot d\mathbf{A}$$

$$= \frac{q_1}{\epsilon_0} + \frac{q_2}{\epsilon_0} = \frac{q_1 + q_2}{\epsilon_0} = \frac{q_3}{\epsilon_0}.$$

(b)

$$\oint_3 \mathbf{B} \cdot d\mathbf{A} = \oint_1 \mathbf{B} \cdot d\mathbf{A} + \oint_2 \mathbf{B} \cdot d\mathbf{A} = 0 + 0 = 0.$$

19P

The Gauss's law for dielectric materials (Eq. 27-38) is $\oint \kappa \mathbf{E} \cdot d\mathbf{A} = q/\epsilon_0$, where we replace $\mathbf{E}$ by $\kappa\mathbf{E}$. The same substitution is made for Eq. III. Eq. II is related with the magnetic field and is unchanged. Finally in Eq. IV we need to replace Φ_E by $\kappa\Phi_E$, since $\Phi_E = \oint \mathbf{E} \cdot d\mathbf{A} \to \oint \kappa \mathbf{E} \cdot d\mathbf{A}$.

20P*

(a) At time t the charge on the right face is given by

$$q = \int_0^t i\, dt = \int_0^t \alpha t\, dt = \frac{1}{2}\alpha t^2 .$$

At that time the charge on the left face is $-\frac{1}{2}\alpha t^2$.

(b) Use a Gaussian surface in the shape of a cylinder, concentric with the rod, with one end in the gap and the other in the rod to the left of the gap, as shown in the diagram to the right. The electric field is in the positive x direction so we need to consider only the faces of the cylinder. The magnitude of the electric field at the left face is given by ρJ, where ρ is the resistivity of the rod and J is the current density.

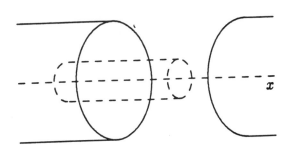

Let E be the magnitude of the field at the right face. Assume the current density is uniform on the left face and the electric field is uniform on the right face. Then

$$\oint \mathbf{E} \cdot d\mathbf{A} = -\rho J A + EA,$$

where A is the area of a face. We suppose the resistivity is so small that the first term can be neglected. Gauss' law becomes $EA = Q/\epsilon_0$, where Q is the charge on the rod end, within the Gaussian surface. The area of the face of the Gaussian cylinder is $A = \pi r^2$, where r it is radius, and the charge enclosed is $Q = (r^2/R^2)q$, where q is the charge on the face of the rod. Thus

$$E = \frac{q}{\pi \epsilon_0 R^2} = \frac{\alpha t^2}{2\pi \epsilon_0 R^2} \, ,$$

where the result of part (a), $q = \frac{1}{2}\alpha t^2$, was used.

(c) The magnetic field lines form circles that are concentric with the rod axis (the x axis) and lie in planes that are parallel to the rod faces.

(d) Use the Ampere-Maxwell law:

$$\oint \mathbf{B} \cdot d\mathbf{s} = \mu_0 i + \mu_0 \epsilon_0 \frac{d\Phi_E}{dt} \, .$$

For the path of integration choose a circle that coincides with a magnetic field line. Suppose its radius is r (with $r < R$) and that B is the magnitude of the field at points on it. Then $\oint \mathbf{B} \cdot d\mathbf{s} = 2\pi r B$. In the gap the current is zero and only the displacement current contributes to the right side of the Ampere-Maxwell equation. Since

$$\frac{d\Phi_E}{dt} = A \frac{dE}{dt} = \pi r^2 \frac{\alpha t}{\pi \epsilon_0 R^2} = \frac{\alpha t r^2}{\epsilon_0 R^2} \, ,$$

the Ampere-Maxwell law yields

$$2\pi r B = \mu_0 \epsilon_0 \frac{\alpha t r^2}{\epsilon_0 R^2} \, .$$

Thus

$$B = \frac{\mu_0 \alpha t r}{2\pi R^2} \, .$$

The magnetic field inside the rod, a distance r from its axis, is given by exactly the same expression. Now only the conduction current contributes to the right side of the Ampere-Maxwell equation. Take the path of integration to be a circle centered at the axis and parallel to the rod faces. The current through the circle is $(r^2/R^2)i$ and the Ampere-Maxwell equation yields

$$2\pi r B = \mu_0 (r^2/R^2)i \, ,$$

so

$$B = \frac{\mu_0 i r}{2\pi R^2} = \frac{\mu_0 \alpha t r}{2\pi R^2} \, ,$$

where αt was substituted for i.

21

(a)

$$E = \frac{J}{\sigma} = \rho J = \frac{\rho i}{A} = \frac{(1.62 \times 10^{-8} \, \Omega \cdot \text{m})(100 \, \text{A})}{5.00 \times 10^{-6} \, \text{m}^2} = 0.324 \, \text{V/m}.$$

(b)

$$i_d = \epsilon_0 \frac{d\Phi_E}{dt} = \epsilon_0 A \frac{dE}{dt} = \epsilon_0 A \frac{d}{dt}\left(\frac{\rho i}{A}\right) = \epsilon_0 \rho \frac{di}{dt}$$
$$= (8.85 \times 10^{-12}\,\text{F})(1.62 \times 10^{-8}\,\Omega)(2000\,\text{A/s}) = 2.87 \times 10^{-16}\,\text{A}.$$

(c)

$$\frac{B(\text{due to } i_d)}{B(\text{due to } i)} = \frac{\mu_0 i_d / 2\pi r}{\mu_0 i / 2\pi r} = \frac{i_d}{i} = \frac{2.87 \times 10^{-16}\,\text{A}}{100\,\text{A}} 2.87 \times 10^{-18}.$$

22

Let the surface change density be σ' and the charge be q' on the plates. Then the displacement current is

$$i_d = \epsilon_0 \frac{d\Phi_E}{dt} = \epsilon_0 \frac{d}{dt}(AE) = \epsilon_0 \frac{d}{dt}\left(\frac{\sigma' A}{\epsilon_0}\right) = \frac{dq'}{dt} = -i,$$

i.e. $B \propto i_d + i = 0$.

23

$$\mathbf{J}_d = \left(\frac{i_d}{A}\right)\frac{\mathbf{E}}{E} = \frac{\epsilon_0}{A}\frac{d}{dt}(\kappa\Phi_E)\frac{\mathbf{E}}{E} = \frac{\epsilon_0}{A}\frac{d}{dt}(\kappa EA)\frac{\mathbf{E}}{E} = \frac{d}{dt}(\kappa\epsilon_0 E)\frac{\mathbf{E}}{E}$$
$$= \frac{d(\kappa\epsilon_0\mathbf{E})}{dt} = \frac{d\mathbf{D}}{dt},$$

where we noted that $d\mathbf{E}/dt = (dE/dt)(\mathbf{E}/E)$, since the direction of $\mathbf{E}$ does not change.

CHAPTER 38

1E

(a)

$$f = \frac{C}{\lambda} = \frac{3.0 \times 10^8 \text{ m/s}}{(1.0 \times 10^5)(6.4 \times 10^6 \text{ m})} = 4.7 \times 10^{-3} \text{ Hz}.$$

(b)

$$T = \frac{1}{f} = \frac{1}{4.7 \times 10^{-3} \text{ Hz}} = 212 \text{ sec} = 3 \text{ min } 32 \text{ s}.$$

2E

The time for light to travel a distance d in free space is $t = d/c$, where c is the speed of light (3.00×10^8 m/s).

(a) Take d to be $150 \text{ km} = 150 \times 10^3$ m. Then

$$t = \frac{d}{c} = \frac{150 \times 10^3 \text{ m}}{3.00 \times 10^8 \text{ m/s}} = 5.00 \times 10^{-4} \text{ s}.$$

(b) At full moon the moon and the sun are on opposite sides of the Earth, so the distance traveled by the light is $d = (1.50 \times 10^8 \text{ km}) + 2(3.82 \times 10^5 \text{ km}) = 1.508 \times 10^8 \text{ km} = 1.508 \times 10^{11}$ m. The time taken by light to travel this distance is

$$t = \frac{d}{c} = \frac{1.508 \times 10^{11} \text{ m}}{3.00 \times 10^8 \text{ m/s}} = 503 \text{ s} = 8.38 \text{ min}.$$

The distances are given in Appendix C.

(c) Take d to be $2(1.3 \times 10^9 \text{ km}) = 2.6 \times 10^{12}$ m. Then

$$t = \frac{d}{c} = \frac{2.6 \times 10^{12} \text{ m}}{3.00 \times 10^8 \text{ m/s}} = 8.7 \times 10^3 \text{ s} = 2.4 \text{ h}.$$

(d) Take d to be 6500 ly and the speed of light to be 1.00 ly/y. Then

$$t = \frac{d}{c} = \frac{6500 \text{ ly}}{1.00 \text{ ly/y}} = 6500 \text{ y}.$$

The explosion took place in the year $1054 - 6500 = -5446$ or B.C. 5446.

3E

(a)

$$f = \frac{C}{\lambda} = \frac{3.0 \times 10^8 \, \text{m/s}}{0.067 \times 10^{-15} \, \text{m}} = 4.5 \times 10^{24} \, \text{Hz}.$$

(b)

$$\lambda = \frac{C}{f} = \frac{3.0 \times 10^8 \, \text{m/s}}{30 \, \text{Hz}} = 1.0 \times 10^7 \, \text{m}.$$

4E

(a) From Fig. 38-2 we find the wavelengths to be about 520 nm and 610 nm.
(b) Again from Fig. 38-2 the wavelength is about 560 nm, the frequency is $C/\lambda = (3 \times 10^8 \, \text{m/s})/560 \, \text{nm} = 5.4 \times 10^{14} \, \text{Hz}$, and the period is $(5.4 \times 10^{14} \, \text{Hz})^{-1} \simeq 1.9 \times 10^{-15}$ s.

5E

Consider two wavelengths, λ_1 and λ_2, whose corresponding frequencies are f_1 and f_2. Then $\lambda_1 = C/f_1$ and $\lambda_2 = C/f_2$. If $\lambda_1/\lambda_2 = 10$ then

$$\frac{\lambda_1}{\lambda_2} = \frac{C/f_1}{C/f_2} = \frac{f_2}{f_1} = 10,$$

i.e. The spaces are the same on both scales.

6E

Since $\Delta\lambda \ll \lambda$ we have

$$\Delta f = \left| \Delta\left(\frac{C}{\lambda}\right) \right| \approx \frac{C\Delta\lambda}{\lambda^2} = \frac{(3.0 \times 10^8 \, \text{m/s})(0.0100 \times 10^{-9} \, \text{m})}{(632.8 \times 10^{-9} \, \text{m})^2} = 7.49 \times 10^9 \, \text{Hz}.$$

7P

(a)
Suppose that at time t_1 the moon is starting a revolution (on the verge of going behind Jupiter, say) and that at this instant the distance between Jupiter and the Earth is ℓ_1. The time of the start of the revolution as seen on Earth is $t_1^* = t_1 + \ell_1/c$. Suppose the moon starts the next revolution at time t_2 and at that instant the Earth-Jupiter distance is ℓ_2. The start of the revolution as seen on Earth is $t_2^* = t_2 + \ell_2/c$. Now the actual period of the moon is given by $T = t_2 - t_1$ and the period as measured on Earth is

$$T^* = t_2^* - t_1^* = t_2 - t_1 + \frac{\ell_2}{c} - \frac{\ell_2}{c} = T + \frac{\ell_2 - \ell_1}{c}.$$

The period as measured on Earth is longer than the actual period because the Earth moves during a revolution and light takes a finite time to travel from Jupiter to the Earth. For the situation depicted in the diagram, light emitted at the end of a revolution travels a longer distance to get to the Earth than light emitted at the beginning.

Suppose the position of the Earth is given by the angle θ, measured from x. Let R be the radius of the Earth's orbit and d be the distance from the sun to Jupiter. Then the law of cosines, applied to the triangle with the sun, the Earth, and Jupiter at the vertices, yields $\ell^2 = d^2 + R^2 - 2dR\cos\theta$. This expression can be used to calculate ℓ_1 and ℓ_2. Since the Earth does not move very far during one revolution of the moon, we may approximate $\ell_2 - \ell_1$ by $(d\ell/dt)T$ and T^* by $T + (d\ell/dt)(T/c)$. Now

$$\frac{d\ell}{dt} = \frac{2Rd\sin\theta}{\sqrt{d^2 + R^2 - 2dR\cos\theta}} \frac{d\theta}{dt} = \frac{2vd\sin\theta}{\sqrt{d^2 + R^2 - 2dR\cos\theta}},$$

where $v = R(d\theta/dt)$ is the speed of the Earth in its orbit. For $\theta = 0$, $(d\ell/dt) = 0$ and $T^* = T$. Since the Earth is then moving perpendicularly to the line from the sun to Jupiter its distance from the planet does not change much during a revolution of the moon. On the other hand, when $\theta = 90°$, $d\ell/dt = vd/\sqrt{d^2 + R^2}$ and

$$T^* = T\left(1 + \frac{vd}{c\sqrt{d^2 + R^2}}\right).$$

The Earth is now moving parallel to the line from the sun to Jupiter and its distance from the planet changes during a revolution of the moon.

(b) Let t be the actual time for the moon to make N revolutions and t^* the time for N revolutions to be observed on Earth. Then

$$t^* = t + \frac{\ell_2 - \ell_2}{c},$$

where ℓ_1 is the Earth-Jupiter distance at the beginning of the interval and ℓ_2 is the Earth-Jupiter distance at the end. Suppose the Earth is at x at the beginning of the interval and at y at the end. Then $\ell_1 = d - R$ and $\ell_2 = \sqrt{d^2 + R^2}$. Thus

$$t^* = t + \frac{\sqrt{d^2 + R^2} - (d - R)}{c}.$$

A value can be found for t by measuring the observed period of revolution when the Earth is at x and multiplying by N. Notice that the observed period is the true period when the Earth is at x. Now measure the time interval as the Earth moves from x to y. This is t^*. The difference is

$$t^* - t = \frac{\sqrt{d^2 + R^2} - (d - R)}{c}.$$

If the radii of the orbits of Jupiter and the Earth are known, the value for $t^* - t$ can be used to compute c.

Since Jupiter is much further from the sun than the Earth, $\sqrt{d^2 + R^2}$ may be approximated by d and $t^* - t$ may be approximated by R/c. In this approximation only the radius of the Earth's orbit need be known.

8E

$$\lambda = \frac{c}{f} = 2\pi c\sqrt{LC}$$

$$= 2\pi(3.0 \times 10^8 \text{ m/s})\sqrt{(0.253 \times 10^{-6} \text{ H})(25.0 \times 10^{-12} \text{ F})} = 4.7 \text{ m}.$$

9E

If f is the frequency and λ is the wavelength of an electromagnetic wave then $f\lambda = c$. The frequency is the same as the frequency of oscillation of the current in the LC circuit of the generator. That is, $f = 1/2\pi\sqrt{LC}$, where C is the capacitance and L is the inductance. Thus

$$\frac{\lambda}{2\pi\sqrt{LC}} = c.$$

The solution for L is

$$L = \frac{\lambda^2}{4\pi^2 C c^2} = \frac{(550 \times 10^{-9} \text{ m})^2}{4\pi^2(17 \times 10^{-12} \text{ F})(3.00 \times 10^8 \text{ m/s})^2} = 5.00 \times 10^{-21} \text{ H}.$$

This is exceedingly small.

10P

(a) The arrangement in Fig. 38-3 features a pair of wire terminals with alternating charges q and $-q$ each, resembling an electric dipole. The arrangement is Fig. 38-19 replaces that with a wire loop through which an alternating current exists, resembling a magnetic dipole. (b) Due to the symmetry of the Maxwell's Equations in free space (where $i = q = 0$), to get the field of a magnetic dipole all you need to do is to take the field of an electric dipole, depicted in Figs. 38-4 and 38-5, and make the following transformation: $\mathbf{E} \to \mathbf{B}$, $\mathbf{B} \to \mathbf{E}$.

11E

$$B_m = \frac{E_m}{c} = \frac{3.20 \times 10^{-4} \text{ V/m}}{3.00 \times 10^8 \text{ m/s}} = 1.07 \times 10^{-12} \text{ T}.$$

12E

Since the **E**-wave oscillates in the z direction and travels in the x direction, we have $B_x = B_z = 0$, and

$$B_y = B_m \cos[\pi \times 10^{15}(t - x/c)] = \frac{(2.0)\cos[10^{15}\pi(t - x/c)]}{3.0 \times 10^8}$$

$$= (6.7 \times 10^{-9} \text{ T})\cos[10^{15}\pi(t - x/c)].$$

13P
Differentiate both sides of Eq. 38-15 with respect to x:

$$\frac{\partial}{\partial x}\left(\frac{\partial E}{\partial x}\right) = \frac{\partial^2 E}{\partial x^2} = -\frac{\partial}{\partial x}\left(\frac{\partial B}{\partial t}\right) = \frac{\partial^2 B}{\partial x \partial t}.$$

Differentiate both sides of Eq. 38-21 with respect to t:

$$\frac{\partial}{\partial t}\left(\frac{\partial B}{\partial x}\right) = \frac{\partial^2 B}{\partial x \partial t} = \frac{\partial}{\partial t}\left(\epsilon_0 \mu_0 \frac{\partial E}{\partial t}\right) = \epsilon_0 \mu_0 \frac{\partial^2 E}{\partial t^2}.$$

Substituting $\partial^2 E/\partial x^2 = -\partial^2 B/\partial x \partial t$ from the first equation above into the second one, we get

$$\epsilon_0 \mu_0 \frac{\partial^2 E}{\partial t^2} = \frac{\partial^2 E}{\partial x^2},$$

or

$$\frac{\partial^2 E}{\partial t^2} = \frac{1}{\epsilon_0 \mu_0}\frac{\partial^2 E}{\partial x^2} = c^2 \frac{\partial^2 E}{\partial x^2}.$$

Similarly, differentiate both sides of Eq. 38-15 with respect to t:

$$\frac{\partial^2 E}{\partial x \partial t} = -\frac{\partial^2 B}{\partial t^2};$$

and differentiate both sides of Eq. 38-21 with respect to x:

$$-\frac{\partial^2 B}{\partial x^2} = \epsilon_0 \mu_0 \frac{\partial^2 E}{\partial x \partial x}.$$

Combining these two equations, we get

$$\frac{\partial^2 B}{\partial t^2} = \frac{1}{\epsilon_0 \mu_0}\frac{\partial^2 B}{\partial x^2} = c^2 \frac{\partial^2 B}{\partial x^2}.$$

14P
(a) From Eq. 38-1 we get

$$\frac{\partial^2 E}{\partial t^2} = \frac{\partial^2}{\partial t^2}[E_m \sin(kx - \omega t)] = -\omega^2 E_m \sin(kx - \omega t),$$

and

$$c^2 \frac{\partial^2 E}{\partial x^2} = c^2 \frac{\partial^2}{\partial x^2}[E_m \sin(kx - \omega t)] = -k^2 c^2 \sin(kx - \omega t)$$
$$= -\omega^2 E_m \sin(kx - \omega t).$$

936

So

$$\frac{\partial^2 E}{\partial t^2} = c^2 \frac{\partial^2 E}{\partial x^2}$$

is satisfied. You can show analogously that Eq. 38-2 satisfies

$$\frac{\partial^2 B}{\partial t^2} = c^2 \frac{\partial^2 B}{\partial x^2}.$$

(b) For $E = E_m f(kx \pm \omega t)$ we have

$$\frac{\partial^2 E}{\partial t^2} = E_m \frac{\partial^2 f(kx \pm \omega t)}{\partial t^2} = \omega^2 E_m \frac{d^2 f}{du^2}\bigg|_{u=kx\pm\omega t},$$

and

$$c^2 \frac{\partial^2 E}{\partial x^2} = c^2 E_m \frac{\partial^2 f(kx \pm \omega t)}{\partial t^2} = c^2 E_m k^2 \frac{d^2 f}{du^2}\bigg|_{u=kx\pm\omega t}.$$

Since $\omega = ck$ the R.H.S. of the two equations above are equal. So

$$\frac{\partial^2 E}{\partial t^2} = c^2 \frac{\partial^2 E}{\partial x^2}.$$

Changes E to B and repeat the derivation above to show that $B = B_m f(kx \pm \omega t)$ satisfies

$$\frac{\partial^2 B}{\partial t^2} = c^2 \frac{\partial^2 B}{\partial x^2}.$$

15E
Use $\mathbf{s} = (1/\mu_0)\mathbf{E} \times \mathbf{B}$, you can easily verify that $\mathbf{s}$ is in the direction of propagation for all these cases.

16E
If P is the power and Δt is the time interval of one pulse, then the energy in a pulse is

$$E = P \Delta t = (100 \times 10^{12}\,\text{W})(1.0 \times 10^{-9}\,\text{s}) = 1.0 \times 10^5\,\text{J}.$$

17E

$$I = \frac{P}{4\pi r^2} = \frac{1.0 \times 10^6\,\text{W}}{4\pi[(4.3\,\text{ly})(9.46 \times 10^{15}\,\text{m/ly})]^2}$$
$$= 4.8 \times 10^{-29}\,\text{W/m}^2.$$

18E

Since $\mathbf{E} \times \mathbf{B} = \mu_0 \mathbf{s}$, where $\mathbf{E} = E\mathbf{k}$ and $\mathbf{s} = s(-\mathbf{j})$. You can verify easily that since $\mathbf{k} \times (-\mathbf{i}) = -\mathbf{j}$, $\mathbf{B}$ has to be in the negative x direction (with unit vector $-\mathbf{i}$). Also

$$B = \frac{E}{c} = \frac{100\,\text{V/m}}{3.0 \times 10^8\,\text{m/s}} = 3.3 \times 10^{-7}\,\text{T}.$$

19E

The fraction is

$$\text{frac} = \frac{\pi R_E^2}{4\pi r_{ES}^2} = \frac{1}{4}\left(\frac{6.37 \times 10^6\,\text{m}}{1.50 \times 10^{11}\,\text{m}}\right)^2 = 4.51 \times 10^{-10}.$$

20E

The region illuminated on the moon is a circle with radius $R = r\theta/2$, where r is the Earth-moon distance $(3.82 \times 10^8\,\text{m})$ and θ is the full-angle beam divergence in radians. The area A illuminated is

$$A = \pi R^2 = \frac{\pi r^2 \theta^2}{4} = \frac{\pi (3.82 \times 10^8\,\text{m})^2 (0.880 \times 10^{-6}\,\text{rad})^2}{4} = 8.88 \times 10^4\,\text{m}^2\,.$$

21E

Solve r from $4\pi r^2 I = P$:

$$r = \sqrt{\frac{P}{4\pi I}} = \sqrt{\frac{1.0 \times 10^3\,\text{W}}{4\pi (100\,\text{W/m}^2)}} = 0.89\,\text{m}.$$

22E

$$\bar{S} = \frac{1}{\mu_0}|\mathbf{E} \times \mathbf{B}|_{\text{av}} = \frac{1}{\mu_0}(EB)_{\text{av}} = \frac{E_{av}B_{av}}{\mu_0} = \frac{(E_m/\sqrt{2})(B_m/\sqrt{2})}{\mu_0}$$

$$= \frac{E_m B_m}{2\mu_0} = \frac{E_m^2}{2\mu_0 c} = \frac{cB_m^2}{2\mu_0},$$

where we used $E_{av}B_{av} = (EB)_{\text{av}}$ since E and B have the same phase, and $E_m = cB_m$.

23E

$$I = \bar{S} = \frac{cB_m^2}{2\mu_0} = \frac{(3.0 \times 10^8 \text{ m/s})(1.0 \times 10^{-4} \text{ T})^2}{2(1.26 \times 10^{-6} \text{ H/m})^2} = 1.2 \times 10^6 \text{ W/m}^2.$$

24E

(a)

$$B_m = \frac{E_m}{c} = \frac{5.00 \text{ V/m}}{3.0 \times 10^8 \text{ m/s}} = 1.67 \times 10^{-8} \text{ T}.$$

(b)

$$I = \bar{S} = \frac{E_m^2}{2\mu_0 c} = \frac{(5.00 \text{ V/m})^2}{2(1.26 \times 10^{-6} \text{ H/m})(3.0 \times 10^8 \text{ m/s})} = 3.31 \times 10^{-2} \text{ W/m}^2.$$

25P

Let the distance in question be r_0. Then

$$P = 4\pi I_0 r_0^2 = 4\pi I_1 r_1^2,$$

where $I_1 = 1.5 I_0$ and $r_1 = r_0 - 150 \text{ m}$. Solve for r_0:

$$f_0 = \frac{\sqrt{1.5}(150 \text{ m})}{\sqrt{1.5} - 1} = 8.2 \times 10^2 \text{ m}.$$

26P

At any point and time the energy density associated with the electric field is given by $u_E = \epsilon_0 E^2/2$, where E is the magnitude of the electric field at that point and that time. The energy density associated with the magnetic field is given by $u_B = B^2/2\mu_0$, where B is the magnitude of the magnetic field. The electric and magnetic fields in an electromagnetic wave are related by $E = cB$, where c is the speed of light. Substitute cB for E and $1/\sqrt{\mu_0 \epsilon_0}$ for c in the expression for the electric-field energy density. You should obtain

$$u_E = \frac{1}{2}\epsilon_0 c^2 B^2 = \frac{\epsilon_0 B^2}{2\mu_0 \epsilon_0} = \frac{B^2}{2\mu_0}.$$

Since this is the energy density associated with the magnetic field, $u_E = u_B$.

27P

Use $I = E_m^2/2\mu_0 c$ to calculate E_{m1}

$$E_m = \sqrt{2\mu_0 I c} = \sqrt{2(1.26 \times 10^{-6} \text{ H/m})(1.40 \times 10^3 \text{ W/m}^2)(3.0 \times 10^8 \text{ m/s})}$$
$$= 1.03 \times 10^3 \text{ V/m}.$$

Also

$$B_m = \frac{E_m}{c} = \frac{1.03 \times 10^4 \text{ V/m}}{3.0 \times 10^8 \text{ m/s}} = 3.43 \times 10^{-6} \text{ T}.$$

28P

(a)

$$B_m = \frac{E_m}{c} = \frac{2.0 \text{ V/m}}{3.0 \times 10^8 \text{ m/s}} = 6.7 \times 10^{-9} \text{ T}.$$

(b)

$$\bar{I} = \frac{E_m^2}{2\mu_0 c} = \frac{(2.0 \text{ V/m})^2}{2(1.26 \times 10^{-6} \text{ H/m})(3.0 \times 10^8 \text{ m/s})} = 5.3 \times 10^{-3} \text{ W/m}^2.$$

(c) $P = 4\pi r^2 \bar{I} = 4\pi (10 \text{ m})^2 (5.3 \times 10^{-3} \text{ W/m}^2) = 6.7 \text{ W}.$

29P

(a) Take the electric field to be $\mathbf{E} = E\mathbf{j}$ and the magnetic field to be $\mathbf{B} = B\mathbf{i}$, where E and B are the magnitudes of the fields. The Poynting vector is

$$\mathbf{S} = \frac{1}{\mu_0}\mathbf{E} \times \mathbf{B} = \frac{1}{\mu_0}(E\mathbf{j}) \times (B\mathbf{i}) = -\frac{EB}{\mu_0}\mathbf{k},$$

where $\mathbf{j} \times \mathbf{i} = -\mathbf{k}$ was used. The Poynting vector is in the negative z direction. If the z axis is upward, the Poynting vector view predicts that energy flows into the top face of the cube at the rate

$$P = SA = \frac{EBa^2}{\mu_0},$$

where A ($= a^2$) is the area of a face. It also predicts that energy flows out of the bottom face at the same rate. The Poynting vector is parallel to all other faces of the cube, so the view predicts that no energy flows through these faces.

(b) The net rate with which energy in the cube is changing is the difference between the rate with which it is flowing into the top face and the rate with which it is flowing out of the bottom face. Since these two rates are the same, the energy in the cube is not changing.

The Poynting vector may not give the actual rate of energy flow through any given portion of a surface. Note that the fields given above may be static, in which case no energy actually flows through any face of the cube. Nevertheless, $\oint \mathbf{S} \cdot d\mathbf{A}$, around a *closed* surface, correctly gives the rate of change of energy within the surface, whether the fields are static or not.

30P

(a) The power received is

$$P_r = (1.0 \times 10^{-12} \text{ W})\frac{\pi[(1000 \text{ ft})(0.3048 \text{ m/ft})]^2/4}{4\pi(6.37 \times 10^6 \text{ m})^2} = 1.4 \times 10^{-22} \text{ W}.$$

(b) The power would be

$$P = 4\pi r^2 I = 4\pi[(2.2 \times 10^4 \text{ ly})(9.46 \times 10^{15} \text{ m/ly})]^2 \left[\frac{1.0 \times 10^{-12} \text{ W}}{4\pi(6.37 \times 10^6 \text{ m})^2} \right]$$

$$= 1.1 \times 10^{15} \text{ W}.$$

31P
(a)

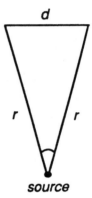

d

r   r

source

$$I = \frac{P}{\pi d^2/4} = \frac{P}{\pi(\theta r)^2/4}$$

$$= \frac{4(3.0 \times 10^{-3} \text{ W})}{\pi[(0.17 \times 10^{-3} \text{ rad})(40\,\text{m})]^2}$$

$$= 83 \text{ W/m}^2.$$

(b) $P' = 4\pi r^2 I = 4\pi(40\,\text{m})^2(83\,\text{W/m}^2) = 1.7 \times 10^6 \text{ W}.$

32P
(a) The average rate of energy flow per unit area, or intensity, is related to the electric field amplitude E_m by $I = E_m^2/2\mu_0 c$, so

$$E_m = \sqrt{2\mu_0 cI} = \sqrt{2(4\pi \times 10^{-7}\,\text{H/m})(3.00 \times 10^8\,\text{m/s})(10 \times 10^{-6}\,\text{W/m}^2)}$$

$$= 8.7 \times 10^{-2}\,\text{V/m}.$$

(b) The amplitude of the magnetic field is given by

$$B_m = \frac{E_m}{c} = \frac{8.7 \times 10^{-2}\,\text{V/m}}{3.00 \times 10^8\,\text{m/s}} = 2.9 \times 10^{-10}\,\text{T}.$$

(c) At a distance r from the transmitter the intensity is $I = P/4\pi r^2$, where P is the power of the transmitter. Thus

$$P = 4\pi r^2 I = 4\pi(10 \times 10^3\,\text{m})^2(10 \times 10^{-6}\,\text{W/m}^2) = 1.3 \times 10^4\,\text{W}.$$

33P
(a)

$$I = \frac{P}{2\pi r^2} = \frac{180 \times 10^3\,\text{W}}{2\pi(90 \times 10^3\,\text{m})^2} = 3.5 \times 10^{-6}\,\text{W/m}^2.$$

(b) $P_r = IA = (3.5 \times 10^{-6}\,\text{W/m}^2)(0.22\,\text{m}^2) = 7.7 \times 10^{-7}\,\text{W}.$

(c)

$$I_r = \frac{P_r}{2\pi r^2} = \frac{7.7 \times 10^{-7}\,\text{W}}{2\pi(90 \times 10^3\,\text{m})^2} = 1.5 \times 10^{-17}\,\text{W/m}^2.$$

(d)

$$E_m = \sqrt{2\mu_0 I_r c} = \sqrt{2(1.26 \times 10^{-6}\,\text{H/m})(1.5 \times 10^{-17}\,\text{W/m}^2)(3.0 \times 10^8\,\text{m/s})}$$
$$= 1.1 \times 10^{-7}\,\text{V/m}.$$

(e)

$$B_{\text{rms}} = \frac{E_m}{\sqrt{2}c} = \frac{1.1 \times 10^{-7}\,\text{V/m}}{\sqrt{2}(3.0 \times 10^8\,\text{m/s})} = 2.6 \times 10^{-16}\,\text{T}.$$

34E

$$p_r = \frac{I}{c} = \frac{10\,\text{W/m}^2}{3.0 \times 10^8\,\text{m/s}} = 3.3 \times 10^{-8}\,\text{N/m}^2.$$

35E

The plasma completely reflects all the energy incident on it, so the radiation pressure is given by $p_r = 2I/c$, where I is the intensity. The intensity is $I = P/A$, where P is the power and A is the area intercepted by the radiation. Thus

$$p_r = \frac{2P}{Ac} = \frac{2(1.5 \times 10^9\,\text{W})}{(1.00 \times 10^{-6}\,\text{m}^2)(3.00 \times 10^8\,\text{m/s})} = 1.0 \times 10^7\,\text{Pa} = 10\,\text{MPa}.$$

36E
(a)

$$p_r = \frac{I}{c} = \frac{1.4 \times 10^3\,\text{W/m}^2}{3.0 \times 10^8\,\text{m/s}} = 4.7 \times 10^{-6}\,\text{N/m}^2.$$

(b)

$$\frac{p_r}{p_0} = \frac{4.7 \times 10^{-6}\,\text{N/m}^2}{1.0 \times 10^5\,\text{N/m}^2} = 4.7 \times 10^{-11}.$$

37E
(a)

$$F_r = p_r(\pi R_E^2) = \left(\frac{I}{c}\right)(\pi R_E^2)$$

$$= \frac{\pi(1.4 \times 10^3\,\text{W/m}^2)(6.37 \times 10^6\,\text{m})^2}{3.0 \times 10^8\,\text{m/s}} = 6.0 \times 10^8\,\text{N}.$$

(b)

$$F_{\text{gravity}} = \frac{GM_SM_E}{r_{ES}^2} = \frac{(6.67 \times 10^{-11}\,\text{N}\cdot\text{m}^2/\text{kg}^2)(2.0 \times 10^{30}\,\text{kg})(5.98 \times 10^{24}\,\text{kg})}{(1.5 \times 10^{11}\,\text{m})^2}$$
$$= 3.6 \times 10^{22}\,\text{N},$$

which is much greater than F_r.

38E

Since the surface is perfectly absorbing the radiation pressure is given by $p_r = I/c$, where I is the intensity. Since the bulb radiates uniformly in all directions the intensity a distance r from it is given by $I = P/4\pi r^2$, where P is the power of the bulb. Thus

$$p_r = \frac{P}{4\pi r^2 c} = \frac{500\,\text{W}}{4\pi(1.5\,\text{m})^2(3.00 \times 10^8\,\text{m/s})} = 5.9 \times 10^{-8}\,\text{Pa}.$$

39P

(a) Since $c = \lambda f$, where λ is the wavelength and f is the frequency of the wave,

$$f = \frac{c}{\lambda} = \frac{3.00 \times 10^8\,\text{m/s}}{3.0\,\text{m}} = 1.0 \times 10^8\,\text{Hz}.$$

(b) The magnetic field amplitude is

$$B_m = \frac{E_m}{c} = \frac{300\,\text{V/m}}{3.00 \times 10^8\,\text{m/s}} = 1.00 \times 10^{-6}\,\text{T}.$$

B must be in the positive z direction when **E** is in the positive y direction in order for **E** $\times$ **B** to be in the positive x direction (the direction of propagation).

(c) The angular wave number is

$$k = \frac{2\pi}{\lambda} = \frac{2\pi}{3.0\,\text{m}} = 2.1\,\text{rad/m}.$$

The angular frequency is

$$\omega = 2\pi f = 2\pi(1.0 \times 10^8\,\text{Hz}) = 6.3 \times 10^8\,\text{rad/s}.$$

(d) The intensity of the wave is

$$I = \frac{E_m^2}{2\mu_0 c} = \frac{(300\,\text{V/m})^2}{2(4\pi \times 10^{-7}\,\text{H/m})(3.00 \times 10^8\,\text{m/s})} = 119\,\text{W/m}^2.$$

(e) Since the sheet is perfectly absorbing, the rate per unit area with which momentum is delivered to it is I/c, so

$$\frac{dp}{dt} = \frac{IA}{c} = \frac{(119\,\text{W/m}^2)(2.0\,\text{m}^2)}{3.00 \times 10^8\,\text{m/s}} = 8.0 \times 10^{-7}\,\text{N}.$$

The radiation pressure is

$$p_r = \frac{dp/dt}{A} = \frac{8.0 \times 10^{-7}\,\text{N}}{2.0\,\text{m}^2} = 4.0 \times 10^{-7}\,\text{Pa}.$$

40P
(a)

$$I = \frac{P}{\pi d^2/4} = \frac{5.00 \times 10^{-3}\,\text{W}}{\pi[(2.00)(633 \times 10^{-9}\,\text{m})]^2/4} = 3.97 \times 10^9\,\text{W/m}^2.$$

(b)

$$p_r = \frac{I}{c} = \frac{3.97 \times 10^9\,\text{W/m}^2}{3.00 \times 10^8\,\text{m/s}} = 13.2\,\text{N/m}^2.$$

(c)

$$F_r = \left(\frac{\pi d^2}{4}\right)p_r = \frac{Pp_r}{I} = \frac{(5.00 \times 10^{-3}\,\text{W})(13.2\,\text{N/m}^2)}{3.97 \times 10^9\,\text{W/m}^2} = 1.67 \times 10^{-11}\,\text{N}.$$

(d)

$$a = \frac{F_r}{m} = \frac{F_r}{\rho(\pi d^3/6)} = \frac{6(1.67 \times 10^{-11}\,\text{N})}{\pi(5.00 \times 10^3\,\text{kg/m}^3)[(2.00)(633 \times 10^{-9}\,\text{m})]^3}$$
$$= 3.14 \times 10^3\,\text{m/s}^2.$$

41P
The mass of the cylinder is $m = \rho(\pi d_1^2/4)H$, where d_1 is the diameter of the cylinder. Since it is in equilibrium

$$F_{\text{net}} = mg - F_r = \frac{\pi H d_1^2 g\rho}{4} - \left(\frac{\pi d_1^2}{4}\right)\left(\frac{2I}{c}\right) = 0.$$

Solve for H:

$$H = \frac{2I}{gc\rho} = \left(\frac{P}{\pi d^2/4}\right)\frac{1}{gc\rho}$$

$$= \frac{8(4.60\,\text{W})}{\pi(2.60 \times 10^{-3}\,\text{m})^2(9.8\,\text{m/s}^2)(3.0 \times 10^8\,\text{m/s})(1.20 \times 10^3\,\text{kg/m}^3)}$$
$$= 4.91 \times 10^{-7}\,\text{m}.$$

42P

Denote the fraction by α. The contribution to P_r due to the absorbed part of the radiation is $P_{r1} = I_{\text{absorbed}}/c = \alpha I/c$, while the contribution to P_r due to the reflected part is $P_{r2} = 2I_{\text{reflected}}/c = 2I(1-\alpha)/c$. Thus

$$P_r = P_{r1} + P_{r2} = \frac{\alpha I}{c} + \frac{2I(1-\alpha)}{c} = \frac{I(2-\alpha)}{c}.$$

43P

Let f be the fraction of the incident beam intensity that is reflected. The fraction absorbed is $1 - f$. The reflected portion exerts a radiation pressure of

$$p_r = \frac{2fI_0}{c}$$

and the absorbed portion exerts a radiation pressure of

$$p_a = \frac{(1-f)I_0}{c},$$

where I_0 is the incident intensity. The factor 2 enters the first expression because the momentum of the reflected portion is reversed. The total radiation pressure is the sum of the two contributions:

$$p_{\text{total}} = p_r + p_a = \frac{2fI_0 + (1-f)I_0}{c} = \frac{(1+f)I_0}{c}.$$

To relate the intensity and energy density, consider a tube with length ℓ and cross-sectional area A, lying with its axis along the propagation direction of an electromagnetic wave. The electromagnetic energy inside is $U = uA\ell$, where u is the energy density. All this energy will pass through the end in time $t = \ell/c$ so the intensity is

$$I = \frac{U}{At} = \frac{uA\ell c}{\ell} = uc.$$

Thus $u = I/c$. The intensity and energy density are inherently positive, regardless of the propagation direction.

For the partially reflected and partially absorbed wave the intensity just outside the surface is $I = I_0 + fI_0 = (1+f)I_0$, where the first term is associated with the incident beam and the second is associated with the reflected beam. The energy density is therefore

$$u = \frac{I}{c} = \frac{(1+f)I_0}{c},$$

the same as radiation pressure.

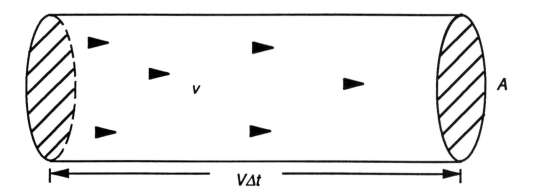

The bullets (of mass m and speed v each) which will strike a surface of area A of the plane within time t to $t + \Delta t$ must all be contained in the cylindrical volume shown above at time t. Since each of the bullets changes its momentum by $\Delta p_b = mv$, the rate of change of the total momentum for the bullets that strike the area is

$$F = \frac{\Delta P_{\text{total}}}{\Delta t} = \frac{(Av\Delta t)nmv}{\Delta t} = Anmv^2,$$

where n is the number density of the bullets. The pressure is then

$$P_r = \frac{F}{A} = nmv^2 = 2nK,$$

where $K = \frac{1}{2}mv^2$. Note that nK is the kinetic energy density.

45P

If the beam carries energy U away from the spaceship then it also carries momentum $p = U/c$ away. Since the total momentum of the spaceship and light is conserved, this is the magnitude of the momentum acquired by the spaceship. If P is the power of the laser, then the energy carried away in time t is $U = Pt$. Thus $p = Pt/c$ and, if m is mass of the spaceship, its speed is

$$v = \frac{p}{m} = \frac{Pt}{mc} = \frac{(10 \times 10^3 \text{ W})(1 \, d)(8.64 \times 10^4 \text{ s}/d)}{(1.5 \times 10^3 \text{ kg})(3.00 \times 10^8 \text{ m/s})} = 1.9 \times 10^{-3} \text{ m/s} = 1.9 \, \text{mm/s}.$$

46P

Let $F_{\text{grav}} = F_r$ or

$$G\frac{mM_S}{r_{ES}^2} = \frac{2IA}{c}$$

and solve for the area A:

$$A = \frac{GmM_Sc}{2Ir_{ES}^2} = \frac{(6.67 \times 10^{-11}\,\text{N} \cdot \text{m}^2\,\text{kg}^2)(1500\,\text{kg})(1.99 \times 10^{30}\,\text{kg})(3.0 \times 10^8\,\text{m/s})}{2(1.40 \times 10^3\,\text{W/m}^2)(1.50 \times 10^{11}\,\text{m})^2}$$
$$= 9.5 \times 10^5\,\text{m}^2 = 0.95\,\text{km}^2.$$

47P

(a) Let r be the radius and ρ be the density of the particle. Since its volume is $(4\pi/3)r^3$, its mass is $m = (4\pi/3)\rho r^3$. Let R be the distance from the sun to the particle and let M be the mass of the sun. Then the gravitational force of attraction of the sun on the particle has magnitude

$$F_g = \frac{GMm}{R^2} = \frac{4\pi GM\rho r^3}{3R^2}.$$

If P is the power output of the sun, then at the position of the particle the radiation intensity is $I = P/4\pi R^2$ and since the particle is perfectly absorbing the radiation pressure on it is

$$p_r = \frac{I}{c} = \frac{P}{4\pi R^2 c}.$$

All of the radiation that passes through a circle of radius r and area $A = \pi r^2$, perpendicular to the direction of propagation, is absorbed by the particle, so the force of the radiation on the particle has magnitude

$$F_r = p_r A = \frac{\pi P r^2}{4\pi R^2 c} = \frac{P r^2}{4R^2 c}.$$

The force is radially outward from the sun. Notice that both the force of gravity and the force of the radiation are inversely proportional to R^2. If one of these forces is larger than the other at some distance from the sun, then that force is larger at all distances.

The two forces depend on the particle radius r differently: F_g is proportional to r^3 and F_r is proportional to r^2. We expect a small radius particle to be blown away by the radiation pressure and a large radius particle with the same density to be pulled inward toward the sun. The critical value for the radius is the value for which the two forces are equal. Equate the expressions for F_g and F_r, then solve for r. You should obtain

$$r = \frac{3P}{16\pi GM\rho c}.$$

947

(b) According to Appendix C, $M = 1.99 \times 10^{30}$ kg and $P = 3.90 \times 10^{26}$ W. Thus,

$$r = \frac{3(3.90 \times 10^{26}\,\text{W})}{16\pi(6.67 \times 10^{-11}\,\text{N} \cdot \text{m}^2/\text{kg}^2)(1.99 \times 10^{30}\,\text{kg})(1.0 \times 10^3\,\text{kg/m}^3)(3.00 \times 10^8\,\text{m/s})}$$
$$= 5.8 \times 10^{-7}\,\text{m}.$$

48E
(a) Negative y direction.
(b) $E_x = E_y = 0$, and $E_z = -cB\sin(kx + \omega t)$. You can check that with this expression for $\mathbf{E}$, $\mathbf{E} \times \mathbf{B}$ is in the direction of propagation.
(c) The wave is plane polarized with $\mathbf{E}$ along the z axis.

49E
(a) Since the incident light is unpolarized half the intensity is transmitted and half is absorbed. Thus the transmitted intensity is $I = 5.0\,\text{mW}/m^2$. The intensity and the electric field amplitude are related by $I = E_m^2/2\mu_0 c$, so

$$E_m = \sqrt{2\mu_0 cI} = \sqrt{2(4\pi \times 10^{-7}\,\text{H/m})(3.00 \times 10^8\,\text{m/s})(5.0 \times 10^{-3}\,\text{W/m}^2)}$$
$$= 1.9\,\text{V/m}.$$

(b) The radiation pressure is $p_r = I_a/c$, where I_a is the absorbed intensity. Thus

$$p_r = \frac{5.0 \times 10^{-3}\,\text{W/m}^2}{3.00 \times 10^8\,\text{m/s}} = 1.7 \times 10^{-11}\,\text{Pa}.$$

50E
As the unpolarized beam of intensity I_0 passes the first polarizer, its intensity is reduced to $\frac{1}{2}I_0$. After passing through the second polarizer whose dirction of polarization is at an angle θ from that of the first one $I = \frac{1}{2}I_0\cos^2\theta = \frac{1}{3}I_0$. Thus $\cos^2\theta = 2/3$, which gives $\theta = 35°$.

51E

Use $I = I_m\cos^2\theta$. The diagram above shows that

$$\frac{I_{\text{final}}}{I_0} = \frac{(I_0/2)\cos^4 45°}{I_0} = \frac{1}{8}.$$

52E
After passing through the first polarizer the initial intensity I_0 reduces by a factor of $1/2$. After passing through the second one it is further reduced by a factor of $\cos^2(\pi - \theta_1 - \theta_2) = \cos^2(\theta_1 + \theta_2)$. Finally after passing through the third one it is again reduced by a factor of $\cos^2(\pi - \theta_2 - \theta_3) = \cos^2(\theta_2 + \theta_3)$. So

$$\frac{I_f}{I_0} = \left(\frac{1}{2}\right)\cos^2(\theta_1 + \theta_2)\cos^2(\theta_2 + \theta_3)$$

$$= \left(\frac{1}{2}\right)\cos^2(50° + 50°)\cos^2(50° + 50°) = 4.5 \times 10^{-4}.$$

53P
By noticing that the direction polarization of the polarizer in the middle is perpendicular to those of the other two, we conclude that no light will get through the system, i.e. $I_f/I_0 = 0$.

54P
After passing through the first polarizer the initial intensity I_0 of the light is reduced to $\frac{1}{2}I_0$. After that it is reduced by a factor of $\cos^2 30°$ each time the light passes through one more polarizer. So

$$\frac{I_f}{I_0} = \frac{1}{2}(\cos^2 30°)^3 = 0.21.$$

55P
After passing through the first polarizer the initial intensity I_0 of the light is reduced to $I_1 = I_0\cos^2\theta$. Since the angle between the polarization directions of the two polarizers if $90° - \theta$, the final intensity of light is $I_f = I_1\cos^2(90° - \theta) = I_0\cos^2\theta\sin^2\theta = (I_0/4)\sin^2(2\theta)$. Let $I_f = 0.10I_0$ to obtain $\sin^2(2\theta) = 0.40$. The angle is $\theta = 20°$ or $\theta = 70°$.

56P
The intensity of the transmitted light is

$$I_f = (i_0\cos^2 70°)\cos^2(90° - 70°) = (43\,\text{W/m}^2)(\cos^2 70°)(\cos^2 20°) = 4.4\,\text{W/m}^2.$$

57P
In this case we replace $I_0\cos^2 70°$ by $\frac{1}{2}I_0$ as the intensity of the light after passing through the first polarizer. So

$$I_f = \frac{1}{2}I_0\cos^2(90° - 70°) = \frac{1}{2}(43\,\text{W/m}^2)(\cos^2 20°) = 19\,\text{W/m}^2.$$

58P

Let I_0 be the intensity of the incident beam and f be the fraction that is polarized. Thus the intensity of the polarized portion is fI_0. After transmission this portion contributes $fI_0 \cos^2 \theta$ to the intensity of the transmitted beam. Here θ is the angle between the direction of polarization of the radiation and the polarizing direction of the filter. The intensity of the unpolarized portion of the incident beam is $(1-f)I_0$ and after transmission this portion contributes $(1-f)I_0/2$ to the transmitted intensity. Thus the transmitted intensity is

$$I = fI_0 \cos^2 \theta + \frac{1}{2}(1-f)I_0 .$$

As the filter is rotated $\cos^2 \theta$ varies from a minimum of 0 to a maximum of 1, so the transmitted intensity varies from a minimum of

$$I_{\min} = \frac{1}{2}(1-f)I_0$$

to a maximum of

$$I_{\max} = fI_0 + \frac{1}{2}(1-f)I_0 = \frac{1}{2}(1+f)I_0 .$$

The ratio of $I_{\max}$ to $I_{\min}$ is

$$\frac{I_{\max}}{I_{\min}} = \frac{1+f}{1-f} .$$

Set the ratio equal to 5.0 and solve for f. You should get $f = 0.67$.

59P

(a) The rotation cannot be done with a single sheet. If a sheet is placed with its polarizing direction at an angle of 90° to the direction of polarization of the incident radiation, no radiation is transmitted.

It can be done with two sheets. Place the first sheet with its polarizing direction at some angle θ, between 0 and 90°, to the direction of polarization of the incident radiation. Place the second sheet with its polarizing direction at 90° to the polarization direction of the incident radiation. The transmitted radiation is then polarized at 90° to the incident polarization direction. The intensity is $I_0 \cos^2 \theta \cos^2(90° - \theta) = I_0 \cos^2 \theta \sin^2 \theta$, where I_0 is the incident radiation. If θ is not 0 or 90° the transmitted intensity is not zero.

(b) Consider n sheets, with the polarizing direction of the first sheet making an angle of $\theta = 90°/n$ with the direction of polarization of the incident radiation and with the polarizing direction of each successive sheet rotated $90°/n$ in the same direction from the polarizing direction of the previous sheet. The transmitted radiation is polarized with its direction of polarization making an angle of 90° with the direction of polarization of the incident radiation. The intensity is $I = I_0 \cos^{2n}(90°/n)$. You want the smallest integer value of n for which this is greater than $0.60I_0$.

950

Start with $n = 2$ and calculate $\cos^{2n}(90°/n)$. If the result is greater than 0.60 you have obtained the solution. If it is less, increase n by 1 and try again. Repeat this process, increasing n by 1 each time, until you have a value for which $\cos^{2n}(90°/n)$ is greater than 0.60. The first one will be $n = 5$.

60P

(a)

$$\frac{I_f}{I_0} = \frac{E_f^2}{E_0^2} = \frac{E_v^2}{E_v^2 + E_h^2} = \frac{E_v^2}{E_v^2 + (2.3E_v)^2} = 0.16.$$

(b) Since now the horizontal component of $\mathbf{E}$ will pass through the glasses

$$\frac{I_f}{I_0} = \frac{E_h^2}{E_v^2 + E_h^2} = \frac{(2.3E_v)^2}{E_v^2 + (2.3E_v)^2} = 0.84.$$

61

From Exercise 22 the rate at which electromagnetic energy is absorbed by the sheet is

$$\frac{d\varepsilon}{dt} = \bar{S}A = \frac{E_m^2 A}{2\mu_0 c}.$$

Thus from $d\varepsilon = c_s m dT$ we get

$$\frac{dT}{dt} = \frac{1}{c_s m}\frac{d\varepsilon}{dt} = \frac{E_m^2 A}{2\mu_0 c_s cm}.$$

62

Let the angle in question be θ. Then

$$\frac{I_f}{I_0} = \frac{1}{2}\cos^2\theta = p\% = \frac{p}{100},$$

or $\theta = \cos^{-1}(\sqrt{p/50})$.

63

First, the intensity of light as detected on the reflecting surface is $I(\theta) = I_\perp \cos\theta$. Second, the change in momentum for the beam of light upon reflection is $\Delta P(\theta) = \Delta P_\perp \cos\theta$. So

$$p_r(\theta) \propto I(\theta)\Delta P(\theta)$$
$$= (I_\perp \cos\theta)(\Delta P_\perp \cos\theta)$$
$$= p_{r\perp} \cos^2\theta.$$

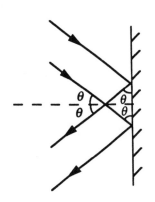

Consider the radiation pressure at the angle θ as shown: $p_r(\theta) = p_{r\perp}\cos^2\theta = (I/c)\cos^2\theta$, where we used the result of Problem 63. Since only the x component of the total F is present (by symmetry),

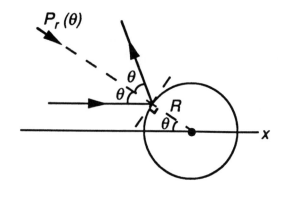

$$dF = p_r(\theta)|_x\, R\, d\theta$$
$$= p_r(\theta)\cos\theta R\, d\theta$$
$$= (2I/c)\cos^3\theta R\, d\theta.$$

Thus

$$F = 2\int_0^{\pi/2} \frac{2IR}{c}\cos^3\theta\, d\theta = \frac{8RI}{3c}.$$

CHAPTER 39

1E

According to the laws of reflection and refraction $\theta_1 = 38.0°$ and

$$\theta_2 = \sin^{-1} \left[\frac{1.58 \sin(38.0°)}{1.22} \right] = 52.9°.$$

2E

Use the law of refraction:

$$n_1 \sin \theta_1 = n_2 \sin \theta_2 .$$

Take medium 1 to be the vacuum, with $n_1 = 1$ and $\theta_1 = 32.0°$. Medium 2 is the glass, with $\theta_2 = 21.0°$. Solve for n_2:

$$n_2 = n_1 \frac{\sin \theta_1}{\sin \theta_2} = (1.00) \left(\frac{\sin 32.0°}{\sin 21.0°} \right) = 1.48 .$$

3E

Note that the normal to the refracting surface is vertical in the diagram. The angle of refraction is $\theta_2 = 90°$ and the angle of incidence is given by $\tan \theta_1 = w/h$, where h is the height of the tank and w is its width. Thus

$$\theta_1 = \tan^{-1} \left(\frac{w}{h} \right) = \tan^{-1} \left(\frac{1.10 \, \text{m}}{0.850 \, \text{m}} \right) = 52.31° .$$

The law of refraction yields

$$n_1 = n_2 \frac{\sin \theta_2}{\sin \theta_1} = (1.00) \left(\frac{\sin 90°}{\sin 52.31°} \right) = 1.26 ,$$

where the index of refraction of air was taken to be unity.

4E

(a) The law of refraction requires that $\sin \theta_1 / \sin \theta_2 = n_{\text{water}} = \text{const.}$ You can check that this is indeed valid for any given pair of θ_1 and θ_2. For example $\sin 10° / \sin 8° = 1.3$, and $\sin 20° / \sin 15°30' = 1.3$, etc.
(b) $n_{\text{water}} = 1.3$, as shown in part (a).

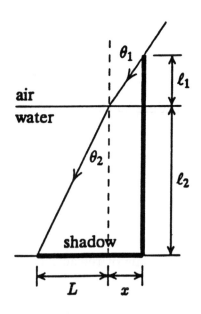

5P

Consider a ray that grazes the top of the pole, as shown in the diagram to the right. Here $\theta_1 = 35°$, $\ell_1 = 0.50$ m, and $\ell_2 = 1.50$ m. The length of the shadow is $x + L$. x is given by $x = \ell_1 \tan \theta_1 = (0.50 \text{ m}) \tan 35° = 0.35$ m. According to the law of refraction $n_2 \sin \theta_2 = n_1 \sin \theta_1$. Take $n_1 = 1$ and $n_2 = 1.33$ (from Table 39–1). Then

$$\theta_2 = \sin^{-1}\left(\frac{\sin \theta_1}{n_2}\right) = \sin^{-1}\left(\frac{\sin 35.0°}{1.33}\right) = 25.55° .$$

L is given by

$$L = \ell_2 \tan \theta_2 = (1.50 \text{ m}) \tan 25.55° = 0.72 \text{ m} .$$

The length of the shadow is $0.35 \text{ m} + 0.72 \text{ m} = 1.07 \text{ m}$.

6P

Let θ be the angle of incidence and θ_2 be the angle of refraction at the left face of the plate. Let n be the index of refraction of the glass. Then the law of refraction yields $\sin \theta = n \sin \theta_2$. The angle of incidence at the right face is also θ_2. If θ_3 is the angle of emergence there, then $n \sin \theta_2 = \sin \theta_3$. Thus $\sin \theta_3 = \sin \theta$ and $\theta_3 = \theta$. The emerging ray is parallel to the incident ray.

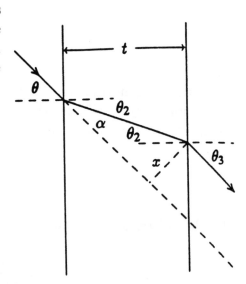

You wish to derive an expression for x in terms of θ. If D is the length of the ray in the glass, then $D \cos \theta_2 = t$ and $D = t/\cos \theta_2$. The angle α in the diagram equals $\theta - \theta_2$ and $x = D \sin \alpha = D \sin(\theta - \theta_2)$. Thus

$$x = \frac{t \sin(\theta - \theta_2)}{\cos \theta_2} .$$

If all the angles θ, θ_2, θ_3, and $\theta - \theta_2$ are small and measured in radians then $\sin \theta \approx \theta$, $\sin \theta_2 \approx \theta_2$, $\sin(\theta - \theta_2) \approx \theta - \theta_2$, and $\cos \theta_2 \approx 1$. Thus $x \approx t(\theta - \theta_2)$. The law of refraction applied to the point of incidence at the left face of the plate is now $\theta \approx n\theta_2$, so $\theta_2 \approx \theta/n$ and

$$x \approx t\left(\theta - \frac{\theta}{n}\right) = \frac{(n-1)t\theta}{n} .$$

7P

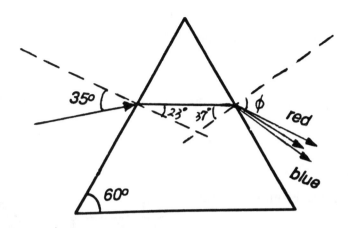

The paths traversed by rays representing these lights are shown above. Here we used the law of refraction for each ray of light at both boundaries. Here $\phi \simeq 61°$ for red light, $62°$ for yellow-green light and $63°$ for blue light.

8P

In the figure shown to the right $x = d_a \tan\theta_2 = d\tan\theta_1$, or

$$d_a = d\left(\frac{\tan\theta_2}{\tan\theta_1}\right).$$

For light rays close to the normal $\tan\theta_{1,2} \approx \sin\theta_{1,2}$ so

$$d_a = d\left(\frac{\tan\theta_2}{\tan\theta_1}\right) \approx d\left(\frac{\sin\theta_2}{\sin\theta_1}\right) = \frac{d}{n},$$

where the law of refraction $\sin\theta_1/\sin\theta_2 = n$ is used.

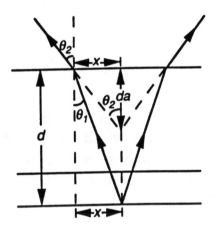

9P

(a) Use the result of Problem 8: $d_a = d/n_{\text{water}} = 2.4\,\text{m}/1.33 = 1.8\,\text{m}$.

(b) From the law of refraction

$$\begin{aligned}
\theta &= \sin^{-1}(n_{\text{water}}\sin 30°) \\
&= \sin^{-1}(1.33\sin 30°) \\
&= 41.7°.
\end{aligned}$$

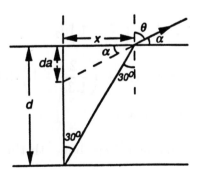

Thus

$$d_a = x \tan \alpha = (d \tan 30°) \tan(90° - \theta)$$
$$= (2.4\,\text{m}) \tan 30° \tan(90° - 41.7°)$$
$$= 1.6\,\text{m}.$$

Note: Since $\theta = 41.7°$, the light rays are not close to the normal so the result of Problem 8 cannot be applied here.

10P

Refer to the diagram to the right. From the result of Problem 8 we get

$$d_{a1} = \frac{d_1'}{n_w} \frac{d_1 + d_{a2}}{n_w}$$
$$= \frac{d_1 + d_2/(n_c/n_w)}{n_w}$$
$$= \frac{20\,\text{mm} + (40\,\text{mm})(1.33/1.46)}{1.33}$$
$$= 42\,\text{mm}.$$

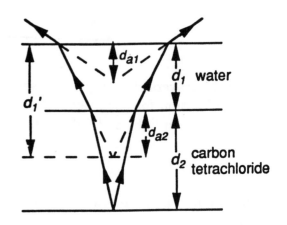

11P

Refer to the diagram to the right. Consider small angles θ_1 and θ_2 which satisfy $\sin\theta_{1,2} \approx \tan\theta_{1,2} \approx \theta_{1,2}$. We have $y \approx d_1\theta_1$, $x \approx d_2(2\theta_2)$, and $d_2 + z \approx (x + y)/\theta_1$. Also $\theta_1/\theta_2 \approx n_{\text{water}} = 1.33$. Thus

$$z \approx \frac{x + y}{\theta_1} - d_2$$
$$= \frac{2\theta_2 d_2 + \theta_1 d_1}{\theta_1} - d_2$$
$$= d_1 + \left(\frac{2}{n} - 1\right) d_2$$
$$= 250\,\text{cm} + \left(\frac{2}{1.33} - 1\right)(200\,\text{cm})$$
$$= 351\,\text{cm}.$$

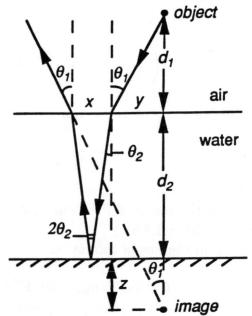

So the image is 351 cm beneath the mirror surface.

12P

(a) A ray diagram is shown to the right. The incident ray is normal to the water surface and so is not refracted. The angle of incidence at the first mirror is $\theta_1 = 45°$. According to the law of reflection the angle of reflection is also 45°. This means the ray is horizontal after reflection and the angle of incidence at the second mirror is $\theta_2 = 45°$. Since the angle of reflection at the second mirror is also 45° the ray

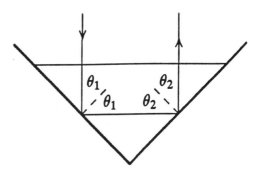

leaves that mirror normal to the water surface. Again there is no refraction at the water surface and the emerging ray is parallel to the incident ray.

(b) A ray diagram is shown below. On incidence the ray makes the angle θ_1 with the normal to the water surface. The angle of refraction θ_2 can be found using the law of refraction: $\sin\theta_1 = n\sin\theta_2$, where n is the index of refraction of the water. The normal to the water surface and the normal to the first mirror make an angle of 45°. If the normal to the water surface is continued downward until it meets the normal to the first mirror the triangle formed has an interior angle of $180° - 45° = 135°$ at the vertex formed by the normal. Since the interior angles of a triangle must sum to 180°, the angle of incidence at the first mirror satisfies $\theta_3 + \theta_2 + 135° = 180°$, so $\theta_3 = 45° - \theta_2$. The angle of reflection at the first mirror is also $45° - \theta_2$.

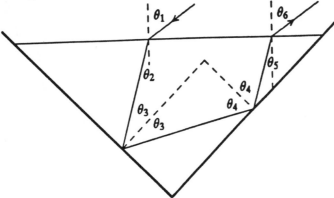

Now look at the triangle formed by the ray and the normals to the two mirrors. It is a right triangle, so $\theta_3 + \theta_4 + 90° = 180°$ and $\theta_4 = 90° - \theta_3 = 90° - 45° + \theta_2 = 45° + \theta_2$. The angle of reflection at the second mirror is also $45° + \theta_2$.

Now continue the normal to the water surface downward from the exit point of the ray to the second mirror. It makes an angle of 45° with the mirror. Consider the triangle formed by the second mirror, the ray, and the normal to the water surface. The angle at the intersection of the normal and the mirror is $180° - 45° = 135°$. The angle at the intersection of the ray and the mirror is $90° - \theta_4 = 90° - (45° + \theta_2) = 45° - \theta_2$. The angle at the intersection of the ray and the water surface is θ_5. These three angles must sum to 180°, so $135° + 45° - \theta_2 + \theta_5 = 180°$. This means $\theta_5 = \theta_2$.

Now use the law of refraction to find θ_6: $\sin\theta_6 = n\sin\theta_5$. But since $\theta_5 = \theta_2$, this means $\sin\theta_6 = n\sin\theta_2$. Finally, since $\sin\theta_1 = n\sin\theta_2$, we conclude that $\sin\theta_6 = \sin\theta_1$ and $\theta_6 = \theta_1$. The exiting ray is parallel to the incident ray.

957

13P

(a) Apply the law of refraction to each successive
pair of layers:

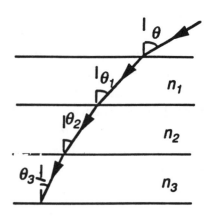

$$\begin{cases} \dfrac{\sin\theta}{\sin\theta_1} = n_1, \\[2mm] \dfrac{\sin\theta_1}{\sin\theta_2} = n_2, \\[2mm] \dfrac{\sin\theta_2}{\sin\theta_3} = n_3. \end{cases}$$

Multiply the three equations above to obtain
$\sin\theta_3 = (1/n_3)\sin\theta_1$.

(b) Now

$$\theta = \sin^{-1}(n_3\sin\theta) = \sin^{-1}[(1.00029)\sin 20.0°] = 20.00605°,$$

so $\theta - \theta_3 = 20.00605° - 20.0° = 0.00605°$.

14P

From the diagram to the right we find $\alpha + 90° +$
$(90° - \phi/2) = 180°$ and $\alpha = \phi - \psi/2$. Solve for θ:
$\theta = (\psi + \phi)/2$. The law of refraction then gives

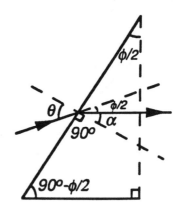

$$n = \frac{\sin\theta}{\sin\alpha} = \frac{\sin\theta}{\sin(\theta - \psi/2)}$$

$$= \frac{\sin\frac{1}{2}(\psi + \phi)}{\sin\frac{1}{2}\phi}.$$

15P

Use the result obtained in Problem 14:

$$n = \frac{\sin\frac{1}{2}(\phi + \psi)}{\sin\frac{1}{2}\phi} = \frac{\sin\frac{1}{2}(60.0° + 30.0°)}{\sin\frac{1}{2}(60.0°)} = 1.41.$$

16E

$$\theta_c = \sin^{-1}(1/n) = \sin^{-1}(1/1.8) = 34°.$$

17E

Let $\theta_1 (= 45°)$ be the angle of incidence at the first surface and θ_2 be the angle of refraction
there. Let θ_3 be the angle of incidence at the second surface. The condition for total internal
reflection at the second surface is $n\sin\theta_3 \geq 1$. You want to find the smallest value of the
index of refraction n for which this inequality holds.

The law of refraction, applied to the first surface, yields $n \sin \theta_2 = \sin \theta_1$. Consideration of the triangle formed by the surface of the slab and the ray in the slab tells us that $\theta_3 = 90° - \theta_2$. Thus the condition for total internal reflection becomes $1 \le n \sin(90° - \theta_2) = n \cos \theta_2$. Square this equation and use $\sin^2 \theta_2 + \cos^2 \theta_2 = 1$ to obtain $1 \le n^2(1 - \sin^2 \theta_2)$. Now substitute $\sin \theta_2 = (1/n) \sin \theta_1$ to obtain

$$1 \le n^2 \left(1 - \frac{\sin^2 \theta_1}{n^2}\right) = n^2 - \sin^2 \theta_1 \,.$$

The largest value of n for which this equation is true is the value for which $1 = n^2 - \sin^2 \theta_1$. Solve for n:

$$n = \sqrt{1 + \sin^2 \theta_1} = \sqrt{1 + \sin^2 45°} = 1.22 \,.$$

18E

(a) No refraction occurs at the surface ab, so the angle of incidence at surface ac is $90° - \phi$. For total internal reflection at the second surface, $n_g \sin(90° - \phi)$ must be greater than n_a. Here n_g is the index of refraction for the glass and n_a is the index of refraction for air. Since $\sin(90° - \phi) = \cos \phi$, you want the largest value of ϕ for which $n_g \cos \phi \ge n_a$. Recall that $\cos \phi$ decreases as ϕ increases from zero. When ϕ has the largest value for which total internal reflection occurs, then $n_g \cos \phi = n_a$, or

$$\phi = \cos^{-1}\left(\frac{n_a}{n_g}\right) = \cos^{-1}\left(\frac{1}{1.52}\right) = 48.9° \,.$$

The index of refraction for air was taken to be unity.

(b) Replace the air with water. If $n_w \, (= 1.33)$ is the index of refraction for water, then the largest value of ϕ for which total internal reflection occurs is

$$\phi = \cos^{-1}\left(\frac{n_w}{n_g}\right) = \cos^{-1}\left(\frac{1.33}{1.52}\right) = 29.0° \,.$$

19E

Refer to the figure to the right. The angle is

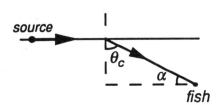

$$\alpha = 90° - \theta_c = 90° - \sin^{-1}(1/n_w)$$
$$= 90° - \sin^{-1}(1/1.33)$$
$$= 41.2° \,.$$

20E

Refer to the figure to the right. The diameter of the circle is

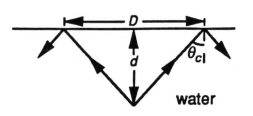

$$D = 2d \tan \theta_c = 2d \tan[\sin^{-1}(1/n_w)]$$
$$= 2(80.0\,\text{cm}) \tan[\sin^{-1}(1/1.33)]$$
$$= 182\,\text{cm}.$$

21P

(a) The diagram on the right shows a cross section, through the center of the cube and parallel to a face. L is the length of a cube edge and S labels the spot. A portion of a ray from the source to a cube face is also shown. Light leaving the source at a small angle θ is refracted at the face and leaves the cube; light leaving at a sufficiently large angle is totally reflected. The light that passes through the cube face forms a circle, the radius r being associated with the critical angle for total internal reflection. If θ_c is that angle then

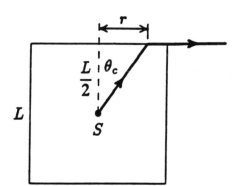

$$\sin \theta_c = \frac{1}{n},$$

where n is the index of refraction for the glass. As the diagram shows, the radius of the circle is given by $r = (L/2) \tan \theta_c$. Now

$$\tan \theta_c = \frac{\sin \theta_c}{\cos \theta_c} = \frac{\sin \theta_c}{\sqrt{1 - \sin^2 \theta_c}} = \frac{1/n}{\sqrt{1 - (1/n)^2}} = \frac{1}{\sqrt{n^2 - 1}}$$

and the radius of the circle is

$$r = \frac{L}{2\sqrt{n^2 - 1}} = \frac{10\,\text{mm}}{2\sqrt{(1.5)^2 - 1}} = 4.47\,\text{mm}.$$

If an opaque circular disk with this radius is pasted at the center of each cube face the spot will not be seen (provided internally reflected light can be ignored).

(b) There must be six opaque disks, one for each face. The total area covered by disks is $6\pi r^2$ and the total surface area of the cube is $6L^2$. The fraction of the surface area that must covered by disks is

$$f = \frac{6\pi r^2}{6L^2} = \frac{\pi r^2}{L^2} = \frac{\pi(4.47\,\text{mm})^2}{(10\,\text{mm})^2} = 0.63.$$

960

22P

The index of refraction n for fused quartz is slightly higher on the bluish side of the visible light spectrum (with shorter wavelength). Since $\sin \theta_c = 1/n$, when this equation first becomes valid for the reddish light the bluish colored light has yet to reach its critical angle so it will not have total internal reflection, leaving the reflected light appear reddish. So (b) is possible while (a) is not.

(c) The angle is about $\theta_c = \sin^{-1}(1/n) = \sin^{-1}(1/1.47) = 43°$.

23P

(a) A ray diagram is shown to the right. Let θ_1 be the angle of incidence and θ_2 be the angle of refraction at the first surface. Let θ_3 be the angle of incidence at the second surface. The angle of refraction there is $\theta_4 = 90°$. The law of refraction, applied to the second surface, yields $n \sin \theta_3 = \sin \theta_4 = 1$. As shown in the diagram, the normals to the surfaces at P and Q make an angle of $90°$

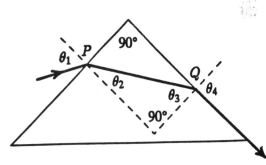

with each other. The interior angles of the triangle formed by the ray and the two normals must sum to $180°$, so $\theta_3 = 90° - \theta_2$ and $\sin \theta_3 = \sin(90° - \theta_2) = \cos \theta_2 = \sqrt{1 - \sin^2 \theta_2}$. According to the law of refraction, applied at Q, $n\sqrt{1 - \sin^2 \theta_2} = 1$.

The law of refraction, applied to point P, yields $\sin \theta_1 = n \sin \theta_2$, so $\sin \theta_2 = (\sin \theta_1)/n$ and

$$n\sqrt{1 - \frac{\sin^2 \theta_1}{n^2}} = 1 .$$

Square both sides and solve for n. You should get

$$n = \sqrt{1 + \sin^2 \theta_1} .$$

(b) The greatest possible value of $\sin^2 \theta_1$ is 1, so the greatest possible value of n is $n_{\max} = \sqrt{2} = 1.41$.

(c) For a given value of n, if the angle of incidence at the first surface is greater than θ_1, the angle of refraction there is greater than θ_2 and the angle of incidence at the second face is less than θ_3 $(= 90° - \theta_2)$. That is, it is less than the critical angle for total internal reflection, so light leaves the second surface and emerges into the air.

(d) If the angle of incidence at the first surface is less than θ_1, the angle of refraction there is less than θ_2 and the angle of incidence at the second surface is greater than θ_3. This is greater than the critical angle for total internal reflection, so all the light is reflected at Q.

24P

(a) When the incident ray is at the minimum angle for which light exits the prism, the light exits along the second face. That is, the angle of refraction at the second face is $90°$ and the angle of incidence there is the critical angle for total internal reflection. Let θ_1 be the angle of incidence and θ_2 be the angle of refraction at the first face and let θ_3 be the angle of incidence at the second face. You want to solve for θ_1.

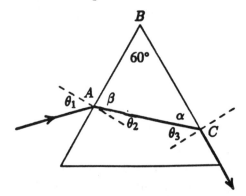

A ray diagram is shown to the right. The law of refraction, applied to point C, yields $n \sin \theta_3 = 1$, so $\sin \theta_3 = 1/n = 1/1.60 = 0.625$ and $\theta_3 = 38.68°$. The interior angles of the triangle ABC must sum to $180°$, so $\alpha + \beta = 120°$. Now $\alpha = 90° - \theta_3 = 51.32°$, so $\beta = 120° - 51.32° = 69.68°$. Thus, $\theta_2 = 90° - \beta = 21.32°$. The law of refraction, applied to point A, yields $\sin \theta_1 = n \sin \theta_2 = 1.60 \sin 21.32° = 0.5817$. Thus $\theta_1 = 35.6°$.

(b) Apply the law of refraction to point C. Since the angle of refraction there is the same as the angle of incidence at A, $n \sin \theta_3 = \sin \theta_1$. Now $\alpha + \beta = 120°$, $\alpha = 90° - \theta_3$, and $\beta = 90° - \theta_2$, as before. This means $\theta_2 + \theta_3 = 60°$. Thus the law of refraction becomes $\sin \theta_1 = n \sin(60° - \theta_2)$, or $\sin \theta_1 = n \sin 60° \cos \theta_2 - n \cos 60° \sin \theta_2$, where the trigonometric identity $\sin(A - B) = \sin A \cos B - \cos A \sin B$ was used.

Now apply the law of refraction to point A: $\sin \theta_1 = n \sin \theta_2$. This means $\sin \theta_2 = (1/n) \sin \theta_1$ and $\cos \theta_2 = \sqrt{1 - \sin^2 \theta_2} = \sqrt{1 - (1/n^2) \sin^2 \theta_1}$. Thus

$$\sin \theta_1 = n \sin 60° \sqrt{1 - (1/n)^2 \sin^2 \theta_1} - \cos 60° \sin \theta_1$$

or

$$(1 + \cos 60°) \sin \theta_1 = \sin 60° \sqrt{n^2 - \sin^2 \theta_1} \, .$$

Square both sides and solve for $\sin \theta_1$. You should get

$$\sin \theta_1 = \frac{n \sin 60°}{\sqrt{(1 + \cos 60°)^2 + \sin^2 60°}} = \frac{1.60 \sin 60°}{\sqrt{(1 + \cos 60°)^2 + \sin^2 60°}} = 0.80$$

and $\theta_1 = 53.1°$.

25P

(a) The light that passes through the surface of the lake is within a cone of apex angle $2\theta_c$, where θ_c is the critical angle for total internal reflection. Imagine a sphere with the light source at its center and suppose that surface area A of the sphere is inside the cone. Since the intensity is the same at every point on the sphere, the fraction of the total energy emitted that passes through the surface is $\text{frac} = A/4\pi R^2$, where R is the radius of the sphere.

You now need to develop an expression for A in terms of the critical angle θ_c. Consider a ring of angular thickness $d\theta$ on the sphere surface. As you can see on the diagram, its radius is $r = R\sin\theta$, so its circumference is $2\pi R\sin\theta$. Its thickness is $R\,d\theta$, so its area is $dA = 2\pi R^2 \sin\theta\,d\theta$. Integrate from zero to θ_c to obtain

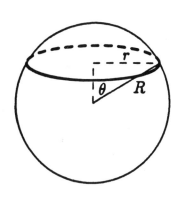

$$A = 2\pi R^2 \int_0^{\theta_c} \sin\theta\,d\theta = -2\pi R^2 \cos\theta \Big|_0^{\theta_c}$$
$$= 2\pi R^2 (1 - \cos\theta_c)\,.$$

The critical angle is given by $\sin\theta_c = 1/n$, so $\cos\theta_c = \sqrt{1 - \sin^2\theta_c} = \sqrt{1 - 1/n^2}$ and

$$\text{frac} = \frac{2\pi R^2 (1 - \cos\theta_c)}{4\pi R^2} = \frac{1}{2}\left[1 - \sqrt{1 - \frac{1}{n^2}}\right]\,.$$

(b) For $n = 1.33$,

$$\text{frac} = \frac{1}{2}\left[1 - \sqrt{1 - \frac{1}{(1.33)^2}}\right] = 0.170\,.$$

26P

From the diagram to the right we have

$$\begin{cases} \dfrac{\sin\theta}{\sin\phi} = n_1, \\[2mm] \cos\phi\sin\theta_c = \dfrac{n_2}{n_1}. \end{cases}$$

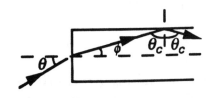

Solve for θ:

$$\sin\theta = n_1\sin\phi = n_1\sqrt{1 - \cos^2\phi} = n_1\sqrt{1 - \left(\frac{n_2}{n_1}\right)^2} = \sqrt{n_1^2 - n_2^2},$$

or $\theta = \sin^{-1}\sqrt{n_1^2 - n_2^2}$.
(b) Now $\theta = \sin^{-1}\sqrt{(1.58)^2 - (1.53)^2} = 23.2°$.

27P

(a) Consider the two light rays a and b, as shown. Obviously the distance traveled by ray a following the zigzag path is longer than that of ray b by

$$\Delta L = \left(\frac{1}{\sin\theta_c} - 1\right) L,$$

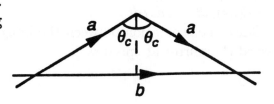

963

So

$$\Delta t = \frac{\Delta L}{c/n_1} = \frac{Ln_1}{c}\left(\frac{1}{\sin\theta_c} - 1\right) = \frac{Ln_1}{c}\left(\frac{1}{n_2/n_1} - 1\right)$$
$$= \frac{L\,n_1}{c\,n_2}(n_1 - n_2).$$

(b) Now

$$\Delta t = \frac{L\,n_1}{c\,n_2}(n_1 - n_2) = \left(\frac{300\,\text{m}}{3.00 \times 10^8\,\text{m/s}}\right)\left(\frac{1.58}{1.53}\right)(1.58 - 1.53) = 5.16 \times 10^{-8}\,\text{s}.$$

28E
(a) Use Eq. 39-5: $\theta_B = \tan^{-1} n_w = \tan^{-1}(1.33) = 53.1°$.
(b) Yes, since n_w depends on the wavelength of the light.

29E
The angle of incidence θ_B for which reflected light is fully polarized is given by Brewster's law, Eq. 39-4 of the text. If n_1 is the index of refraction for the medium of incidence and n_2 is the index of refraction for the second medium, then $\theta_B = \tan^{-1}(n_2/n_1) = \tan^{-1}(1.53/1.33) = 63.8°$.

30E
From Fig. 39-2 we find $n_{max} = 1.470$ for $\lambda = 400\,\text{nm}$ and $n_{min} = 1.456$ for $\lambda = 700\,\text{nm}$. The corresponding Brewster's angles are $\theta_{B,max} = \tan^{-1} n_{max} = \tan^{-1}(1.470) = 55.77°$ and $\theta_{B,min} = \tan^{-1}(1.456) = 55.52°$.

31P
(a) and(b) At the Brewster angle $\theta_{incident} + \theta_{refracted} = \theta_B + 32.0° = 90.0°$, so $\theta_B = 58.0°$ and $n_{glass} = \tan\theta_B = \tan 58.0° = 1.60$.

32E
(a) Let the separation between you and the mirror be s, then the separation between you and your image is $2s$. The speed of your image then moves toward you at a speed $v_i = d(2s)/dt = 2\,ds/dt = 2v$.
(b) Since the separation between the image and the mirror is also s, the image also moves toward the mirror at speed v.

33E

You see easily that the angle of incidence for the light ray on mirror B is $90° - \theta$. So the outgoing ray r' makes an angle $90° - (90° - \theta) = \theta$ with the vertical direction and is antiparallel to the incoming one. The angle between i and r' is therefore 180°.

34E

The image is 10 cm behind the mirror and you are 30 cm in front of the mirror. You must focus your eyes for a distance of 10 cm + 30 cm = 40 cm.

35E

Refer to the diagram to the right. The focus distance is

$$d = \sqrt{(d_1 + d_2)^2 + d_3^2}$$
$$= \sqrt{(4.30\,\text{m} + 3.30\,\text{m})^2 + (5.00\,\text{m})^2}$$
$$= 9.10\,\text{m}.$$

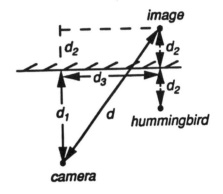

36E

The nearest image of O in A is the direct image of O, which is at $d/3$ from mirror A; the second nearest one is the image in A of the direct image of O in mirror B, which is a distance $d/3 + 2(d - d/3) = 5d/3$ from A; etc. You can show easily that the third and fourth nearest images in A are at $7d/3$ and $11d/3$ from mirror A, respectively.

37E

Draw the various images of a, b and c produced by each mirror. You will find that a and c are visible from the entrance x but b is not.

38E

(a) There are three images. Two are formed by single reflections from each of the mirrors and the third is formed by successive reflections from both mirrors.

(b) The positions of the images are shown on the two diagrams below. The diagram on the left shows the image I_1, formed by reflections from the left-hand mirror. It is the same distance behind the mirror as the object O is in front and is on the line that is perpendicular to the mirror and through the object. Image I_2 is formed by light that is reflected from both mirrors. You may consider I_2 to be the image of I_1 formed by the right-hand mirror, extended. I_2 is the same distance behind the line of the right-hand mirror as I_1 is in front and it is on the line that is perpendicular to the line of the mirror. The diagram on the right shows image I_3, formed by reflections from the right-hand mirror. It is the same

965

distance behind the mirror as the object is in front and is on the line that is perpendicular to the mirror and through the object. As the diagram shows, light that is first reflected from the right-hand mirror and then from the left-hand mirror forms an image at I_2.

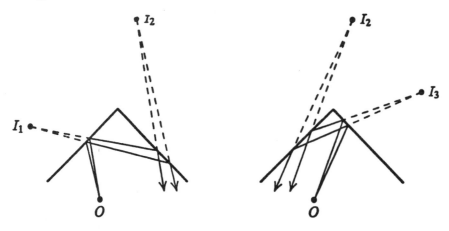

39P

(a) The number of images produced is equal to the greatest integer n which satisfies the inequality $n \le 360°/\theta - 1$. So $n = 360°/45° - 1 = 7$.

(b) $n = 360°/60° - 1 = 5$.

(c) There can be 1 to 3 images, depending on the position of the object and your perspective.

40P

When S is barelay able to see B the light rays from B reflect to S off the edge of the mirror, as shown. So

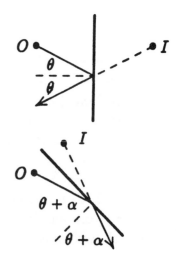

$$\frac{x}{d/2} = \frac{d}{d},$$

or $x = d/2 = 3.0\,\mathrm{m}/2 = 1.5\,\mathrm{m}.$

41P

Consider a single ray from the source to the mirror and let θ be the angle of incidence. The angle of reflection is also θ and the reflected ray makes an angle of 2θ with the incident ray. Now rotate the mirror through the angle α so the angle of incidence increases to $\theta + \alpha$. The reflected ray now makes an angle of $2(\theta + \alpha)$ with the incident ray. The reflected ray has been rotated through an angle of 2α. If the mirror is rotated so the angle of incidence is decreased, then the reflected ray makes an angle of $2(\theta - \alpha)$ with the incident ray. Again it has been rotated through 2α. The diagrams show the situation for $\alpha = 45°$. The ray from the object to the mirror is the same in both cases and the reflected rays are 90° apart.

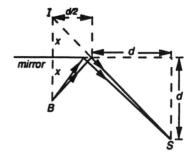

966

42P

Consider the two light rays, r and r', which are reflected off the mirror and reach the edge of the pupil. In the figure to the right

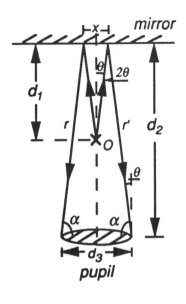

$$x = d_3 - 2d_2/\tan\alpha$$
$$= d_3 - 2d_2\tan\theta$$
$$= d_3 - 2d_2\left(\frac{x/2}{d_1}\right),$$

which gives

$$x = \frac{d_1 d_3}{d_1 + d_2}$$
$$= \frac{(10\,\text{cm})(5.0\,\text{mm})}{10\,\text{cm} + 20\,\text{cm}} = 1.67\,\text{mm}.$$

The area of the mirror used to observe the image of the object is therefore

$$A = \frac{1}{4}\pi x^2 = \frac{\pi}{4}(1.67\,\text{mm})^2 = 2.2\,\text{mm}^2.$$

43P

The intensity of light from a point source varies as the inverse of the square of the distance from the source. Before the mirror is in place, the intensity at the center of the screen is given by $I_0 = A/d^2$, where A is a constant of proportionality. After the mirror is in place, the light that goes directly to the screen contributes intensity I_0, as before. Reflected light also reaches the screen. This light appears to come from the image of the source, a distance d behind the mirror and a distance $3d$ from the screen. Its contribution to the intensity at the center of the screen is

$$I_r = \frac{A}{(3d)^2} = \frac{A}{9d^2} = \frac{I_0}{9}.$$

The total intensity at the center of the screen is

$$I = I_0 + I_r = I_0 + \frac{I_0}{9} = \frac{10}{9}\,I_0.$$

The ratio of the new intensity to the original intensity is $I/I_0 = 10/9$.

44P

You may think of the final image as the image formed by the bottom mirror of the image in the top mirror. Consider an object a distance ℓ in front of a plane mirror that is tilted at 45° to the horizontal, as shown. The image is on the normal to the mirror, a distance ℓ behind it. It is on the vertical line shown. If L is the horizontal distance from the object to the mirror then the vertical distance from the mirror to the image is also L. If the object is extended its image has the same orientation and size.

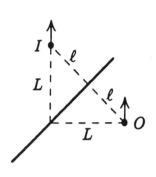

(a) The final image is behind the bottom mirror. No light passes through it, so it is virtual.

(b) The image in a plane mirror of an upright object is itself upright. The image in the top mirror is upright and this becomes an upright object for the bottom mirror. The final image is therefore upright.

(c) The image in a plane mirror is the same size as the object. The image in the top mirror is the same size as the penguin and the image in the bottom mirror is the same size as the first image and therefore the same size as the penguin. The magnification is $+1$.

(d) The image formed by the top mirror is a distance D directly above it. This image, which is the object for the bottom mirror, is therefore a distance $L + D$ from the bottom mirror. The final image is directly in front of the bottom mirror, a distance $L + D$ from it.

45P*

Set up a coordiante system as shown. Suppose an incident ray of light i first strikes one of the mirrors in the xy plane. If the unit vector denoting the direction of i is given by $\mathbf{i}\cos\alpha + \mathbf{j}\cos\beta + \mathbf{k}\cos\gamma$, where α, β, γ are the angles i makes with the x, y and z axis, then after reflection off the xy plane the unit vector becomes $\mathbf{i}\cos\alpha + \mathbf{j}\cos\beta + \mathbf{k}\cos(\pi - \gamma) = \mathbf{i}\cos\alpha + \mathbf{j}\cos\beta - \mathbf{k}\cos\gamma$. Next suppose it strikes the mirror in the xz plane. The unit vector of the reflected ray is $\mathbf{i}\cos\alpha + \mathbf{j}\cos(\pi - \beta) - \mathbf{k}\cos\gamma = \mathbf{i}\cos\alpha - \mathbf{j}\cos\beta - \mathbf{k}\cos\gamma$. Finally

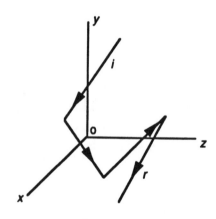

as it reflects off the mirror in the yz plane α becomes $\pi - \alpha$, so the unit vector in the direction of the reflected ray, r, is given by $\mathbf{i}\cos(\pi - \alpha) - \mathbf{j}\cos\beta - \mathbf{k}\cos\gamma = -(\mathbf{i}\cos\alpha + \mathbf{j}\cos\beta + \mathbf{k}\cos\gamma)$, exactly reversed from the direction of i.

46E

Use Eqs. 39-9 and 39-10, and note that $m = -i/p$ so

$$\frac{1}{p} - \frac{1}{pm} = \frac{2}{r},$$

968

$$p = \frac{r}{2}\left(1 - \frac{1}{m}\right)^{-1} = \frac{35.0\,\text{cm}}{2}\left(1 - \frac{1}{-2.50}\right)^{-1} = 12.5\,\text{cm}.$$

47E
In Fig. 39-15(b) we have $p = 8.50\,\text{mm}$ and $r = 25.5\,\text{mm}$, so

$$i = \left(\frac{2}{r} - \frac{1}{p}\right)^{-1} = \left(\frac{2}{25.5\,\text{mm}} - \frac{1}{8.50\,\text{mm}}\right)^{-1} = -25.5\,\text{mm}$$

according to the prediction by Eq. 39-10. The measured value of i is $-17.0\,\text{mm}$. In Fig. 39-15 (c) we also have $p = 8.5\,\text{mm}$ and $r = 3.2\,\text{mm}$ so

$$i = \left(-\frac{2}{r} - \frac{1}{p}\right)^{-1} = -\left(\frac{2}{25.5\,\text{mm}} + \frac{1}{8.5\,\text{mm}}\right)^{-1} = -5.1\,\text{mm}$$

according to Eq. 39-10. The measured valued value is $-6.5\,\text{mm}$.

48P
(a) $f = +20\,\text{cm}$ (positive, because the mirror is concave), $r = 2f = 2(+20\,\text{cm}) = +40\,\text{cm}$, $i = (1/f - 1/p)^{-1} = (1/20\,\text{cm} - 1/10\,\text{cm})^{-1} = -20\,\text{cm}$, $m = -i/p = -(-20\,\text{cm})/10\,\text{cm} = +2.0$, the image is virtual (not real) and upright.

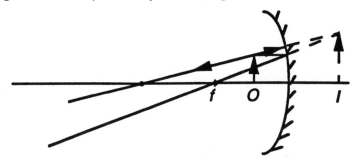

Similarly:
(b) plane, ∞, ∞, $-10\,\text{cm}$, yes;

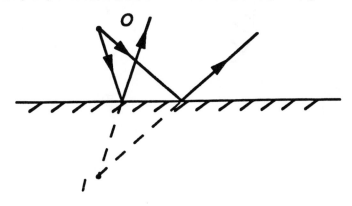

(*c*) concave, +40 cm, +60 cm, −2.0, yes, no;

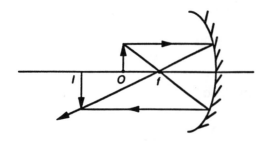

(*d*) concave, +20 cm, +40 cm, +30 cm, yes, no;

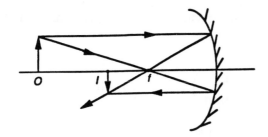

(*e*) convex, −20 cm, +20 cm, +50 cm, no, yes;

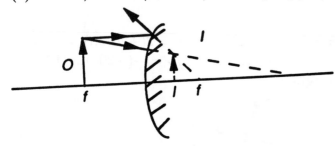

(f) convex, −, −40 cm, −18 cm, +18 cm, no, yes;

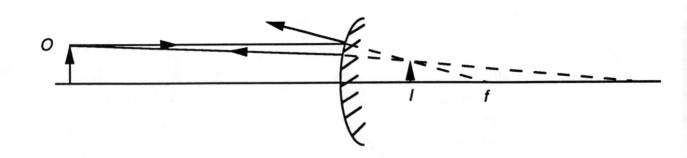

(g) $-20\,\text{cm}$, $-$, $-$, $+50\,\text{cm}$, $+0.8\,\text{cm}$, no, yes;

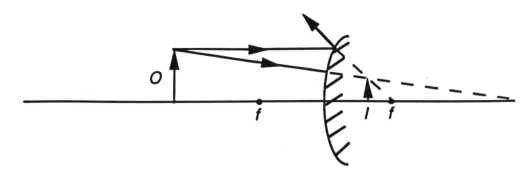

(h) concave, $+8\,\text{cm}$, $+16\,\text{cm}$, $+12\,\text{cm}$, $-$, yes.

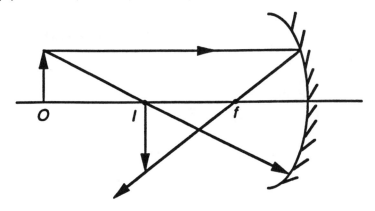

49P

(a) Suppose one end of the object is a distance p from the mirror and the other end is a distance $p + L$. The position i_1 of the image of the first end is given by

$$\frac{1}{p} + \frac{1}{i_1} = \frac{1}{f},$$

where f is the focal length of the mirror. Thus

$$i_1 = \frac{fp}{p - f}.$$

The image of the other end is at

$$i_2 = \frac{f(p + L)}{p + L - f},$$

so the length of the image is

$$L' = i_1 - i_2 = \frac{fp}{p - f} - \frac{f(p + L)}{p + L - f} = \frac{f^2 L}{(p - f)(p + L - f)}.$$

Since the object is short compared to $p - f$ we may neglect the L in the denominator and write

$$L' = L\left(\frac{f}{p-f}\right)^2.$$

(b) The lateral magnification is $m = -i/p$ and since $i = fp/(p - f)$, this can be written $m = -f/(p - f)$. The longitudinal magnification is

$$m' = \frac{L'}{L} = \left(\frac{f}{p-f}\right)^2 = m^2.$$

50P
(a) Solve i from Eqs. 39-9 and 39-10 $i = pf/(p - f) = pr/(2p - r)$. Differentiate both sides with respect to time and use $v_O = dp/dt$:

$$v_I = \frac{di}{dt} = \frac{d}{dt}\left(\frac{pr}{2p-r}\right) = \frac{rv_O(2p-r) - 2v_Opr}{(2p-r)^2}$$

$$= -\left(\frac{r}{2p-r}\right)^2 v_O.$$

(b)
$$v_I = -\left[\frac{15\,\text{cm}}{2(30\,\text{cm}) - 15\,\text{cm}}\right]^2 (5.0\,\text{cm/s}) = -0.56\,\text{cm/s}.$$

(c)
$$v_I = -\left[\frac{15\,\text{cm}}{2(8.0\,\text{cm}) - 15\,\text{cm}}\right]^2 (5.0\,\text{cm/s}) = -1.1 \times 10^3\,\text{cm/s}.$$

(d)
$$v_I = -\left[\frac{15\,\text{cm}}{2(0.10\,\text{cm}) - 15\,\text{cm}}\right]^2 (5.0\,\text{cm/s}) = -5.1\,\text{cm/s}.$$

51P
(a) Use Eq. 39-14 and note that $n_1 = 1.00$(air), $n_2 = n$, $p = \infty$, and $i = 2r$:

$$\frac{n}{2r} = \frac{n-1}{r}.$$

Solve for n: $n = 2.00$.
(b) Now $i = r$ so Eq. 39-14 becomes

$$\frac{n}{r} = \frac{n-1}{r},$$

which is not valid unless n
the sphere.

52P

Use Eq. 39-14.

(a)

$$i = n_2 \left[\frac{n_2 - n_1}{r} - \frac{n_1}{p} \right]^{-1}$$

$$= 1.5 \left[\frac{1.5 - 1.0}{30\,\text{cm}} - \frac{1.0}{10\,\text{cm}} \right]^{-1} = -18\,\text{cm},$$

The image is not real (as $i < 0$).

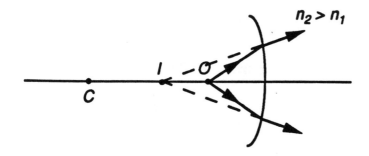

Similarly:
(b) $-33\,\text{cm}$, no;
(c) $+71\,\text{cm}$, yes;
(d) any value of n_2 is possible, no;
(e) $+30\,\text{cm}$, no;
(f) $+10\,\text{cm}$, no;
(g) $-26\,\text{cm}$, no;
(h) $1.1\,\text{cm}$, yes.

53P

Light refracted at the left surface of the sphere passes through and is refracted again at the right surface. Apply Eq. 39–14 twice, using the image formed by the first surface as the object for the second surface. For refraction at the first surface the object distance is $p_1 = \infty$ and the radius of curvature is $r = R$, where R is the radius of the sphere. The surface is convex to the incoming light so the radius of curvature is positive. The medium of incidence is air (or vacuum) and the medium of refraction is glass, so $n_1 = 1$ and $n_2 = n$, where n is the index of refraction of the glass. If i_1 is the image distance for the image formed by the left surface, then

$$\frac{n}{i_1} = \frac{n - 1}{R},$$

$$i_1 = \frac{nR}{n-1}.$$

The image distance is measured from the left edge of the sphere. Since n is less than 2, i_1 is greater than $2R$ and the image is formed to the right of the sphere, a distance $i_1 - 2R$ from its right edge.

The object distance for refraction at the right surface is

$$p_2 = 2R - i_1 = 2R - \frac{nR}{n-1} = \frac{n-2}{n-1}R.$$

This is a negative number, indicating that the light is converging as it strikes the right surface of the sphere. Now the medium of incidence is glass and the medium of the refracted light is air, so $n_1 = n$ and $n_2 = 1$. The surface is concave to the incoming light so the radius of curvature is $r = -R$. Eq. 39–14 yields

$$\frac{n(n-1)}{(n-2)R} + \frac{1}{i_2} = \frac{n-1}{R},$$

where i_2 is the image distance for the second refraction. Thus

$$\frac{1}{i_2} = \frac{n-1}{R} - \frac{n(n-1)}{(n-2)R} = \frac{2(n-1)}{(2-n)R}.$$

The image distance is

$$i_2 = \frac{2-n}{2(n-1)}R.$$

This is positive, indicating that the final image is to the right of the sphere.

54E

Solve Eq. 39–15 for the image distance i: $i = pf/(p-f)$. The lens is diverging, so its focal length is $f = -30\,\text{cm}$. The object distance is $p = 20\,\text{cm}$. Thus

$$i = \frac{(20\,\text{cm})(-30\,\text{cm})}{(20\,\text{cm}) - (-30\,\text{cm})} = -12\,\text{cm}.$$

The negative sign indicates that the image is virtual and is on the same side of the lens as the object. The ray diagram, drawn to scale, is shown on the right.

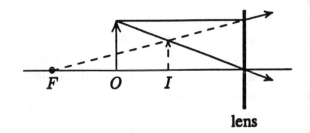

55E

(a) In the two shaded triangles as shown $W_2/f_2 = W_1/f_1$, so

$$W_2 = \left(\frac{f_2}{f_1}\right) W_1.$$

(b)

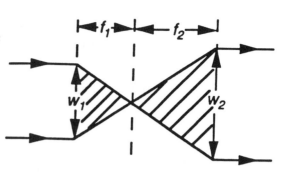

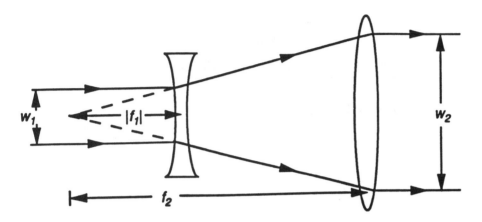

See the arrangement depicted above. The two lenses are separated by $f_2 - |f_1|$. Here $W_2/W_1 = f_2/|f_1|$.

56E

$$\frac{I_2}{I_1} = \frac{P/A_2^2}{P/A_1^2} = \left(\frac{A_1}{A_2}\right)^2 = \left(\frac{W_1}{W_2}\right)^2 = \left(\frac{f_1}{f_2}\right)^2.$$

57E

Use the lens maker's equation, Eq. 39–16:

$$\frac{1}{f} = (n-1)\left(\frac{1}{r_1} - \frac{1}{r_2}\right),$$

where f is the focal length, n is the index of refraction, r_1 is the radius of curvature of the first surface encountered by the light and r_2 is the radius of curvature of the second surface. Since one surface has twice the radius of the other and since one surface is convex to the incoming light while the other is concave, set $r_2 = -2r_1$ to obtain

$$\frac{1}{f} = (n-1)\left(\frac{1}{r_1} + \frac{1}{2r_1}\right) = \frac{3(n-1)}{2r_1}.$$

Solve for r_1:

$$r_1 = \frac{3(n-1)f}{2} = \frac{3(1.5-1)(60\,\text{mm})}{2} = 45\,\text{mm}.$$

The radii are 45 mm and 90 mm.

58E

Let the diameter of the sun be d_p and that of the image be d_i. Then

$$d_i = md_p = \left(\frac{i}{p}\right)d_p = \left(\frac{f}{p}\right)d_p$$

$$= \frac{(20.0 \times 10^{-2}\,\text{m})(2)(6.96 \times 10^8\,\text{m})}{1.50 \times 10^{11}\,\text{m}}$$

$$= 1.86 \times 10^{-3}\,\text{m} = 1.86\,\text{mm}.$$

59E

(a) Use Eq. 39-16:

$$f = \left[(n-1)\left(\frac{1}{r_1} - \frac{1}{r_2}\right)\right]^{-1}$$

$$= \left[(1.5-1)\left(\frac{1}{\infty} - \frac{1}{-20\,\text{cm}}\right)\right]^{-1} = 40\,\text{cm}.$$

(b) Solve i from Eq. 39-15

$$i = \left(\frac{1}{f} - \frac{1}{p}\right)^{-1} = \left(\frac{1}{40\,\text{cm}} - \frac{1}{40\,\text{cm}}\right)^{-1} = \infty,$$

i.e. The image is located at infinity.

60E

From Eq. 39-16, if

$$f \propto \left(\frac{1}{r_1} - \frac{1}{r_2}\right)^{-1} = \frac{r_1 r_2}{r_2 - r_1}$$

is positive, i.e. $r_2 > r_1$, then the lens is converging, ect.
(a) Converging, since $r_2 \to \infty$ and r_1 is finite (i.e. $r_2 > r_1$).
(b) Diverging, since $r_1 \to \infty$ and r_2 is finite (i.e. $r_2 < r_1$).
(c) Converging, since $r_2 > r_1$.
(d) Diverging, since $r_2 < r_1$.

61E

Eq. 39-16 is valid when the lens is immersed in vaccum whose index of refraction is 1. When immersed in a fluid with index of refraction n' the law of refraction applied to both the imcoming and outgoing rays of light has to be rewritten, with n replaced by n/n'. So Eq. 39-16 should also be rewritten as

$$\frac{1}{f} = \left(\frac{n}{n'} - 1\right)\left(\frac{1}{r_1} - \frac{1}{r_2}\right) = \frac{n - n'}{n'}\left(\frac{1}{r_1} - \frac{1}{r_2}\right).$$

62E

Solve i from Eq. 39-15:

$$i = \left(\frac{1}{f} - \frac{1}{p}\right)^{-1} = \frac{fp}{p - f}.$$

So the height of the image is

$$h_i = mh_p = \left(\frac{i}{p}\right)h_p = \frac{fh_p}{p - f}$$

$$= \frac{(75\,\text{mm})(1.80\,\text{m})}{27\,\text{m} - 75 \times 10^{-3}\,\text{m}} = 5.0\,\text{mm}.$$

63P

Use Eq. 39-16.

(a)

$$f = \left[(n - 1)\left(\frac{1}{r_1} - \frac{1}{r_2}\right)\right]^{-1} = \left[(1.5 - 1)\left(\frac{1}{40\,\text{cm}} - \frac{1}{-40\,\text{cm}}\right)\right]^{-1} = 40\,\text{cm}.$$

Since $f > 0$ the lens forms a real image of the sun.

(b) Now

$$f = \left[(1.5 - 1)\left(\frac{1}{\infty} - \frac{1}{-40\,\text{cm}}\right)\right]^{-1} = 80\,\text{cm},$$

forming a real image ($f > 0$).

(c) Now

$$f = \left[(1.5 - 1)\left(\frac{1}{40\,\text{cm}} - \frac{1}{60\,\text{cm}}\right)\right]^{-1} = 240\,\text{cm},$$

forming a real image ($f > 0$).

(d) Now

$$f = \left[(1.5 - 1)\left(\frac{1}{-40\,\text{cm}} - \frac{1}{40\,\text{cm}}\right)\right]^{-1} = -40\,\text{cm},$$

forming a virtual image ($f < 0$).

(e) Now

$$f = \left[(1.5 - 1)\left(\frac{1}{\infty} - \frac{1}{40\,\text{cm}}\right)\right]^{-1} = -80\,\text{cm},$$

forming a virtual image ($f < 0$).

(f) Now

$$f = \left[(1.5 - 1)\left(\frac{1}{60\,\text{cm}} - \frac{1}{40\,\text{cm}}\right)\right]^{-1} = -240\,\text{cm},$$

forming a virtual image ($f < 0$).

64P

For a thin lens $(1/p) + (1/i) = (1/f)$, where p is the object distance, i is the image distance, and f is the focal length. Solve for i:

$$i = \frac{fp}{p - f}.$$

Let $p = f + x$, where x is positive if the object is outside the focal point and negative if it is inside. Then

$$i = \frac{f(f + x)}{x}.$$

Now let $i = f + x'$, where x' is positive if the image is outside the focal point and negative if it is inside. Then

$$x' = i - f = \frac{f(f + x)}{x} - f = \frac{f^2}{x}$$

and $xx' = f^2$.

65P

(a) $f = +10\,\text{cm}$ (positive, because the lens is a converging one), r_1 and r_2 cannot be determined (since n is not given), $i = (1/f - 1/p)^{-1} = (1/10\,\text{cm} - 1/20\,\text{cm})^{-1} = 20\,\text{cm}$, n cannot be determined, $m = -i/p = -20\,\text{cm}/20\,\text{cm} = -1.0$, the image is real (since $i > 0$) and inverted (since $m < 0$).

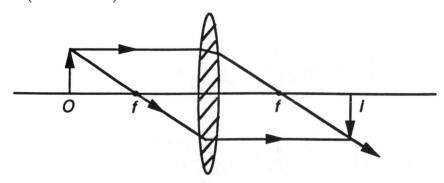

Using an X to denote a quantity which cannot be determined from the given data, we have

(b) converging, X, X, $-10\,\text{cm}$, X, $+2.0$, no, yes;
(c) converging, $+$, X, X, $-10\,\text{cm}$, X, no, yes;
(d) diverging, $-$, X, X, -3.3, X, no, yes;
(e) converging, $+30\,\text{cm}$, $-15\,\text{cm}$, $+1.5$, no, yes;
(f) converging, $-30\,\text{cm}$, $-7.5\,\text{cm}$, $+0.75$, no, yes;
(g) diverging, $-120\,\text{cm}$, $-9.2\,\text{cm}$, $+0.92$, no, yes;
(h) diverging, $-10\,\text{cm}$, X, X, $-5\,\text{cm}$, X, $+$, no;
(i) converging, $+3.3\,\text{cm}$, X, X, $+5\,\text{cm}$, X, no.

66P
Without the diverging lens (lens 2), the real image formed by the converging lens (lens 1) is located at a distance

$$i_1 = \left(\frac{1}{f_1} - \frac{1}{p_1}\right)^{-1} = \left(\frac{1}{20\,\text{cm}} - \frac{1}{40\,\text{cm}}\right)^{-1} = 40\,\text{cm}$$

to the right of lens 1. This image now serves as an object for lens 2, with $p_2 = -(40\,\text{cm} - 10\,\text{cm}) = -30\,\text{cm}$. So

$$i_2 = \left(\frac{1}{f_2} - \frac{1}{p_2}\right)^{-1} = \left(\frac{1}{-15\,\text{cm}} - \frac{1}{-30\,\text{cm}}\right)^{-1} = -30\,\text{cm}$$

i.e. The image formed by lens 2 is located 30 cm to the left of lens 2. It is upright and virtual, as you can easily check by drawing a ray diagram.

67P
Suppose that the lens is placed to the left of the mirror. The image formed by the converging lens is located at a distnace

$$i = \left(\frac{1}{f} - \frac{1}{p}\right)^{-1} = \left(\frac{1}{0.50\,\text{m}} - \frac{1}{1.0\,\text{m}}\right)^{-1} = 1.0\,\text{m}$$

to the right of the lens, or $2.0\,\text{m} - 1.0\,\text{m} = 1.0\,\text{m}$ in front of the mirror. The image formed by the mirror for this real image is then at 1.0 m to the right of the the mirror, or $2.0\,\text{m} + 1.0\,\text{m} = 3.0\,\text{m}$ to the right of the lens. This image then results in another image formed by the lens, located at a distance

$$i' = \left(\frac{1}{f} - \frac{1}{p'}\right)^{-1} = \left(\frac{1}{0.50\,\text{m}} - \frac{1}{3.0\,\text{m}}\right)^{-1} = 0.60\,\text{m}$$

to the left of the lens.
(b) and (c) The final image is real and upright, as you can easily check by drawing a ray diagram.

(d)
$$m = \left(-\frac{i}{p}\right)\left(-\frac{i'}{p'}\right) = \left(-\frac{1.0\,\text{m}}{1.0\,\text{m}}\right)\left(-\frac{0.60\,\text{m}}{3.0\,\text{m}}\right) = +0.20.$$

68P
(a) First, the lens forms a real image of the objet located at a distance

$$i_1 = \left(\frac{1}{f_1} - \frac{1}{p_1}\right)^{-1} = \left(\frac{1}{f_1} - \frac{1}{2f_1}\right)^{-1} = 2f_1$$

to the right of the lens, or at $p_2 = 2(f_1 + f_2) - 2f_1 = 2f_2$ in front of the mirror. The subsequent image formed by the mirror is located at a distance

$$i_2 = \left(\frac{1}{f_2} - \frac{1}{p_2}\right)^{-1} = \left(\frac{1}{f_2} - \frac{1}{2f_2}\right)^{-1} = 2f_2$$

to the left of the mirror, or at $p'_1 = 2(f_1 + f_2) - 2f_2 = 2f_1$ to the right of the lens. The final image formed by the lens is that at a distance i'_1 to the left of the lens, where

$$i'_1 = \left(\frac{1}{f_1} - \frac{1}{p'_1}\right)^{-1} = \left(\frac{1}{f_1} - \frac{1}{2f_1}\right)^{-1} = 2f_1,$$

i.e. right at the location of the object. The image is real and inverted. The lateral magnification is

$$m = \left(-\frac{i_1}{p_1}\right)\left(-\frac{i_2}{p_2}\right)\left(-\frac{i'_1}{p'_1}\right) = \left(-\frac{2f_1}{2f_1}\right)\left(-\frac{2f_2}{2f_2}\right)\left(-\frac{2f_1}{2f_1}\right) = -1.0.$$

(b)

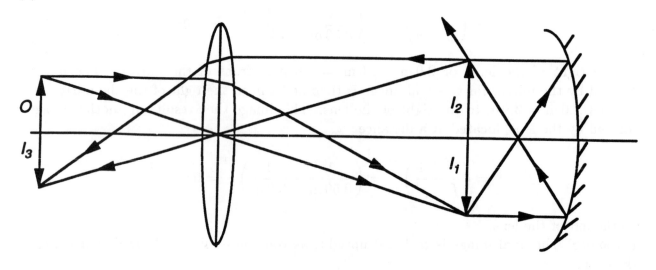

980

69P

(a) A convex lens, since a real image is formed.

(b) Since $i = d - p$ and $i/p = 1/2$, we find

$$p = \frac{2d}{3} = \frac{2(40.0\,\text{cm})}{3} = 26.7\,\text{cm}.$$

(c)

$$f = \left(\frac{1}{i} + \frac{1}{p}\right)^{-1} = \left(\frac{1}{d/3} + \frac{1}{2d/3}\right)^{-1} \qquad \frac{2d}{9} - \frac{2(40.0\,\text{cm})}{9} = 8.89\,\text{cm}.$$

70P

(a) For the image formed by the first lens

$$i_1 = \left(\frac{1}{f_1} - \frac{1}{p_1}\right)^{-1} = \left(\frac{1}{10\,\text{cm}} - \frac{1}{20\,\text{cm}}\right)^{-1} = 20\,\text{cm}.$$

For the subsequent image formed by the second lens $p_2 = 30\,\text{cm} - 20\,\text{cm} = 10\,\text{cm}$, so

$$i_2 = \left(\frac{1}{f_2} - \frac{1}{p_2}\right)^{-1} = \left(\frac{1}{12.5\,\text{cm}} - \frac{1}{10\,\text{cm}}\right)^{-1} = -50\,\text{cm},$$

i.e. the final image is 50 cm to the left of the second lens, which means it coincides with the object. The magnification is

$$m = \left(\frac{i_1}{p_1}\right)\left(\frac{i_2}{p_2}\right) = \left(\frac{20\,\text{cm}}{20\,\text{cm}}\right)\left(\frac{-50\,\text{cm}}{10\,\text{cm}}\right) = -5.0,$$

i.e. the object is enlarged 5 times in its final image.

(b)

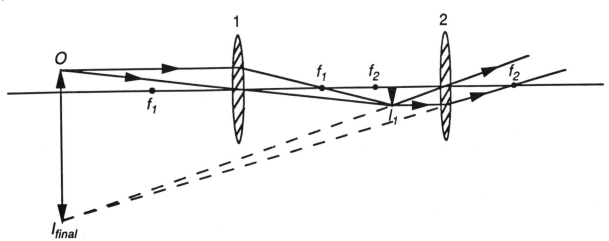

(c) It is virtual (see diagram above) and inverted.

71P

Place an object far away from the composite lens and find the image distance i. Since the image is at a focal point $i = f$, the effective focal length of the composite. The final image is produced by two lenses, with the image of the first lens being the object for the second. For the first lens $(1/p_1) + (1/i_1) = (1/f_1)$, where f_1 is the focal length of this lens and i_1 is the image distance for the image it forms. Since $p_1 = \infty$, $i_1 = f_1$.

The thin lens equation, applied to the second lens, is $(1/p_2) + (1/i_2) = (1/f_2)$, where p_2 is the object distance, i_2 is the image distance, and f_2 is the focal length. If the thicknesses of the lenses can be ignored the object distance for the second lens is $p_2 = -i_1$. The negative sign must be used since the image formed by the first lens is beyond the second lens if i_1 is positive. This means the object for the second lens is virtual and the object distance is negative. If i_1 is negative the image formed by the first lens is in front of the second lens and p_2 is positive. In the thin lens equation, replace p_2 with $-f_1$ and i_2 with f to obtain

$$-\frac{1}{f_1} + \frac{1}{f} = \frac{1}{f_2}$$

or

$$\frac{1}{f} = \frac{1}{f_1} + \frac{1}{f_2} = \frac{f_1 + f_2}{f_1 f_2}.$$

Thus

$$f = \frac{f_1 f_2}{f_1 + f_2}.$$

72P

(a) Since a beam of parallel light will be focused at a distance f from the lens, the shorter the focal length f the greater the ability for the lens to focus. Therefore $p = 1/f$ is a reasonable definition.

(b) Use the result of Problem 71:

$$p = \frac{1}{f} = \frac{f_1 + f_2}{f_1 f_2} = \frac{1}{f_1} + \frac{1}{f_2} = p_1 + p_2.$$

73P

Use Eq. 39-15 and note that $p + i = d = 44\,\text{cm}$, we obtain $p^2 - dp + df = 0$. Solve for p:

$$p = \frac{1}{2}(d \pm \sqrt{d^2 - 4df})$$

$$= 22\,\text{cm} \pm \frac{1}{2}\sqrt{(44\,\text{cm})^2 - 4(44\,\text{cm})(11\,\text{cm})} = 22\,\text{cm}.$$

74P

For an object in front of a thin lens, the object distance p and the image distance i are related by $(1/p) + (1/i) = (1/f)$, where f is the focal length of the lens. For the situation described by the problem all quantities are positive, so the distance x between the object and image is $x = p + i$. Substitute $i = x - p$ into the thin lens equation and solve for x. You should get

$$x = \frac{p^2}{p - f}.$$

To find the minimum value of x, set $dx/dp = 0$ and solve for p. Since

$$\frac{dx}{dp} = \frac{p(p - 2f)}{(p - f)^2},$$

the result is $p = 2f$. The minimum distance is

$$x_{min} = \frac{p^2}{p - f} = \frac{(2f)^2}{2f - f} = 4f.$$

This is a minimum, rather than a maximum, since the image distance i becomes large without bound as the object approaches the focal point.

75P

(a) If the object distance is x, then the image distance is $D - x$ and the thin lens equation becomes

$$\frac{1}{x} + \frac{1}{D - x} = \frac{1}{f}.$$

Multiply each term in the equation by $fx(D - x)$ to obtain $x^2 - Dx + Df = 0$. Solve for x. The two object distances for which images are formed on the screen are

$$x_1 = \frac{D - \sqrt{D(D - 4f)}}{2}$$

and

$$x_2 = \frac{D + \sqrt{D(D - 4f)}}{2}.$$

The distance between the two object positions is

$$d = x_2 - x_1 = \sqrt{D(D - 4f)}.$$

(b) The ratio of the image sizes is the same as the ratio of the lateral magnifications. If the object is at $p = x_1$ the lateral magnification is

$$m_1 = \frac{i_1}{p_1} = \frac{D - x_1}{x_1}.$$

983

Now $x_1 = \frac{1}{2}(D - d)$, where $d = \sqrt{D(D - f)}$, so

$$m_1 = \frac{D - (D - d)/2}{(D - d)/2} = \frac{D + d}{D - d}.$$

Similarly, when the object is at x_2 the magnification is

$$m_2 = \frac{I_2}{p_2} = \frac{D - x_2}{x_2} = \frac{D - (D + d)/2}{(D + d)/2} = \frac{D - d}{D + d}.$$

The ratio of the magnifications is

$$\frac{m_2}{m_1} = \frac{(D - d)/(D + d)}{(D + d)/(D - d)} = \left(\frac{D - d}{D + d}\right)^2.$$

76E

(a) If L is the distance between the lenses, then according to Fig. 39–26, the tube length is $s = L - f_{ob} - f_{ey} = 25.0\,\text{cm} - 4.00\,\text{cm} - 8.00\,\text{cm} = 13.0\,\text{cm}$.

(b) Solve $(1/p) + (1/i) = (1/f_{ob})$ for p. The image distance is $i = f_{ob} + s = 4.00\,\text{cm} + 13.0\,\text{cm} = 17.0\,\text{cm}$, so

$$p = \frac{i f_{ob}}{i - f_{ob}} = \frac{(17.0\,\text{cm})(4.00\,\text{cm})}{17.0\,\text{cm} - 4.00\,\text{cm}} = 5.23\,\text{cm}.$$

(c) The magnification of the objective is

$$m = -\frac{i}{p} = -\frac{17.0\,\text{cm}}{5.23\,\text{cm}} = -3.25.$$

(d) The angular magnification of the eyepiece is

$$m_\theta = \frac{15\,\text{cm}}{f_{ey}} = \frac{15\,\text{cm}}{8.00\,\text{cm}} = 1.88.$$

(e) The overall magnification of the microscope is

$$M = m m_\theta = (-3.25)(1.88) = -6.09.$$

77E

The minimum diameter of the eyepiece is

$$d_{ey} = \frac{d_{ob}}{m_\theta} = \frac{75\,\text{mm}}{36} = 2.1\,\text{mm}.$$

78P

(a) In this case $i < 0$ so $i = -|i|$, and Eq. 39-15 becomes

$$\frac{1}{f} = \frac{1}{p} - \frac{1}{|i|}.$$

Differentiate with respect to t to obtain

$$v_I = \frac{d|i|}{dt} = \left(\frac{i}{p}\right)^2 \left(\frac{dp}{dt}\right).$$

As the object is moved toward the lens $dp/dt < 0$. So $d|i|/dt < 0$, i.e. the image moves in from infinity. The angle $\theta' \approx \tan^{-1}(h/p)$ increases since p decreases.
(b) When the image appears to be at P_n, i.e. $|i| = P_n$.
(c) In this case

$$p = \left(\frac{1}{f} - \frac{1}{i}\right)^{-1} = \left(\frac{1}{f} + \frac{1}{|i|}\right)^{-1} = \left(\frac{1}{f} + \frac{1}{P_n}\right)^{-1},$$

so

$$m_\theta = \frac{\theta'}{\theta} = \frac{h/p}{h/P_n} = P_n\left(\frac{1}{f} + \frac{1}{P_n}\right)$$
$$= 1 + \frac{15\,\text{cm}}{f}.$$

(d) The linear magnigication is

$$m = \frac{|i|}{p} = |i|\left(\frac{1}{f} + \frac{1}{|i|}\right) = 1 + \frac{|i|}{f} = 1 + \frac{P_n}{f} = 1 + \frac{15\,\text{cm}}{f} = m_\theta.$$

79P

(a) When the eye muscle is relaxed we have $p \to \infty$ so $i = f = 40.0\,\text{cm}$. Now

$$\frac{1}{f'} = \frac{1}{i} + \frac{1}{p} = \frac{1}{f} + \frac{1}{p} = \frac{1}{2.50\,\text{cm}} + \frac{1}{40.0\,\text{cm}}$$

so $f' = 2.35\,\text{cm}$.
(b) Decrease, since $f' \propto r$ is decreased.

80P

(a) A parallel ray of light focuses at the focal point behind the lens. In the case of far-sightedness we need to bring the focal point closer, i.e. to reduce the focal length. From Problem 71 we know that we need to use a converging lens of certain focal lenght f_1 which, when combined with the eye of focal length f_2, gives $f = f_1 f_2/(f_1 + f_2) < f_2$. Similarly you can see that in the case of nearsightness we need to do just the opposite, i.e. to bring in a diverging lens.

(b) As an object is brought closer to a fixed-focus lens the image formed also moves away from the lens. Reading requires that the object be close to the eyes. If you need visual aid for reading it means that your eyes cannot fully adjust themselves to prevent the image from moving further away from your retina. Therefore you are farsighted.

<u>81P</u>

(a)

$$i = \left(\frac{1}{f} - \frac{1}{p}\right)^{-1} = \left(\frac{1}{5.0\,\text{cm}} - \frac{1}{100\,\text{cm}}\right)^{-1} = 5.3\,\text{cm}.$$

(b) The charge in the lens-film distance is $5.3\,\text{cm} - 5.0\,\text{cm} = 0.30\,\text{cm}.$

<u>82P</u>

(a) As far as magnification is concerned the mirror M has exactly the same effect as a lens with the same focal length, at the same position. The only difference is that the image produced by the mirror is in front while the image produced by the lens is behind. Thus Eq. 39–21 is directly applicable and $m_\theta = -f_{ob}/f_{ey}$.

(b) Solve the mirror equation $(1/p) + (1/i) = (1/f)$ for i. Here the object distance is $p = 2.0 \times 10^3\,\text{m}$ and the focal length is $f = 16.8\,\text{m}$. The result is

$$i = \frac{pf}{p - f} = \frac{(2.0 \times 10^3\,\text{m})(16.8\,\text{m})}{2.0 \times 10^3\,\text{m} - 16.8\,\text{m}} = 16.94\,\text{m}.$$

The magnification is

$$m = -\frac{i}{p} = -\frac{16.94\,\text{m}}{2.0 \times 10^3\,\text{m}} = -8.47 \times 10^{-3}.$$

Since the length of the object is $\ell = 1.0\,\text{m}$, the length of its image is

$$\ell' = |m|\ell = (8.47 \times 10^{-3})(1.0\,\text{m}) = 8.47 \times 10^{-3}\,\text{m}.$$

(c) Use $m_\theta = -f_{ob}/f_{ey}$. If R is the radius of curvature of the objective mirror, its focal length is $f_{ob} = R/2 = 5.0\,\text{m}$. Take the angular magnification to be -200. Then

$$f_{ey} = -\frac{f_{ob}}{m_\theta} = \frac{5.0\,\text{m}}{200} = 0.025\,\text{m} = 2.5\,\text{cm}.$$

83P

Refer to Fig. 39-26. For the intermediate image we have $p = 10\,\text{mm}$ and $i = (f_{ob} + s + f_{ey}) - f_{ey} = 300\,\text{m} - 50\,\text{mm} = 250\,\text{mm}$, so

$$\frac{1}{f_{ob}} = \frac{1}{i} + \frac{1}{p} = \frac{1}{250\,\text{mm}} + \frac{1}{10\,\text{mm}} = \frac{1}{9.62\,\text{mm}},$$

and $s = (f_{ob} + s + f_{ey}) - f_{ob} - f_{ey} = 300\,\text{mm} - 9.62\,\text{mm} - 50\,\text{mm} = 240\,\text{mm}$. Then from Eq. 39-20 we get

$$M = -\frac{s}{f_{ob}} \frac{15\,\text{cm}}{f_{ey}} = -\left(\frac{240\,\text{mm}}{9.62\,\text{mm}}\right)\left(\frac{150\,\text{mm}}{50\,\text{mm}}\right) = -75.$$

84

(a) Let the focal length of the eyes be f_0. Then without visual aid $p_{max} = 50\,\text{cm}$, and $p_{max}^{-1} + i_{min}^{-1} = f_0^{-1}$. With a corrective lens of focal length f_c, the combined focal length f satisfies $f^{-1} = f_0^{-1} + f_c^{-1}$ (see Problem 71), and p_{max} is extended to infinity:

$$\frac{1}{\infty} + \frac{1}{i_{min}} = \frac{1}{f} = \frac{1}{f_0} + \frac{1}{f_c} = \left(\frac{1}{p_{max}} + \frac{1}{i_{min}}\right) + \frac{1}{f_c}.$$

Solve for f_c: $f_c = -p_{max} = -50\,\text{cm} < 0$.

(b) It is a divergent lens, since $f_c < 0$.

(c) $P = 1/f_c = 1/(-50\,\text{cm}) = 1/(-50\,\text{m}) = -2.0\,\text{diopters}$.

85

Consider A', the image of A in the mirror. The actual path of light from A to B is AOB, for which the angle of incidence θ satisfies $\theta + \alpha = 90°$ and the angle of reflection ϕ satisfies $\phi + \alpha = 90°$. So $\theta = \phi$. To show that any other path, such as $AO'B$ as shown, is longer than AOB, just note in the figure that

$$AO' + O'B = A'O' + O'B > A'B$$
$$= A'O + OB = AO + OB.$$

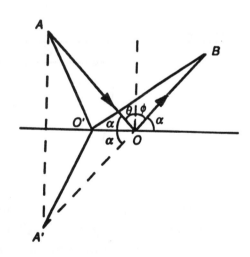

86

(a) Without the magnifier we have $\theta = h/P_n$ (see Fig. 39-25). With the magnifier, let $p = P_n$ and $i = -|i| = -P_n$ we have

$$\frac{1}{p} = \frac{1}{f} - \frac{1}{i} = \frac{1}{f} + \frac{1}{|i|} = \frac{1}{f} + \frac{1}{P_n}$$

$$m_\theta = \frac{\theta'}{\theta} = \frac{h/p}{h/P_n} = \frac{1/f + 1/P_n}{1/P_n}$$

$$= 1 + \frac{P_n}{f} = 1 + \frac{25\,\text{cm}}{f}.$$

(b) Now $i = -|i| \to -\infty$ so $1/p + 1/i = 1/p = 1/f$ and

$$m_\theta = \frac{\theta'}{\theta} = \frac{h/p}{h/P_n} = \frac{1/f}{1/P_n} = \frac{P_n}{f} = \frac{25\,\text{cm}}{f}.$$

(c) For $f = 10\,\text{cm}$ we have

$$f = \begin{cases} 1 + 25\,\text{cm}/10\,\text{cm} = 3.5 & \text{(case a)} \\ 25\,\text{cm}/10\,\text{cm} = 2.5 & \text{(case b)}. \end{cases}$$

<u>87</u>

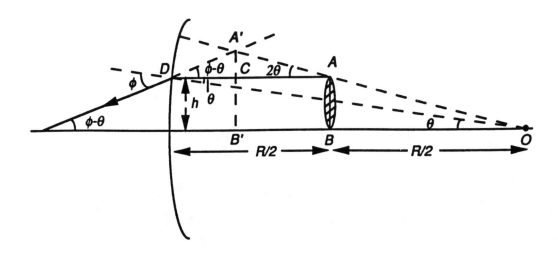

Refer to the ray diagram shown above. Although the angles shown are not small (for clarity) we consider only very small angles since the size of the goldfish is (hopefully) much less than R. In this approximation $\sin\phi/\sin\theta \approx \phi/\theta = m_w$, or $\phi \approx n_w\theta$. In the triangle $DA'A$ we have

$$\frac{R}{2} = DA = DC + CA = \frac{A'C}{\tan(\phi - \theta)} + \frac{A'C}{\tan(2\theta)} \approx A'C\left(\frac{1}{\phi - \theta} + \frac{1}{2\theta}\right)$$

$$= \frac{A'C}{\theta}\left(\frac{1}{n_w - 1} + \frac{1}{2}\right) = \frac{A'C}{h/R}\left(\frac{1}{n_w - 1} + \frac{1}{2}\right),$$

which gives

$$A'C = \frac{h}{2}\left(\frac{1}{n_w - 1} + \frac{1}{2}\right)^{-1}.$$

The magnification is therefore

$$m = \frac{A'B}{AB} = \frac{A'C + h}{h} = 1 + \frac{1}{2}\left(\frac{1}{n_w - 1} + \frac{1}{2}\right)^{-1}$$

$$= 1 + \frac{1}{2}\left(\frac{1}{1.33 - 1} + \frac{1}{2}\right)^{-1} = 1.14.$$

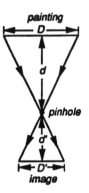

88

In the figure to the right $d'/D' = d/D$, which gives

$$d = \frac{Dd}{D'} = \frac{(50\,\text{cm})(12\,\text{cm})}{6.0\,\text{cm}}$$

$$= 1.0 \times 10^2\,\text{cm}.$$

CHAPTER 40

1E

(*a*)

$$f = \frac{c}{\lambda} = \frac{3.00 \times 10^8 \, \text{m/s}}{589 \times 10^{-0} \, \text{m}} = 5.09 \times 10^{14} \, \text{Hz}.$$

(*b*)

$$\lambda' = \frac{v}{f} = \frac{c/n}{f} = \frac{\lambda}{n} = \frac{589 \, \text{nm}}{1.52} = 388 \, \text{nm}.$$

(*c*) $v = \lambda' f = (388 \times 10^{-9} \, \text{m})(5.09 \times 10^{14} \, \text{Hz}) = 1.97 \times 10^8 \, \text{m/s}.$

2E

$$\Delta v = v_s - v_d = c \left(\frac{1}{n_s} - \frac{1}{n_d} \right)$$

$$= (3.00 \times 10^8 \, \text{m/s}) \left(\frac{1}{1.77} - \frac{1}{2.42} \right) = 4.55 \times 10^7 \, \text{m/s}.$$

3E

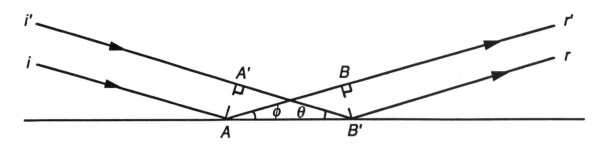

Consider a wave front AA' of the incident wave. Suppose the time it takes for the wave at point A' to travel to point B' is t, then $A'B' = vt$ where v is the speed of light in the medium. Meanwhile the wave which was reflected at point A must have reached point B, where $AB = vt$. Thus

$$\cos \phi = \frac{AB}{AB'} = \frac{A'B'}{AB'} = \cos \theta,$$

or $\phi = \theta$. This is equivalent to the law of reflection.

4E

$$n = \frac{v}{c} = \frac{1.92 \times 10^8 \text{ m/s}}{3.00 \times 10^8 \text{ m/s}} = 1.56.$$

5E

The index of refraction of fused quartz at $\lambda = 550$ nm is about 1.459, which is obtained from Fig. 39-2. So

$$v = \frac{c}{n} = \frac{3.00 \times 10^8 \text{ m/s}}{1.459} = 2.06 \times 10^8 \text{ m/s}.$$

6E

$v_{\min} = c/n = (3.00 \times 10^8 \text{ m/s})/1.54 = 1.95 \times 10^8 \text{ m/s}.$

7E

The travel time would be greater when the tube is filled with air, as the speed of light in air is less than that in vacuum. The time difference is

$$\Delta t = \frac{d}{c} - \frac{d}{v} = \frac{d}{c}\left(1 - \frac{1}{n_{\text{air}}}\right)$$

$$= \frac{1.609 \times 10^3 \text{ m}}{3.00 \times 10^8 \text{ m/s}}\left(1 - \frac{1}{1.00029}\right) = 1.55 \times 10^{-9} \text{ s}.$$

8P

Refer to Fig. 18-21. Suppose that the stick starts from point S_1 at $t = 0$ and moves to point S during time t, then $S_1 S = vt$. Meanwhile the wave front produced by the stick at $t = 0$ at point S_1 has grown to a circular cross section of radius $r = ut$. Thus a conical wave front is set up, with

$$\sin\theta = \frac{r}{S_1 S} = \frac{ut}{vt} = \frac{u}{v}.$$

9P

Use the law of refraction: $\sin\theta/\sin 30° = v_s/v_d$. So

$$\theta = \sin^{-1}\left(\frac{v_s \sin 30°}{v_d}\right) = \sin^{-1}\left[\frac{(3.0 \text{ m/s})\sin 30°}{4.0 \text{ m/s}}\right] = 22°.$$

The angle of incidence is gradually reduced due to refraction, such as shown in the calculation above. This is why most waves come in normal to a shore ($\theta \approx 0°$).

10P

(a) The time t_2 it takes for pulse 2 to travel through the plastic is

$$t_2 = \frac{L}{c/1.55} + \frac{L}{c/1.70} + \frac{L}{c/1.60} + \frac{L}{c/1.40} = \frac{6.25L}{c}.$$

Similarly for pulse 1

$$t_1 = \frac{2L}{c/1.59} + \frac{L}{c/1.65} + \frac{L}{c/1.50} = \frac{6.33L}{c}.$$

So pulse 2 travels through the plastic in a shorter time.

(b)

$$\Delta t = t_2 - t_1 = 6.33L/c - 6.25L/c = 0.08L/c.$$

11P

(a) Take the phases of both waves to be zero at the front surfaces of the layers. The phase of the first wave at the back surface of the glass is given by $\phi_1 = k_1 L - \omega t$, where k_1 $(= 2\pi/\lambda_1)$ is the angular wave number and λ_1 is the wavelength in glass. Similarly, the phase of the second wave at the back surface of the plastic is given by $\phi_2 = k_2 L - \omega t$, where k_2 $(= 2\pi/\lambda_2)$ is the angular wave number and λ_2 is the wavelength in plastic. The angular frequencies are the same since the waves have the same wavelength in air and the frequency of a wave does not change when the wave enters another medium. The phase difference is

$$\phi_1 - \phi_2 = (k_1 - k_2)L = 2\pi \left(\frac{1}{\lambda_1} - \frac{1}{\lambda_2} \right) L.$$

Now $\lambda_1 = \lambda_{air}/n_1$, where λ_{air} is the wavelength in air and n_1 is the index of refraction of the glass. Similarly $\lambda_2 = \lambda_{air}/n_2$, where n_2 is the index of refraction of the plastic. This means that the phase difference is $\phi_1 - \phi_2 = (2\pi/\lambda_{air})(n_1 - n_2)L$. The value of L that makes this 5.65 rad is

$$L = \frac{(\phi_1 - \phi_2)\lambda_{air}}{2\pi(n_1 - n_2)} = \frac{5.65(400 \times 10^{-9}\,\text{m})}{2\pi(1.60 - 1.50)} = 3.60 \times 10^{-6}\,\text{m}.$$

(b) 5.65 rad is less than 2π rad $(= 6.28\,\text{rad})$, the phase difference for completely constructive interference, and greater than π rad $(= 3.14\,\text{rad})$, the phase difference for completely destructive interference. The interference is therefore intermediate, neither completely constructive nor completely destructive. It is, however, closer to completely constructive than to completely destructive.

12P

Use

$$\Delta\phi = \omega\Delta t = \left(\frac{2\pi}{t}\right)\left(\frac{L}{v_1} - \frac{L}{v_2}\right) = \frac{2\pi}{T}\left(\frac{L}{c/n_1} - \frac{L}{c/n_2}\right)$$

$$= \frac{2\pi L}{\lambda}(n_1 - n_2).$$

(a)

$$\frac{\Delta\phi_a}{2\pi} = \frac{(8.50 \times 10^{-6}\,\text{m})}{500 \times 10^{-9}\,\text{m}}(1.50 - 1.60) = -1.70.$$

(b)

$$\frac{\Delta\phi_b}{2\pi} = \frac{(8.50 \times 10^{-6}\,\text{m})}{500 \times 10^{-9}\,\text{m}}(1.62 - 1.72) = -1.70.$$

(c)

$$\frac{\Delta\phi_c}{2\pi} = \frac{(3.25 \times 10^{-6}\,\text{m})}{500 \times 10^{-9}\,\text{m}}(1.59 - 1.79) = -1.30.$$

(d) Since $\Delta\phi_a = \Delta\phi_b$ the brightness must be the same for (a) and (b). As for (c) since $\Delta\phi_c/2\pi$ and $\Delta\phi_a/2\pi$ each differs from an integer by 0.30, the brightness in case (c) is also the same as that in (a) and (b).

13P

(a) Use the formula obtained in Problem 12. Let

$$\Delta\phi = \frac{2\pi L}{\lambda}|n_1 - n_2| = (2n + 1)\pi \qquad (n = 0, 1, 2, \cdots)$$

we get

$$L_{\text{min}} = L|_{n=0} = \frac{\lambda}{2|n_1 - n_2|} = \frac{620\,\text{nm}}{2|1.45 - 1.65|} = 1550\,\text{nm} = 1.55\mu\text{m}.$$

(b) For the next smallest one $n = 1$, so

$$L_1 = \frac{3\lambda}{2|n_1 - n_2|} = 3(1.55\mu\text{m}) = 4.65\mu\text{m}.$$

14P

(a)

$$\Delta\phi = \omega\Delta t = \frac{2\pi}{T}\left(\frac{L_1}{c/n_1} - \frac{L_2}{c/n_2}\right) = \frac{2\pi}{\lambda}(n_1 L_1 - n_2 L_2)$$

$$= \frac{2\pi}{600.0 \times 10^{-9}\,\text{m}}\left[(1.40)(4.00 \times 10^{-6}\,\text{m}) - (1.60)(3.50 \times 10^{-6}\,\text{m})\right]$$

$$= 0.$$

(b) Constructive interference, since $\Delta\phi = 0$.

15E
Use Eq. 40-12 with $m = 3$:
(a)
$$\theta = \sin^{-1}\left(\frac{m\lambda}{d}\right) = \sin^{-1}\left[\frac{2(550 \times 10^{-9}\,\text{m})}{7.70 \times 10^{-6}\,\text{m}}\right] = 0.216\,\text{rad}.$$
(b) $\theta = (0.216\,\text{rad})(180°/\pi\,\text{rad}) = 12.4°$.

16E
For the first dark fringe $\Delta\phi_1 = \pm\pi$, and for the second one $\Delta\phi_2 = \pm 3\pi$, etc. For the mth one $\Delta\phi_m = \pm(2m + 1)\pi$.

17E
In Fig. 40-9 (a) $\sin\theta \approx y/D$ so the fringe separation (say, between adjacent bright fringes) is
$$\Delta y = \Delta(D\sin\theta) = D\Delta\sin\theta = D\Delta\left(\frac{m\lambda}{d}\right) = \frac{D\lambda}{d}\Delta m = \frac{D\lambda}{d},$$
where we used Eq. 40-12. So to keep $\Delta y \propto D/d$ a constant we need to double D if d is doubled.

18E
The condition for a maximum in the two-slit interference pattern is $d\sin\theta = m\lambda$, where d is the slit separation, λ is the wavelength, m is an integer, and θ is the angle made by the interfering rays with the forward direction. If θ is small, $\sin\theta$ may be approximated by θ in radians. Then $d\theta = m\lambda$ and the angular separation of adjacent maxima, one associated with the integer m and the other associated with the integer $m + 1$, is given by $\Delta\theta = \lambda/d$. The separation on a screen a distance D away is given by $\Delta y = D\,\Delta\theta = \lambda D/d$. Thus

$$\Delta y = \frac{(500 \times 10^{-9}\,\text{m})(5.40\,\text{m})}{1.20 \times 10^{-3}\,\text{m}} = 2.25 \times 10^{-3}\,\text{m} = 2.25\,\text{mm}.$$

19E
In the case of a distant screen $\sin\theta \approx \theta$ so from Eq. 40-12

$$\Delta\theta \approx \Delta\sin\theta = \Delta\left(\frac{m\lambda}{d}\right) = \frac{\lambda}{d}\Delta m = \frac{\lambda}{d},$$

or $d \approx \lambda/\Delta\theta = 589 \times 10^{-9}\,\text{m}/0.018\,\text{rad} = 3.3 \times 10^{-5}\,\text{m} = 33\mu\text{m}$.

20E

The angular positions of the maxima of a two-slit interference pattern are given by $d \sin \theta = m\lambda$, where d is the slit separation, λ is the wavelength, and m is an integer. If θ is small, $\sin \theta$ may be approximated by θ in radians. Then $d\theta = m\lambda$. The angular separation of two adjacent maxima is $\Delta\theta = \lambda/d$. Let λ' be the wavelength for which the angular separation is 10.0% greater. Then $1.10\lambda/d = \lambda'/d$ or $\lambda' = 1.10\lambda = 1.10(589\,\text{nm}) = 648\,\text{nm}$.

21E

(a) For the maximum adjacent to the central one we have $m = 1$, so

$$\theta_1 = \sin^{-1}\left(\frac{m\lambda}{d}\right)\bigg|_{m=1} = \sin^{-1}\left[\frac{(1)(\lambda)}{100\lambda}\right] = 0.010\,\text{rad}.$$

(b) Since $y_1 = D \sin \theta_1 = (50.0\,\text{cm}) \sin(0.010\,\text{rad}) = 5.0\,\text{mm}$, the separation is $\Delta y = y_1 - y_0 = y_1 - 0 = 5.0\,\text{mm}$.

22E

For the fifth maximum $y_5 = D \sin \theta_5 = D(4\lambda/d)$, and for the seventh minimum $y_7' = D \sin \theta_7' = D[(7 + 1/2)\lambda/d]$. So

$$\Delta y = y_7' - y_5 = \frac{D(7 + 1/2)\lambda}{d} - D\left(\frac{4\lambda}{d}\right) = \frac{3\lambda D}{2d}$$

$$= \frac{3(546 \times 10^{-9}\,\text{m})(20 \times 10^{-2}\,\text{m})}{2(0.10 \times 10^{-3}\,\text{m})} = 1.6 \times 10^{-3}\,\text{m} = 1.6\,\text{mm}.$$

23E

From $\Delta\theta = \lambda/d$ which is obtained in Exercise 19 we have, in our case,

$$\Delta\theta' = \frac{\lambda'}{d} = \frac{v/f}{d} = \frac{(c/f)/n}{d} = \frac{\lambda}{nd} = \frac{\Delta\theta}{n} = \frac{0.20°}{1.33} = 0.15°.$$

24P

The maxima of a two-slit interference pattern are at angles θ given by $d \sin \theta = m\lambda$, where d is the slit separation, λ is the wavelength, and m is an integer. If θ is small, $\sin \theta$ may be replaced by θ in radians. Then $d\theta = m\lambda$. The angular separation of two maxima associated with different wavelengths but the same value of m is $\Delta\theta = (m/d)(\lambda_2 - \lambda_1)$ and the separation on a screen a distance D away is

$$\Delta y = D \tan \Delta\theta \approx D \Delta\theta = \left[\frac{mD}{d}\right](\lambda_2 - \lambda_1)$$

$$= \left[\frac{3(1.0\,\text{m})}{5.0 \times 10^{-3}\,\text{m}}\right](600 \times 10^{-9}\,\text{m} - 480 \times 10^{-9}\,\text{m}) = 7.2 \times 10^{-5}\,\text{m}.$$

The small angle approximation $\tan \Delta\theta \approx \Delta\theta$ was made. $\Delta\theta$ must be in radians.

25P

The separation between adjacent maxima is obtained in Exercise 17: $\Delta y = D\lambda/d = (D/d)(v/f)$. Solve for f:

$$f = \frac{Dv}{d\Delta y} = \frac{(2.00\,\text{m})(25.0 \times 10^{-2}\,\text{m/s})}{(120 \times 10^{-3}\,\text{m})(180 \times 10^{-3}\,\text{m})} = 23.1\,\text{Hz}.$$

26P

For the first maximum $m = 0$ and for the tenth one $m = 9$. So the separation is $\Delta y = (D\lambda/d)\Delta m = 9D\lambda/d$. Solve for λ:

$$\lambda = \frac{d\Delta y}{9D} = \frac{(0.15 \times 10^{-3}\,\text{m})(18 \times 10^{-3}\,\text{m})}{9(50 \times 10^{-2}\,\text{m})} = 6.0 \times 10^{-7}\,\text{m} = 600\,\text{nm}.$$

27P

Let the distance in question be x. Then

$$|\Delta\phi_{AB}| = |\phi_B - \phi_A| = \frac{2\pi}{\lambda}\left(\sqrt{d^2 + x_m^2} - x_m\right) = (2m + 1)\pi,$$

where $m = 0, 1, 2, \cdots$. Solve for x:

$$x_m = \frac{d^2}{(2m+1)\lambda} - \frac{(2m+1)\lambda}{4}.$$

For the largest value of x_m let $m = 0$, we find

$$x_c = \frac{d^2}{\lambda} - \frac{\lambda}{4} = \frac{(3.00\lambda)^2}{\lambda} - \frac{\lambda}{4} = 8.75\lambda.$$

28P

Consider the two waves, one from each slit, that produce the seventh bright fringe in the absence of the mica. They are in phase at the slits and travel different distances to the seventh bright fringe, where they are out of phase by $2\pi m = 14\pi$. Now a piece of mica with thickness x is placed in front of one of the slits and the waves are no longer in phase at the slits. In fact, their phases at the slits differ by

$$\frac{2\pi x}{\lambda_m} - \frac{2\pi x}{\lambda} = \frac{2\pi x}{\lambda}(n - 1),$$

where λ_m is the wavelength in the mica and n is the index of refraction of the mica. The relationship $\lambda_m = \lambda/n$ was used to substitute for λ_m. Since the waves are now in phase at the screen

$$\frac{2\pi x}{\lambda}(n-1) = 14\pi$$

or

$$x = \frac{7\lambda}{n-1} = \frac{7(550 \times 10^{-9}\,\text{m})}{1.58 - 1} = 6.64 \times 10^{-6}\,\text{m}.$$

29P
The figure to the right shows a part of the distribution of interference maxima in a plane containing the two point sources P_1 and P_2. Each of the hyperbolic curves labeled with various values of m corresponds to a specific line of maxima. For example $P_1 P - P_2 P = \lambda$. The full three-dimensional picture is obtained by rotating this figure about the line $P_1 P_2$.

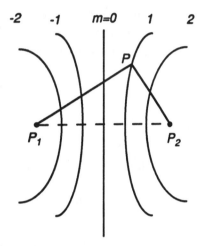

30P
Interference maxima occur at angles θ such that $d \sin \theta = m\lambda$, where d is the separation of the sources, λ is the wavelength, and m is an integer. Since $d = 2.0\,\text{m}$ and $\lambda = 0.50\,\text{m}$, this means that $\sin \theta = 0.25m$. You want all values of m (positive and negative) for which $|0.25m| \leq 1$. These are -4, -3, -2, -1, 0, $+1$, $+2$, $+3$, and $+4$. For each of these except -4 and $+4$ there are 2 different values for θ. A single value of θ $(-90°)$ is associated with $m = -4$ and a single value $(-90°)$ is associated with $m = +4$. There are 16 different angles in all and therefore 16 maxima.

31P
Let the thickness of meca be t, then

$$\Delta\phi = 2m\pi = \Delta(kt) = \Delta\left(\frac{2\pi t}{\lambda}\right) = \frac{2\pi t}{\lambda}(n-1),$$

where we used $\Delta\lambda^{-1} = (\lambda')^{-1} - \lambda^{-1} = n/\lambda - \lambda^{-1}$. Solve for L:

$$t = \frac{m\lambda}{n-1} = \frac{(30)(480\,\text{nm})}{1.6 - 1} = 2.4 \times 10^4\,\text{nm} = 24\mu\text{m}.$$

32P

(a) Use $\Delta y = D\lambda/d$ (see Exercise 17) to solve for d:

$$d = \frac{D\lambda}{\Delta y} = \frac{2(20.0\,\text{m})(632.8\,\text{nm})}{10.0\,\text{cm}} = 0.253\,\text{mm}.$$

(b) In this case the interference pattern will be shifted. For example, since at the location of the original central maximum the phase difference is now $\Delta\phi = \Delta(kL) = k\Delta L = (2\pi/\lambda)(2.50\lambda) = 5.0\pi$, there will be a minimum instead of a maximum.

33P

Use the result of Problem 31. Now

$$|\Delta\phi| = |\Delta\phi_1 - \Delta\phi_2| = \left| \frac{2\pi t}{\lambda}(n_1 - 1) - \frac{2\pi t}{\lambda}(n_2 - 1) \right|$$

$$= 2m\pi,$$

so

$$t = \frac{m\lambda}{|n_1 - n_2|} = \frac{5(480\,\text{nm})}{|1.7 - 1.4|} = 8.0 \times 10^3\,\text{nm} = 8.0\mu\text{m}.$$

34P

Let the $m = 10$ bright fringe on the screen be a distance y from the central maximum. Then from Fig. 40-9 (a)

$$r_1 - r_2 = \sqrt{(y + d/2)^2 + D^2} - \sqrt{(y - d/2)^2 + D^2} = 10\lambda.$$

To the order of $(d/D)^2$, we find

$$y = y_0 + \frac{y(y^2 + d^2/4)}{2D^2},$$

where $y_0 = 10D\lambda/d$. Let $y \simeq y_0$ and we find the percentage error to be

$$\alpha \simeq \frac{y_0(y_0^2 + d^2/4)}{2D^2 y_0} = \frac{1}{2}\left(\frac{10\lambda}{D}\right)^2 + \frac{1}{8}\left(\frac{d}{D}\right)^2$$

$$= \frac{1}{2}\left(\frac{5.89\mu\text{m}}{2000\mu\text{m}}\right)^2 + \frac{1}{8}\left(\frac{2.0\,\text{mm}}{40\,\text{mm}}\right)^2 = 0.03\%.$$

35P
For constant phase difference

$$\Delta\phi = k(r_1 - r_2) = \frac{2\pi}{\lambda}(r_1 - r_2),$$

so $r_1 - r_2 = \lambda\Delta\phi/2\pi = $ const., i.e. the curve is a hyperbola.

36E
The phasor is shown to the right. For the resultant phasor

$$A_x = A_2 \cos 30° + A_1 + A_3 \cos 45°$$
$$= 15 \cos 30° + 10 + 5 \cos 45°$$
$$= 26.5$$

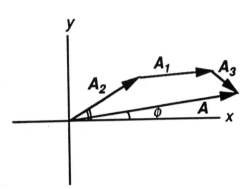

and

$$A_y = A_2 \sin 30° - A_3 \sin 45°$$
$$= 15 \sin 30° - 5 \sin 45°$$
$$= 3.96.$$

Thus

$$\phi = \tan^{-1}\left(\frac{A_y}{A_x}\right) = \tan^{-1}\left(\frac{3.96}{26.5}\right) = 8.5°,$$

and

$$y = A \sin(\omega t + \phi) = \sqrt{A_x^2 + A_y^2}\, \sin(\omega t + \phi)$$
$$= \sqrt{(26.5)^2 + (3.96)^2}\, \sin(\omega t + 8.5°)$$
$$= 27 \sin(\omega t + 8.5°).$$

37E
Use $\phi = kr - \omega t + \phi_0$. Now

$$\Delta\phi = \phi_A - \phi_B = -90° + k\Delta r = 90° + \frac{2\pi}{\lambda}(r_A - r_B)$$
$$= -90° + 360°\left(\frac{100\,\text{m}}{400\,\text{m}}\right) = 0°.$$

The angular separation $\Delta\theta$ between adjacent maxima satisfies

$$\Delta(d\sin\theta) \approx \Delta(d\theta) = d\Delta\theta = \Delta(m\lambda) = \lambda\Delta m = \lambda,$$

or

$$\Delta\theta \approx \frac{\lambda}{d} = \frac{600\,\text{nm}}{0.60\,\text{mm}} = 0.0010\,\text{rad}.$$

The intensity pattern is as shown.

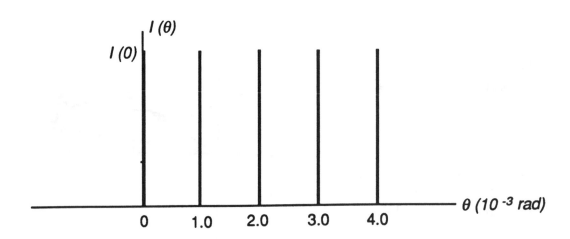

39P

The phasor diagram is shown to the right. Here $E_1 = 1.00$, $E_2 = 2.00$, and $\phi = 60°$. The resultant amplitude E_m is given by the trigonometric law of cosines:

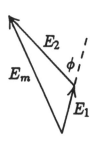

$$E_m^2 = E_1^2 + E_2^2 - 2E_1E_2\cos(180° - \phi),$$

so

$$E_m = \sqrt{(1.00)^2 + (2.00)^2 - 2(1.00)(2.00)\cos 120°} = 2.65.$$

40P

(a) To get to the detector the wave from A travels a distance x and the wave from B travels a distance $\sqrt{d^2 + x^2}$. The difference in phase of the two waves is

$$\Delta\phi = \frac{2\pi}{\lambda}\left[\sqrt{d^2 + x^2} - x\right],$$

where λ is the wavelength. For a maximum in intensity this must be a multiple of 2π. Solve

$$\sqrt{d^2 + x^2} - x = m\lambda$$

for x. Here m is an integer. Write the equation as $\sqrt{d^2 + x^2} = x + m\lambda$, then square both sides to obtain $d^2 + x^2 = x^2 + m^2\lambda^2 + 2m\lambda x$. The solution is

$$x = \frac{d^2 - m^2\lambda^2}{2m\lambda}.$$

The largest value of m that produces a positive value for x is $m = 3$. This corresponds to the maximum that is nearest A, at

$$x = \frac{(4.00\,\text{m})^2 - 9(1.00\,\text{m})^2}{(2)(3)(1.00\,\text{m})} = 1.17\,\text{m}.$$

For the next maximum $m = 2$ and $x = 3.00\,\text{m}$. For the third maximum $m = 1$ and $x = 7.50\,\text{m}$.

(b) Minima in intensity occur where the phase difference is π rad; the intensity at a minimum, however, is not zero because the amplitudes of the waves are different. Although the amplitudes are the same at the sources, the waves travel different distances to get to the points of minimum intensity and each amplitude decreases in inverse proportion to the distance traveled.

41P

See the phasor diagram to the right. We have $y = A\sin(\omega t + \phi)$, where

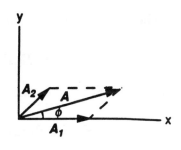

$$A = \sqrt{A_x^2 + A_y^2} = \sqrt{(A_2\cos 30° + A_1)^2 + (A_2\sin 30°)^2}$$
$$= \sqrt{(8.0\cos 30° + 10)^2 + (8.0\sin 30°)^2}$$
$$= 17$$

and

$$\phi = \tan^{-1}\left(\frac{A_y}{A_x}\right) = \tan^{-1}\left(\frac{8.0\sin 30°}{8.0\cos 30° + 10}\right) = 13°.$$

Thus $y = y_1 + y_2 = A\sin(\omega t + \phi) = 17\cos(\omega t + 13°)$.

42P

According to Eqs. 40–18 and 40–19, the intensity is given by

$$I = 4I_0\cos^2(\phi/2),$$

1001

where

$$\phi = \left(\frac{2\pi d}{\lambda}\right)\sin\theta.$$

Here d is the slit separation and λ is the wavelength. The intensity at the center of the interference pattern is $4I_0$, so you want the value of θ for which $I = 2I_0$. First solve $2I_0 = 4I_0\cos^2(\frac{1}{2}\phi)$ for ϕ:

$$\phi = 2\cos^{-1}\left(\frac{1}{\sqrt{2}}\right) = \frac{\pi}{2}\,\text{rad}.$$

Now solve

$$\frac{\pi}{2} = \left(\frac{2\pi d}{\lambda}\right)\sin\theta$$

for θ. Since θ is small, $\sin\theta \approx \theta$, provided θ is measured in radians. Then

$$\frac{\pi}{2} = \frac{2\pi d\theta}{\lambda}$$

and

$$\theta = \frac{\lambda}{4d}.$$

Another point of half intensity, at $\theta = -\lambda/4d$, is symmetrically placed relative to the central point of the pattern, so the width of the pattern at half intensity is $2(\lambda/4d) = \lambda/2d$.

43P*
Take the electric field of one wave, at the screen, to be

$$E_1 = E_0\sin(\omega t)$$

and the electric field of the other to be

$$E_2 = 2E_0\sin(\omega t + \phi),$$

where the phase difference is given by

$$\phi = \left(\frac{2\pi d}{\lambda}\right)\sin\theta.$$

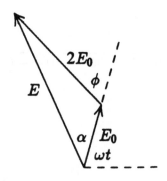

Here d is the center-to-center slit separation and λ is the wavelength. The resultant wave can be written $E = E_1 + E_2 = E\sin(\omega t + \alpha)$, where α is a phase constant. The phasor diagram is shown above.

The resultant amplitude E is given by the trigonometric law of cosines:

$$E^2 = E_0^2 + (2E_0)^2 - 4E_0^2\cos(180° - \phi) = E_0^2(5 + 4\cos\phi).$$

The intensity is given by $I = I_0(5 + 4\cos\phi)$, where I_0 is the intensity that would be produced by the first wave if the second were not present. Since $\cos\phi = 2\cos^2(\phi/2) - 1$, this may also be written $I = I_0\left[1 + 8\cos^2(\phi/2)\right]$.

44E
Let $\Delta\phi = k(2L) = (2\pi/\lambda)(2L) = \pi$ and solve for L: $L = \lambda/4$.

45E
Now $\Delta\phi = \pi + k(2L) = \pi + (2\pi/\lambda)(2L) = 2m\pi$ so

$$L = \frac{(2m-1)}{4\lambda}, \qquad m = 1, 2, 3, \cdots$$

46E
Since the thickness of the air layer is much less than λ we only need to consider the possible phase difference due to the reflection on the two boundaries.
(a) Since $n_1 > n_{\text{air}}$ there is a π-phase shift upon reflection off the lower boundary. So the two reflected light rays from the two boundaries are almost out of phase, so the lignt reflected is approximately eliminated.
(b) Since $n_2 > n_{\text{air}}$ there is only a π-phase shift upon reflection off the upper boundary so again the lignt reflected is approxmately eliminated.
(c) Now there is only a π-phase shift upon reflection off the lower boundary so again the lignt reflected is approxmately eliminated.
(d) Now there is only a π-phase shift upon reflection off the lower boundary so again the lignt reflected is approxmately eliminated.

47E
The wave reflected from the front surface suffers a phase change of π rad since it is incident in air on a medium of higher index of refraction. The phase of the wave reflected from the back surface does not change on reflection since the medium beyond the soap film is air and has a lower index of refraction than the film. If L is the thickness of the film this wave travels a distance $2L$ further than the wave reflected from the front surface. The phase difference of the two waves is $2L(2\pi/\lambda_f) + \pi$, where λ_f is the wavelength in the film. If λ is the wavelength in vacuum and n is the index of refraction of the soap film, then $\lambda_f = \lambda/n$ and the phase difference is

$$2nL\left(\frac{2\pi}{\lambda}\right) + \pi = 2(1.33)(1.21 \times 10^{-6}\,\text{m})\left(\frac{2\pi}{585 \times 10^{-9}\,\text{m}}\right) + \pi = 12\pi\,\text{rad}.$$

Since the phase difference is an even multiple of π the interference is completely constructive.

48E

For constructive interference, use Eq. 40-27: $2n_2L = (m+1/2)\lambda$. For the two smallest valuses of L let $m = 0$ and 1:

$$L_0 = \frac{\lambda/2}{2n_2} = \frac{624\,\text{nm}}{4(1.33)} = 117\,\text{nm} = 0.117\mu\text{m},$$

$$L_1 = \frac{(1+1/2)\lambda}{2n_2} = \frac{3\lambda}{2n_2} = 3L_0 = 3(0.117\mu\text{m}) = 0.352\mu\text{m}.$$

49E

Since the lens has a greater index of refraction than the film there is a π-phase shift upon reflecting off the lens-film boundary, which cancels with the π-phase shift due to the reflection off the film-air boundary. Therefore the condition for destructive interference is $2n_2L = (n+1/2)\lambda$. For the smallest value of L let $m = 0$:

$$L_{\min} = \frac{\lambda}{4n_2} = \frac{680\,\text{nm}}{4(1.30)} = 131\,\text{nm} = 0.131\mu\text{m}.$$

50E

Use the formula obtained in Exercise 49:

$$L_{\min} = \frac{\lambda}{4n_2} = \frac{\lambda}{4(1.25)} = \frac{\lambda}{5}.$$

51E

Use Eq. 40-27 for constructive interference: $2n_2L = (m+1/2)\lambda$, or

$$\lambda = \frac{2n_2L}{m+1/2} = \frac{2(1.50)(410\,\text{nm})}{m+1/2} = \frac{1230\,\text{nm}}{m+1/2}.$$

The only value of m which corresponds to a wavelength which falls within the visible light range is $m = 1$, so

$$\lambda = \frac{1230\,\text{nm}}{1+1/2} = 492\,\text{nm}.$$

52E

Light reflected from the front surface of the coating suffers a phase change of π rad while light reflected from the back surface does not change phase. If L is the thickness of the coating, light reflected from the back surface travels a distance $2L$ further than light reflected from the front surface. The difference in phase of the two waves is $2L(2\pi/\lambda_c) - \pi$, where λ_c is the wavelength in the coating. If λ is the wavelength in vacuum, then $\lambda_c = \lambda/n$, where n is the index of refraction of the coating. Thus the phase difference is $2nL(2\pi/\lambda) - \pi$. For fully constructive interference this should be a multiple of 2π. Solve

$$2nL\left(\frac{2\pi}{\lambda}\right) - \pi = 2m\pi$$

for L. Here m is an integer. This equation is a slightly rearranged version of Eq. 40–27. The solution is

$$L = \frac{(2m+1)\lambda}{4n}.$$

To find the smallest coating thickness, take $m = 0$. Then

$$L = \frac{\lambda}{4n} = \frac{560 \times 10^{-9}\,\text{m}}{4(2.00)} = 7.00 \times 10^{-8}\,\text{m}.$$

53E

For complete destructive interference, you want the waves reflected from the front and back of the coating to differ in phase by an odd multiple of π rad. Each wave is incident on a medium of higher index of refraction from a medium of lower index, so both suffer phase changes of π rad on reflection. If L is the thickness of the coating, the wave reflected from the back surface travels a distance $2L$ further than the wave reflected from the front. The phase difference is $2L(2\pi/\lambda_c)$, where λ_c is the wavelength in the coating. If n is the index of refraction of the coating, $\lambda_c = \lambda/n$, where λ is the wavelength in vacuum, and the phase difference is $2nL(2\pi/\lambda)$. Solve

$$2nL\left(\frac{2\pi}{\lambda}\right) = (2m+1)\pi$$

for L. Here m is an integer. The result is

$$L = \frac{(2m+1)\lambda}{4n}.$$

To find the least thickness for which destructive interference occurs, take $m = 0$. Then

$$L = \frac{\lambda}{4n} = \frac{600 \times 10^{-9}\,\text{m}}{4(1.25)} = 1.2 \times 10^{-7}\,\text{m}.$$

1005

54P

Let the thickness of the structure at a certain section be $t = \alpha L$. The condition for constructive interference is

$$t = \alpha L = \frac{(m+1/2)\lambda}{2n_2},$$

or

$$\alpha = \frac{(m+1/2)\lambda}{2n_2 L} = \frac{(m+1/2)(600\,\text{nm})}{2(1.50)(4.00 \times 10^3\,\text{nm})} = \frac{2m+1}{40},$$

where $m = 0, 1, 2 \cdots$. You can check that no values of m would produce any of the values of α (1, 2, 1/2, 3 and 1/10) given. So none of the sections will provide the right thickness for constructive interference.

55P

If the expression $m\lambda = 2Ln_2$ gives the condition for constructive interferene then there should be no net π-phase shift upon the two reflections off the film-media boundary. This requires that either $n_2 > n_1$ and $n_2 > n_3$, or $n_2 < n_1$ and $n_2 < n_3$. Here n_1, n_3 are the indices of refraction for the upper and lower medium, respectively. You can easily check that this condition is satisfied in case (a) and (c).

56P

(a) In this case there are π-phase shifts for both of the waves reflected, so there is no net π-phase shift, thus $m\lambda = 2Ln_2$. Solve for λ:

$$\lambda = \frac{2Ln_2}{m} = \frac{2(460\,\text{nm})(1.20)}{m} = \frac{1104\,\text{nm}}{m}.$$

In the visible light range the only possible value for m is 2, so $\lambda = 1104\,\text{nm}/2 = 552\,\text{nm}$.
(b) Now there is a π-phase shift upon reflection off the kerosen-air boundary but no π-phase shift off the water-kerosen boundary. So a net π-phase shift is present, and for constructive interference

$$\lambda = \frac{2Ln_2}{m+1/2} = \frac{2(460\,\text{nm})(1.20)}{m+1/2} = \frac{1104\,\text{nm}}{m+1/2}.$$

In the visible light range m can only be 2, in which case $\lambda = 1104\,\text{nm}/(1+1/2) = 442\,\text{nm}$.

57P

There is no net π-phase shift in this case so for constructive interference $\lambda = 2Ln_2/m$, i.e.

$$\begin{cases} \lambda_1 = 700\,\text{nm} = \dfrac{2Ln_2}{m_1} \\ \lambda_2 = 500\,\text{nm} = \dfrac{2Ln_2}{m_1+1}. \end{cases}$$

Solve for L:

$$L = \frac{\lambda_1 \lambda_2}{2n_2(\lambda_1 - \lambda_2)} = \frac{(700\,\text{nm})(500\,\text{nm})}{2(1.30)(700\,\text{nm} - 500\,\text{nm})} = 673\,\text{nm}.$$

58P
For the maximum at $\lambda_1 = 600\,\text{nm}$ we have

$$\lambda_1 = 600\,\text{nm} = \frac{2Ln_2}{m_1 + 1/2}.$$

For the minimum at $\lambda_2 = 450\,\text{nm}$ we have

$$\lambda_2 = 450\,\text{nm} = \frac{2Ln_2}{m_2} = \frac{2Ln_2}{m_1 + 1}.$$

Solve for L:

$$L = \frac{\lambda_1 \lambda_2}{4n_2(\lambda_1 - \lambda_2)} = \frac{(600\,\text{nm})(450\,\text{nm})}{4(1.30)(600\,\text{nm} - 450\,\text{nm})} = 338\,\text{nm}.$$

59P
(a) In this case there is no π-phase shift (see Problem 55) and the condition for constructive interference is $m\lambda = 2Ln_2$. Solve for L:

$$L = \frac{m\lambda}{2n_2} = \frac{m(525\,\text{nm})}{2(1.55)} = (169\,\text{nm})m.$$

For the minimum value of L we let $m = 1$ and obtain $L_{\min} = 169\,\text{nm}$.
(b) The light of wavelength λ that would be preferentially transmitted satisfies $m'\lambda = 2n_2 L$, or

$$\lambda = \frac{2n_2 L}{m'} = \frac{2(1.55)(169\,\text{nm})}{m'} = \frac{525\,\text{nm}}{m'}.$$

Since $m' = 1, 2, 3, \cdots$, no values of m' will give a value of λ which falls into the visible light range except for $m' = 1$, which corresponds to the green light.
(c) For a sharp reduction of transmission let

$$\lambda = \frac{2n_2 L}{m' + 1/2} = \frac{525\,\text{nm}}{m' + 1/2},$$

where $m' = 0, 1, 2, 3, \cdots$. In the visible light range the only possible value for m' is $m' = 1$ and $\lambda = 350\,\text{nm}$. This correspouds to the blue-violet light.

60P
Light reflected from the upper oil surface (in contact with air) changes phase by π rad. Light reflected from the lower surface (in contact with glass) changes phase by π rad if the index of refraction of the oil is less than that of the glass and does not change phase if the index of refraction of the oil is greater than that of the glass.

First suppose the index of refraction of the oil is greater than the index of refraction of the glass. The condition for fully destructive interference is $2n_od = m\lambda$, where d is the thickness of the oil film, n_o is the index of refraction of the oil, λ is the wavelength in vacuum, and m is an integer. For the shorter wavelength $2n_od = m_1\lambda_1$ and for the longer $2n_od = m_2\lambda_2$. Since λ_1 is less than λ_2, m_1 is greater than m_2 and since fully destructive interference does not occur for any wavelengths between, $m_1 = m_2 + 1$. Solve $(m_2 + 1)\lambda_1 = m_2\lambda_2$ for m_2. The result is

$$m_2 = \frac{\lambda_1}{\lambda_2 - \lambda_1} = \frac{500\,\text{nm}}{700\,\text{nm} - 500\,\text{nm}} = 2.50\,.$$

Since m_2 must be an integer the oil cannot have an index of refraction that is greater than that of the glass.

Now suppose the index of refraction of the oil is less than that of the glass. The condition for fully destructive interference is then $2n_od = (2m + 1)\lambda$. For the shorter wavelength $2m_od = (2m_1 + 1)\lambda_1$ and for the longer $2n_od = (2m_2 + 1)\lambda_2$. Again $m_1 = m_2 + 1$, so $(2m_2 + 3)\lambda_1 = (2m_2 + 1)\lambda_2$. This means the value of m_2 is

$$m_2 = \frac{3\lambda_1 - \lambda_2}{2(\lambda_2 - \lambda_1)} = \frac{3(500\,\text{nm}) - 700\,\text{nm}}{2(700\,\text{nm} - 500\,\text{nm})} = 2.00\,.$$

This is an integer. Thus the index of refraction of the oil is less than that of the glass.

61P
In this case there is a π-phase shift (see Problem 55). So for destructive interference at $\lambda_1 = 600\,\text{nm}$ we have $m_1\lambda_1 = 2n_2L$, and for constructive interference at $\lambda_2 = 700\,\text{nm}$ we have $(m_2 + 1/2)\lambda_2 = 2n_2L$. Thus $(m_2 + 1/2)\lambda_2 = m_1\lambda_1$, which gives

$$\frac{m_2 + 1/2}{m_1} = \frac{\lambda_1}{\lambda_2} = \frac{700\,\text{nm}}{600\,\text{nm}} = \frac{7}{6}\,.$$

This gives $m_1 = m_2 = 3$. Thus

$$L = \frac{m_1\lambda_1}{2n_2} = \frac{3(700\,\text{nm})}{2(1.25)} = 840\,\text{nm} = 0.840\,\mu\text{m}.$$

62P
Since the index of refraction of water is greater than that of the oil, which in turn is greater than that of air, both the wave reflected from the upper surface of the oil drop and the wave reflected from the lower surface undergo phase changes of π rad on reflection. At a place where the thickness of the drop is L the condition for a bright fringe is $2nL = m\lambda$ and the condition for a dark fringe is $2nL = (m + \frac{1}{2})\lambda$, where λ is the wavelength in vacuum, n is the index of refraction of the oil, and m is an integer. Near the rim of the drop, where $L < \lambda/4$, only the condition for a bright fringe (with $m = 0$) can be met, so the rim is bright.

1008

(b) Take λ to be 475 nm and m to be 3. Then

$$L = \frac{3\lambda}{2n} = \frac{3(475\,\text{nm})}{2(1.20)} = 594\,\text{nm}.$$

(c) At places where the drop is thick, fractionally small variations in thickness from place to place may amount to variations of many wavelengths. The fringes are quite close together and cannot be distinguished by an unaided eye.

63P

You can check easily that the condition for no net π-phase shift in the transmitted light is $n_2 > n_1, n_3$ or $n_2 < n_1, n_3$, and that in the reflected light is $n_1 < n_2 < n_3$ or $n_3 < n_2 < n_1$.
(a) There is no net π-phase shift for transmission in this case so for maximum transmission $m\lambda = 2n_2 L$, or $L_{\text{min}} = \lambda/2n_2$.
(b) There is no net π-phase shift for reflection so for minimum reflection $(m+1/2)\lambda = 2n_2 L$, or $L_{\text{min}} = \lambda/4n_2$.
(c) Now $m\lambda = 2n_2 L$ for maximum reflection, or $L_{\text{min}} = \lambda/2n_2$.

64P

Use Eq. 40-18: $I = I_{\text{max}} = \cos^2(\phi/2)$ where $\phi = k(2n_2 L) + \pi = (2\pi/\lambda)(2n_2 L) + \pi$. At $\lambda = 450\,\text{nm}$

$$\frac{I}{I_{\text{max}}} = \cos^2\phi = \cos^2\left[\frac{2\pi n_2 L}{\lambda} + \frac{\pi}{2}\right]$$

$$= \cos^2\left[\frac{2\pi(1.38)(99.6\,\text{nm})}{450\,\text{nm}} + \frac{\pi}{2}\right] = 0.883.$$

and at $\lambda = 650\,\text{nm}$

$$\frac{I}{I_{\text{max}}} = \cos^2\left[\frac{2\pi(1.38)(99.6\,\text{nm})}{650\,\text{nm}} + \frac{\pi}{2}\right] = 0.942.$$

65P

Consider the interference of waves reflected from the top and bottom surfaces of the air film. The wave reflected from the upper surface does not change phase on reflection but the wave reflected from the bottom surface changes phase by π rad. At a place where the thickness of the air film is L the condition for fully constructive interference is $2L = (m + \frac{1}{2})\lambda$, where λ ($= 680\,\text{nm}$) is the wavelength and m is an integer. The largest value of m for which L is less than $48.0\,\mu\text{m}$ is 140. Note that for $m = 140$

$$L = \frac{(m + \frac{1}{2})\lambda}{2} = \frac{(140.5)(680 \times 10^{-9}\,\text{m})}{2} = 4.78 \times 10^{-5}\,\text{m} = 47.8\,\mu\text{m}$$

and for $m = 141$

$$L = \frac{(141.5)(680 \times 10^{-9}\,\text{m})}{2} = 4.81 \times 10^{-5}\,\text{m} = 48.1\,\mu\text{m}.$$

At the thin end of the air film there is a bright fringe associated with $m = 0$. There are therefore 141 bright fringes in all.

66P
(a) Because of destructive interference due to π-phase shift.
(b) Violet, since it has the shortest wavelength, which corresponds to the shortest thickness of the air gap between the two plates that satisfy the condition for destructive interference.
(c) The yellow-red end of the visible light spectrum, since the violet end is missing.

67P
(a) Every time one more destructive (constructive) fringe appears the thickness of the air gap increases by $\lambda/2$. Now that there are 6 more destructive fringes in addition to the one at point A, the thickness at B is $t_B = 6(\lambda/2) = 3(600\,\text{nm}) = 1.80\mu\text{m}$.
(b) Now we must replace λ by $\lambda' = \lambda/n_w$. Since t_B is unchanged $t_B = N(\lambda'/2) = N(\lambda/2n_w)$, or

$$N = \frac{2t_B n_w}{\lambda} = \frac{2(3\lambda)n_2}{\lambda} = 6n_w = 6(1.33) = 8.$$

68P
Refer to the figure to the right. The separation between adjacent fringes is $\Delta x \approx \lambda/2\theta$ (see Problem 67). If you fill the air gap with a liquid whose index of refraction is n, then you need to change λ to $\lambda' = \lambda/n$. So the new separation is

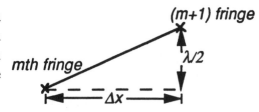

$$\Delta x' = \frac{\lambda'}{2\theta} = \frac{\lambda/n}{2\theta} = \frac{\Delta x}{n} = \frac{3\Delta x}{4}.$$

Thus the spacing decreases by a factor of 3/4.

69P
Assume the wedge-shaped film is in air, so the wave reflected from one surface undergoes a phase change of π rad while the wave reflected from the other surface does not. At a place where the film thickness is L the condition for fully constructive interference is $2nL = (m + \frac{1}{2})\lambda$, where n is the index of refraction of the film, λ is the wavelength in vacuum, and m is an integer. The ends of the film are bright. Suppose the end where the film is narrow has thickness L_1 and the bright fringe there corresponds to $m = m_1$. Suppose

the end where the film is thick has thickness L_2 and the bright fringe there corresponds to $m = m_2$. Since there are 10 bright fringes $m_2 = m_1 + 9$. Subtract $2nL_1 = (m_1 + \frac{1}{2})\lambda$ from $2nL_2 = (m_1 + 9 + \frac{1}{2})\lambda$ to obtain $2n\,\Delta L = 9\lambda$, where $\Delta L = L_2 - L_1$ is the change in the film thickness over its length. Thus

$$\Delta L = \frac{9\lambda}{2n} = \frac{9(630 \times 10^{-9}\,\mathrm{m})}{2(1.50)} = 1.89 \times 10^{-6}\,\mathrm{m}\,.$$

70P
See Problem 67, part (a). The difference in thickness is

$$\Delta t = \frac{\lambda}{2}\Delta m = \left(\frac{480\,\mathrm{nm}}{2}\right)(16 - 6) = 2400\,\mathrm{nm} = 2.4\,\mu\mathrm{m}.$$

71P
Use $\Delta x' = \Delta x/n$ (see Problem 68). If the total length of the wedge is x then $x = N\Delta x = N'\Delta x' = N'\Delta x/n$, where $N = 4000$ and $N' = 4001$. Solve for n:

$$n = \frac{N'}{N} = \frac{4001}{4000} = 1.00025.$$

72P
Consider the interference pattern formed by waves reflected from the upper and lower surfaces of the air wedge. The wave reflected from the lower surface undergoes a π rad phase change while the wave reflected from the upper surface does not. At a place where the thickness of the wedge is d the condition for a maximum in intensity is $2d = (m + \frac{1}{2})\lambda$, where λ is the wavelength in air and m is an integer. Thus $d = (2m + 1)\lambda/4$. As the geometry of Fig. 40–31 shows, $d = R - \sqrt{R^2 - r^2}$, where R is the radius of curvature of the lens and r is the radius of a Newton's ring. Thus $(2m + 1)\lambda/4 = R - \sqrt{R^2 - r^2}$. Solve for r. First rearrange the terms so the equation becomes

$$\sqrt{R^2 - r^2} = R - \frac{(2m + 1)\lambda}{4}\,.$$

Now square both sides and solve for r^2. When you take the square root you should get

$$r = \sqrt{\frac{(2m + 1)R\lambda}{2} - \frac{(2m + 1)^2\lambda^2}{16}}\,.$$

If R is much larger than a wavelength the first term dominates the second and

$$r = \sqrt{\frac{(2m + 1)R\lambda}{2}}\,.$$

73P

(a) Solve m from the last formula obtained in Problem 72:

$$m = \frac{r^2}{R\lambda} - \frac{1}{2} = \frac{(20 \times 10^{-3}\,\text{m}/2)^2}{(5.0\,\text{m})(589 \times 10^{-9}\,\text{m})} - \frac{1}{2} = 33.$$

(b) Counting the largest one, the total number of bright rings is $33 + 1 = 34$. Replace λ by $\lambda' = \lambda/n_w$:

$$\begin{aligned}
m' &= \frac{r^2}{R\lambda'} - \frac{1}{2} = \frac{n_w r^2}{R\lambda} - \frac{1}{2} \\
&= \frac{(1.33)(20 \times 10^{-3}\,\text{m}/2)^2}{(5.0\,\text{m})(589 \times 10^{-9}\,\text{m})} - \frac{1}{2} = 45.
\end{aligned}$$

So the number of bright rings is $45 + 1 = 46$.

74P

Solve n from the formula $r = \sqrt{(2n+1)R\lambda/2}$ obtained in Problem 72: $n = r^2/R\lambda - 1/2$. Now when n is changed to $n + 20$, r becomes r', so $n + 20 = r'^2/R\lambda - 1/2$. Taking the difference between the two equations above, we eliminate n and find

$$F = \frac{r'^2 - r^2}{20\lambda} = \frac{(0.368\,\text{cm})^2 - (0.162\,\text{cm})^2}{20(546 \times 10^{-7}\,\text{cm})} = 1.00\,\text{m}.$$

75P

$$\begin{aligned}
\Delta r = r_{m+1} - r_m &\approx \left(\frac{dr}{dm}\right)\Delta m \bigg|_{\Delta m = 1} \\
&= \frac{d}{dm}\sqrt{\frac{(2m+1)\lambda R}{2}} = \frac{1}{2}\sqrt{\frac{\lambda R}{m + 1/2}} \approx \frac{1}{2}\sqrt{\frac{\lambda R}{m}}.
\end{aligned}$$

76P

Use the result of Problems 72 and 75:

$$A \approx 2\pi r_m \Delta r \approx 2\pi \sqrt{\left(m + \frac{1}{2}\right)\lambda R}\left(\frac{1}{2}\sqrt{\frac{\lambda R}{m}}\right) \approx \pi\lambda R,$$

where we used $m + 1/2 \approx m$ since $m \gg 1$.

77P

(a) There is a π-phase shift due to the reflection: $\Delta\phi = \pi$.

(b) Dark, because of the π-phase shift.

(c) We can replace the mirror by introducing another source S' located at the image of S, which is initially out of phase with S (because of the π-phase shift). Comparing with the Young's double-slit arrangement we find that we should replace d by $2h$, and exchange the conditions for constructive/destructive interference. So

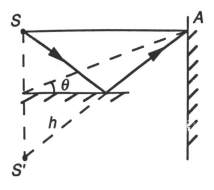

$$\begin{cases} 2h\sin\theta = m\lambda, & m = 0, 1, 2, \cdots \text{ for minima}, \\ 2h\sin\theta = \left(m + \dfrac{1}{2}\right)\lambda, & m = 0, 1, 2, \cdots \text{ for maxima}. \end{cases}$$

78E

A shift of one fringe corresponds to a change in the optical path length of one wavelength. When the mirror moves a distance d the path length changes by $2d$ since the light traverses the mirror arm twice. Let N be the number of fringes shifted. Then $2d = N\lambda$ and

$$\lambda = \frac{2d}{N} = \frac{2(0.233 \times 10^{-3}\,\text{m})}{792} = 5.88 \times 10^{-7}\,\text{m} = 588\,\text{nm}.$$

79P

From Eq. 40-31, the number of fringes shifted (ΔN) due to the insertion of the film of thickness L is $\Delta N = (2L/\lambda)(n - 1)$. So

$$L = \frac{\lambda\Delta N}{2(n-1)} = \frac{(589\,\text{nm})(7.0)}{2(1.40 - 1)} = 5.2\mu\text{m}.$$

80P

Let ϕ_1 be the phase difference of the waves in the two arms when the tube has air in it and let ϕ_2 be the phase difference when the tube is evacuated. These are different because the wavelength in air is different from the wavelength in vacuum. If λ is the wavelength in vacuum then the wavelength in air is λ/n, where n is the index of refraction of air. This means

$$\phi_1 - \phi_2 = 2L\left[\frac{2\pi n}{\lambda} - \frac{2\pi}{\lambda}\right] = \frac{4\pi(n-1)L}{\lambda},$$

where L is the length of the tube. The factor 2 arises because the light traverses the tube twice, once on the way to a mirror and once after reflection from the mirror.

Each shift by 1 fringe corresponds to a change in phase of 2π rad so if the interference pattern shifts by N fringes as the tube is evacuated,

$$\frac{4\pi(n-1)L}{\lambda} = 2N\pi$$

and

$$n - 1 = \frac{N\lambda}{2L} = \frac{60(500 \times 10^{-9}\,\text{m})}{2(5.0 \times 10^{-2}\,\text{m})} = 3.0 \times 10^{-4}.$$

Thus $n = 1.00030$.

81P
The phase difference between the two light paths is $\Delta\phi = 2kd_2 = 2(2\pi/\lambda)d_2 = 4\pi d_2/\lambda$. Then from Eq. 40-18

$$I(d_2) = I_{\text{max}} \cos^2\left(\frac{\Delta\phi}{2}\right) = I_{\text{max}} \cos^2\left(\frac{2\pi d_2}{\lambda}\right).$$

82P
In this case the path traveled by ray no.2 is longer than ray no.1 by $2L\cos\theta_r$, instead of $2L$. Here $\sin\theta_i/\sin\theta_r = n_2$, or $\theta_r = \sin^{-1}(\sin\theta_i/n_2)$. So we replace $2L$ by $2L\cos\theta_r$ in Eqs. 40-27 and 40-28 to obtain

$$2n_2 L \cos\theta_r = \left(m + \frac{1}{2}\right)\lambda, \qquad \text{for } m = 0, 1, 2, \cdots \text{(maxima)},$$

and

$$2n_2 L \cos\theta_r = m\lambda, \qquad \text{for } m = 0, 1, 2, \cdots \text{(minima)}.$$

83
Set up a coordinate system as shown. Let $A = (0, A_y)$ and $B = (B_x, B_y)$. If $OC = x$ then $CD = B_x - x$. The time t it takes for light to travel form point A to B is

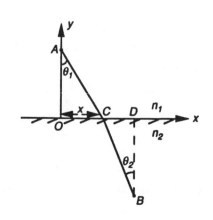

$$t = t_{AC} + t_{CB}$$

$$= \frac{\sqrt{A_x^2 + x^2}}{c/n_1} + \frac{\sqrt{(B_x - x)^2 + B_y^2}}{c/n_2}.$$

To minimize t, set $dt/dx = 0$:

$$c\frac{dt}{dx} = n_1\left(\frac{x}{\sqrt{A_x^2 + x^2}}\right) - n_2\left(\frac{B_x - x}{\sqrt{(B_x - x)^2 + B_y^2}}\right)$$

$$= n_1 \sin\theta_1 - n_2 \sin\theta_2 = 0.$$

Thus $n_1 \sin\theta_1 = n_2 \sin\theta_2$.

84

The reflection does cause a phase change of π. The situation here is analogous with that of Problem 77, from which we obtain the condition for maximum reception:

$$2a \sin\theta \approx 2a\left(\frac{x}{D}\right) = \left(m + \frac{1}{2}\right)\lambda.$$

Thus

$$x = \frac{(2m + 1)\lambda D}{4a}, \qquad \text{for } m = 0,\, 1,\, 2, \cdots$$

85

Denote the two wavelengths as λ and λ'. Then from $\Delta\phi = 2kd_2 = 2(2\pi/\lambda)d_2$, we have

$$\Delta\phi - \Delta\phi' = \frac{4\pi d_2}{\lambda} - \frac{4\pi d_2}{\lambda'} = 2\pi,$$

or

$$d_2 = \frac{1}{2}\left(\frac{1}{\lambda} - \frac{1}{\lambda'}\right)^{-1}$$

$$= \frac{1}{2}\left(\frac{1}{589.10\,\text{nm}} - \frac{1}{589.59\,\text{nm}}\right)^{-1} = 3.54 \times 10^5\,\text{nm} = 0.354\,\text{mm}.$$

CHAPTER 41

1E

Use Eq. 41-3: $\lambda = a \sin \theta / m = (0.022 \, \text{mm})(\sin 1.8°)/1 = 6.9 \times 10^{-3} \, \text{mm} = 690 \, \text{nm}$.

2E

(a) $\theta = \sin^{-1}(1.50 \, \text{cm}/2.00 \, \text{m}) = 0.430°$.

(b) For the mth diffraction minimum $a \sin \theta = m\lambda$. Solve for a:

$$a = \frac{m\lambda}{\sin \theta} = \frac{2(441 \, \text{nm})}{\sin 0.430°} = 0.118 \, \text{mm}.$$

3E

The condition for a minimum of a single-slit diffraction pattern is

$$a \sin \theta = m\lambda \,,$$

where a is the slit width, λ is the wavelength, and m is an integer. The angle θ is measured from the forward direction, so for the situation described in the problem it is 0.60°, for $m = 1$. Thus

$$a = \frac{m\lambda}{\sin \theta} = \frac{633 \times 10^{-9} \, \text{m}}{\sin 0.60°} = 6.04 \times 10^{-5} \, \text{m} \,.$$

4E

(a) The condition for a minimum in a single-slit diffraction pattern is given by $a \sin \theta = m\lambda$, where a is the slit width, λ is the wavelength, and m is an integer. For $\lambda = \lambda_a$ and $m = 1$ the angle θ is the same as for $\lambda = \lambda_b$ and $m = 2$. Thus $\lambda_a = 2\lambda_b$.

(b) Let m_a be the integer associated with a minimum in the pattern produced by light with wavelength λ_a and let m_b be the integer associated with a minimum in the pattern produced by light with wavelength λ_b. A minimum in one pattern coincides with a minimum in the other if they occur at the same angle. This means $m_a \lambda_a = m_b \lambda_b$. Since $\lambda_a = 2\lambda_b$, the minima coincide if $2m_a = m_b$. Thus every other minimum of the λ_b pattern coincides with a minimum of the λ_a pattern.

5E

(a) Use Eq. 41-3 to calculate the separation between the first ($m_1 = 1$) and fifth ($m_2 = 5$) minima:

$$\Delta y = D\Delta \sin \theta = D\Delta \left[\frac{m\lambda}{a} \right] = \frac{D\lambda}{a} \Delta m = \frac{D\lambda}{a}(m_2 - m_1).$$

Sovle for a:

$$a = \frac{d\lambda(m_2 - m_1)}{\Delta y} = \frac{(400\,\text{mm})(550 \times 10^{-6}\,\text{mm})(5-1)}{0.35\,\text{mm}} = 2.5\,\text{mm}.$$

(b) For $m = 1$

$$\sin\theta = \frac{m\lambda}{a} = \frac{(1)(550 \times 10^{-6}\,\text{mm})}{2.5\,\text{mm}} = 2.2 \times 10^{-4}.$$

The angle is $\theta = \sin^{-1}(2.2 \times 10^{-4}) = 2.2 \times 10^{-4}\,\text{rad}$.

6E
From Eq. 41-3

$$\frac{a}{\lambda} = \frac{m}{\sin\theta} = \frac{1}{\sin 45.0°} = 1.41.$$

7E
(a) A plane wave is incident on the lens so it is brought to focus in the focal plane of the lens, a distance of 70 cm from the lens.

(b) Waves leaving the lens at an angle θ to the forward direction interfere to produce an intensity minimum if $a\sin\theta = m\lambda$, where a is the slit width, λ is the wavelength, and m is an integer. The distance on the screen from the center of the pattern to the minimum is given by $y = D\tan\theta$, where D is the distance from the lens to the screen. For the conditions of this problem

$$\sin\theta = \frac{m\lambda}{a} = \frac{(1)(590 \times 10^{-9}\,\text{m})}{0.40 \times 10^{-3}\,\text{m}} = 1.475 \times 10^{-3}.$$

This means $\theta = 1.475 \times 10^{-3}\,\text{rad}$ and $y = (70 \times 10^{-2}\,\text{m})\tan(1.475 \times 10^{-3}\,\text{rad}) = 1.03 \times 10^{-3}\,\text{m}$.

8P
The condition for a minimum of intensity in a single-slit diffraction pattern is $a\sin\theta = m\lambda$, where a is the slit width, λ is the wavelength, and m is an integer. To find the angular position of the first minimum to one side of the central maximum set $m = 1$:

$$\theta_1 = \sin^{-1}\left(\frac{\lambda}{a}\right) = \sin^{-1}\left(\frac{589 \times 10^{-9}\,\text{m}}{1.00 \times 10^{-3}\,\text{m}}\right) = 5.89 \times 10^{-4}\,\text{rad}.$$

If D is the distance from the slit to the screen, the distance on the screen from the center of the pattern to the minimum is $y_1 = D\tan\theta_1 = (3.00\,\text{m})\tan(5.89 \times 10^{-4}\,\text{rad}) = 1.767 \times 10^{-3}\,\text{m}$.

To find the second minimum set $m = 2$:

$$\theta_2 = \sin^{-1}\left(\frac{2(589 \times 10^{-9}\,\text{m})}{1.00 \times 10^{-3}\,\text{m}}\right) = 1.178 \times 10^{-3}\,\text{rad}.$$

The distance from the pattern center to the minimum is $y_2 = D \tan\theta_2 = (3.00\,\text{m})\tan(1.178 \times 10^{-3}\,\text{rad}) = 3.534 \times 10^{-3}\,\text{m}$. The separation of the two minima is $\Delta y = y_2 - y_1 = 3.534\,\text{mm} - 1.767\,\text{mm} = 1.77\,\text{mm}$.

9P

Let the first minimum be a distnce y from the line perpendicular to the speaker. Then $\sin\theta = y/(D^2 + y^2)^{1/2} = m\lambda/a = \lambda/a$ (for $m = 1$). Solve for y:

$$y = \frac{D}{\sqrt{(a/\lambda)^2 - 1}} = \frac{D}{\sqrt{(af/v_s)^2 - 1}}$$

$$= \frac{100\,\text{m}}{\sqrt{[0.300\,\text{m}(3000\,\text{Hz})/(343\,\text{m/s})]^2 - 1}} = 41.2\,\text{m}.$$

10P

From $y = m\lambda D/a$ we get

$$\Delta y = \Delta\left(\frac{m\lambda D}{a}\right) = \frac{\lambda D}{a}\Delta m$$

$$= \frac{(632.8\,\text{nm})(2.60)}{1.37\,\text{mm}}[10 - (-10)] = 24.0\,\text{mm}.$$

11E

From Eq. 41-4

$$\Delta\phi = \left(\frac{2\pi}{\lambda}\right)(\Delta x \sin\theta) = \left(\frac{2\pi}{589\,\text{nm}}\right)\left(\frac{0.10\,\text{mm}}{2}\right)(\sin 30°) = 267\,\text{rad}.$$

This is equivalent to $267\,\text{rad} - 84\pi = 2.79\,\text{rad} = 160°$.

12E

(a) $\theta = \sin^{-1}(1.1\,\text{cm}/3.5\,\text{m}) = 0.18°$.

(b) Use Eq. 41-6:

$$\alpha = \left(\frac{\pi a}{\lambda}\right)\sin\theta = \frac{\pi(0.025\,\text{mm})(\sin 0.18°)}{538\,\text{nm}} = 0.46\,\text{rad}.$$

(c) Use Eq. 41-5:

$$\frac{I}{I_m} = \left(\frac{\sin\alpha}{\alpha}\right)^2 = \left[\frac{\sin(0.46\,\text{rad})}{0.46}\right]^2 = 0.93.$$

13P

If you divide the original slit into N strips and represent the light from each strip, when it reaches the screen, by a phasor, then at the central maximum in the diffraction pattern you add N phasors, all in the same direction and each with the same amplitude. The intensity there is proportional to N^2. If you double the slit width you need $2N$ phasors if they are each to have the amplitude of the phasors you used for the narrow slit. The intensity at the central maximum is proportional to $(2N)^2$ and is therefore 4 times the intensity for the narrow slit. The energy reaching the screen per unit time, however, is only twice the energy reaching it per unit time when the narrow slit is in place. The energy is simply redistributed. For example, the central peak is now half as wide and the integral of the intensity over the peak is only twice the analogous integral for the narrow slit.

14P

Think of the Huygens' explanation of diffraction phenomenon. When A is in place only the Huygens' wavelets that pass through the hole get to point P. Suppose they produce a resultant electric field E_A. When B is in place the light that was blocked by A gets to P and the light that passed through the hole in A is blocked. Suppose the electric field at P is now E_B. The sum $E_A + E_B$ is the resultant of all waves that get to P when neither A nor B are present. Since P is in the geometric shadow this is zero. Thus $E_A = -E_B$ and since the intensity is proportional to the square of the electric field, the intensity at P is the same when A is present as when B is present.

15P

(a) The intensity for a single-slit diffraction pattern is given by

$$I = I_m \frac{\sin^2\alpha}{\alpha^2},$$

where $\alpha = (\pi a/\lambda)\sin\theta$, a is the slit width and λ is the wavelength. The angle θ is measured from the forward direction. You want $I = I_m/2$, so

$$\sin^2\alpha = \frac{1}{2}\alpha^2.$$

(b) Evaluate $\sin^2\alpha$ and $\alpha^2/2$ for $\alpha = 1.39\,\text{rad}$ and compare the results. To be sure that 1.39 rad is closer to the correct value for α than any other value with 3 significant digits, you should also try 1.385 rad and 1.395 rad.

(c) Since $\alpha = (\pi a/\lambda) \sin \theta$,

$$\theta = \sin^{-1}\left(\frac{\alpha\lambda}{\pi a}\right).$$

Now $\alpha/\pi = 1.39/\pi = 0.442$, so

$$\theta = \sin^{-1}\left(\frac{0.442\lambda}{a}\right).$$

The angular separation of the two points of half intensity, one on either side of the center of the diffraction pattern, is

$$\Delta\theta = 2\theta = 2\sin^{-1}\left(\frac{0.442\lambda}{a}\right).$$

(d) For $a/\lambda = 1.0$,

$$\Delta\theta = 2\sin^{-1}(0.442/1.0) = 0.916\,\text{rad}\,,$$

for $a/\lambda = 5.0$,

$$\Delta\theta = 2\sin^{-1}(0.442/5.0) = 0.177\,\text{rad}\,,$$

and for $a/\lambda = 10$,

$$\Delta\theta = 2\sin^{-1}(0.442/10) = 0.0884\,\text{rad}\,.$$

16P

(a) The intensity for a single-slit diffraction pattern is given by

$$I = I_m \frac{\sin^2 \alpha}{\alpha^2}\,,$$

where $\alpha = (\pi a/\lambda) \sin \theta$. Here a is the slit width and λ is the wavelength. To find the maxima and minima, set the derivative of I with respect to α equal to zero and solve for α.

The derivative is

$$\frac{dI}{d\alpha} = 2I_m \frac{\sin \alpha}{\alpha^3} \left(\alpha \cos \alpha - \sin \alpha\right).$$

The derivative vanishes if $\alpha \neq 0$ but $\sin \alpha = 0$. This yields $\alpha = m\pi$, where m is an integer. Except for $m = 0$ these are the intensity minima: $I = 0$ for $\alpha = m\pi$.

The derivative also vanishes for $\alpha \cos \alpha - \sin \alpha = 0$. This condition can be written $\tan \alpha = \alpha$. These are the maxima.

(b) The values of α that satisfy $\tan\alpha = \alpha$ can be found by trial and error on a pocket calculator or computer. Each of them is slightly less than one of the values $(m + \frac{1}{2})\pi$ rad, so start with these values. The first few are 0, 4.4934, 7.7252, 10.9041, 14.0662, and 17.2207. They can also be found graphically. As in the diagram to the right, plot $y = \tan\alpha$ and $y = \alpha$ on the same graph. The intersections of the line with the $\tan\alpha$ curves are the solutions. The first two solutions listed above are shown on the diagram.

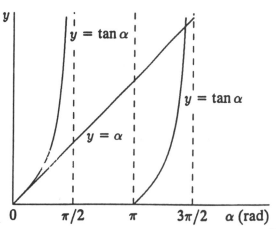

(c) Write $\alpha = (m + \frac{1}{2})\pi$ for the maxima. For the central maximum, $\alpha = 0$ and $m = -\frac{1}{2}$. For the next, $\alpha = 4.4934$ and $m = 0.930$. For the next $\alpha = 7.7252$ and $m = 1.959$.

17P*

Since the slit width is much less than the wavelength of the light, the central peak of the single-slit diffraction pattern is spread across the screen and the diffraction envelope can be ignored. Consider 3 waves, one from each slit. Since the slits are evenly spaced the phase difference for waves from the first and second slits is the same as the phase difference for waves from the second and third slits. The electric fields of the waves at the screen can be written $E_1 = E_0\sin(\omega t)$, $E_2 = E_0\sin(\omega t + \phi)$, and $E_3 = E_0\sin(\omega t + 2\phi)$, where $\phi = (2\pi d/\lambda)\sin\theta$. Here d is the separation of adjacent slits and λ is the wavelength. The phasor diagram is shown to the right. It yields

$$E = E_0\cos\phi + E_0 + E_0\cos\phi = E_0(1 + 2\cos\phi)$$

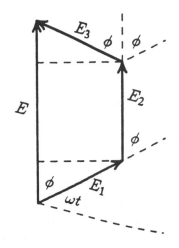

for the amplitude of the resultant wave. Since the intensity of a wave is proportional to the square of the electric field, we may write $I = AE_0^2(1 + 2\cos\phi)^2$, where A is a constant of proportionality. If I_m is the intensity at the center of the pattern, for which $\phi = 0$, then $I_m = 9AE_0^2$. Take A to be $I_m/9E_0^2$ and obtain

$$I = \frac{I_m}{9}\left(1 + 2\cos\phi\right)^2 = \frac{I_m}{9}\left(1 + 4\cos\phi + 4\cos^2\phi\right).$$

18E

(a) Use the Rayleigh criteria. To resolve two point sources the central maximum of the diffraction pattern of one must lie at or beyond the first minimum of the diffraction pattern of the other. This means the angular separation of the sources must be at least $\theta_R =$

$1.22\lambda/d$, where λ is the wavelength and d is the diameter of the aperture. For the headlights of this problem

$$\theta_R = \frac{1.22(550 \times 10^{-9}\,\text{m})}{5.0 \times 10^{-3}\,\text{m}} = 1.34 \times 10^{-4}\,\text{rad}.$$

(b) If D is the distance from the headlights to the eye when the headlights are just resolvable and ℓ is the separation of the headlights, then $\ell = D \tan\theta_R \approx D\theta_R$, where the small angle approximation $\tan\theta_R \approx \theta_R$ was made. This is valid if θ_R is measured in radians. Thus $D = \ell/\theta_R = (1.4\,\text{m})/(1.34 \times 10^{-4}\,\text{rad}) = 1.0 \times 10^4\,\text{m} = 10\,\text{km}.$

19E
(a) Use Eq. 41-11:

$$\theta_R = 1.22\frac{\lambda}{d} = \frac{(1.22)(540 \times 10^{-6}\,\text{mm})}{5.0\,\text{mm}} = 1.3 \times 10^{-4}\,\text{rad}.$$

(b) The linear separation is $l = D\theta_R = (160 \times 10^3\,\text{m})(1.3 \times 10^{-4}\,\text{rad}) = 21\,\text{m}.$

20E
The minimum separation is

$$l = D_{\text{EM}}\theta_R = D_{\text{EM}}\left(1.22\frac{\lambda}{d}\right) = \frac{(1.22)(3.8 \times 10^8\,\text{m})(550 \times 10^{-9}\,\text{m})}{5.1\,\text{m}} = 50\,\text{m}.$$

21E

$$D_{\max} = \frac{l}{\theta_R} = \frac{l}{1.22\lambda/d} = \frac{(5.0 \times 10^{-3}\,\text{m})(4.0 \times 10^{-3}\,\text{m})}{1.22(550 \times 10^{-9}\,\text{m})} = 30\,\text{m}.$$

22E

$$l_{\min} = D\theta_R = D\left(\frac{1.22\lambda}{d}\right) = \frac{(1.22)(250\,\text{mm})(500 \times 10^{-3}\,\mu\text{m})}{5.00\,\text{mm}} = 30.5\,\mu\text{m}.$$

23E
(a) Use the Rayleigh criteria: two objects can be resolved if their angular separation at the observer is greater than $\theta_R = 1.22\lambda/d$, where λ is the wavelength of the light and d is the diameter of the aperture (the eye or mirror). If D is the distance from the observer to the objects then the smallest separation ℓ they can have and still be resolvable is $\ell = D \tan\theta_R \approx D\theta_R$, where θ_R is measured in radians. The small angle approximation $\tan\theta_R \approx \theta_R$ was made. Thus

$$\ell = \frac{1.22D\lambda}{d} = \frac{1.22(8.0 \times 10^{10}\,\text{m})(550 \times 10^{-9}\,\text{m})}{5.0 \times 10^{-3}\,\text{m}} = 1.1 \times 10^7\,\text{m} = 1.1 \times 10^4\,\text{km}.$$

This distance is greater than the diameter of Mars. One part of the planet's surface cannot be resolved from another part.

(b) Now $d = 5.1$ m and

$$\ell = \frac{1.22(8.0 \times 10^{10}\,\mathrm{m})(550 \times 10^{-9}\,\mathrm{m})}{5.1\,\mathrm{m}} = 1.1 \times 10^4\,\mathrm{m} = 11\,\mathrm{km}\,.$$

24E

$$D_{\max} = \frac{l}{\theta_R} = \frac{l}{1.22\lambda/d} = \frac{(5.0 \times 10^{-2}\,\mathrm{m})(4.0 \times 10^{-3}\,\mathrm{m})}{1.22(0.10 \times 10^{-9}\,\mathrm{m})} = 1.6 \times 10^6\,\mathrm{m} = 1600\,\mathrm{km}.$$

25E

$$l_{\min} = D\theta_R = D\left(\frac{1.22\lambda}{d}\right) = \frac{(6.2 \times 10^3\,\mathrm{m})(1.22)(1.6 \times 10^{-2}\,\mathrm{m})}{2.3\,\mathrm{m}} = 53\,\mathrm{m}.$$

26P
(a) The diameter is

$$l = D\theta_R = D\left(\frac{1.22\lambda}{d}\right) = \frac{(2000 \times 10^3\,\mathrm{m})(1.22)(1.40 \times 10^{-9}\,\mathrm{m})}{0.200 \times 10^{-3}\,\mathrm{m}} = 17.1\,\mathrm{m}.$$

(b) $I/I_0 = (l/d)^2 = (1.71\,\mathrm{m}/0.200 \times 10^{-3}\,\mathrm{m})^2 = 1.37 \times 10^{-10}$.

27P
(a)

$$D_{\max} = \frac{l}{1.22\lambda/d} = \frac{2(50 \times 10^{-6}\,\mathrm{m})(1.5 \times 10^{-3}\,\mathrm{m})}{1.22(650 \times 10^{-9}\,\mathrm{m})} = 0.19\,\mathrm{m}.$$

(b) The wavelength of the blue light is shorter so $D_{\max} \propto \lambda^{-1}$ will be larger.

28P
(a) Use Eq. 41-9:

$$\theta = \sin^{-1}\left(\frac{1.22\lambda}{d}\right) = \sin^{-1}\left[\frac{1.22(v_s/f)}{d}\right]$$

$$= \sin^{-1}\left[\frac{(1.22)(1450\,\mathrm{m/s})}{(25 \times 10^3\,\mathrm{Hz})(0.60\,\mathrm{m})}\right] = 6.8°.$$

(b) Now $f = 1.0 \times 10^3$ Hz so

$$\frac{1.22\lambda}{d} = \frac{(1.22)(1450\,\mathrm{m/s})}{(1.0 \times 10^3\,\mathrm{Hz})(0.60\,\mathrm{m})} = 2.9 > 1.$$

Thus there is no minimum.

29P

Use $2\theta = 1.22\lambda/d = l/D$:

$$d = \frac{1.22D\lambda}{l} = \frac{(1.22)(220\,\text{mi})(1610\,\text{m/mi})(500 \times 10^{-9}\,\text{m})}{(30\,\text{ft})(0.305\,\text{m/ft})} = 4.7\,\text{cm}.$$

30P

From $\theta_R = 1.22\lambda/d = l/D$ we get

$$d = \frac{1.22\lambda D}{l} = \frac{(1.22)(550 \times 10^{-9}\,\text{m})(160 \times 10^3\,\text{m})}{0.30\,\text{m}} = 0.36\,\text{m}.$$

31P

(a) The first minimum in the diffraction pattern is at an angular position θ, measured from the center of the pattern, such that $\sin\theta = 1.22\lambda/d$, where λ is the wavelength and d is the diameter of the antenna. If f is the frequency then the wavelength is $\lambda = c/f = (3.00 \times 10^8\,\text{m/s})/(220 \times 10^9\,\text{Hz}) = 1.36 \times 10^{-3}\,\text{m}$. Thus

$$\theta = \sin^{-1}\left(\frac{1.22\lambda}{d}\right) = \sin^{-1}\left(\frac{1.22(1.36 \times 10^{-3}\,\text{m})}{55.0 \times 10^{-2}\,\text{m}}\right) = 3.02 \times 10^{-3}\,\text{rad}.$$

The angular width of the central maximum is twice this, or $6.04 \times 10^{-3}\,\text{rad}$ $(0.346°)$.
(b) Now $\lambda = 1.6\,\text{cm}$ and $d = 2.3\,\text{m}$, so

$$\theta = \sin^{-1}\left(\frac{1.22(1.6 \times 10^{-2}\,\text{m})}{2.3\,\text{m}}\right) = 8.5 \times 10^{-3}\,\text{rad}.$$

The angular width of the central maximum is $1.7 \times 10^{-2}\,\text{rad}$ $(0.97°)$.

32P

(a) The angular separation is

$$\theta = \theta_R = \frac{1.22\lambda}{d} = \frac{(1.22)(550 \times 10^{-9}\,\text{m})}{0.76\,\text{m}} = 8.8 \times 10^{-7}\,\text{rad} = 0.18''.$$

(b) The distance is

$$D = \frac{(10\,\text{ly})(9.46 \times 10^{12}\,\text{km/ly})(0.18)\pi}{(3600)(180)} = 8.4 \times 10^7\,\text{km}.$$

(c) The diameter is

$$d = 2\theta_R f = \frac{2(0.18)(\pi)(14\,\text{km})}{(3600)(180)} = 2.5 \times 10^{-5}\,\text{m} = 0.025\,\text{mm}.$$

33P
(a) Since $\theta = 1.22\lambda/d$, the larger the wavelength the larger the radius of the first minimum (and second maximum, ect). Therefore the white pattern is outlined by red lights (with longer wavelength than blue lights).
(b)

$$d = \frac{1.22\lambda}{\theta} \approx \frac{1.22(700 \times 10^{-3}\,\mu\text{m})}{1.5(0.50°)(\pi/180°)/2} = 130\mu\text{m}.$$

34P
The energy of the beam of light which is projected onto the moon is concentrated is a circular spot of diameter d_1, where $d_1/D_{\text{EM}} = 2\theta = 2(1.22\lambda/d_0)$, with d_0 the diameter of the mirror on the earth. The fraction of energy picked up by the reflector of diameter d_2 on the moon is then $\eta' = (d_2/d_1)^2$. This reflected light, upon reaching the Earth, has a circular cross section of diameter d_3 satisfying $d_3/D_{\text{EM}} = 2\theta = 2(1.22\lambda/d_2)$. The fraction of the reflected energy that is picked up by the telescope is then $\eta'' = (d_0/d_3)^2$. Thus the fraction of the original energy picked up by the detector is

$$\eta = \eta'\eta'' = \left(\frac{d_0}{d_3}\right)^2 \left(\frac{d_2}{d_1}\right)^2 = \left[\frac{d_0 d_2}{(2.44\lambda D_{\text{EM}}/d_0)(2.44\lambda D_{\text{EM}}/d_2)}\right]^2$$

$$= \left(\frac{d_0 d_2}{2.44\lambda D_{\text{EM}}}\right)^4$$

$$= \left[\frac{(2.6\,\text{m})(0.10\,\text{m})}{2.44(0.69 \times 10^{-6}\,\text{m})(3.82 \times 10^8\,\text{m})}\right]^4 = 4.3 \times 10^{-13}.$$

35E
Bright interference fringes occur at angles θ given by $d\sin\theta = m\lambda$, where d is the slit separation, λ is the wavelength, and m is an integer. For the slits of this problem $d = 11a/2$, so $a\sin\theta = 2m\lambda/11$ (see Sample Problem 41–7). The first minimum of the diffraction pattern occurs at the angle θ_1 given by $a\sin\theta_1 = \lambda$ and the second occurs at the angle θ_2 given by $a\sin\theta_2 = 2\lambda$, where a is the slit width. You want to count the values of m for which $\theta_1 < \theta < \theta_2$, or what is the same, the values of m for which $\sin\theta_1 < \sin\theta < \sin\theta_2$. This means $1 < (2m/11) < 2$. The values are $m = 6, 7, 8, 9$, and 10. There are five bright fringes in all.

1025

36E

The number is $2(d/a) - 1 = 2(2a/a) - 1 = 3$.

37P

Now $\alpha = (\pi a/\lambda)\sin\theta = (\pi d/\lambda)\sin\theta = \beta$ so Eq. 41-15 reads

$$I = I_m(\cos^2\beta)\left(\frac{\sin\alpha}{a}\right)^2 = I_m\left(\frac{\sin\alpha\cos\alpha}{\alpha}\right)^2$$
$$= I_m\left(\frac{\sin 2\alpha}{2\alpha}\right)^2.$$

Since $2\alpha = \pi(2a)\sin\theta/\lambda$, the expression above is indeed the intensity distribution of a single slit with width $2a$. Here we used $\sin 2\alpha = 2\sin\alpha\cos\alpha$.

38P

(a) Let the location of the fourth light fringe coincide with the first minmum of diffraction partern: $\sin\theta = 4\lambda/d = \lambda/a$, or $d = 4a$.

(b) The fringe which happens to be where a diffraction minimum exits will vanish. So let $\sin\theta = m_1\lambda/d = m_2\lambda/a = m_1\lambda/4a = m_2\lambda/a$, or $m_1 = 4m_2$ where $m_2 = 1, 2, 3, \cdots$. The fringes missng are thus the 4th, the 8th, the 12th, $\cdots$, i.e. every fourht fringe is missing.

39P

The angular location of the mth bright fringe is given by $d\sin\theta = m\lambda$ so the linear separation between two adjacent fringe is

$$\Delta y = \Delta(D\sin\theta) = \Delta\left(\frac{D_m\lambda}{d}\right) = \frac{D\lambda}{d}\Delta m = \frac{D\lambda}{d}.$$

40P

(a) The angular positions θ of the bright interference fringes are given by $d\sin\theta = m\lambda$, where d is the slit separation, λ is the wavelength, and m is an integer. The first diffraction minimum occurs at the angle θ_1 given by $a\sin\theta_1 = \lambda$, where a is the slit width. The diffraction peak extends from $-\theta_1$ to $+\theta_1$, so you want to count the number of values of m for which $-\theta_1 < \theta < +\theta_1$, or what is the same, the number of values of m for which $-\sin\theta_1 < \sin\theta < +\sin\theta_1$. This means $-1/a < m/d < 1/a$ or $-d/a < m < +d/a$. Now $d/a = (0.150 \times 10^{-3}\,\text{m})/(30.0 \times 10^{-6}\,\text{m}) = 5.00$, so the values of m are $m = -4, -3, -2, -1, 0, +1, +2, +3$, and $+4$. There are 9 fringes.

(b) The intensity at the screen is given by

$$I = I_m \left(\cos^2 \beta\right) \left(\frac{\sin \alpha}{\alpha}\right)^2,$$

where $\alpha = (\pi a/\lambda) \sin \theta$, $\beta = (\pi d/\lambda) \sin \theta$, and I_m is the intensity at the center of the pattern. For the third bright interference fringe $d \sin \theta = 3\lambda$, so $\beta = 3\pi$ rad and $\cos^2 \beta = 1$. Similarly, $\alpha = 3\pi a/d = 3\pi/5.00 = 0.600\pi$ rad and $(\sin \alpha)^2/\alpha^2 = (\sin 0.600\pi)^2/(0.600\pi)^2 = 0.255$. The intensity ratio is $I/I_m = 0.255$.

41P
(a) The first minimum of the diffraction pattern is at $5.00°$ so $a = \lambda/\sin \theta = 0.440\mu m/\sin 5.00°$ = $5.05\mu m$.
(b) Since the fourth bright fringe is missing $d = 4a = 4(5.05\mu m) = 20.2\mu m$. (see Problem 38).
(c) For the $m = 1$ bright fringe

$$\alpha = \frac{\pi a \sin \theta}{\lambda} = \frac{\pi(5.05\mu m) \sin(1.25°)}{0.440\mu m} = 0.787 \, \text{rad}.$$

So the intensity of the $m = 1$ fringe is

$$I = I_0 \left(\frac{\sin \alpha}{\alpha}\right)^2 = (7.0 \, \text{mW/cm}^2) \left(\frac{\sin 0.787 \, \text{rad}}{0.787}\right)^2 = 5.7 \, \text{mW/cm}^2,$$

which agrees with what Fig. 41-28 inicates. Similarly for $m = 2$ we have $I = 2.9 \, \text{mW/cm}^2$, also in agreement with Fig. 41-28.

42P
As the phase difference $\Delta\phi$ is varied from zero to π, both the intensity profile of the diffracion and the location of the interference maximum change. At $\Delta\phi = \pi$, the original central diffraction envelop is now a minimum, and the two maxima of the diffraction intensity profile are now centered where there the first minma were. The locaions of the intensity maxima/minima due to interference exchange, with the original locations of the maxima now those of minima, and vice versa.
As $\Delta\phi$ is further varied from π to 2π, the intensity pattern is gradually changed back, resuming the original parttern at $\Delta\phi = 2\pi$.

43E
(a) $d = 20.0 \, \text{mm}/6000 = 0.00333 \, \text{mm} = 3.33\mu m$.
(b) Let $d \sin \theta = m\lambda$ ($m = 0, \pm 1, \pm 2, \cdots$) and we find $\theta = \sin^{-1}(\pm\lambda/d) = \sin^{-1}(\pm0.589\mu m$

$/3.30\,\mu\text{m}) = \pm10.2°$ for $m = \pm1$, and similarly $\pm20.7°$ for $m = \pm2$, $\pm32.0°$ for $m = \pm3$, $\pm45°$ for $m = \pm4$, and $\pm62.2°$ for $m = \pm5$. Since $|m|\lambda/d > 1$ for $|m| \geq 6$ these are all the maxima.

44E

(a) Let $d\sin\theta = m\lambda$ and solve for λ:

$$\lambda = \frac{d\sin\theta}{m} = \frac{(1.0\,\text{mm}/200)(\sin 30°)}{m} = \frac{2500\,\text{nm}}{m},$$

where $m = 1, 2, 3\cdots$. In the visible light range m can assume the following values: $m_1 = 4$, $m_2 = 5$ and $m_3 = 6$. The corresponding wavelengths are $\lambda_1 = 2500\,\text{nm}/4 = 625\,\text{nm}$, $\lambda_2 = 2500\,\text{nm}/5 = 500\,\text{nm}$, and $\lambda_3 = 2500\,\text{nm}/6 = 416\,\text{nm}$.
(b) The colors are orange (for $\lambda_1 = 625\,\text{nm}$), blue-green (for $\lambda_2 = 500\,\text{nm}$), and violet (for $\lambda_3 = 416\,\text{nm}$).

45E

The angular location of the mth order diffraction maximum is given by $m\lambda = d\sin\theta$. To be able to observe the fifth-order one we must let $\sin\theta|_{m=5} = 5\lambda/d < 1$, or

$$\lambda < \frac{d}{5} = \frac{1.00\,\text{mm}/315}{5} = 635\,\text{nm}.$$

So all wavelengths shorter than 635 nm can be used.

46E

The ruling separation is $d = 1/(400\,\text{mm}^{-1}) = 2.5 \times 10^{-3}\,\text{mm}$. Diffraction lines occur at angles θ such that $d\sin\theta = m\lambda$, where λ is the wavelength and m is an integer. Notice that for a given order the line associated with a long wavelength is produced at a greater angle than the line associated with a shorter wavelength. Take λ to be the longest wavelength in the visible spectrum (700 nm) and find the greatest integer value of m such that θ is less than 90°. That is, find the greatest integer value of m for which $m\lambda < d$. Since $d/\lambda = (2.5 \times 10^{-6}\,\text{m})/(700 \times 10^{-9}\,\text{m}) = 3.57$ that value is $m = 3$. There are 3 complete orders on each side of the $m = 0$ order. As stated in Problem 56, the second and third orders overlap.

47E

Let the total number of lines on the grating be N, then $d = L/N$ where $L = 3.00\,\text{cm}$. For the second order diffraction maxmimum $d\sin\theta = (L/N)\sin\theta = m\lambda = 2\lambda$, so

$$N = \frac{L\sin\theta}{2\lambda} = \frac{(3.00 \times 10^{-2}\,\text{m})(\sin 33°)}{2(600 \times 10^{-9}\,\text{m})} = 13,600.$$

48E

Let $d \sin \theta = (L/N) \sin \theta = m\lambda$, we get

$$\lambda = \frac{(L/N) \sin \theta}{m} = \frac{(1.0 \times 10^7 \, \text{nm})(\sin 30°)}{(1)(10,000)} = 500 \, \text{nm}.$$

49P

(a) Maxima of a two-slit interference pattern occur at angles θ given by $d \sin \theta = m\lambda$, where d is the slit separation, λ is the wavelength, and m is an integer. The two lines are adjacent so their order numbers differ by unity. Let m be the order number for the line with $\sin \theta = 0.2$ and $m + 1$ be the order number for the line with $\sin \theta = 0.3$. Then $0.2d = m\lambda$ and $0.3d = (m + 1)\lambda$. Subtract the first equation from the second to obtain $0.1d = \lambda$, or $d = \lambda/0.1 = (600 \times 10^{-9} \, \text{m})/0.1 = 6.0 \times 10^{-6} \, \text{m}$.

(b) Minima of the single-slit diffraction pattern occur at angles θ given by $a \sin \theta = m\lambda$, where a is the slit width. Since the fourth order interference maximum is missing it must fall at one of these angles. If a is the smallest slit width for which this order is missing the angle must be given by $a \sin \theta = \lambda$. It is also given by $d \sin \theta = 4\lambda$, so $a = d/4 = (6.0 \times 10^{-6} \, \text{m})/4 = 1.5 \times 10^{-6} \, \text{m}$.

(c) First set $\theta = 90°$ and find the largest value of m for which $m\lambda < d \sin \theta$. This is the highest order that is diffracted toward the screen. The condition is the same as $m < d/\lambda$ and since $d/\lambda = (6.0 \times 10^{-6} \, \text{m})/(600 \times 10^{-9} \, \text{m}) = 10.0$, the highest order seen is the $m = 9$ order. The fourth and eighth orders are missing so the observable orders are $m = 0, 1, 2, 3, 5, 6, 7,$ and 9.

50P

(a) For the maximum with the greatest value of $m (= M)$ we have $M\lambda = a \sin \theta < d$. Thus $M = d/\lambda = 900 \, \text{nm}/600 \, \text{nm} 1.5$ or $M = 1$. Thus three maxima can be seen, with $m = 0, \pm 1$.

(b)

$$\Delta \theta = \frac{\lambda}{Nd \cos \theta} = \frac{d \sin \theta}{Nd \cos \theta} = \frac{\tan \theta}{N} = \frac{1}{N}\left[\sin^{-1}\left(\frac{\lambda}{d}\right) \right]$$

$$= \frac{1}{1000} \tan\left[\sin^{-1}\left(\frac{600 \, \text{nm}}{900 \, \text{nm}}\right) \right] = 0.051°.$$

51P

The angular positions of the first-order diffraction lines are given by $d \sin \theta = \lambda$, where d is the slit separation and λ is the wavelength. Let λ_1 be the shorter wavelength (430 nm) and θ be the angular position of the line associated with it. Let λ_2 be the longer wavelength (680 nm) and let $\theta + \Delta \theta$ be the angular position of the line associated with it. Here

$\Delta\theta = 20°$. Then $d\sin\theta = \lambda_1$ and $d\sin(\theta + \Delta\theta) = \lambda_2$. Use a trigonometric identity to replace $\sin(\theta + \Delta\theta)$ with $\sin\theta\cos\Delta\theta + \cos\theta\sin\Delta\theta$, then use the equation for the first line to replace $\sin\theta$ with λ_1/d and $\cos\theta$ with $\sqrt{1 - \lambda_1^2/d^2}$. After multiplying by d you should obtain $\lambda_1\cos\Delta\theta + \sqrt{d^2 - \lambda_1^2}\sin\Delta\theta = \lambda_2$. Rearrange to get $\sqrt{d^2 - \lambda_1^2}\sin\Delta\theta = \lambda_2 - \lambda_1\cos\Delta\theta$. Square both sides and solve for d. You should get

$$d = \sqrt{\frac{(\lambda_2 - \lambda_1\cos\Delta\theta)^2 + (\lambda_1\sin\Delta\theta)^2}{\sin^2\Delta\theta}}$$

$$= \sqrt{\frac{[(680\,\text{nm}) - (430\,\text{nm})\cos 20°]^2 + [(430\,\text{nm})\sin 20°]^2}{\sin^2 20°}}$$

$$= 914\,\text{nm} = 9.14 \times 10^{-4}\,\text{mm}.$$

There are $1/d = 1/(9.14 \times 10^{-4}\,\text{mm}) = 1090\,\text{rulings per mm}$.

52P
Use Eq. 41-18: $m\lambda = d\sin\theta$. For $m = \pm1$ we get

$$\lambda = \frac{d\sin\theta}{m} = \frac{(1.73\mu\,\text{m})\sin(\pm17.6°)}{\pm1} = 523\,\text{nm},$$

and for $m = \pm2$

$$\lambda = \frac{(1.73\mu\text{m})\sin(\pm37.3°)}{\pm2} = 524\,\text{nm}.$$

Similarly we may compute the values of λ corresponding to the angles for $m = \pm3$. The average value of these λ's is $523\,\text{nm}$.

53P
The difference in path lengths between the two adjacent light rays shown to the right is $\Delta x = AB + BC = d\sin\psi + d\sin\theta$. The condition for bright fringes to occur is thus

$$\Delta x = d(\sin\psi + \sin\theta) = m\lambda,$$

for $m = 0, 1, 2, \cdots$.

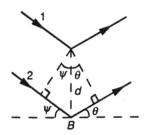

54P
From the figure to the right we see that the angular deviation of the first-order maximum from the incident direction is $\Delta = \psi + \theta_1$. Here $\sin\theta_1 = \lambda/d - \sin\psi = (600\,\text{nm}/1.50\mu\,\text{m}) - \sin\psi = 0.400 = \sin\psi$. Thus

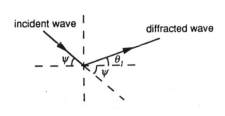

$$\Delta = \psi + \theta_1 = \psi + \sin^{-1}\left(\frac{\lambda}{d} - \sin\psi\right)$$

$$= \psi + \sin^{-1}(0.400 - \sin\psi).$$

The plot is as follows. The angles are given in radians.

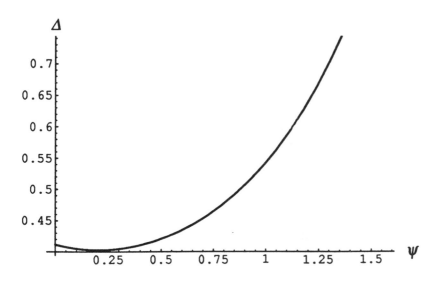

55P
From Eq. 41-18 we get

$$\Delta(\sin\theta) = \Delta\left(\frac{m\lambda}{d}\right) = \frac{m\Delta\lambda}{d},$$

but for small $\Delta\theta$, $\Delta\sin\theta \approx (d\sin\theta/d\theta)\Delta\theta = \cos\theta\Delta\theta$ so

$$\Delta\theta \approx \frac{m\Delta\lambda}{d\cos\theta} = \frac{m\Delta\lambda}{d\sqrt{1-\sin^2\theta}} = \frac{m\Delta\lambda}{d\sqrt{1-(m\lambda/d)^2}}$$

$$= \frac{\Delta\lambda}{\sqrt{(d/m)^2 - \lambda^2}}.$$

56P
From $d\sin\theta = m\lambda$ we see that if the spectra corresponding to $m_1\lambda_1 = m_2\lambda_2$, or

$$\frac{\lambda_1}{\lambda_2} = \frac{m_2}{m_1} = \frac{3}{2}.$$

Since $400\,\text{nm} < \lambda_2 < \lambda_1 < 700\,\text{nm}$ we can always find suitable values of λ_1 and λ_2 which satisfy this condition. For example $\lambda_1 = 600\,\text{nm}$ and $\lambda_2 = 400\,\text{nm}$, or $\lambda_1 = 660\,\text{nm}$ and $\lambda_2 = 440\,\text{nm}$, etc. So these two spectra always overlap, regardless of the value of d.

57P

In this case $a = d/2$, and the formula for the locations of the mth diffraction minimum, $m\lambda = a \sin\theta = (d/2)\sin\theta$, may be re-written as $(2m)\lambda = d\sin\theta$, which we recognize as the formula for the location of the $2m$th maximum of interference. Thus all the $2m$th (i.e. even) orders of maxima will be eliminated (expect $m = 0$).

58P

At the location of the hole $\sin\theta \approx 50\,\text{mm}/30\,\text{cm} = 0.164$, and from $m\lambda = d\sin\theta$ we find $\sin\theta \approx 5.0\,\text{cm}/\sqrt{(30\,\text{cm})^2 + (5.0\,\text{cm})^2} = 0.164$,

$$m = \frac{d\sin\theta}{\lambda} = \frac{(1.00 \times 10^6\,\text{nm}/350)(0.164)}{\lambda} = \frac{470\,\text{nm}}{\lambda}.$$

Since for white light $\lambda > 400\,\text{nm}$ so the only integer m allowed is $m = 1$. At one edge of the hole $\lambda = 477\,\text{nm}$ and at the other edge

$$\lambda = d\sin\theta' = \left(\frac{1.00 \times 10^6\,\text{nm}}{350}\right)\left[\frac{50\,\text{mm} + 10\,\text{mm}}{\sqrt{(30\,\text{cm})^2 + (6.0\,\text{cm})^2}}\right] = 560\,\text{nm}.$$

So the range of wavelengths is from 470 to 560 nm.

59P

The derivation is similar to that used to obtain Eq. 41–21. At the first minimum beyond the mth principal maximum two waves from adjacent slits have a phase difference of $\Delta\phi = 2\pi m + (2\pi/N)$, where N is the number of slits. This implies a difference in path length of $\Delta L = (\Delta\phi/2\pi)\lambda = m\lambda + (\lambda/N)$. If θ_m is the angular position of the mth maximum then the difference in path length is also given by $\Delta L = d\sin(\theta_m + \Delta\theta)$. Thus $d\sin(\theta_m + \Delta\theta) = m\lambda + (\lambda/N)$. Use the trigonometric identity $\sin(\theta_m + \Delta\theta) = \sin\theta_m\cos\Delta\theta + \cos\theta_m\sin\Delta\theta$. Since $\Delta\theta$ is small, we may approximate $\sin\Delta\theta$ by $\Delta\theta$ in radians and $\cos\Delta\theta$ by unity. Thus $d\sin\theta_m + d\Delta\theta\cos\theta_m = m\lambda + (\lambda/N)$. Use the condition $d\sin\theta_m = m\lambda$ to obtain $d\Delta\theta\cos\theta_m = \lambda/N$ and

$$\Delta\theta = \frac{\lambda}{Nd\cos\theta_m}.$$

60E

Let $R = \lambda/\Delta\lambda = Nm$ and solve for N:

$$N = \frac{\lambda}{m\Delta\lambda} = \frac{(589.6\,\text{nm} + 589.0\,\text{nm})/2}{2(589.6\,\text{nm} - 589.0\,\text{nm})} = 491.$$

61E

(a) Solve $\Delta\lambda$ from $R = \lambda/\Delta\lambda = Nm$:

$$\Delta\lambda = \frac{\lambda}{Nm} = \frac{500\,\mathrm{nm}}{(600/\,\mathrm{mm})(5.0\,\mathrm{mm})(3)} = 0.056\,\mathrm{nm}$$

(b) Since $\sin\theta = m_{\max}\lambda/d < 1$ we find

$$m_{\max} < \frac{d}{\lambda} = \frac{1}{(600/\,\mathrm{mm})(500 \times 10^{-6}\,\mathrm{mm})} = 3.3,$$

i.e. $m_{\max} = 3$. So no higher orders of maxima can be seen.

62E

If a grating just resolves two wavelengths whose mean is λ and whose separation is $\Delta\lambda$ then its resolving power is defined by $R = \lambda/\Delta\lambda$. The text shows this is Nm, where N is the number of rulings in the grating and m is the order of the lines. Thus $\lambda/\Delta\lambda = Nm$ and

$$N = \frac{\lambda}{m\,\Delta\lambda} = \frac{656.3\,\mathrm{nm}}{(1)(0.18\,\mathrm{nm})} = 3650\,\mathrm{rulings}\,.$$

63E

(a) From $R = \lambda/\Delta\lambda = Nm$ we find

$$N = \frac{\lambda}{m\Delta\lambda} = \frac{(415.496\,\mathrm{nm} + 415.487\,\mathrm{nm})/2}{2(415.496\,\mathrm{nm} - 415.487\,\mathrm{nm})} = 23,100.$$

(b) The maxima are found at

$$\theta = \sin^{-1}\left[\frac{m\lambda}{d}\right] = \sin^{-1}\left[\frac{(2)(415.5\,\mathrm{nm})}{4.0 \times 10^7\,\mathrm{nm}/23,100}\right]$$
$$= 28.7°.$$

64E

(a) From $d\sin\theta = m\lambda$ we find

$$d = \frac{m\lambda}{\sin\theta} = \frac{3(589.3\,\mathrm{nm})}{\sin 10°} = 1.0 \times 10^4\,\mathrm{nm} = 10\mu\mathrm{m}.$$

(b) The total width of the ruling is

$$L = Nd = \frac{Rd}{m} = \frac{\lambda d}{m\Delta\lambda}$$
$$= \frac{(589.3\,\mathrm{nm})(10\mu\mathrm{m})}{3(589.59\,\mathrm{nm} - 589.00\,\mathrm{nm})} = 3.3 \times 10^3\,\mu\mathrm{m} = 3.3\,\mathrm{mm}.$$

65E

The dispersion of a grating is given by $D = d\theta/d\lambda$, where θ is the angular position of a line associated with wavelength λ. The angular position and wavelength are related by $d \sin \theta = m\lambda$, where d is the slit separation and m is an integer. Differentiate this with respect to θ to obtain $(d\theta/d\lambda) d \cos \theta = m$ or

$$D = \frac{d\theta}{d\lambda} = \frac{m}{d \cos \theta}.$$

Now $m = (d/\lambda) \sin \theta$, so

$$D = \frac{d \sin \theta}{d\lambda \cos \theta} = \frac{\tan \theta}{\lambda}.$$

The trigonometric identity $\tan \theta = \sin \theta / \cos \theta$ was used.

66E

(a) For the first order maxima $\lambda = d \sin \theta$, which gives

$$\theta = \sin^{-1} \left(\frac{\lambda}{d} \right) = \sin^{-1} \left(\frac{589 \, \text{nm}}{76 \times 10^6 \, \text{nm}/40,000} \right) = 18°$$

so from Exercise 65, $D = \tan \theta/\lambda = \tan 18°/589 \, \text{nm} = 0.032°/\,\text{nm}$. Similarly for $m = 2$ and $m = 3$ we have $\theta = 38°$ and $68°$, and the corresponding values of dispersion are $0.076°/\,\text{nm}$ and $0.24°/\,\text{nm}$, respectively.

(b) $R = mN = 40000m = 40,000$ (for $m = 1$); $80,000$ (for $m = 2$); and $120,000$ (for $m = 3$).

67E

(a) We requir that $\sin \theta = m\lambda_{1,2}/d \leq \sin 30°$, where $m = 1, 2$ and $\lambda_1 = 500 \, \text{nm}$. This gives

$$d \geq \frac{2\lambda_2}{\sin 30°} = \frac{2(600 \, \text{nm})}{\sin 30°} = 2400 \, \text{nm}.$$

For a grating of given total width L we have $N = L/d \propto d^{-1}$, so we need to minimize d to maximize $R = mN \propto d^{-1}$. Thus we choose $d = 2400 \, \text{nm}$.

(b) Let the third-order maximum for $\lambda_2 = 600 \, \text{nm}$ be the first minimum for the single-slit diffraction profile. This requires that $d \sin \theta = 3\lambda_2 = a \sin \theta$, or $a = d/3 = 2400 \, \text{nm}/3 = 800 \, \text{nm}$.

(c) Let $\sin \theta = m_{\text{max}} \lambda_2 / d \leq 1$ we get

$$m_{\text{max}} \leq \frac{d}{\lambda_2} = \frac{2400 \, \text{nm}}{800 \, \text{nm}} = 3.$$

Since the third order is missing the only maxima present are the ones with $m = 0, 1$ and 2.

$$R\Delta\theta = (Nm)\left(\frac{\lambda}{Nd\cos\theta}\right) = \frac{m\lambda}{d\cos\theta} = \frac{d\sin\theta}{d\cos\theta} = \tan\theta$$

$$= \tan\left[\sin^{-1}\left(\frac{\lambda}{d}\right)\right] = \tan\left[\sin^{-1}\left(\frac{600\,\text{nm}}{900\,\text{nm}}\right)\right] = 0.89.$$

69P

(a) Since the resolving power of a grating is given by $R = \lambda/\Delta\lambda$ and by Nm, the range of wavelengths that can just be resolved in order m is $\Delta\lambda = \lambda/Nm$. Here N is the number of rulings in the grating. The frequency f is related to the wavelength by $f\lambda = c$, where c is the speed of light. This means $f\Delta\lambda + \lambda\Delta f = 0$, so $\Delta\lambda = -(\lambda/f)\Delta f = -(\lambda^2/c)\Delta f$, where $f = c/\lambda$ was used. The negative sign means simply that an increase in frequency corresponds to a decrease in wavelength. If we interpret Δf as the range of frequencies that can be resolved we may take it to be positive. Then

$$\frac{\lambda^2}{c}\Delta f = \frac{\lambda}{Nm}$$

and

$$\Delta f = \frac{c}{Nm\lambda}.$$

(b) The difference in travel time for waves traveling along the two extreme rays is $\Delta t = \Delta L/c$, where ΔL is the difference in path length. The waves originate at slits that are separated by $(N-1)d$, where d is the slit separation and N is the number of slits, so the path difference is $\Delta L = (N-1)d\sin\theta$ and the time difference is

$$\Delta t = \frac{(N-1)d\sin\theta}{c}.$$

If N is large this may be approximated by $\Delta t = (Nd/c)\sin\theta$. The lens does not affect the travel time.

(c) Substitute the expressions you derived for Δt and Δf to obtain

$$\Delta f\,\Delta t = \left(\frac{c}{Nm\lambda}\right)\left(\frac{Nd\sin\theta}{c}\right) = \frac{d\sin\theta}{m\lambda} = 1.$$

The condition $d\sin\theta = m\lambda$ for a diffraction line was used to obtain the last result.

70E

Bragg's law gives the condition for a diffraction maximum:

$$2d\sin\theta = m\lambda,$$

where d is the spacing of the crystal planes and λ is the wavelength. The angle θ is measured from the normal to the planes. For a second order reflection $m = 2$, so

$$d = \frac{m\lambda}{2\sin\theta} = \frac{2(0.12 \times 10^{-9}\,\text{m})}{2\sin 28°} = 2.56 \times 10^{-10}\,\text{m} = 256\,\text{pm}.$$

71E
Use Eq. 41-29. For smallest value of θ let $m = 1$:

$$\theta_{\min} = \sin^{-1}\left[\frac{m\lambda}{2d}\right] = \sin^{-1}\left[\frac{(1)(30\,\text{pm})}{2(0.30 \times 10^3\,\text{pm})}\right] = 2.9°.$$

72E
For first order reflection $2d\sin\theta_1 = \lambda$ and for the second order one $2d\sin\theta_2 = 2\lambda$. Solve for θ_2:

$$\theta_2 = \sin^{-1}(2\sin\theta_1) = \sin^{-1}(2\sin 3.4°) = 6.8°.$$

73E
Use Eq. 41-29. From the peak on the left at angle θ_1 $2d\sin\theta_1 = \lambda_1$, or $\lambda_1 = 2d\sin\theta_1 = 2(0.94\,\text{nm})\sin(0.75°) = 0.025\,\text{nm} = 25\,\text{pm}$. From the next peak $\lambda_2 = 2d\sin\theta_2 = 2(0.94\,\text{nm})\sin(1.15°) = 0.038\,\text{nm} = 38\,\text{pm}$. You can check that the third peak from left is just the second-order one for λ_1.

74E
For the first beam $2d\sin\theta_1 = \lambda_R$ and for the second one $2d\sin\theta_2 = 3\lambda_B$. Solve for d and λ_A:
(a)

$$d = \frac{3\lambda_B}{2\sin\theta_2} = \frac{3(100\,\text{pm})}{2\sin 60°} = 1.7 \times 10^2\,\text{pm}.$$

(b) $\lambda_A = 2d\sin\theta_1 = 2(1.7 \times 10^2\,\text{pm})(\sin 23°) = 1.3 \times 10^2\,\text{pm}$. (Note that the condition $\lambda_B = 100\,\text{pm}$ is missing in the problem statement.)

75E

$$\lambda = 2d\sin\theta = 2(39.8\,\text{pm})(\sin 30.0°) = 39.8\,\text{pm}.$$

76P

There are two unknowns, the x-ray wavelength λ and the plane separation d, so data for scattering at two angles from the same planes should suffice. The observations obey Bragg's law, so

$$2d \sin \theta_1 = m_1 \lambda$$

and

$$2d \sin \theta_2 = m_2 \lambda.$$

However, these cannot be solved for the unknowns. For example, use first equation to eliminate λ from the second. You obtain $m_2 \sin \theta_1 = m_1 \sin \theta_2$, an equation that does not contain either of the unknowns.

77P

The wavelengths satisfy $m\lambda = 2d \sin \theta = 2(275 \, \text{pm})(\sin 45°) = 389 \, \text{pm}$. In the range of wavelengths given, the allowed values of m are $m = 3, 4$, with corresponding wavelengths being $389 \, \text{pm}/3 = 130 \, \text{pm}$ and $389 \, \text{pm}/4 = 97.2 \, \text{pm}$.

78P

The angle of incidence on the reflection planes is $\theta = 63.8° - 45.0° = 18.8°$, and the plane-plane separation is $d = a_0/\sqrt{2}$. Thus from $2d \sin \theta = \lambda$ we get

$$a_0 = \sqrt{2}d = \frac{\sqrt{2}\lambda}{2 \sin \theta} = \frac{0.260 \, \text{nm}}{\sqrt{2} \sin 18.8°} = 0.570 \, \text{nm}.$$

79P

(a) The sets of planes with the next five smaller interplanar spacings (after a_0) are shown in the diagram to the right. In terms of a_0 the spacings are:

(i): $a_0/\sqrt{2} = 0.7071 a_0$

(ii): $a_0/\sqrt{5} = 0.4472 a_0$

(iii): $a_0/\sqrt{10} = 0.3162 a_0$

(iv): $a_0/\sqrt{13} = 0.2774 a_0$

(v): $a_0/\sqrt{17} = 0.2425 a_0$.

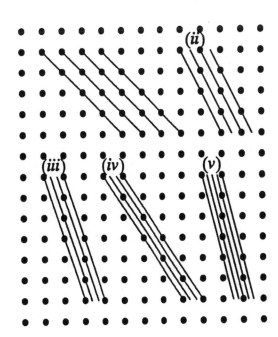

(b) Since any crystal plane passes through lattice points its slope can be written as the ratio of two integers. Consider a set planes with slope m/n, as shown in the diagram to the right. The first and last planes shown pass through adjacent lattice points along a horizontal line and there are $m-1$ planes between. If h is the separation of the first and last planes, then the interplanar spacing is $d = h/m$. If the planes make the angle θ with the horizontal, then the normal to planes (shown dotted) makes the angle $\phi = 90° - \theta$. The distance h is given by $h = a_0 \cos \phi$ and the interplanar spacing is $d = h/m = (a_0/m) \cos \phi$. Since $\tan \theta = m/n$, $\tan \phi = n/m$ and $\cos \phi = 1/\sqrt{1 + \tan^2 \phi} = m/\sqrt{n^2 + m^2}$. Thus

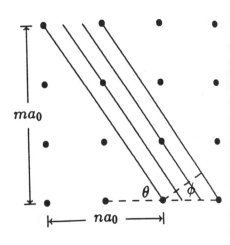

$$d = \frac{h}{m} = \frac{a_0 \cos \phi}{m} = \frac{a_0}{\sqrt{n^2 + m^2}} .$$

80P

The angles of incidence which correspond to intensity maxima in reflected beam of light satisfy $2d \sin \theta = m\lambda$, or

$$\sin \theta = \frac{m\lambda}{2d} = \frac{m(0.125\,\text{nm})}{2(0.252\,\text{nm})} = \frac{m}{4.032} .$$

Since $|\sin \theta| < 1$ the allowed values for m are $m = 1, 2, 3, 4$. Correspondingly the values of θ are $\theta = 14.4°$, $29.7°$, $48.1°$, and $82.8°$. Therefore the crystal should be rotated counterclockwise by $48.1° - 45.0° = 3.1°$ or $82.8° - 45.0° = 37.8°$, or clockwise by $45.0° - 14.4° = 30.6°$ or $45.0° - 29.7° = 15.3°$.

CHAPTER 42

1E

(a)
$$\beta = \frac{v}{c} = \frac{(1\,\text{in./y})(0.2540 \times 10^{-2}\,\text{m/in.})(1\,\text{y}/3.15 \times 10^7\,\text{s})}{3.0 \times 10^8\,\text{m/s}} = 3 \times 10^{-18}.$$

(b)
$$\beta = \frac{v}{c} = \frac{0.5 \times 10^{-3}\,\text{m/s}}{3.0 \times 10^8\,\text{m/s}} = 2 \times 10^{-12}.$$

(c)
$$\beta = \frac{v}{c} = \frac{(55\,\text{mi/h})(1.609 \times 10^3\,\text{m/mi})(1\,\text{h}/3600\,\text{s})}{3.00 \times 10^8\,\text{m/s}} = 8.2 \times 10^{-8}.$$

(d) The rms speed of a hydrogen molecule at room temperature is $v = 1920\,\text{m/s}$ (see Table 21-1). So
$$\beta = \frac{v}{c} = \frac{1920\,\text{m/s}}{3.00 \times 10^8\,\text{m/s}} = 6.4 \times 10^{-6}.$$

(e)
$$\beta = \frac{(1200\,\text{km/h})(10^3\,\text{m/km})(1\,\text{h}/3600\,\text{s})}{3.00 \times 10^8\,\text{m/s}} = 1.1 \times 10^{-6}.$$

(f)
$$\beta = \frac{(11.2\,\text{km/s})(10^3\,\text{m/km})}{3.00 \times 10^8\,\text{m/s}} = 3.7 \times 10^{-5}.$$

(g) The orbital speed of the Earth is
$$v = \frac{2\pi R_{\text{ES}}}{T} = \frac{2\pi(1.50 \times 10^{11}\,\text{m})}{(1\,\text{y})(3.154 \times 10^7\,\text{s/y})} = 3.0 \times 10^4\,\text{m/s}.$$

Thus
$$\beta = \frac{v}{c} = \frac{3.0 \times 10^4\,\text{m/s}}{3.0 \times 10^8\,\text{m/s}} = 1.0 \times 10^{-4}.$$

(h)
$$p = \frac{v}{c} = \frac{(3.0 \times 10^4\,\text{km/s})(10^3\,\text{m/km})}{3.00 \times 10^8\,\text{m/s}} = 0.10.$$

2E

(a) The time an electron with a horizontal component of velocity v takes to travel a horizontal distance L is
$$t = \frac{L}{v} = \frac{20 \times 10^{-2}\,\text{m}}{(0.992)(3.00 \times 10^8\,\text{m/s})} = 6.72 \times 10^{-10}\,\text{s}.$$

(b) During this time it falls a vertical distance $y = \frac{1}{2}gt^2 = \frac{1}{2}(9.8\,\text{m/s}^2)(6.72 \times 10^{-10}\,\text{s})^2 = 2.21 \times 10^{-18}\,\text{m}$.

3P

$$v = \frac{s}{t} = \frac{6.0\,\text{ly}}{2.0\,\text{y} + 6.0\,\text{y}} = \frac{(6.0\,c)(1.0\,\text{y})}{2.0\,\text{y} + 6.0\,\text{y}} = 0.75\,c.$$

4E

Solve β from $\gamma = (1 - \beta^2)^{-1/2}$: $\beta = (1 - r^{-2})^{1/2}$.
(a) $\beta = \sqrt{1 - (1.01)^{-2}} = 0.140$.
(b) $\beta = \sqrt{1 - (10.0)^{-2}} = 0.9950$.
(c) $\beta = \sqrt{1 - (100)^{-2}} = 0.999950$.
(c) $\beta = \sqrt{1 - (1000)^{-2}} = 0.99999950$.

5E

Use the time dilation equation $\Delta t = \gamma \Delta t_0$, where Δt_0 is the proper time interval, $\gamma = 1/\sqrt{1 - \beta^2}$, and $\beta = v/c$. Thus $\Delta t = \Delta t_0 / \sqrt{1 - \beta^2}$ and the solution for β is

$$\beta = \sqrt{1 - \left(\frac{\Delta t_0}{\Delta t}\right)^2}.$$

The proper time interval is measured by a clock at rest relative to the muon. That is, $\Delta t_0 = 2.2\,\mu\text{s}$ and $\Delta t = 16\,\mu\text{s}$. This means

$$\beta = \sqrt{1 - \left(\frac{2.2\,\mu\text{s}}{16\,\mu\text{s}}\right)^2} = 0.9905.$$

The muon speed is $v = \beta c = 0.9905(3.00 \times 10^8\,\text{m/s}) = 2.97 \times 10^8\,\text{m/s}$.

6P

Use Eqs. 42-6 to 42-8:

$$\Delta t_0 = \frac{\Delta t}{\gamma} = \frac{s}{v\gamma} = \frac{s}{v}\sqrt{1 - \left(\frac{v}{c}\right)^2}$$

$$= \frac{1.05 \times 10^{-3}\,\text{m}\sqrt{1 - (0.992)^2}}{(0.992)(3.00 \times 10^8\,\text{m/s})} = 4.45 \times 10^{-13}\,\text{s}.$$

7P

The mean life time of a pion measured in a frame fixed on the Earth is $\Delta t = \gamma \Delta t_0$ so the distance it can travel is

$$s = v\Delta t = \gamma v \Delta t_0 = \frac{(0.99)(3.00 \times 10^8 \text{ m/s})(26 \times 10^{-9} \text{ s})}{\sqrt{1 - (0.99)^2}} = 55 \text{ m}.$$

8P

(a) Find $v = \beta c$ from $\gamma = (1 - \beta^2)^{-1/2} = \Delta t / \Delta t_0$:

$$v = \beta c = \sqrt{1 - \left(\frac{\Delta t_0}{\Delta t}\right)^2}\, c = \sqrt{1 - \left(\frac{1 \text{ y}}{1000 \text{ y}}\right)^2}\, c = 0.99999950.$$

(b) Yes. In fact if you do not travel in a straight line then you are no longer in an inertial frame of reference in which the Lorentz transformation is valid.

9E

The length L of the rod, as measured in a frame in which it is moving with speed v parallel to its length, is related to its rest length L_0 by $L = L_0/\gamma$, where $\gamma = 1/\sqrt{1 - \beta^2}$ and $\beta = v/c$. Since γ must be greater than 1, L is less than L_0. For this problem $L_0 = 1.70 \text{ m}$ and $\beta = 0.630$, so $L = (1.70 \text{ m})\sqrt{1 - (0.630)^2} = 1.32 \text{ m}$.

10E

(a) Use Eq. 42-10 and solve for $v = \beta c$:

$$v = \beta c = c\sqrt{1 - \left(\frac{L}{L_0}\right)^2} = c\sqrt{1 - \left(\frac{1}{2}\right)^2} = 0.866\, c.$$

(b) The factor is $\gamma = (1 - \beta^2)^{-1/2} = [1 - (0.866)^2]^{-1/2} = 2.00$.

11E

$$L = \frac{L_0}{\gamma} = L_0\sqrt{1 - \beta^2} = (3.00 \text{ m})\sqrt{1 - (0.999987)^2} = 0.0153 \text{ m}.$$

12E

$$|\Delta L| = L_0 - L = L_0\left(1 - \frac{1}{\gamma}\right) = L_0(1 - \sqrt{1 - \beta^2})$$

$$= 2(6.370 \times 10^4 \text{ m})\left[1 - \sqrt{1 - \left(\frac{3.0 \times 10^4 \text{ m/s}}{3.00 \times 10^8 \text{ m/s}}\right)^2}\right] = 0.064 \text{ m}.$$

13E

(a) The rest length L_0 (= 130 m) of the spaceship and its length L as measured by the timing station are related by $L = L_0/\gamma = L_0\sqrt{1-\beta^2}$, where $\gamma = 1/\sqrt{1-\beta^2}$ and $\beta = v/c$. Thus $L = (130\,\text{m})\sqrt{1-(0.740)^2} = 87.4\,\text{m}$.

(b) The time interval for the passage of the spaceship is

$$\Delta t = \frac{L}{v} = \frac{87.4\,\text{m}}{(0.740)(3.00\times 10^8\,\text{m/s})} = 3.94\times 10^{-7}\,\text{s}.$$

14P

(a) The speed of the traveler is $v = 0.99c$ which is the same as $0.99\,\text{ly/y}$. Let d be the distance traveled. Then the time for the trip, as measured in the frame of the Earth, is $\Delta t = d/v = (26\,\text{ly})/(0.99\,\text{ly/y}) = 26.3\,\text{y}$.

(b) The signal, presumed to be a radio wave, travels with speed c and so takes $26.0\,\text{y}$ to reach Earth. The total time elapsed, in the frame of the Earth, is $26.3\,\text{y} + 26.0\,\text{y} = 52.3\,\text{y}$.

(c) The proper time interval is measured by a clock in the spaceship, so $\Delta t_0 = \Delta t/\gamma$. Now $\gamma = 1/\sqrt{1-\beta^2} = 1/\sqrt{1-(0.99)^2} = 7.09$. Thus $\Delta t_0 = (26.3\,\text{y})/(7.09) = 3.7\,\text{y}$.

15P

(a)

$$\frac{|\Delta L|}{L_0} = \frac{L_0(1-\gamma^{-1})}{L_0} = 1 - \sqrt{1-\beta^2} \approx 1 - (1 - \tfrac{1}{2}\beta^2) = \tfrac{1}{2}\beta^2$$

$$= \frac{1}{2}\left(\frac{630\,\text{m/s}}{3.00\times 10^8\,\text{m/s}}\right)^2 = 2.21\times 10^{-12}.$$

(b) Let $|\Delta t - \Delta t_0| = \Delta t_0(\gamma - 1) = \tau = 1.00\,\mu\text{s}$ and solve for Δt_0:

$$\Delta t_0 = \frac{\tau}{\gamma - 1} = \frac{\tau}{(1-\beta^2)^{-1/2} - 1} \approx \frac{\tau}{1 + \tfrac{1}{2}\beta^2 - 1} = \frac{2\tau}{\beta^2}$$

$$= \frac{2(1.00\times 10^{-6}\,\text{s})(1\,\text{d}/86400\,\text{s})}{[(630\,\text{m/s})/(3.00\times 10^8\,\text{m/s})]^2} = 5.25\,\text{d}.$$

16P

(a) In principle, yes. If the person moves fast enough, then from the time dilation argument his travel time measured from the Earth is much longer than a normal lifetime, or from the length contraction argument the distance he needs to cover (measured with respect to his spaceship) is much less than 23,000 ly. Either way, we conclude that it is possible for him to reach the center of the galaxy in a normal lifetime.

(b) Solve v from $\gamma = (1 - \beta^2)^{-1/2} = \Delta t / \Delta t_0 \approx 23{,}000\,\text{y}/30\,\text{y}$:

$$v = \beta c = c\sqrt{1 - \left(\frac{30\,\text{y}}{23000\,\text{y}}\right)^2} = 0.99999915\,c.$$

17E

The proper time is not measured by clocks in either frame S or frame S' since a single clock at rest in either frame cannot be present at the origin and at the event. The full Lorentz transformation must be used:

$$x' = \gamma[x - vt]$$

$$t' = \gamma[t - \beta x/c]\,,$$

where $\beta = v/c = 0.950$ and $\gamma = 1/\sqrt{1 - \beta^2} = 1/\sqrt{1 - (0.950)^2} = 3.2026$. Thus

$$x' = (3.2026)\left[100 \times 10^3\,\text{m} - (0.950)(3.00 \times 10^8\,\text{m/s})(200 \times 10^{-6}\,\text{s}\right]$$
$$= 1.38 \times 10^5\,\text{m} = 138\,\text{km}$$

and

$$t' = (3.2026)\left[200 \times 10^{-6}\,\text{s} - \frac{(0.950)(100 \times 10^3\,\text{m})}{3.00 \times 10^8\,\text{m/s}}\right] = -3.74 \times 10^{-4}\,\text{s} = -374\,\mu\text{s}\,.$$

18E

(a) The coordinates in the S' are:

$$x' = \gamma(x - vt) = \frac{x - vt}{\sqrt{1 - \beta^2}}$$
$$= \frac{3.00 \times 10^8\,\text{m} - (0.400)(3.00 \times 10^8\,\text{m/s})(2.50\,\text{s})}{\sqrt{1 - (0.400)^2}} = 0,$$

$y' = y = 0$, $z' = z = 0$, and

$$t' = \gamma\left(\left(t - \frac{vx}{c^2}\right)\right) = \frac{1}{\sqrt{1 - (0.400)^2}}\left[2.50\,\text{s} - \frac{(0.400)(3.00 \times 10^8\,\text{m})}{3.00 \times 10^8\,\text{m/s}}\right]$$
$$= 2.29\,\text{s}.$$

(b) Let $v \rightarrow -v$ to obtain

$$x' = \frac{x + vt}{\sqrt{1 - \beta^2}} = \frac{3.00 \times 10^8\,\text{m} + (0.400)(3.00 \times 10^8\,\text{m/s})(2.50\,\text{s})}{\sqrt{1 - (0.400)^2}} = 6.55 \times 10^8\,\text{m},$$

$y' = y = 0$, $z' = z = 0$, and

$$t' = \gamma\left(\left(t + \frac{vx}{c^2}\right)\right) = \frac{1}{\sqrt{1 - (0.400)^2}}\left[2.50\,\text{s} + \frac{(0.400)(3.00 \times 10^8\,\text{m})}{3.00 \times 10^8\,\text{m/s}}\right]$$
$$= 3.16\,\text{s}.$$

19E
For event 1:

$$t_1' = \gamma\left(t_1 + \frac{vx_1}{c^2}\right) = \gamma(0) = 0.$$

For event 2:

$$t_2' = \gamma\left(t_2 - \frac{vx_2}{c^2}\right) = \frac{1}{\sqrt{1 - (0.60)^2}}\left[4.0 \times 10^{-6}\,\text{s} - \frac{(0.60)(3.0 \times 10^3\,\text{m})}{3.00 \times 10^8\,\text{m/s}}\right]$$
$$= -2.5 \times 10^{-6}\,\text{s} = -2.5\mu\,\text{s}.$$

Since $x_2/t_2 = 3.0 \times 10^3\,\text{m}/(4.0 \times 10^{-6}\,\text{s}) = 7.5 \times 10^8\,\text{m/s} > c$, the two events are independent. Therefore the difference in time order is possible.

20E
(a) Take the flashbulbs to be at rest in frame S and let frame S' be the rest frame of the second observer. Clocks in neither frame measure the proper time interval between the flashes, so the full Lorentz transformation must be used. Let t_b be the time and x_b be the coordinate of the blue flash, as measured in frame S. Then the time of the blue flash, as measured in frame S', is

$$t_b' = \gamma\left[t_b - \frac{\beta x_b}{c}\right],$$

where $\beta = v/c = 0.250$ and $\gamma = 1/\sqrt{1 - \beta^2} = 1/\sqrt{1 - (0.250)^2} = 1.0328$. Similarly, let t_r be the time and x_r be the coordinate of the red flash, as measured in frame S. Then the time of the red flash, as measured in frame S', is

$$t_r' = \gamma\left[t_r - \frac{\beta x_r}{c}\right].$$

Now subtract the first Lorentz transformation equation from the second. Recognize that $t_b = t_r$ since the flashes are simultaneous in S. Let $\Delta x = x_r - x_b = 30.0\,\text{km}$ and let $\Delta t' = t_r' - t_b'$. Then

$$\Delta t' = -\frac{\gamma\beta\,\Delta x}{c} = -\frac{(1.0328)(0.250)(30 \times 10^3\,\text{m})}{3.00 \times 10^8\,\text{m/s}} = -2.58 \times 10^{-5}\,\text{s}.$$

(b) Since $\Delta t'$ is negative, t'_b is greater than t'_r. The red bulb flashes first in S'.

21E
From Eq. 1 in Table 42-3, $\Delta x' = \Delta x/\gamma - v\Delta t'$. Then from Eq. 2 $\Delta t' = \Delta t/\gamma - v\Delta x'/c^2$. Combining these two equations:

$$\Delta x' = \frac{\Delta x}{\gamma} - v\left(\frac{\Delta t}{\gamma} - \frac{v\Delta x'}{c^2}\right).$$

Solve for $\Delta x'$: $\Delta x' = \gamma(\Delta x - v\Delta t)$. Here we used $\gamma^{-1} = \sqrt{1 - v^2/c^2}$. This is Eq. 1'. Similarly we can get from Eq. 2 to Eq. 2'.

22P
(a) The Lorentz factor is

$$\gamma = \frac{1}{\sqrt{1 - \beta^2}} = \frac{1}{\sqrt{1 - (0.600)^2}} = 1.25.$$

(b) In the unprimed frame the time for the clock to travel from the origin to $x = 180\,\text{m}$ is

$$t = \frac{x}{v} = \frac{180\,\text{m}}{(0.600)(3.00 \times 10^8\,\text{m/s})} = 1.00 \times 10^{-6}\,\text{s}.$$

The proper time interval between the two events (clock at origin and clock at $x = 180\,\text{m}$) is measured by the clock itself. The reading on the clock at the beginning of the interval is zero, so the reading at the end is

$$t' = \frac{t}{\gamma} = \frac{1.00 \times 10^{-6}\,\text{s}}{1.25} = 8.00 \times 10^{-7}\,\text{s}.$$

23E
(a) Let the separation between the two events in S' be

$$\Delta x' = \gamma(\Delta x - v\Delta t) = 0,$$

we get

$$v = \frac{\Delta x}{\Delta t} = \frac{(720\,\text{m})c}{(5.00 \times 10^{-6}\,\text{s})(3.00 \times 10^8\,\text{m/s})} = 0.480\,c.$$

(b) Since

$$\Delta t' = \gamma\left(\Delta t - \frac{v\Delta x}{c^2}\right) = [1 - (0.48)^2]^{-1/2}\left[5.00\mu\text{s} - \frac{(0.48)(720\,\text{m})}{3.00 \times 10^8\,\text{m/s}}\right]$$

$$= 4.39\mu\text{s} > 0,$$

the "red" flash would occur first.

(c) $\Delta t' = 4.39 \mu$s, as calculated in (b).

24P

Let $\Delta x' = \gamma(\Delta x - v\Delta t) = 0$ to get the speed v of the S' frame: $v = \Delta x/\Delta t$. Now $v < c$ so $\Delta x/\Delta t < c$, or

$$\Delta t > \frac{\Delta x}{c} = \frac{720\,\text{m}}{3.00 \times 10^8\,\text{m/s}} = 2.40 \mu\text{s},$$

i.e. the time interval in S frame cannot be less than 2.40μs.

25E

There are two possible solutions, depending on the relative directions of the velocity of the particle and the velocity of frame S, both as measured in S'. First suppose both are in the positive x direction. Then $v = 0.40c$ and $u = -0.60c$. According to the velocity transformation equation (Eq. 42–23)

$$v = \frac{v' + u}{1 + uv'/c^2} = \frac{0.40c - 0.60c}{1 + (0.40c)(-0.60c)/c^2} = -0.263c.$$

Notice that in the equation u is the velocity of S' relative to S. Since S is moving with speed $0.60c$ in the positive x direction according to S', S' is moving with the same speed but in the negative x direction according to S.

Now suppose the velocity of frame S is in the negative x direction when viewed from S'. Then $u = +0.60c$ and

$$v = \frac{0.40c + 0.60c}{1 + (0.40c)(0.60c)/c^2} = 0.81c.$$

26P

(a) Use Eq. 42-23:

$$v = \frac{v' + u}{1 + uv'/c^2} = \frac{0.47\,c + 0.62\,c}{1 + (0.47\,c)(0.62\,c)/c^2} = 0.84\,c,$$

in the direction of increasing x (since $v > 0$). The classical theory predicts that $v = 0.47\,c + 0.62\,c = 1.1\,c > c$.

(b) Now $v' = -0.47\,c$ so

$$v = \frac{v' + u}{1 + uv'/c^2} = \frac{-0.47\,c + 0.62\,c}{1 + (-0.47\,c)(0.62\,c)/c^2} = 0.21\,c,$$

still in the direction of increasing x. The classical prediction is $v = 0.62\,c - 0.47\,c = 0.15\,c$.

27E

Let the reference frame be S in which in particle approaching the South Pole is at rest, and the frame that is fixed on the Earth be S'. Then $u = 0.60\,c$ and $v' = 0.80\,c$. The relative speed is now the speed of the other particle in S:

$$v = \frac{v' + u}{1 + uv'/c^2} = \frac{0.80\,c + 0.60\,c}{1 + (0.8\,c)(0.60\,c)/c^2} = 0.95\,c.$$

28E

(a) Let frame S' be attached to us and frame S be attached to Galaxy A. Take the positive axis to be in the direction of motion of Galaxy A, as seen by us. In S' our velocity is $v' = 0$ and the velocity of Galaxy A is $0.35c$ in the positive x direction. This means $u = -0.35c$. Our velocity, as observed from Galaxy A, is

$$v = \frac{v' + u}{1 + uv'/c^2} = u = -0.35c.$$

The negative sign indicates motion in the negative x direction.

(b) In frame S' the velocity of Galaxy B is $v' = -0.35c$, so in S it is

$$v = \frac{v' + u}{1 + uv'} = \frac{-0.35c - 0.35c}{1 + (-0.35c)(-0.35c)/c^2} = -0.62c.$$

The negative sign again indicates motion in the negative x direction.

29E

Denote tha reference frame fixed on the Earth as S and that fixed on Q_1 be S'. Then the velocity of Q_2 measured by Q_1 is

$$v' = \frac{v - u}{1 - vu/c^2} = \frac{0.400\,c - 0.800\,c}{1 - (0.400\,c)(0.800\,c)/c^2} = -0.588\,c,$$

where the minus sign indicates that Q_2 is moving away form Q_1 (i.e. towards the Earth).

30P

Calculate the speed of the micrometeorite relative to the spaceship. Let S' be the reference frame for which the data is given and attach frame S to the spaceship. Suppose the micrometeorite is going in the positive x direction and the spaceship is going in the negative x direction, both as viewed from S'. Then in Eq. 42–23, $v' = 0.82c$ and $u = 0.82c$. Notice that u in the equation is the velocity of S' relative to S. Thus the velocity of the micrometeorite in the frame of the spaceship is

$$v = \frac{v' + u}{1 + uv'/c^2} = \frac{0.82c + 0.82c}{1 + (0.82c)(0.82c)/c^2} = 0.9806c.$$

The time for the micrometeorite to pass the spaceship is

$$\Delta t = \frac{L}{v} = \frac{350\,\text{m}}{(0.9806)(3.00 \times 10^8\,\text{m/s})} = 1.19 \times 10^{-6}\,\text{s}.$$

31P

(a) $v_r = 2v = 2(17,000\,\text{mi/h}) = 34,000\,\text{mi/h}$.

(b) The correct formula for v_r is $v_r = 2v/(1 + v^2/c^2)$ so the percentage error is

$$1 - \frac{1}{1 + v^2/c^2} = 1 - \frac{1}{1 + [(17,000\,\text{mi/h})/(6.17 \times 10^8\,\text{mi/h})]^2} = 6.4 \times 10^{-10}.$$

32P

The speed of the spaceship after the first increment is $v_1 = 0.5\,c$. After the second one, it becomes

$$v_2 = \frac{v' + v_1}{1 + v'v_1/c^2} = \frac{0.50\,c + 0.50\,c}{1 + (0.50\,c)^2/c^2} = 0.80\,c.$$

After the third one,

$$v_3 = \frac{v' + v_2}{1 + v'v_2/c^2} = \frac{0.50\,c + 0.80\,c}{1 + (0.50\,c)(0.80\,c)/c^2} = 0.929\,c.$$

Continuing with this process, you can get $v_4 = 0.976\,c$, $v_5 = 0.992\,c$, $v_6 = 0.997\,c$ and $v_7 = 0.999\,c$. Thus seven increments are needed.

33E

The spaceship is moving away from the Earth, so the frequency received is given by Eq. 42–26:

$$f = f_0 \sqrt{\frac{1 - \beta}{1 + \beta}},$$

where f_0 is the frequency in the frame of the spaceship, $\beta = v/c$, and v is the speed of the spaceship relative to the Earth. Thus

$$f = (100\,\text{MHz})\sqrt{\frac{1 - 0.9000}{1 + 0.9000}} = 22.9\,\text{MHz}.$$

34E

(a) Use Eq. 18-51, the classical Doppler shift equation: $f' = fv/(v+v_s)$, or $\lambda' = \lambda(v+v_s)/v$. Solve for v_s:

$$v_s = v\left(\frac{\lambda'}{\lambda} - 1\right) = c\left(\frac{3\lambda}{\lambda} - 1\right) = 2c > c.$$

(b) Now use Eq. 42-26 to find $v_s = \beta_s c$:

$$\beta_s = \frac{1 - (f/f_0)^2}{1 + (f/f_0)^2} = \frac{1 - (\lambda'/\lambda)^2}{1 + (\lambda'/\lambda)^2} = \frac{1 - (1/3)^2}{1 + (1/3)^2} = 0.8,$$

so $v_s = \beta_s c = 0.8\,c$.

35E

Use the transverse Doppler shift formula, Eq. 42-30: $f = f_0\sqrt{1 - \beta^2}a$, or $\lambda^{-1} = \lambda_0^{-1}\sqrt{1 - \beta^2}$. Solve for $\lambda - \lambda_0$:

$$\lambda - \lambda_0 = \lambda_0\left(\frac{1}{\sqrt{1-\beta^2}} - 1\right) = (589.00\,\text{nm})\left[\frac{1}{\sqrt{1-(0.100)^2}} - 1\right] = 2.97\,\text{nm}.$$

36P

The spaceship is moving away from the Earth, so the frequency received is given by Eq. 42-26:

$$f = f_0\sqrt{\frac{1-\beta}{1+\beta}},$$

where f_0 is the frequency in the frame of the spaceship, $\beta = v/c$, and v is the speed of the spaceship relative to the Earth. The frequency f and wavelength λ are related by $f\lambda = c$, so if λ_0 is the wavelength of the light as seen on the spaceship and λ is the wavelength detected on Earth, then

$$\lambda = \lambda_0\sqrt{\frac{1+\beta}{1-\beta}} = (450\,\text{nm})\sqrt{\frac{1+0.20}{1-0.20}} = 550\,\text{nm}.$$

This is in the yellow-green portion of the visible spectrum.

37P

(a) This is a time dilation problem. The answer is (see Eqs. 42-6 to 42-8)

$$\tau_s = \gamma\tau_0 = \frac{\tau_0}{\sqrt{1-\beta^2}}.$$

(b) Use Eq. 42-26 and note that $f_R = \tau_R^{-1}$, $f_0 = \tau_0^{-1}$:

$$\tau_R = \frac{1}{f_R} = \left(f_0 \sqrt{\frac{1-\beta}{a+\beta}}\right)^{-1} = \tau_0 \sqrt{\frac{1+\beta}{1-\beta}} = \tau_0 \sqrt{\frac{c+v}{c-v}}.$$

(c) τ_R has to do with the Doppler shift of the radar pulse and is not the same as τ_s, which is purely due to time dilation. So $\tau_R \neq \tau_s$.

38E
Use $W = \Delta K = mc^2 - m_0 c^2 = m_0 c^2 (\gamma - 1)$ and $m_0 c^2 = 0.511\,\text{MeV}$:
(a)

$$W = m_0 c^2 \left(\frac{1}{\sqrt{1-\beta^2}} - 1\right) = (0.511\,\text{MeV})\left[\frac{1}{\sqrt{1-(0.50)^2}} - 1\right] = 0.079\,\text{MeV}.$$

(b)

$$W = (0.511\,\text{MeV})\left[\frac{1}{\sqrt{1-(0.990)^2}} - 1\right] = 3.11\,\text{MeV}.$$

(c)

$$W = (0.511\,\text{MeV})\left[\frac{1}{\sqrt{1-(0.9990)^2}} - 1\right] = 10.9\,\text{MeV}.$$

39E
(a)

$$v = \left(\frac{2\pi R_E}{Tc}\right)c = \frac{2\pi(6.37 \times 10^6\,\text{m})c}{(1.00\,\text{s})(3.00 \times 10^8\,\text{m/s})} = 0.134\,c.$$

(b)

$$K = (m - m_0)c^2 = m_0 c^2 (\gamma - 1)$$
$$= (0.511\,\text{MeV})\left[\frac{1}{\sqrt{1-(0.134)^2}} - 1\right] = 4.65\,\text{keV}.$$

(c) The classical value of K is

$$K_c = \frac{1}{2}m_0 v^2 = \frac{1}{2}m_0 c^2 \beta^2 = \frac{1}{2}(0.511\,\text{MeV})(0.134)^2 = 4.59\,\text{keV}.$$

The percent error is then

$$\frac{|K - K_c|}{K} = \frac{4.65\,\text{keV} - 4.59\,\text{keV}}{4.65\,\text{keV}} = 1.3\%.$$

40E

Solve β and γ from $K = m_0c^2(\gamma - 1) = m_0c^2[(1 - \beta^2)^{-1/2} - 1]$:

$$\beta = \sqrt{1 - \left(\frac{K}{m_0c^2} + 1\right)^{-2}},$$

and $\gamma = K/m_0c^2 + 1$.

(a) Now $K = 1.00\,\text{keV}$ so

$$\beta = \sqrt{1 - \left(\frac{1.00\,\text{keV}}{0.511\,\text{MeV}} + 1\right)^{-2}} = 0.0625$$

and $\gamma = 1.00\,\text{keV}/0.511\,\text{MeV} + 1 = 1.00196$.

(b) Now $K = 1.00\,\text{MeV}$ so

$$\beta = \sqrt{1 - \left(\frac{1.00\,\text{MeV}}{0.511\,\text{MeV}} + 1\right)^{-2}} = 0.941$$

and $\gamma = 1.00\,\text{MeV}/0.511\,\text{MeV} + 1 = 2.96$.

(c) Now $K = 1.00\,\text{GeV}$ so

$$\beta = \sqrt{1 - \left(\frac{1.00\,\text{GeV}}{0.511\,\text{MeV}} + 1\right)^{-2}} = 0.99999987$$

and $\gamma = 1.00\,\text{GeV}/0.511\,\text{MeV} + 1 = 1960$.

41E

Use the formulas found in Exercise 40.

(a) $m_0c^2 = 0.511\,\text{MeV}$ so $\gamma = 10.0\,\text{MeV}/0.511\,\text{MeV} + 1 = 20.6$ and $\beta = \sqrt{1 - \gamma^{-2}} = \sqrt{1 - (20.6)^{-2}} = 0.9988$.

(b) Now $m_0c^2 = 937\,\text{MeV}$ so $\gamma = 10.0\,\text{MeV}/938\,\text{MeV} + 1 = 1.01$ and $\beta = \sqrt{1 - \gamma^{-2}} = \sqrt{1 - (1.01)^{-2}} = 0.145$.

(c) Now $m_0c^2 = (4.00\,\text{u})(932\,\text{MeV/u}) = 3.73 \times 10^3\,\text{MeV}$ so $\gamma = 10.0\,\text{MeV}/3.73 \times 10^3\,\text{MeV} = 1.0027$ and $\beta = \sqrt{1 - \gamma^{-2}} = \sqrt{1 - (1.0027)^{-2}} = 0.073$.

42E

Use the two expressions for the total energy: $E = mc^2 + K$ and $E = \gamma mc^2$, where m is the mass of an electron, K is the kinetic energy, and $\gamma = 1/\sqrt{1 - \beta^2}$. Thus $mc^2 + K = \gamma mc^2$ and $\gamma = (mc^2 + K)/mc^2$. This means $\sqrt{1 - \beta^2} = (mc^2)/(mc^2 + K)$ and

$$\beta = \sqrt{1 - \left(\frac{mc^2}{mc^2 + K}\right)^2}.$$

Now $mc^2 = 0.511\,\text{MeV}$ so

$$\beta = \sqrt{1 - \left(\frac{0.511\,\text{MeV}}{0.511\,\text{MeV} + 100\,\text{MeV}}\right)^2} = 0.999987.$$

The speed of the electron is $0.999987c$ or 99.9987% the speed of light.

43E
(a)

$$E = m_p c^2 = \gamma m_{p0} c^2 = \frac{938\,\text{MeV}}{\sqrt{1 - (0.990)^2}} = 6.65\,\text{GeV},$$

$$K = E - m_{p0} c^2 = 6.65\,\text{GeV} - 938\,\text{MeV} = 5.71\,\text{GeV},$$

and

$$p = m_p v = \gamma m_{p0} v \approx \frac{(938\,\text{MeV})(0.990)/c}{\sqrt{1 - (0.990)^2}} = 6.59\,\text{GeV}/c.$$

(b)

$$E = m_e c^2 = \gamma m_{e0} c^2 = \frac{0.511\,\text{MeV}}{\sqrt{1 - (0.990)^2}} = 3.62\,\text{MeV},$$

$$K = E - m_{e0} c^2 = 3.625\,\text{MeV} - 0.511\,\text{MeV} = 3.11\,\text{MeV},$$

and

$$p = m_e v = \gamma m_{e0} v = \frac{(0.511\,\text{MeV})(0.990)/c}{\sqrt{1 - (0.990)^2}} = 3.59\,\text{MeV}/c.$$

44E

$$m = \frac{E}{c^2} = \frac{(2.2 \times 10^{12}\,\text{kW} \cdot \text{h})(10^3\,\text{W/kW})(3600\,\text{s/h})}{(3.00 \times 10^8\,\text{m/s})} = 88\,\text{kg}.$$

It doesn't matter how the energy is generated, just how much the total amount is.

45E
Since the rest energy E_0 and the mass m of the quasar are related by $E_0 = mc^2$, the rate P of energy radiation and the rate of mass loss are related by $P = dE_0/dt = (dm/dt)c^2$. Thus

$$\frac{dm}{dt} = \frac{P}{c^2} = \frac{10^{41}\,\text{W}}{(3.00 \times 10^8\,\text{m/s})^2} = 1.11 \times 10^{24}\,kg/s.$$

Since a solar mass is 2.0×10^{30} kg and a year is 3.156×10^7 s,

$$\frac{dm}{dt} = (1.11 \times 10^{24}\,\text{kg} / \text{s}) \left(\frac{3.156 \times 10^7\,\text{s/y}}{2.0 \times 10^{30}\,\text{kg/smu}}\right) = 17.5\,\text{smu/y}.$$

46P

Use the work-energy theorem:

$$W = \Delta K = (\gamma_f - 1)m_0 c^2 - (\gamma_i - 1)m_0 c^2 = (\gamma_f - \gamma_i)m_0 c^2.$$

(a)

$$W = \left(\frac{1}{\sqrt{1 - \beta_f^2}} - \frac{1}{\sqrt{1 - \beta_i^2}} \right) m_0 c^2$$

$$= (0.511\,\text{MeV}) \left[\frac{1}{\sqrt{1 - (0.19)^2}} - \frac{1}{\sqrt{1 - (0.18)^2}} \right] = 1.0\,\text{keV}.$$

(b)

$$W = (0.511\,\text{MeV}) \left[\frac{1}{\sqrt{1 - (0.99)^2}} - \frac{1}{\sqrt{1 - (0.98)^2}} \right] = 1.1\,\text{MeV}.$$

Note that $1.1\,\text{MeV} \gg 1.0\,\text{keV}$, meaming that it gets more difficult to accelerate the electron as its speed approaches c.

47P

(a) Let $K = (\gamma - 1)m_0 c^2 = 2m_0 c^2$ or $\gamma = 3$. Thus $v = \beta c = \sqrt{1 - \gamma^{-2}}\,c = \sqrt{1 - 3^{-2}}\,c = 0.943\,c$.
(b) Now $E = mc^2 = \gamma m_0 c^2 = 2m_0 c^2$ so $\gamma = 2$. Thus $v = \sqrt{1 - 2^{-2}} = 0.866\,c$.

48P

(a) Classically, let $e\Delta V = \Delta K = \frac{1}{2}m_0 c^2$, we get

$$\Delta V = \frac{m_0 c^2}{2e} = \frac{0.511\,\text{MeV}}{2e} = 256\,\text{kV}.$$

(b) Now $K = e\Delta V = (\gamma - 1)m_0 c^2$ so

$$v = c\beta = c\sqrt{1 - \frac{1}{\gamma^2}} = c\sqrt{1 - \left(\frac{e\Delta V}{m_0 c^2} + 1 \right)^{-2}}$$

$$= c\sqrt{1 - \left(\frac{1}{2} + 1 \right)^{-2}} = 0.746\,c.$$

49P

(a)

In general, the momentum of a particle with mass m and speed v is given by $p = \gamma m v$, where γ is the Lorentz factor. Since the particle of the problem has momentum mc, $mc = \gamma m v$ or $1 = \gamma \beta$, where $\beta = v/c$. Now find an expression for β in terms of γ. Since $\gamma = 1/\sqrt{1 - \beta^2}$, $\beta^2 = 1 - (1/\gamma^2) = (\gamma^2 - 1)/\gamma^2$. Thus $\beta = \sqrt{\gamma^2 - 1}/\gamma$ and $1 = \sqrt{\gamma^2 - 1}$. The solution is $\gamma = \sqrt{2} = 1.41$.

(b) The speed parameter is

$$\beta = \frac{\sqrt{\gamma^2 - 1}}{\gamma} = \frac{\sqrt{2-1}}{\sqrt{2}} = 0.707 \,.$$

The speed of the particle is $v = \beta c = 0.707c$.

(c) The kinetic energy is $K = (\gamma - 1)mc^2 = (\sqrt{2} - 1)mc^2 = 0.414mc^2$.

50P

Let $E = \sqrt{p^2 c^2 + (mc^2)^2} = 3mc^2$ and solve for p: $\; p = \sqrt{8}mc$.

51P

(a) The photon, at speed $v = c$.

(b) For the electron, $\gamma_e = K_e/m_{e0}c^2 + 1 = 0.40/0.511 + 1 = 1.78$. For the proton, $\gamma_p = K_p/m_{p0}c^2 + 1 = 10/938 + 1 = 1.011$. Since $\gamma_e > \gamma_p$ we have $v_e > v_p$, so the proton is moving the slowest.

(c) and (d) For the photon $p_{ph} = E_p/c = 2.0\,\mathrm{eV}/c$. For the electron $p_e = \sqrt{E_e^2 - m_{e0}^2 c^4}/c = \sqrt{(0.40 + 0.51)^2 - (0.511)^2}\,\mathrm{MeV}/c = 0.75\,\mathrm{MeV}/c$. For the proton $p_p = \sqrt{E_p^2 - m_{p0}^2 c^4}/c = \sqrt{(938 + 10)^2 - (938)^2}\,\mathrm{MeV}/c = 137\,\mathrm{MeV}/c$. So the photon has the greatest momentum while the photon has the least.

52P

The energy equivalent of one tablet is $mc^2 = (320 \times 10^{-6}\,\mathrm{kg})(3.00 \times 10^8\,\mathrm{m/s})^2 = 2.88 \times 10^{13}\,\mathrm{J}$. This provides the same energy as $(2.88 \times 10^{13}\,\mathrm{J})/(1.30 \times 10^8\,\mathrm{J/gal}) = 2.21 \times 10^5\,\mathrm{gal}$ of gasoline. The distance the car can go is $d = (2.21 \times 10^5\,\mathrm{gal})(30.0\,\mathrm{mi/gal}) = 6.65 \times 10^6\,\mathrm{mi}$.

53P

(a) From $E = K + mc^2 = \sqrt{p^2 c^2 + (mc^2)^2}$ we solve for m:

$$m = \frac{(pc)^2 - K^2}{2Kc^2} \,.$$

(b) As $u/c \to 0$ we have $p = \gamma mv \approx mv \ll mc$ so

$$E = K + mc^2 = mc^2 \sqrt{1 + \left(\frac{p}{mc}\right)^2} \approx mc^2 \left[1 + \frac{1}{2}\left(\frac{p}{mc}\right)^2\right].$$

Here we used $(1 + x)^n \approx 1 + nx$ for $|x| \ll 1$. Thus

$$K \simeq mc^2 \left[1 + \frac{1}{2}\left(\frac{p}{mc}\right)^2\right] - mc^2 = \frac{p^2}{2m},$$

as expected from classical mechanics.

(c)

$$m = \frac{[(121\,\mathrm{MeV}/c)c]^2 - (55.0\,\mathrm{MeV})^2}{2(55.0\,\mathrm{MeV})c^2} = \left(\frac{106\,\mathrm{MeV}/c^2}{0.511\,\mathrm{MeV}/c^2}\right)m_e = 207m_e.$$

(The particle is a muon).

54P

The distance traveled by the pion in the frame of the Earth is $d = v\,\Delta t$, where v is the speed of the pion and Δt is the pion lifetime, both as measured in that frame. The proper time interval Δt_0 is measured in the rest frame of the pion, so $\Delta t = \gamma\Delta t_0$. We must calculate the speed of the pion and the Lorentz factor γ.

Since the total energy of the pion is given by $E = \gamma m c^2$,

$$\gamma = \frac{E}{mc^2} = \frac{1.35 \times 10^5\,\mathrm{MeV}}{139.6\,\mathrm{MeV}} = 967.1\,.$$

Since $\gamma = 1/\sqrt{1-\beta^2}$,

$$\beta = \frac{\sqrt{\gamma^2 - 1}}{\gamma} = \frac{\sqrt{(967.1)^2 - 1}}{967.1} = 0.9999995\,.$$

The speed of the pion is extremely close to the speed of light and we may approximate β as 1. Thus $v = 3.00 \times 10^8\,\mathrm{m/s}$.

The pion lifetime as measured in the frame of the Earth is $\Delta t = (967.1)(35.0\,\mathrm{ns}) = 3.385 \times 10^4\,\mathrm{ns} = 3.385 \times 10^{-5}\,\mathrm{s}$. The distance traveled is $d = (3.00 \times 10^8\,\mathrm{m/s})(3.385 \times 10^{-5}\,\mathrm{s}) = 1.02 \times 10^4\,\mathrm{m} = 10.2\,\mathrm{km}$. The altitude at which the pion decays is $120\,\mathrm{km} - 10.2\,\mathrm{km} = 110\,\mathrm{km}$.

55P

(a) Use $\gamma = \tau/\tau_0 = (1 - \beta^2)^{-1/2}$ to find $v = \beta c$:

$$\beta = \sqrt{1 - \frac{1}{\gamma^2}} = \sqrt{1 - \left(\frac{\tau_0}{\tau}\right)^2} = \sqrt{1 - \left(\frac{2.20\mu\,\mathrm{s}}{6.90\mu\,\mathrm{s}}\right)^2} = 0.948$$

so $v = 0.948\,c$.

(b)

$$K = (\gamma - 1)m_0 c^2 = \left(\frac{6.90\mu\,\mathrm{s}}{2.20\mu\,\mathrm{s}} - 1\right)(106\,\mathrm{MeV}) = 226\,\mathrm{MeV}.$$

(c)

$$p = \sqrt{E^2 - (m_0 c^2)^2}/c = \sqrt{(K + m_0 c^2)^2 - (m_0 c^2)^2}/c$$
$$= \sqrt{(226 + 106)^2 - (106)^2}\,\mathrm{MeV}/c = 314\,\mathrm{MeV}/c.$$

56P

(a) $\Delta E = \Delta m c^2 = (3.0\,\text{kg})(0.10\%)(3.00 \times 10^8\,\text{m/s})^2 = 2.7 \times 10^{14}\,\text{J}$.

(b) The mass of TNT is

$$m_{\text{TNT}} = \frac{(2.7 \times 10^{14}\,\text{J})(0.227\,\text{kg/mol})}{3.4 \times 10^6\,\text{J}} = 1.8 \times 10^7\,\text{kg}.$$

(c) The fraction of mass converted in the TNT case is

$$\frac{\Delta m_{\text{TNT}}}{m_{\text{TNT}}} = \frac{(3.0\,\text{kg})(0.10\%)}{1.8 \times 10^7\,\text{kg}} = 1.6 \times 10^{-9}.$$

So the fraction in question is $(0.10\%)/1.6 \times 10^{-9} = 6.0 \times 10^6$.

57P

(a) From $K = (\gamma - 1)m_e c^2$ we get

$$\beta = \sqrt{1 - \left(\frac{K}{m_e c^2} + 1\right)^{-2}} = \sqrt{1 - \left(\frac{10.0\,\text{MeV}}{0.511\,\text{MeV}} + 1\right)^{-2}} = 0.9988.$$

So classically

$$r = \frac{mv}{qB} = \frac{(9.11 \times 10^{-31}\,\text{kg})(0.9988)(3.00 \times 10^8\,\text{m/s})}{(1.60 \times 10^{-19}\,\text{C})(2.20\,\text{T})} = 7.76 \times 10^{-4}\,\text{m}.$$

(b) Using relativistic formula, we have

$$r = \frac{\gamma m v}{qB} = \frac{mv/qB}{\sqrt{1 - \beta^2}} = \frac{7.76 \times 10^{-4}\,\text{m}}{\sqrt{1 - (0.9988)^2}} = 1.60 \times 10^{-2}\,\text{m}.$$

(c) The true period is

$$T = \frac{2\pi r}{v} = \frac{2\pi(1.60 \times 10^{-2}\,\text{m})}{(0.9988)(3.00 \times 10^8\,\text{m/s})} = 3.35 \times 10^{-10}\,\text{s}.$$

The result is not speed-independent. In fact

$$T = \frac{2\pi r}{v} = \frac{2\pi}{v}\left(\frac{mv}{qB\sqrt{1 - \beta^2}}\right) = \frac{2\pi m}{qB\sqrt{1 - \beta^2}},$$

which is a function of $\beta = v/c$.

58P

The radius r of the path is given in Problem 57 as

$$r = \frac{mv}{qB\sqrt{1 - \beta^2}},$$

so

$$m = \frac{qBr\sqrt{1 - \beta^2}}{v} = \frac{2(1.60 \times 10^{-19}\,\text{C})(1.00\,\text{T})(6.28\,\text{m})\sqrt{1 - (0.710)^2}}{(0.710)(3.00 \times 10^8\,\text{m/s})}$$

$$= 6.64 \times 10^{-27}\,\text{kg}.$$

Since $1.00\,\text{u} = 1.66 \times 10^{-27}\,\text{u}$, $m = 4.00\,\text{u}$. The nuclear particle contains 4 nucleons. Since there must be 2 protons to provide the charge $2e$, the nuclear particle is a helium nucleus with 2 protons and 2 neutrons.

59P

Now $\gamma = K/mc^2 + 1$ and

$$\beta = \sqrt{1 - \left(\frac{K}{mc^2} + 1\right)^{-2}} = \sqrt{1 - \left(\frac{10\,\text{GeV}}{938\,\text{MeV}} + 1\right)^{-2}} = 0.9963,$$

so the radius is (see Problem 57)

$$r = \frac{\gamma mv}{qB} = \frac{(10\,\text{GeV}/938\,\text{MeV} + 1)(1.67 \times 10^{-27}\,\text{kg})(0.9963)(3.00 \times 10^8\,\text{m/s})}{(1.60 \times 10^{-19}\,\text{C})(55 \times 10^{-6}\,\text{T})}$$

$$= 6.6 \times 10^5\,\text{m} = 660\,\text{km}.$$

60P

Now $\gamma = K/mc^2 + 1 = 2.50\,\text{MeV}/0.511\,\text{MeV} + 1 = 5.892$ and $\beta = \sqrt{1 - \gamma^{-2}} = 0.9855$, so from $r = \gamma mv/qB$ we get

$$B = \frac{\gamma mv}{qr} = \frac{(5.892)(9.11 \times 10^{-31}\,\text{kg})(0.9855)(3.00 \times 10^8\,\text{m/s})}{(1.60 \times 10^{-19}\,\text{C})(3.0 \times 10^{-2}\,\text{m})}$$

$$= 0.330\,\text{T}.$$

61P

(a)

$$\gamma = \frac{K}{mc^2} + 1 = \frac{500\,\text{GeV}}{938\,\text{MeV}} + 1 = 534.$$

(b) $\beta = \sqrt{1 - \gamma^{-2}} = \sqrt{1 - (534)^{-2}} = 0.99999825.$

(c)

$$B = \frac{\gamma m v}{qr} = \frac{(534)(1.67 \times 10^{-27}\,\text{kg})(0.99999825)(3.00 \times 10^8\,\text{m/s})}{(1.60 \times 10^{-19}\,\text{C})(750\,\text{m})}$$

$$= 2.23\,\text{T}.$$

62

(a) From time dilation formula $\Delta t = \gamma \Delta t_0$ we get the pulse rate

$$f = \frac{1}{\Delta t} = \frac{1}{\gamma \Delta t_0} = \frac{f_0}{\gamma} = f_0 \sqrt{1 - \beta^2}$$

$$= (150/\min)\sqrt{1 - (0.900)^2} = 65.4/\min.$$

(b) Since the length walked in the reference frame fixed in the spaceship is $L_0 = (1.0\,\text{m/s})$ $(3600\,\text{s}) = 3600\,\text{m}$. Length contraction then gives the length measured at the ground station to be

$$L = \frac{L_0}{\gamma} = L_0\sqrt{1 - \beta^2} = 3600\,\text{m}\sqrt{1 - (0.900)^2} = 1570\,\text{m}.$$

63

(a) In the messenger's rest system (called S_m), the velocity of the armade i s

$$v' = \frac{v - v_m}{1 - vv_m/c^2} = \frac{0.80\,c - 0.95\,c}{1 - (0.80\,c)(0.95\,c)/c^2} = -0.625\,c.$$

The length of the armada as measured in S_m is

$$L' = \frac{L_0}{\gamma_{v'}} = (1.0\,\text{ly})\sqrt{1 - (-0.625)^2} = 0.781\,\text{ly}.$$

Thus the length of the trip is

$$t' = \frac{L'}{|v'|} = \frac{0.781\,\text{ly}}{0.625\,c} = 1.25\,\text{y}.$$

(b) In the armada's rest frame (called S_a), the velocity of the messenger is

$$v' = \frac{v - v_a}{1 - vv_a/c^2} = \frac{0.95\,c - 0.80\,c}{1 - (0.95\,c)(0.80\,c)/c^2} = 0.625\,c.$$

Thus the length of the trip is

$$t' = \frac{L_0}{v'} = \frac{1.0\,\text{ly}}{0.625\,c} = 1.6\,\text{ly}.$$

(c) Measured in system S, the length of the armada is

$$L = \frac{L_0}{\gamma} = 1.0\,\text{ly}\sqrt{1-(0.80)^2} = 0.60\,\text{ly}$$

so the length of the trip is

$$t = \frac{L}{v_m - v_a} = \frac{0.60\,\text{ly}}{0.95\,c - 0.80\,c} = 4.0\,\text{y}.$$

64

The coordinate differences between the two ends of the meter stick in S' frame is $\Delta x' = L_0 \cos 30° = (1.0\,\text{m})(\sqrt{3}/2) = \sqrt{3}\,\text{m}/2$ and $\Delta y' = L_0 \sin 30° = 0.50\,\text{m}$. When meaused in S, length contraction gives $\Delta x = \Delta x'/\gamma$ and $\Delta y = \Delta y'$. So the length is

$$L = \sqrt{(\Delta x)^2 + (\Delta y)^2} = \sqrt{\left(\frac{\Delta x'}{\gamma}\right)^2 + (\Delta y')^2} = \sqrt{(\Delta x'\sqrt{1-\beta^2})^2 + (\Delta y')^2}$$

$$= \sqrt{(\sqrt{3}\,\text{m}/2)^2[1-(0.90)^2] + (0.50\,\text{m})^2} = 0.63\,\text{m}.$$

65

Since the total momentum of the two particles is zero in S', it must be that the velocities of these two particles is equal in magnitude and opposite in direction in S'. Let the velocity of S' be u relative to S, then the particle which is at rest in S must have a velocity of $v_1' = -u$ in S', and the velocity of the other particle is

$$v_2' = \frac{v_2 - u}{1 - uv_2/c^2} = \frac{c/2 - u}{1 - uc/2c^2}.$$

Let $v_2' = -v_1' = u$ to obtain

$$\frac{c/2 - u}{1 - u/2c} = u.$$

Solve for u: $u = 0.27\,c$.

CHAPTER 43

1E

The energy of a photon is given by $E = hf$, where h is the Planck constant and f is the frequency. The wavelength λ is related to the frequency by $\lambda f = c$, so $E = hc/\lambda$. Since $h = 6.63 \times 10^{-34}$ J $\cdot$ s and $c = 3.00 \times 10^8$ m/s,

$$hc = 1.99 \times 10^{-25} \text{ J} \cdot \text{m} = \frac{1.99 \times 10^{-25} \text{ J} \cdot \text{m}}{(1.602 \times 10^{-19} \text{ J/eV}) \times (10^{-9} \text{ m/nm})} = 1240 \text{ eV} \cdot \text{nm} .$$

Thus

$$E = \frac{1240 \text{ eV} \cdot \text{nm}}{\lambda} .$$

2E

$E = 1240/\lambda = 1240/589 = 2.11$ eV.

3E

Let $E = 1240/\lambda_{\min} = 0.6$ to get $\lambda = 2.1 \times 10^3$ nm $= 2.1\mu$ m. It is in the infrared region.

4E

(a) $E = 1240/(21 \times 10^7) = 5.9 \times 10^{-6}$ eV $= 5.9\mu$ eV.
(b) Since $\lambda = (1,650,763.73)^{-1}$ m $= 6.05 \times 10^{-7}$ m $= 605\mu$ m, the energy is $E = 1240$ nm $\cdot$ eV/605 nm $= 2.05$ eV.

5E

(a) $E = 1240$ nm $\cdot$ eV/$(35.0 \times 10^{-3}$ nm$) = 3.54 \times 10^4$ eV $= 35.4$ keV.
(b) $f = C/\lambda = (3.00 \times 10^8$ m/s$)/(35.0 \times 10^{-12}$ m$) = 8.57 \times 10^{18}$ Hz.
(c) $p = h/\lambda = (6.63 \times 10^{-34}$ J $\cdot$ s$)/(3.50 \times 10^{-11}$ m$) = 1.89 \times 10^{-23}$ kg $\cdot$ m/s.

6P

$$P = \frac{E}{t} = \left(\frac{1240}{\lambda}\right)(100/\text{s}) = \left(\frac{1240 \text{ eV}}{550}\right)(1.60 \times 10^{-19} \text{ J/eV})(100/\text{s})$$
$$= 3.6 \times 10^{-17} \text{ W} .$$

7P

The energy of the photon is now $E = 0.511\,\text{MeV} = 5.11 \times 10^5\,\text{eV}$.

(a) $f = E/h = (5.11 \times 10^5\,\text{eV})/(4.14 \times 10^{-15}\,\text{eV} \cdot \text{s}) = 1.24 \times 10^{20}\,\text{Hz}$.

(b) $\lambda = (1240/5.11 \times 10^5)\,\text{nm} = 2.43 \times 10^{-3}\,\text{nm} = 2.43\,\text{pm}$.

(c) $p = h/\lambda = (6.63 \times 10^{-34}\,\text{J} \cdot \text{s})/(2.43 \times 10^{-12}\,\text{m}) = 2.73 \times 10^{-22}\,\text{kg} \cdot \text{m/s}$.

8P

Let the intensity of each of the two beams (labeled 1 and 2) be I. Then $I + n_1 E_1 = n_1(hc/\lambda_1) = n_2 E_2 = n_2(hc/\lambda_2)$, where $n_{1,2}$ is the rate at which photons pass through a unit cross sectional area. Thus $n_1/n_2 = \lambda_1/\lambda_2$.

9P

(a) Let R be the rate of photon emission (number of photons emitted per unit time) and let E be the energy of a single photon. Then the power output of a bulb is given by $P = RE$ if all the power goes into photon production. Now $E = hf = hc/\lambda$, where h is the Planck constant, f is the frequency of the light emitted, and λ is the wavelength. Thus

$$P = \frac{Rhc}{\lambda}$$

and

$$R = \frac{\lambda P}{hc}.$$

The bulb emitting light with the longer wavelength (the 700 nm bulb) emits more photons per unit time. The energy of each photon is less so it must emit photons at a greater rate.

(b) Let R_ℓ be the rate of photon production at the longer wavelength (λ_ℓ) and let R_s be the rate of production at the shorter wavelength (λ_s). Then

$$R_\ell - R_s = \frac{(\lambda_\ell - \lambda_s)P}{hc} = \frac{(700\,\text{nm} - 400\,\text{nm})(400\,\text{J/s})}{(1.60 \times 10^{-19}\,\text{J/eV})(1240\,\text{eV} \cdot \text{nm})} = 6.0 \times 10^{20}\,\text{photon/s}.$$

The result $hc = 1240\,\text{eV} \cdot \text{nm}$, developed in Exercise 1, was used.

10P

(a) $dE/dt = PA = (1.39\,\text{kW/m}^2)(2.60\,\text{m}^2) = 3.61\,\text{kW}$.

(b) The rate is

$$\frac{dN}{dt} = \frac{1}{E_{\text{photon}}}\frac{dE}{dt} = \frac{3.61\,\text{kW}}{(1240/550)\,\text{eV}(1.60 \times 10^{-19}\,\text{J/eV})} = 1.00 \times 10^{22}/\text{s}.$$

(c)

$$t = \frac{N_A}{dN/dt} = \frac{6.02 \times 10^{23}}{1.00 \times 10^{22}/\text{s}} = 60.2\,\text{s}.$$

11P

The total energy emitted by the bulb is $E_{total} = 93\% Pt$, where $P = 60\,\text{W}$ and $t = 730\,\text{h} = (730\,\text{h})(3600\,\text{s/h}) = 2.68 \times 10^6\,\text{s}$. The energy of each photon emitted is $E_{total} = h/\lambda$. Thus the number of photons emitted is

$$N = \frac{E_{total}}{E_{photon}} = \frac{93\% Pt}{h/\lambda} = \frac{(93\%)(60\,\text{W})(2.628 \times 10^6\,\text{s})}{(1240/630)\,\text{eV}(1.60 \times 10^{-19}\,\text{J/eV})} = 4.7 \times 10^{26}.$$

12P

(a)

$$\frac{dN}{dt} = \frac{1}{E_{photon}}\frac{dE}{dt} = \frac{(1.5\,\text{W})(1.0\,\text{m}^2)/[\pi(3.0 \times 10^{-3}\,\text{m})^2/4]}{(1240/515)\,\text{eV}(1.60 \times 10^{-19}\,\text{J/eV})}$$
$$= 5.5 \times 10^{23}\ \text{photons/m}^2 \cdot \text{s}.$$

(b)

$$\frac{dN'}{dt} = \left(\frac{dN}{dt}\right)\left(\frac{84\% A}{A'}\right) = \left(\frac{dN}{dt}\right)\left(\frac{1.22 f_L \lambda/d}{d/2}\right)^{-2}(84\%)$$
$$= (5.5 \times 10^{23}\ \text{photon/m}^2 \cdot \text{s})\left[\frac{2(1.22)(2.5\,\text{mm})(515 \times 10^{-6}\,\text{mm})}{(3.0\,\text{mm})^2}\right]^2(84\%)$$
$$= 3.8 \times 10^{30}\ \text{photons/m}^2 \cdot \text{s}.$$

13P

(a) Assume all the power results in photon production at the wavelength $\lambda = 589\,\text{nm}$. Let R be the rate of photon production and E be the energy of a single photon. Then $P = RE = Rhc/\lambda$, where $E = hf$ and $f = c/\lambda$ were used. Here h is the Planck constant, f is the frequency of the emitted light, and λ is its wavelength. Thus

$$R = \frac{\lambda P}{hc} = \frac{(589 \times 10^{-9}\,\text{m})(100\,\text{W})}{(6.63 \times 10^{-34}\,\text{J} \cdot \text{s})(3.00 \times 10^8\,\text{m/s})} = 2.96 \times 10^{20}\ \text{photon/s}.$$

(b) Let I be the photon flux a distance r from the source. Since photons are emitted uniformly in all directions $R = 4\pi r^2 I$ and

$$r = \sqrt{\frac{R}{4\pi I}} = \sqrt{\frac{2.96 \times 10^{20}\ \text{photon/s}}{4\pi(1.00 \times 10^4\ \text{photon/m}^2 \cdot \text{s})}} = 4.85 \times 10^7\,\text{m}.$$

(c) Let n be the photon density and consider a narrow column with cross-sectional area A and length ℓ, with its axis along the direction of photon motion. At any instant the number of photons in the column is $N = nA\ell$. All of them will move through one end in time $t = \ell/c$, so the photon flux through the end is $I = N/At = nA\ell c/A\ell = nc$. Now $I = R/4\pi r^2$, so $R/4\pi r^2 = nc$ and

$$r = \sqrt{\frac{R}{4\pi nc}} = \sqrt{\frac{2.96 \times 10^{20}\,\text{photon/s}}{4\pi(1.00 \times 10^6\,\text{photon/m}^3)(3.00 \times 10^8\,\text{m/s})}} = 280\,\text{m}.$$

(d) The photon flux is

$$I = \frac{R}{4\pi r^2} = \frac{2.96 \times 10^{20}\,\text{photon/s}}{4\pi(2.00\,\text{m})^2} = 5.89 \times 10^{18}\,\text{photon/m}^2 \cdot \text{s}$$

and the photon density is

$$n = \frac{I}{c} = \frac{5.89 \times 10^{18}\,\text{photon/m}^2 \cdot \text{s}}{3.00 \times 10^8\,\text{m/s}} = 1.96 \times 10^{10}\,\text{photon/m}^3.$$

14E
Th energy of the most energetic photon in the visible light range (with wavelength of about $400\,\text{nm}$) is about $E = (1240/400)\,\text{eV} = 3.1\,\text{eV}$. So barium and lithium can be used, since their work functions are lower than $3.1\,\text{eV}$.

15E
Let $\phi = E_{\text{photon}} = h/\lambda_{\text{max}}$, we get $\lambda_{\text{max}} = h/\phi = (1240\,\text{eV} \cdot \text{nm})/(5.32\,\text{eV}) = 233\,\text{nm}$.

16E
(a) Since $E_{\text{photon}} = h/\lambda = (1240/680)\,\text{eV} = 1.82\,\text{eV} < \phi = 2.28\,\text{eV}$, there is no photoelectric emission.
(b) The longest (cut off) wavelength of photons which will cause photoelectric emission in sodium is given by $E_{\text{photon}} = h/\lambda_{\text{max}} = \phi$, or $\lambda_{\text{max}} = h/\phi = (1240\,\text{eV} \cdot \text{nm})/2.28\,\text{eV} = 544\,\text{nm}$. This corresponds to the green color.

17E
Use Eq. 43-8:

$$K_{\text{m}} = hf - \phi = (4.14 \times 10^{-15}\,\text{eV} \cdot \text{s})(3.0 \times 10^{15}\,\text{Hz}) - 2.3\,\text{eV} = 10\,\text{eV}.$$

18E

The energy of an incident photon is $E = hf = hc/\lambda$, where h is the Planck constant, f is the frequency of the electromagnetic radiation, and λ is its wavelength. The kinetic energy of the most energetic electron emitted is $K_m = E - \phi = (hc/\lambda) - \phi$, where ϕ is the work function for sodium. The stopping potential V_0 is related to the maximum kinetic energy by $eV_0 = K_m$, so $eV_0 = (hc/\lambda) - \phi$ and

$$\lambda = \frac{hc}{eV_0 + \phi} = \frac{1240\,\text{eV} \cdot \text{nm}}{5.0\,\text{eV} + 2.2\,\text{eV}} = 170\,\text{nm}.$$

Here $eV_0 = 5.0\,\text{eV}$ and $hc = 1240\,\text{eV} \cdot \text{nm}$ were used. See Exercise 1.

19E

The speed v of the electron satisfies $K_m = \frac{1}{2}mv^2 = E_{\text{photon}} - \phi$, or

$$v = \sqrt{\frac{2(E_{\text{photon}} - \phi)}{m}} = \sqrt{\frac{2(E_{\text{photon}} - \phi)c^2}{mc^2}}$$
$$= \sqrt{\frac{2(5.80\,\text{eV} - 4.50\,\text{eV})(3.00 \times 10^8\,\text{m/s})^2}{0.511 \times 10^6\,\text{eV}}} = 6.76 \times 10^5\,\text{m/s}.$$

20E

(a) The kinetic energy K_m of the fastest electron emitted is given by $K_m = hf - \phi = (hc/\lambda) - \phi$, where ϕ is the work function of aluminum, f is the frequency of the incident radiation, and λ is its wavelength. The relationship $f = c/\lambda$ was used to obtain the second form. Thus

$$K_m = \frac{1240\,\text{eV} \cdot \text{nm}}{200\,\text{nm}} - 4.20\,\text{eV} = 2.00\,\text{eV},$$

where the result of Exercise 1 was used.

(b) The slowest electron just breaks free of the surface and so has zero kinetic energy.

(c) The stopping potential V_0 is given by $K_m = eV_0$, so $V_0 = K_m/e = (2.00\,\text{eV})/e = 2.00\,\text{V}$.

(d) The value of the cutoff wavelength is such that $K_m = 0$. Thus $hc/\lambda = \phi$ or

$$\lambda = \frac{hc}{\phi} = \frac{1240\,\text{eV} \cdot \text{nm}}{4.2\,\text{eV}} = 295\,\text{nm}.$$

If the wavelength is longer the photon energy is less and a photon does not have sufficient energy to knock even the most energetic electron out of the aluminum sample.

21E

(a) Use Eq. 43-9:

$$V_0 = \frac{hf - \phi}{e} = \frac{hc/\lambda - \phi}{e} = \frac{(1240/400)\,\text{eV} - 1.8\,\text{eV}}{e} = 1.3\,\text{V}.$$

(b)

$$v = \sqrt{\frac{2(E_{\text{photon}} - \phi)}{m}} = \sqrt{\frac{2eV_0}{m}} = \sqrt{\frac{2eV_0 c^2}{mc^2}}$$

$$= \sqrt{\frac{2e(1.3\,\text{V})(3.00 \times 10^8\,\text{m/s})^2}{0.511 \times 10^6\,\text{eV}}} = 6.8 \times 10^5\,\text{m/s}.$$

22E

$$K_m = E_{\text{photon}} - \phi = hc/\lambda - hc/\lambda_{\max}$$
$$= (1240/254)\,\text{eV} - (1240/325)\,\text{eV}$$
$$= 1.07\,\text{eV}.$$

23P

(a) Use the photoelectric effect equation (Eq. 43–8) in the form $hc/\lambda = \phi + K_m$. The work function depends only on the material and the condition of the surface and not on the wavelength of the incident light. Let λ_1 be first wavelength described and λ_2 be the second. Let K_{m1} (= 0.710 eV) be the maximum kinetic energy of electrons ejected by light with the first wavelength and K_{m2} (= 1.43 eV) be the maximum kinetic energy of electron ejected by light with the second wavelength. Then

$$\frac{hc}{\lambda_1} = \phi + K_{m1}$$

and

$$\frac{hc}{\lambda_2} = \phi + K_{m2}.$$

Solve these equations simultaneously for λ_2.

The first equation yields $\phi = (hc/\lambda_1) - K_{m1}$. When this is used to substitute for ϕ in the second equation the result is $(hc/\lambda_2) = (hc/\lambda_1) - K_{m1} + K_{m2}$. The solution for λ_2 is

$$\lambda_2 = \frac{hc\lambda_1}{hc + \lambda_1(K_{m2} - K_{m1})} = \frac{(1240\,\text{eV} \cdot \text{nm})(491\,\text{nm})}{1240\,\text{eV} \cdot \text{nm} + (491\,\text{nm})(1.43\,\text{eV} - 0.710\,\text{eV})}$$
$$= 382\,\text{nm}.$$

Here $hc = 1240\,\text{eV} \cdot \text{nm}$, calculated in Exercise 1, was used.

(*b*) The first equation displayed above yields

$$\phi = \frac{hc}{\lambda_1} - K_{m1} = \frac{1240\,\text{eV} \cdot \text{nm}}{491\,\text{nm}} - 0.710\,\text{eV} = 1.82\,\text{eV}.$$

24P

For the first and second case (labeled 1 and 2) we have $eV_{01} = hc/\lambda_1 - \phi$ and $eV_{02} = hc/\lambda_2 - \phi$. Solve for h and ϕ:

(*a*)

$$h = \frac{e(V_1 - V_2)}{c(\lambda_1^{-1} - \lambda_2^{-1})} = \frac{1.85\,\text{eV} - 0.820\,\text{eV}}{(3.00 \times 10^{17}\,\text{nm/s})[(300\,\text{nm})^{-1} - (400\,\text{nm})^{-1}]}$$
$$= 4.12 \times 10^{-15}\,\text{eV} \cdot \text{s}.$$

(*b*)

$$\phi = \frac{3(V_2\lambda_2 - V_1\lambda_1)}{\lambda_1 - \lambda_2} = \frac{(0.820\,\text{eV})(400\,\text{nm}) - (1.85\,\text{eV})(300\,\text{nm})}{300\,\text{nm} - 400\,\text{nm}} = 2.27\,\text{eV}.$$

(*c*) Let $\phi = hc/\lambda_{\max}$ we get

$$\lambda_{\max} = \frac{hc}{\phi} = \frac{1240\,\text{nm} \cdot \text{eV}}{2.27\,\text{eV}} = 545\,\text{nm}.$$

25P

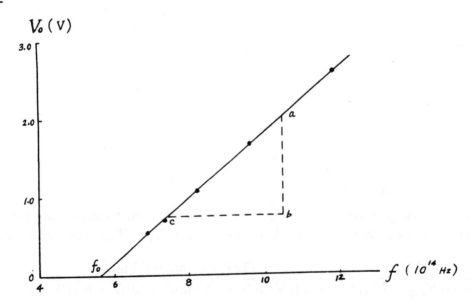

(*a*) From

$$\frac{h}{c} = \frac{ab}{bc} = \frac{2.0\,\text{V} - 0.75\,\text{V}}{(10.5 \times 10^{14} - 7.5 \times 10^{14})\,\text{Hz}} = 4.17 \times 10^{-15}\,\text{V} \cdot \text{s},$$

we get $h = (4.17 \times 10^{-15} \, \text{V} \cdot \text{s})(1.6 \times 10^{-19} \, \text{C}) = 6.7 \times 10^{-34} \, \text{J} \cdot \text{s}$.

(b) From the graph above we find $f_0 = 5.7 \times 10^{14} \, \text{Hz}$ so

$$\phi = hf_0 = \frac{(6.63 \times 10^{-34} \, \text{J} \cdot \text{s})(5.7 \times 10^{14} \, \text{Hz})}{1.6 \times 10^{-19} \, \text{J/C}} = 2.4 \, \text{eV}.$$

This compares favourably with actual value of 2.3 eV.

26P
The number of photons emitted from the laser per unit time is

$$\frac{dn}{dt} = \frac{P}{E_{\text{photon}}} = \frac{2.00 \times 10^{-3} \, \text{w}}{(1240/600) \, \text{eV}(1.60 \times 10^{-19} \, \text{J/eV})} = 6.05 \times 10^{15}/\text{s},$$

of which $(1.0 \times 10^{-16})(6.05 \times 10^{15}/\text{s}) = 0.605/\text{s}$ actually cause photoelectron emissions. Thus the current is $i = (0.605/\text{s})(1.60 \times 10^{-19} \, \text{J}) = 9.68 \times 10^{-20} \, \text{A}$.

27
(a) Find the speed v of the electron from $r = mv/eB$: $v = (rB)(e/m)$. Thus

$$K_m = \frac{1}{2}mv^2 = \frac{1}{2}m\left(\frac{rBe}{m}\right)^2$$

$$= \frac{(1.88 \times 10^{-4} \, \text{T} \cdot \text{m})^2(1.60 \times 10^{-19} \, \text{C})^2}{2(9.11 \times 10^{-31} \, \text{kg})(1.60 \times 10^{-19} \, \text{J/eV})} = 3.10 \, \text{keV}.$$

(b) The work done is

$$W = E_{\text{photon}} - K_m = (1240/71 \times 10^{-3}) \, \text{eV} - 3.10 \, \text{keV} = 14 \, \text{keV}.$$

28P*
The momentum of the photon is given by hf/c, where f is the frequency of the radiation. The momentum of the electron is initially zero. After the collision the momentum of the electron is $mv/\sqrt{1 - v^2/c^2}$, where v is its velocity. Assume the photon is absorbed. Then conservation of momentum yields

$$\frac{hf}{c} = \frac{mv}{\sqrt{1 - v^2/c^2}}.$$

Initially the photon has energy hf and the electron has energy mc^2, its rest energy. After the collision the electron energy is $mc^2/\sqrt{1 - v^2/c^2}$. Conservation of energy yields

$$hf + mc^2 = \frac{mc^2}{\sqrt{1 - v^2/c^2}}.$$

Solve the momentum conservation equation for hf and substitute the result into the energy conservation equation. You should get

$$v = c \left[1 - \sqrt{1 - v^2/c^2}\right].$$

There are two solutions for v: either $v = 0$ or $v = c$. If $v = 0$ then the momentum conservation equation tells us that $f = 0$. There really is no interaction since no radiation energy is incident on the electron. The solution $v = c$ is prohibited since this means the electron has infinite momentum and energy after the collision and the photon has infinite momentum and energy before.

29E

(a) When a photon scatters from an electron initially at rest the change in wavelength is given by

$$\Delta\lambda = \frac{h}{mc}(1 - \cos\phi),$$

where m is the mass of an electron and ϕ is the scattering angle. Now $h/mc = 2.43 \times 10^{-12}$ m $= 2.43$ pm, so $\Delta\lambda = (2.43\,\text{pm})(1 - \cos 30°) = 0.326$ pm. The final wavelength is $\lambda' = \lambda + \Delta\lambda = 2.4\,\text{pm} + 0.326\,\text{pm} = 2.73\,\text{pm}$.

(b) Now $\Delta\lambda = (2.43\,\text{pm})(1 - \cos 120°) = 3.645$ pm and $\lambda' = 2.4\,\text{pm} + 3.645\,\text{pm} = 6.05\,\text{pm}$.

30E

(a) $\lambda = hc/E = 1240\,\text{nm} \cdot \text{eV}/0.511\,\text{MeV} = 2.43 \times 10^{-3}\,\text{nm} = 2.43\,\text{pm}$.
(b) $\lambda' = \lambda + \Delta\lambda = \lambda + (h/mc)(1 - \cos\phi) = 2.43\,\text{pm} + (2.43\,\text{pm})[1 - \cos 90.0°] = 4.86\,\text{pm}$.
(c) $E' = E(\lambda/\lambda') = (0.511\,\text{MeV})(2.43\,\text{pm}/4.86\,\text{pm}) = 0.255\,\text{MeV}$.

31E

(a) $\Delta\lambda = (h/mc)(1 - \cos\phi) = (2.43\,\text{pm})(1 - \cos 180°) = 4.86\,\text{pm}$.
(b) $\Delta E = hc/\lambda' - hc/\lambda = (1240\,\text{nm} \cdot \text{eV})[(0.01\,\text{nm} + 4.86\,\text{pm})^{-1} - (0.01\,\text{nm})^{-1}]$
$= -41\,\text{keV}$.
(c) $\Delta K = -\Delta E = 41\,\text{keV}$ (from conservation of energy).

32E

(a) Since the mass of an electron is $m = 9.109 \times 10^{-31}$ kg, its Compton wavelength is

$$\lambda_C = \frac{h}{mc} = \frac{6.626 \times 10^{-34}\,\text{J} \cdot \text{s}}{(9.109 \times 10^{-31}\,\text{kg})(2.998 \times 10^8\,\text{m/s})} = 2.426 \times 10^{-12}\,\text{m} = 2.43\,\text{pm}.$$

(b) Since the mass of a proton is $m = 1.673 \times 10^{-27}$ kg, its Compton wavelength is

$$\lambda_C = \frac{6.626 \times 10^{-34}\,\text{J} \cdot \text{s}}{(1.673 \times 10^{-27}\,\text{kg})(2.998 \times 10^8\,\text{m/s})} = 1.321 \times 10^{-15}\,\text{m} = 1.32\,\text{fm}.$$

(c) Use the formula developed in Exercise 1: $E = (1240 \, \text{eV} \cdot \text{nm})/\lambda$, where E is the energy and λ is the wavelength. Thus for the electron

$$E = \frac{1240 \, \text{eV} \cdot \text{nm}}{2.426 \times 10^{-3} \, \text{nm}} = 5.11 \times 10^5 \, \text{eV} = 0.511 \, \text{MeV}.$$

(d) For the proton

$$E = \frac{1240 \, \text{eV} \cdot \text{nm}}{1.321 \times 10^{-6} \, \text{nm}} = 9.39 \times 10^8 \, \text{eV} = 939 \, \text{MeV}.$$

33E

The percent change is

$$\frac{\Delta E}{E} = \frac{\Delta(hc/\lambda)}{hc/\lambda} = \lambda \Delta \left(\frac{1}{\lambda}\right) = \lambda \left(\frac{1}{\lambda'} - \frac{1}{\lambda}\right) = \frac{\lambda}{\lambda'} - 1 = \frac{\lambda}{\lambda + \Delta\lambda} - 1$$

$$= -\frac{1}{\lambda/\Delta\lambda + 1} = -\frac{1}{(\lambda/\lambda_C)(1 - \cos\phi)^{-1} + 1}$$

(a) Now $\lambda = 3.0 \, \text{cm} = 3.0 \times 10^{10} \, \text{pm}$ and $\phi = 90°$ so

$$\frac{\Delta E}{E} = -\frac{1}{(3.0 \times 10^{10} \, \text{pm}/2.43 \, \text{pm})(1 - \cos 90°)^{-1} + 1} = -8.1 \times 10^{-11}.$$

(b) Now $\lambda = 500 \, \text{nm} = 5.00 \times 10^5 \, \text{pm}$ and $\phi = 90°$ so

$$\frac{\Delta E}{E} = -\frac{1}{(5.00 \times 10^5 \, \text{pm}/2.43 \, \text{pm})(1 - \cos 90°)^{-1} + 1} = -4.9 \times 10^{-6}.$$

(c) Now $\lambda = 25 \, \text{pm}$ and $\phi = 90°$ so

$$\frac{\Delta E}{E} = -\frac{1}{(25 \, \text{pm}/2.43 \, \text{pm})(1 - \cos 90°)^{-1} + 1} = -8.9 \times 10^{-2}.$$

(d) Now $\lambda = hc/E = 1240 \, \text{nm} \cdot \text{eV}/1.0 \, \text{MeV} = 1.24 \times 10^{-3} \, \text{nm} = 1.24 \, \text{pm}$ so

$$\frac{\Delta E}{E} = -\frac{1}{(1.24 \, \text{pm}/2.43 \, \text{pm})(1 - \cos 90°)^{-1} + 1} = -0.66.$$

Obviously since $\Delta E/E$ is virtually zero for the microwave and visible light, Compton effect is important only in the X ray to gamma ray range of electromagnetic spectrum.

34E

If E is the original energy of the photon and E' is the energy after scattering, then the fractional energy loss is

$$frac = \frac{E - E'}{E}.$$

Sample Problem 43–6 shows that this is

$$frac = \frac{\Delta\lambda}{\lambda + \Delta\lambda}.$$

Thus

$$\frac{\Delta\lambda}{\lambda} = \frac{frac}{1 - frac} = \frac{0.75}{1 - 0.75} = 3.$$

A 300% increase in the wavelength leads to a 75% decrease in the energy of the photon.

35E

$$\Delta\lambda_{max} = \left[\frac{h}{m_p c}(1 - \cos\phi)\right]_{max} = \frac{2h}{m_p c} = \frac{2(4.14 \times 10^{-15}\,\text{eV} \cdot \text{s})(3.00 \times 10^8\,\text{m/s})}{(938\,\text{MeV})}$$
$$= 2.65 \times 10^{-15}\,\text{m} = 2.65\,\text{fm}.$$

36P

(a) Use the result developed in Sample Problem 43–6:

$$\frac{E - E'}{E} = \frac{\Delta\lambda}{\lambda + \Delta\lambda},$$

where E is the initial energy of the photon, E' is its final energy, λ is the initial wavelength of the wave associated with the photon, and $\Delta\lambda$ is the change in wavelength. Substitute $E = hf$ and $E' = hf'$ to obtain

$$\frac{f - f'}{f} = \frac{\Delta\lambda}{\lambda + \Delta\lambda}.$$

If $(f - f')/f = frac$, the solution for $\Delta\lambda$ is

$$\Delta\lambda = \frac{\lambda frac}{1 - frac}.$$

The wavelength of a 6.2-keV photon is $\lambda = (hc)/E = (1240\,\text{eV} \cdot \text{nm})/(6.2 \times 10^3\,\text{eV}) = 0.200\,\text{nm}$, where the result of Exercise 1 was used. Thus

$$\Delta\lambda = \frac{(0.200\,\text{nm})(1.0 \times 10^{-4})}{1 - 1.0 \times 10^{-4}} = 2.0 \times 10^{-5}\,\text{nm} = 2.0 \times 10^{-2}\,\text{pm}.$$

Now use the Compton scattering equation $\Delta\lambda = \lambda_C(1 - \cos\phi)$, where λ_C is the Compton wavelength for an electron (2.43 pm) and ϕ is the scattering angle. This means

$$\phi = \cos^{-1}\left(1 - \frac{\Delta\lambda}{\lambda_C}\right) = \cos^{-1}\left(1 - \frac{2.0 \times 10^{-2}\,\text{pm}}{2.43\,\text{pm}}\right) = 7.4°.$$

(b) The kinetic energy imparted to the electron equals the energy lost by the photon. That is,

$$K = \frac{hc}{\lambda} - \frac{hc}{\lambda'} = \frac{hc(\lambda' - \lambda)}{\lambda\lambda'} = \frac{hc\,\Delta\lambda}{\lambda(\lambda + \Delta\lambda)}$$

$$= \frac{(1240\,\text{eV}\cdot\text{nm})(2.00 \times 10^{-5}\,\text{nm})}{(0.200\,\text{nm})(0.200\,\text{nm} + 2.00 \times 10^{-5}\,\text{nm})} = 0.62\,\text{eV}.$$

37P
From Exercise 33

$$\frac{\Delta E}{E} = \frac{\lambda}{\lambda'} - 1 = \frac{\lambda - \lambda'}{\lambda'} = \frac{-\Delta\lambda}{\lambda'} = -\frac{(h/mc)(1 - \cos\phi)}{c/f'}$$

$$= -(hf'/mc^2)(1 - \cos\phi).$$

Here the minum sign indicates that photon energy is lost during the scattering.

38P
From Exercise 33 we find

$$\cos\phi = 1 + \left(\frac{\lambda}{\lambda_C}\right)\left[1 + \left(\frac{\Delta E}{E}\right)^{-1}\right]^{-1}.$$

Now $\lambda = hc/E = (1240\,\text{eV}\cdot\text{nm})/200\,\text{keV} = 6.20\,\text{pm}$ so

$$\cos\phi = 1 + \left(\frac{6.2\,\text{pm}}{2.43\,\text{pm}}\right)[1 + (-10\%)^{-1}]^{-1} = 0.717.$$

The angle is $\phi = 44°$.

39P
The maximum energy of the electron is attained when the loss of energy of the photon is the greatest:

$$\frac{\Delta E}{E} = \left[-\frac{1}{(\lambda/\lambda_C)(1 - \cos\phi)^{-1} + 1}\right]_{\text{max}} = -\frac{1}{\lambda/2\lambda_C + 1}$$

Conservation of energy then gives

$$K_{\text{max}} = -\Delta E_{\text{max}} = \frac{E}{\lambda/2\lambda_C + 1} = \frac{E}{(hc/E)(mc/2h) + 1}$$

$$= \frac{E^2}{mc^2/2 + E}.$$

40P
Use the fomula obtained in Problem 39:

$$K_{\text{mas}} = \frac{E^2}{E + mc^2/2} = \frac{(17.5\,\text{keV})^2}{17.5\,\text{keV} + 511\,\text{keV}/2} = 1.12\,\text{keV}.$$

41P
Rewrite Eq. 43-12 as

$$\frac{h}{m\lambda} - \frac{h}{m\lambda'}\cos\phi = \frac{v}{\sqrt{1-(v/c)^2}}\cos\theta$$

and Eq. 43-13 as

$$\frac{h}{m\lambda'}\sin\phi = \frac{v}{\sqrt{1-(v/c)^2}}\sin\theta.$$

Square both equations and add up the two sides:

$$\left(\frac{h}{m}\right)^2\left[\left(\frac{1}{\lambda} - \frac{1}{\lambda'}\cos\phi\right)^2 + \left(\frac{1}{\lambda'}\sin\phi\right)^2\right] = \frac{v^2}{1-(v/c)^2},$$

where we used $\sin^2\theta + \cos^2\theta = 1$ to eliminate θ. Now the RHS can be written as

$$\frac{v^2}{1-(v/c)^2} = -c^2\left[1 - \frac{1}{1-(v/c)^2}\right]$$

so

$$\frac{1}{1-(v/c)^2} = \left(\frac{h}{mc}\right)^2\left[\left(\frac{1}{\lambda} - \frac{1}{\lambda'}\cos\phi\right)^2 + \left(\frac{1}{\lambda'}\sin\phi\right)^2\right] + 1.$$

Now rewrite Eq. 43-10 as

$$\frac{h}{mc}\left(\frac{1}{\lambda} - \frac{1}{\lambda'}\right) + 1 = \frac{1}{\sqrt{1-(v/c)^2}},$$

and compare with the previous equation we obtained for $[1 - (v/c)^2]^{-1}$, we get

$$\left[\frac{h}{mc}\left(\frac{1}{\lambda} - \frac{1}{\lambda'}\right) + 1\right]^2 = \left(\frac{h}{mc}\right)^2\left[\frac{1}{\lambda} - \frac{1}{\lambda'}\cos\phi\right)^2 + \left(\frac{1}{\lambda'}\sin\phi\right)^2\right] + 1.$$

We have so far eliminated θ and v. Working out the squares on both sides and noting that $\sin^2 \phi + \cos^2 \phi = 1$, we get

$$\lambda' - \lambda = \Delta\lambda = \frac{h}{mc}(1 - \cos\phi).$$

42E

Since $\lambda_{max}T = 2898\,\mu\mathrm{m}\cdot\mathrm{K}$,

$$\lambda_{max} = \frac{2898\,\mu\mathrm{m}\cdot\mathrm{K}}{5800\,\mathrm{K}} = 0.500\,\mu\mathrm{m} = 500\,\mathrm{nm}.$$

This is in the blue-green portion of the visible spectrum. The sun appears yellow because the human eye is more sensitive to light at about 550 nm than to light at 500 nm and the sun has a high intensity at the somewhat redder wavelengths. See Fig. 38–2.

43E

From the formula in Exercise 42

$$\lambda_{max} = \frac{2898\mu\,\mathrm{m}\cdot\mathrm{K}}{290\,\mathrm{K}} = 9.99\mu\,\mathrm{m}.$$

44E

From Exercise 42

$$T = \frac{2898\mu\,\mathrm{m}\cdot\mathrm{K}}{550 \times 10^{-3}\mu\,\mathrm{m}} = 5270\,\mathrm{K}.$$

45E

From Exercise 42

$$T = \frac{2898\mu\,\mathrm{m}\cdot\mathrm{K}}{32\mu\,\mathrm{m}} = 91\,\mathrm{K}.$$

46E

(a) From Exercise 42

$$\lambda_{max} = \frac{2898\mu\,\mathrm{m}\cdot\mathrm{K}}{2.00 \times 10^{-3}\,\mathrm{K}} = 1.45 \times 10^6\,\mu\,\mathrm{m} = 1.45\,\mathrm{m}.$$

(b) From Fig. 38-1 we see that this radiation corresponds to the radio wave region.

(*c*) You are being subject to interferences from existing broadcasting radio waves that fill the air.

47E
Use the formula in Exercise 42. See Fig. 38-1 for the corresponding regions of electromagnetic spectrum.

(*a*) $\lambda_{\max} = (2898\mu\,\mathrm{m}\cdot\mathrm{K})/(3.0\,\mathrm{K}) = 9.7\times10^2\,\mu\,\mathrm{m} = 0.97\,\mathrm{mm}$, in the microwave region.

(*b*) $\lambda_{\max} = (2898\mu\,\mathrm{m}\cdot\mathrm{K})/(20+273)\,\mathrm{K} = 9.9\mu\,\mathrm{m}$, in the infrared region.

(*c*) $\lambda_{\max} = (2898\mu\,\mathrm{m}\cdot\mathrm{K})/(1800\,\mathrm{K}) = 1.6\mu\,\mathrm{m}$, in the infrared region.

(*d*) $\lambda_{\max} = (2898\mu\,\mathrm{m}\cdot\mathrm{K})/(10^7\,\mathrm{K}) = 2.6\times10^{-4}\,\mu\,\mathrm{m} = 0.26\,\mathrm{nm}$, in the X ray region.

(*e*) $\lambda_{\max} = (2898\mu\,\mathrm{m}\cdot\mathrm{K})/(10^{38}\,\mathrm{K}) = 2.9\times10^{-41}\,\mathrm{m}$, in the very high energy gamma ray region.

48P
Set $ds/d\lambda = 0$ in Eq. 43-18:

$$\frac{ds(\lambda)}{d\lambda} = \frac{-10\pi c^2 h}{\lambda^6}\frac{1}{e^{hc/\lambda kT}-1} + \frac{2\pi c^2 h}{\lambda^5}\frac{hc/\lambda^2 kT}{(e^{hc/\lambda kT}-1)^2}$$

$$= \frac{2\pi c^2 h}{\lambda^6}\left[-5 + \frac{hc}{\lambda kT(e^{hc/\lambda kT}-1)}\right] = 0.$$

Let $hc/\lambda kT = x$, we get

$$-5 + \frac{x}{e^x - 1} = 0,$$

whose solution is 4.965. So $hc/\lambda_{\max}kT = x = 4.965$, or

$$\lambda_{\max}T = \frac{hc}{kx} = \frac{1.24\,\mathrm{eV}\cdot\mu\,\mathrm{m}}{(8.62\times10^{-5}\,\mathrm{eV/K})(4.965)} = 2898\mu\,\mathrm{m}\cdot\mathrm{K}.$$

49P
(*a*) If $S(\lambda)$ is the spectral radiancy then the power emitted per unit area is

$$P = \int_0^\infty S(\lambda)\,d\lambda = (2\pi c^2 h)\int_0^\infty \frac{\lambda^{-5}\,d\lambda}{e^{hc/\lambda kT}-1}.$$

Let $x = hc/\lambda kT$; then $\lambda = hc/kTx$ and $d\lambda = -(hc/kTx^2)\,dx$. When $\lambda = \infty$ then $x = 0$ and when $\lambda = \infty$ then $x = 0$. The negative sign in $d\lambda$ can be used to reverse the limits on the integral. Hence

$$P = (2\pi c^2 h)\left(\frac{kT}{hc}\right)^4\int_0^\infty \frac{x^3\,dx}{e^x - 1} = (2\pi c^2 h)\left(\frac{k}{hc}\right)^4\left(\frac{\pi^4}{15}\right)T^4 = \left(\frac{2\pi^5 k^4}{15h^3 c^2}\right)T^4.$$

This can be written $P = \sigma T^4$, where $\sigma = (2\pi^5 k^4)/(15h^3 c^2)$.

(b) Use values of the fundamental constants given in Appendix B to obtain

$$\sigma = \frac{2\pi^5(1.3807 \times 10^{-23} \, \text{J}/K)^4}{15(6.6261 \times 10^{-34} \, \text{J} \cdot \text{s})^3(2.9979 \times 10^8 \, \text{m/s})^2} = 5.67 \times 10^{-8} \, \text{W/m}^2 \cdot \text{K}^4.$$

50P
The rate of energy radiation is

$$P = \sigma T^4 A = [5.67 \times 10^{-8} \, \text{W}/(\text{m}^2 \cdot \text{K}^4)][(500 + 273) \, \text{K}]^4(0.50 \, \text{m}^2)$$
$$= 1.0 \times 10^4 \, \text{W} = 10 \, \text{kW}.$$

51P
(a)
$$P = \sigma T^4 A = [5.67 \times 10^{-8} \, \text{W}/(\text{m}^2 \cdot \text{K}^4)][(31 + 273) \, \text{K}]^4(1.8 \, \text{m}^2) = 872 \, \text{W}.$$

(b) Since $\lambda_{\text{max}} = 2898\mu \text{m} \cdot \text{K}/(31 + 273) \, \text{K} = 9.5\mu \text{m}$, the radiation is primarily in the infrared region and is therefroe invisible.

52P
Since $P \propto T^4$, at $T = 2T_1$ the rate of energy radiation is

$$P_2 = \left(\frac{2T_1}{T_1}\right)^4 P_1 = 2^4(12.0 \, \text{mW}) = 192 \, \text{mW}.$$

53P
(a) Use $P = \sigma T^4$. We have

$$\frac{\Delta P}{P} = \frac{\Delta(\sigma T^4)}{\sigma T^4} \approx \frac{4\sigma T^3 \Delta T}{\sigma T^4} = \frac{4\Delta T}{T}.$$

(b) Now $\Delta T = 1° \text{C} = 1 \, \text{K}$ so

$$\frac{\Delta P}{P} \approx \frac{4(1 \, \text{K})}{(34 + 273) \, \text{K}} = 1.3\%.$$

54P
Let T_o be the temperature of the oven in kelvins $(227 + 273 = 500 \, \text{K})$ and T_r be the temperature of the room in kelvins $(27 + 273 = 300 \, \text{K})$. The oven radiates energy into

the room at the rate $\sigma A T_o^4$ and the room radiates energy into the oven at the rate $\sigma A T_r^4$, where A is the area of the opening and σ is the Stefan-Boltzmann constant, developed in Problem 49. The net rate at which energy is transferred from the oven to the room is

$$P = \sigma A \left(T_o^4 - T_r^4 \right) = (5.67 \times 10^{-8}\,\text{W/m}^2 \cdot \text{K}^4)(5.0 \times 10^{-4}\,\text{m}^2) \left[(500\,\text{K})^4 - (300\,\text{K})^4 \right]$$
$$= 1.5\,\text{W}.$$

55E
$$\Delta E = hf = (4.14 \times 10^{-15}\,\text{eV} \cdot \text{s})(6.2 \times 10^{14}\,\text{Hz}) = 2.6\,\text{eV}.$$

56E
The net energy absorbed is

$$\Delta E = h\Delta f = hc\Delta\left(\frac{1}{\lambda}\right) = (1240\,\text{eV} \cdot \text{nm})\left(\frac{1}{375\,\text{nm}} - \frac{1}{580\,\text{nm}}\right) = 1.17\,\text{eV}.$$

57E
Since energy is conserved the energy E of the emitted photon equals $E_i - E_f$, where E_i is the energy of the initial state of the gold atom and E_f is the energy of the final state. Now $E = hf = hc/\lambda = (1240\,\text{eV} \cdot \text{nm})/(18.5 \times 10^{-3}\,\text{nm}) = 6.70 \times 10^4\,\text{eV} = 67.0\,\text{keV}$. Hence

$$E_f = E_i - hf = -13.7\,\text{keV} - 67.0\,\text{keV} = -80.7\,\text{keV}.$$

58E
(a)

$$E_i = -\frac{me^4}{8\epsilon_0^2 h^2} = -\frac{(9.11 \times 10^{-31}\,\text{kg})(1.60 \times 10^{-19}\,\text{C})^4}{8(8.85 \times 10^{-12}\,\text{F/m})^2(6.63 \times 10^{-34}\,\text{J} \cdot \text{s})^2(1.60 \times 10^{-19}\,\text{J/eV})}$$
$$= -13.6\,\text{eV}.$$

(b)

$$R = \frac{me^4}{8\epsilon_0^2 h^3 c} = \frac{(9.11 \times 10^{-31}\,\text{kg})(1.6 \times 10^{-19}\,\text{C})^4(1\,\text{m}/10^9\,\text{nm})}{8(8.85 \times 10^{-12}\,\text{F/m})^2(6.63 \times 10^{-34}\,\text{J} \cdot \text{s})^3(3.00 \times 10^8\,\text{m/s})}$$
$$= 0.01097\,\text{nm}^{-1}.$$

59E

For the Lyman series $l = 1$ so

(a)

$$\frac{1}{\lambda} = R\left(\frac{1}{l^2} - \frac{1}{u^2}\right) = (0.01097\,\text{nm}^{-1})\left(\frac{1}{1^2} - \frac{1}{2^2}\right)$$
$$= 8.2275 \times 10^{-3}\,\text{nm}^{-1}.$$

Thus $\lambda_n = (8.2275 \times 10^{-3}\,\text{nm}^{-1})^{-1} = 121.5\,\text{nm}$.

(b)

$$\frac{1}{\lambda} = (0.01097\,\text{nm}^{-1})\left(\frac{1}{1^2}\right) = 0.01097\,\text{nm}^{-1}.$$

so $\lambda = (0.01097\,\text{nm}^{-1})^{-1} = 91.2\,\text{nm}$.

60E

(a) Since energy is conserved the energy E of the photon is given by $E = E_i - E_f$, where E_i is the initial energy of the electron and E_f is the final energy. The electron energy is given by $(-13.6\,\text{eV})/n^2$, where n is the principal quantum number. Thus

$$E = E_i - E_f = \frac{-13.6\,\text{eV}}{(3)^2} - \frac{-13.6\,\text{eV}}{(1)^2} = 12.1\,\text{eV}.$$

(b) The photon momentum is given by

$$p = \frac{E}{c} = \frac{(12.1\,\text{eV})(1.60 \times 10^{-19}\,\text{J/eV})}{3.00 \times 10^8\,\text{m/s}} = 6.45 \times 10^{-27}\,\text{kg} \cdot \text{m/s}.$$

(c) The wavelength is given by

$$\lambda = \frac{1240\,\text{eV} \cdot \text{nm}}{12.1\,\text{eV}} = 102\,\text{nm},$$

where the result of Exercise 1 was used.

61E

For the Belmer series $l = 2$ so Eq. 43-24 gives

$$\frac{1}{\lambda} = R\left(\frac{1}{4} - \frac{1}{u^2}\right).$$

(a) Now $u = 3$ so

$$\lambda = \frac{1}{(0.01097\,\text{nm}^{-1})(1/4 - 1/3^2)} = 656.3\,\text{nm}.$$

(b) Now $u = 4$ so

$$\lambda = \frac{1}{(0.01097\,\text{nm}^{-1})(1/4 - 1/4^2)} = 486.2\,\text{nm}.$$

(c) Now $u = 5$ so

$$\lambda = \frac{1}{(0.01097\,\text{nm}^{-1})(1/4 - 1/5^2)} = 434.1\,\text{nm}.$$

62E

Use Eq. 43–24 for the wavelengths of the electromagnetic radiation emitted by hydrogen:

$$\frac{1}{\lambda} = R\left(\frac{1}{\ell^2} - \frac{1}{u^2}\right),$$

where R is the Rydberg constant, ℓ is the principal quantum number associated with the lower electron state, and u is the principal quantum number associated with the upper electron state. A series limit is obtained if $u = \infty$. For the Balmer series $\ell = 2$ and $\lambda_B = 4/R$. For the Lyman series $\ell = 1$ and $\lambda_L = 1/R$. The ratio is

$$\frac{\lambda_B}{\lambda_L} = \frac{4/R}{1/R} = 4.$$

63E

(a) $\Delta E = -(13.6\,\text{eV})(4^{-2} - 1^{-2}) = 12.8\,\text{eV}.$
(b) The various photon energies are depcted in the diagram below.

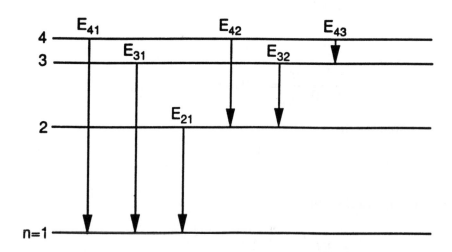

The values of the photon energies are: $E_{41} = \Delta E = 12.8\,\text{eV}$, $E_{31} = -(13.6\,\text{eV})(3^{-2} - 1^{-2}) = 12.1\,\text{eV}$, $E_{21} = -(13.6\,\text{eV})(2^{-2} - 1^{-2}) = 10.2\,\text{eV}$, $E_{42} = -(13.6\,\text{eV})(4^{-2} - 2^{-2}) = 2.55\,\text{eV}$, $E_{32} = -(13.6\,\text{eV})(3^{-2} - 2^{-2}) = 1.89\,\text{eV}$, and $E_{43} = -(13.6\,\text{eV})(4^{-2} - 3^{-2}) = 0.66\,\text{eV}$.

64P

(a) Take the electrostatic potential energy to be zero when the electron and proton are far removed from each other. Then the final energy of the atom is zero and the work done in pulling it apart is $W = -E_i$, where E_i is the energy of the initial state. The energy of the initial state is given by $E_i = (-13.6\,\text{eV})/n^2$, where n is the principal quantum number of the state. For the ground state $n = 1$ and $W = 13.6\,\text{eV}$.

(b) For the state with $n = 2$, $W = (13.6\,\text{eV})/(2)^2 = 3.40\,\text{eV}$.

65P

(a) From Eq. 43-24 we get

$$\lambda_{\min}^{-1} = R\left(\frac{1}{n_1^2}\right)$$

and

$$\lambda_{\min}^{-1} = R\left(\frac{1}{n_1^2} - \frac{1}{n_2^2}\right) = R\left[\frac{1}{n_1^2} - \frac{1}{(n_1+1)^2}\right].$$

For the Lyman series $n_1 = 1$, so

$$\Delta\lambda = \frac{1}{R}\left[\frac{1}{n_1^2} - \frac{1}{(n_1+1)^2}\right]^{-1} - \frac{n_1^2}{R}$$

$$= \frac{1}{R}\left[\frac{1}{1^2} - \frac{1}{2^2}\right]^{-1} - \frac{1^2}{R} = \frac{1}{3R} = \frac{1}{3(0.01097\,\text{nm}^{-1})} = 30.4\,\text{nm}.$$

For the Balmer series $n_1 = 2$, so

$$\Delta\lambda = \frac{1}{R}\left[\frac{1}{2^2} - \frac{1}{3^2}\right]^{-1} - \frac{2^2}{R} = \frac{36}{5R} = \frac{6}{5(0.01097\,\text{nm}^{-1})} = 292\,\text{nm}.$$

For the Paschen series $n_1 = 3$, so

$$\Delta\lambda = \frac{1}{R}\left[\frac{1}{3^2} - \frac{1}{4^2}\right]^{-1} - \frac{3^2}{R} = \frac{81}{7R} = \frac{81}{6(0.01097\,\text{nm}^{-1})} = 1055\,\text{nm}.$$

(b) The frequency interval is

$$\Delta f = c\Delta\left(\frac{1}{\lambda}\right) = cR\left[\frac{1}{n_1^2} - \left(\frac{1}{n_2^2} - \frac{1}{(n_1+1)^2}\right)\right] = \frac{cR}{(n_1+1)^2}.$$

So for the Lyman series

$$\Delta f = \frac{(3.00 \times 10^8\,\text{m/s})(0.01097\,\text{nm}^{-1})}{(1+1)^2} = 8.23 \times 10^{14}\,\text{Hz};$$

for the Balmer series

$$\Delta f = \frac{(3.00 \times 10^8\,\text{m/s})(0.01097\,\text{nm}^{-1})}{(2+1)^2} = 3.66 \times 10^{14}\,\text{Hz};$$

and for the Balmer series

$$\Delta f = \frac{(3.00 \times 10^8\,\text{m/s})(0.01097\,\text{nm}^{-1})}{(3+1)^2} = 2.06 \times 10^{14}\,\text{Hz}.$$

66P

(a) Let

$$hf = \frac{hc}{\lambda} = hcR\left(\frac{1}{n_1^2} - \frac{1}{n_2^2}\right)$$

or

$$\frac{1}{n_1^2} - \frac{1}{n_2^2} = \frac{1}{\lambda R} = \frac{1}{(486.1\,\text{nm})(0.01097\,\text{nm}^{-1})} = 0.1875.$$

You can easily verify that the only pair of integers n_1, n_2 which satisfy this formula is $n_1 = 2$ and $n_2 = 4$. So the transition is from the $n_2 = 4$ to the $n_1 = 2$ state.

(b) The Balmer series (since $n_1 = 2$).

67P

Now

$$\frac{1}{\lambda} = R\left(\frac{1}{n_1^2} - \frac{1}{n_2^2}\right)$$

or

$$\frac{1}{n_1^2} - \frac{1}{n_2^2} = \frac{1}{\lambda R}$$

$$= \frac{1}{(121.6\,\text{nm})(0.01097\,\text{nm}^{-1})}$$

$$= \frac{3}{4},$$

So $n_1 = 1$ and $n_2 = 2$. The transition is shown in the energy diagram above.

68P

(a) Since $E_i = -0.85\,\text{eV}$ and $E_f = -13.6\,\text{eV} + 10.2\,\text{eV} = -3.4\,\text{eV}$, the photon energy is $E_{\text{photon}} = E_i - E_f = -0.85\,\text{eV} - (-3.4\,\text{eV}) = 2.6\,\text{eV}.$

(*b*) Since

$$E_i - E_f = (-13.6\,\text{eV})\left(\frac{1}{n_i^2} - \frac{1}{n_f^2}\right)$$

$$= 2.55\,\text{eV},$$

$$\frac{1}{n_i^2} - \frac{1}{n_f^2} = -\frac{2.55\,\text{eV}}{13.6\,\text{eV}} = -\frac{3}{16}.$$

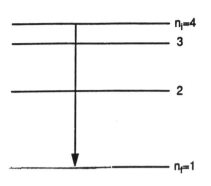

Thus $n_i = 4$ and $n_f = 2$.

69P

Conservation of linear momentum gives $P_{\text{recoil}} = P_{\text{photon}}$, or $mv_{\text{recoil}} = E_{\text{photon}}/c$. Thus

$$v_{\text{recoil}} = \frac{E_4}{mc} = \frac{(-13.6\,\text{eV})(4^{-2} - 1^{-2})}{938\,\text{MeV}/(3.00 \times 10^8\ \text{m/s})} = 4.1\,\text{m/s}.$$

70P

If kinetic energy is not conserved some of the neutron's initial kinetic energy is used to excite the hydrogen atom. The least energy that the hydrogen atom can accept is the difference between the first excited state ($n = 2$) and the ground state ($n = 1$). Since the energy of a state with principal quantum number n is $-(13.6\,\text{eV})/n^2$, the smallest excitation energy is $13.6\,\text{eV} - (13.6\,\text{eV})/(2)^2 = 10.2\,\text{eV}$. The neutron does not have sufficient kinetic energy to excite the hydrogen atom, so the hydrogen atom is left in its ground state and all the initial kinetic energy of the neutron ends up as the final kinetic energies of the neutron and atom. The collision must be elastic.

71P

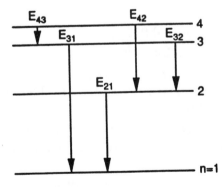

From the energy diagram shown to the right $E_{31} = E_{21} + E_{32}$, or $hf_{31} = hf_{21} + hf_{32}$. Thus $f_{31} = f_{21} + f_{32}$. An example of other valid combinations is $f_{42} = f_{43} + f_{32}$. In general,

$$f_{n_1, n_3} = f_{n_1, n_2} + f_{n_2, n_3},$$

where $n_1 > n_2 > n_3$.

72P

(*a*)Rewrite Eq. 43-24 as

$$\frac{1}{\lambda R} = \frac{1}{n^2} - \frac{1}{(n + \Delta n)^2} \approx \frac{2\Delta n}{n^3},$$

1081

where the approximation is valid for large n ($\Delta n/n \ll 1$). For the smallest value of n let $\Delta n = 1$. Then $n = (2\lambda R)^{1/3}$.

(b) $n = [2(21.0 \times 10^7 \, \text{nm})(0.01097 \, \text{nm}^{-1})]^{1/3} = 166$.

73E

$$r_B = \frac{h^2 \epsilon_0}{\pi m e^2} = \frac{(6.63 \times 10^{-34} \, \text{J} \cdot \text{s})^2 (8.85 \times 10^{-12} \, \text{F/m})}{\pi (9.11 \times 10^{-31} \, \text{kg})(1.60 \times 10^{-19} \, \text{C})^2} = 0.0531 \, \text{nm}.$$

74E
From Eq. 43-33

$$n = \sqrt{\frac{r}{r_B}} = \sqrt{\frac{0.847 \, \text{nm}}{0.05292 \, \text{nm}}} = 4.00.$$

75E
(a) Let $L = M_E v_E R_{\text{ES}} = nh/2\pi$ and solve for n:

$$n = \frac{2\pi M_E v_E R_{\text{ES}}}{h} = \frac{2\pi (5.98 \times 10^{24} \, \text{kg})(29.8 \, \text{km/s})(1.50 \times 10^{11} \, \text{m})}{6.63 \times 10^{-34} \, \text{J} \cdot \text{s}}$$
$$\approx 3 \times 10^{74}.$$

(b) No, because one would need to arrange measurements with relative error of less than 10^{-74}.

76P
(a) $n = 1$.

(b) $r = r_B = 0.0529 \, \text{nm}$.

(c) $L = nh/2\pi = h/2\pi$.

(d) $p = L/r_B = h/(2\pi r_B) = (6.63 \times 10^{-34} \, \text{J} \cdot \text{s})/[2\pi(0.0529 \, \text{nm})] = 1.99 \times 10^{-24} \, \text{kg} \cdot \text{m/s}$.

(e) $\omega = v/r = p/(m r_B) = (1.99 \times 10^{-24} \, \text{kg} \cdot \text{m/s})/[(9.11 \times 10^{-31} \, \text{kg})(0.0529 \, \text{nm})] = 4.14 \times 10^{16} \, \text{rad/s}$.

(f) $v = p/m = (1.99 \times 10^{-24} \, \text{kg} \cdot \text{m/s})/(9.11 \times 10^{-31} \, \text{kg}) = 2.19 \times 10^6 \, \text{m/s}$.

(g) $F = (4\pi\epsilon_0)^{-1} e^2/r_B^2 = (9.0 \times 10^9 \, \text{N} \cdot \text{m}^2/\text{C}^2)(1.60 \times 10^{-19} \, \text{C})^2/(0.0529 \, \text{nm})^2 = 8.26 \times 10^{-8} \, \text{N}$.

(h) $a = v^2/r_B = (2.19 \times 10^6 \, \text{m/s})^2/0.0529 \, \text{nm} = 9.07 \times 10^{22} \, \text{m/s}^2$.

(i) $K = \frac{1}{2} m v^2 = \frac{1}{2}(9.11 \times 10^{-31} \, \text{kg})(2.19 \times 10^6 \, \text{m/s}^2)/(1.60 \times 10^{-19} \, \text{J/eV}) = 13.6 \, \text{eV}$.

(j) $U = -(4\pi\epsilon_0)^{-1}(e^2/r_B) = -(9.0 \times 10^9 \, \text{N} \cdot \text{m}^2/\text{C}^2)(1.60 \times 10^{-19} \, \text{C})^2/[(0.0529 \, \text{nm})(1.60 \times 10^{-19} \, \text{J/eV})] = -27.2 \, \text{eV}$.

(k) $E = K + U = 13.6 \, \text{eV} - 27.2 \, \text{eV} = -13.6 \, \text{eV}$.

77P
(b) $r = n^2 r_B \propto n^2$.
(c) $L = hn/2\pi \propto n$.
(d) $p = L/r \propto n/n^2 = n^{-1}$.
(e) $\omega L/(mr^2) \propto n/n^4 = n^{-3}$.
(f) $v = \omega r \propto (n^{-3})(n^2) = n^{-1}$.
(g) $F = (4\pi\epsilon_0)^{-1}(e^2/r^2) \propto r^{-2} \propto (n^2)^{-2} = n^{-4}$.
(h) $a = F/m \propto n^{-4}$.
(i) $K = \dfrac{1}{2}mv^2 \propto v^2 \propto (n^{-1})^2 = n^{-2}$.
(j) $U = (4\pi\epsilon_0)^{-1}(e^2/r) \propto r^{-1} \propto n^{-2}$.
(k) $T = K + U \propto n^{-2}$.

78P
(a) If angular momentum is quantized as in the Bohr model of the hydrogen atom, then $L = nh/2\pi$, where n is the principal quantum number and h is the Planck constant. Since $L = I\omega$, where I is the rotational inertia and ω is the angular velocity, $I\omega = nh/2\pi$ and $\omega = nh/2\pi I$. The rotational inertia of the two-particle system shown is $I = 2m(d/2)^2 = md^2/2$, so

$$\omega = \frac{nh}{2\pi} \frac{2}{md^2} = \frac{nh}{\pi md^2}.$$

(b) The kinetic energy of rotation is

$$E = \frac{1}{2}I\omega^2 = \frac{1}{2}\left(\frac{md^2}{2}\right)\left(\frac{nh}{\pi md^2}\right)^2 = \frac{n^2 h^2}{4\pi^2 md^2}.$$

79
The charge in energy for the electron-proton system is $\Delta E = E_1 - K = -13.6\,\text{eV} - 3.0\,\text{eV} = -16.6\,\text{eV}$. So the photon frequency is $f = |\Delta E|/h = 16.6\,\text{eV}/(4.14 \times 10^{-15}\,\text{eV} \cdot \text{s}) = 4.0 \times 10^{15}$ Hz.

80
The energy difference is

$$\Delta E = \Delta(hf) = \Delta\left(\frac{hc}{\lambda}\right) = hc\Delta\left(\frac{1}{\lambda}\right)$$

$$= (1240\,\text{eV} \cdot \text{nm})\left(\frac{1}{500\,\text{nm}} - \frac{1}{510\,\text{nm}}\right) = 0.049\,\text{eV}.$$

81

Let the separation be $r_{\min}$. Then

$$\phi = \frac{1}{4\pi\epsilon_0}\frac{e^2}{r_{\min}}.$$

Solve for $r_{\min}$:

$$r_{\min} = \frac{e^2}{4\pi\epsilon_0\phi} = \frac{(1.60\times10^{-19}\,\text{C})^2(9.0\times10^9\,\text{N}\cdot\text{m}^2/\text{C}^2)}{(1.8\,\text{eV})(1.60\times10^{-19}\,\text{J/eV})} = 0.80\,\text{nm}.$$

82

$$E_{\text{photon}} = \frac{hc}{\lambda} = \frac{hc}{(2898\mu\text{m}\cdot\text{K})/T} = \frac{(1240\,\text{nm}\cdot\text{eV})(3K)}{2898\mu\text{m}\cdot\text{K}} = 1\times10^{-3}\,\text{eV}.$$

83

A He^+ ion contains a nucleus with charge $+2e$ and an electron with charge $-e$ orbiting around it with radius r_e. Since $r_e = n^2h^2\epsilon_0/(\pi m_e e^2)\propto m_e^{-1}$, we have $r_\mu/r_e = (m_\mu/m_e)^{-1} = 207^{-1}\ll 1$, i.e. The muon orbits in a circular orbit of radius $r_\mu \ll r_e$. So the muon is attrated by charge Ze ($Z = +2$ in our case). Note that we need to replace one of the two e's by Ze in Eq. 43-26 or, effectively, change ϵ_0^{-1} to $Z\epsilon_0^{-1}$. Thus Eq. 43-21 becomes

$$E_\mu = -\left[\frac{m_\mu e^2}{8(\epsilon_0/Z)^2h^2}\right]\frac{1}{n^2} = -\left(\frac{Z^2 m_\mu}{m_e}\right)\left(\frac{m_e e^2}{8\epsilon_0^2 h^2}\right)\frac{1}{n^2}$$

$$= -\frac{2^2(207)(13.6\,\text{eV})}{n^2} = -\frac{11.3\,\text{keV}}{n^2}.$$

84

$mv\gamma$ •———→ electron

hf_0/c ←———• photon (before collision)

p_e •———→

hf/c •———→ (after collision)

The momenta of the electron and the photon both before and after the collision are depicted in the figure above. Conservation of linear momentum reads

$$mv\gamma - hf_0/c = p_e + hf/c,$$

1084

and conseration of energy gives

$$m\gamma c^2 + h f_0 = \sqrt{p_e^2 + (mc^2)^2} + hf,$$

where $\gamma = (1 - v^2/c^2)^{-1/2}$. Elininate p_e from the above equations to obtain

$$(mvc\gamma - h f_0 - hf)^2 = (mc^2\gamma + h f_0 - hf)^2 - m^2 c^4.$$

A little algebra leads to

$$2hf\left[mc^2\gamma\left(1 - \frac{v}{c}\right) + 2h f_0\right] = 2h f_0 mc^2\gamma\left(1 - \frac{v}{c}\right) + m^2 c^4\left[\gamma^2\left(1 - \frac{v^2}{c^2}\right) - 1\right].$$

Note that $\gamma^2(1 - v^2/c^2) = 1$ so the last term on the R.H.S. above is zero. Thus

$$E = hf = \frac{(h f_0)mc^2\gamma\left(1 - \dfrac{v}{c}\right)}{mc^2\gamma\left(1 - \dfrac{v}{c}\right) + 2h f_0} = \frac{h f_0}{1 + \dfrac{2h f_0}{mc^2\gamma(1 - v/c)}} = \frac{h f_0}{1 + \dfrac{2h f_0}{mc^2}\sqrt{\dfrac{1 + v/c}{1 - v/c}}},$$

where in the last step we used $\gamma(1 - v/c) = (1 - v^2/c^2)^{-1}(1 - v/c) = \sqrt{(1 - v/c)/(1 + v/c)}$.

CHAPTER 44

1E

(a)

$$\lambda = \frac{h}{p} = \frac{h}{mv} = \frac{6.63 \times 10^{-34}\,\text{J} \cdot \text{s}}{(40 \times 10^{-3}\,\text{kg})(1000\,\text{m/s})} = 1.7 \times 10^{-35}\,\text{m}.$$

(b) Since the wavelength of the bullet is much smaller than any reasonable microscopic distance, that is why the wave nature of the bullet does not reveal itself through diffraction effects.

2E

(a) Substitute the classical relationship between momentum p and velocity v, $v = p/m$ into the classical definition of kinetic energy, $K = \frac{1}{2}mv^2$, to obtain $K = p^2/2m$. Here m is the mass of an electron. Solve for p: $p = \sqrt{2mK}$. The relationship between the momentum and the de Broglie wavelength λ is $\lambda = h/p$, where h is the Planck constant. Thus

$$\lambda = \frac{h}{\sqrt{2mK}}.$$

If K is given in electron volts then

$$\lambda = \frac{6.626 \times 10^{-34}\,\text{J} \cdot \text{s}}{\sqrt{2(9.109 \times 10^{-31}\,\text{kg})}\sqrt{(1.602 \times 10^{-19}\,\text{J/eV})K}} = \frac{1.226 \times 10^{-9}\,\text{m} \cdot \text{eV}^{1/2}}{\sqrt{K}}$$

$$= \frac{1.226\,\text{nm} \cdot \text{eV}^{1/2}}{\sqrt{K}}.$$

(b) Replace K with eV, where V is the accelerating potential and e is the charge on the electron, to obtain

$$\lambda = \frac{h}{\sqrt{2meV}} = \frac{6.626 \times 10^{-34}\,\text{J} \cdot \text{s}}{\sqrt{2(9.109 \times 10^{-31}\,\text{kg})(1.602 \times 10^{-19}\,\text{C})V}}$$

$$= \sqrt{\frac{1.50 \times 10^{-18}\,\text{nm}^2 \cdot \text{V}}{V}} = \sqrt{\frac{1.50\,\text{nm}^2 \cdot \text{V}}{V}}.$$

3E

Use the result of Exercise 2:

$$\lambda = \sqrt{\frac{1.50\,\text{nm}^2 \cdot \text{V}}{V}} = \sqrt{\frac{1.50\,\text{nm}^2 \cdot \text{V}}{25.0 \times 10^3\,\text{V}}} = 7.75 \times 10^{-3}\,\text{nm} = 7.75\,\text{pm}.$$

4E

(a)

$$\lambda = \frac{h}{p} = \frac{h}{\sqrt{2m_eK}} = \frac{hc}{\sqrt{2m_ec^2K}} = \frac{1240\,\text{eV} \cdot \text{nm}}{\sqrt{2(0.511\,\text{MeV})(1.00\,\text{keV})}} = 38.7\,\text{pm}.$$

(b)

$$\lambda = \frac{hc}{E} = \frac{1240\,\text{eV} \cdot \text{nm}}{1.00\,\text{keV}} = 1.24\,\text{nm}.$$

(c)

$$\lambda = \frac{hc}{\sqrt{m_nc^2K}} = \frac{1240\,\text{eV} \cdot \text{nm}}{\sqrt{2(939\,\text{MeV})(1.00\,\text{KeV})}} = 0.904\,\text{nm} = 904\,\text{pm}.$$

5E

(a) and (b) For the electron

$$p_e = \frac{h}{\lambda} = \frac{6.63 \times 10^{-34}\,\text{J} \cdot \text{s}}{0.20 \times 10^{-9}\,\text{m}} = 3.3 \times 10^{-24}\,\text{kg} \cdot \text{m/s}$$

and

$$K_e = \frac{p_e^2}{2m_e} = \frac{(3.3 \times 10^{-24}\,\text{kg} \cdot \text{m/s})^2}{2(9.11 \times 10^{-31}\,\text{kg})} = 6.0 \times 10^{-18}\,\text{J} = 38\,\text{eV}.$$

For the photon $p_{\text{ph}} = h/\lambda = p_e = 3.3 \times 10^{-24}\,\text{kg} \cdot \text{m/s}$ and $K_{\text{ph}} = p_{\text{ph}}c = (3.3 \times 10^{-24}\,\text{kg} \cdot$ m/s$)(3.00 \times 10^8\,\text{m/s}) = 9.9 \times 10^{-16}\,\text{J} = 6.2\,\text{keV}.$

6E

Use the result of Exercise 2: $\lambda = (1.226\,\text{nm} \cdot \text{eV}^{1/2})/\sqrt{K}$, where K is the kinetic energy. Thus

$$K = \left(\frac{1.226\,\text{nm} \cdot \text{eV}^{1/2}}{\lambda}\right)^2 = \left(\frac{1.226\,\text{nm} \cdot \text{eV}^{1/2}}{590\,\text{nm}}\right)^2 = 4.32 \times 10^{-6}\,\text{eV}.$$

7E

(a) $K = \frac{3}{2}kT = \frac{3(1.38 \times 10^{-23}\,\text{J/K})(300\,\text{K})}{2(1.60 \times 10^{-19}\,\text{J/eV})} = 3.88 \times 10^{-2}\,\text{eV} = 38.8\,\text{meV}.$

(b)

$$\lambda = \frac{h}{\sqrt{2m_nK}} = \frac{hc}{\sqrt{2(m_nc^2)K}} = \frac{1240\,\text{nm} \cdot \text{eV}}{\sqrt{2(939\,\text{MeV})(3.88 \times 10^{-2}\,\text{eV})}}$$

$$= 1.46 \times 10^{-10}\,\text{m} = 146\,\text{pm}.$$

8E

(a) Solve v from $\lambda = h/p = h/(mv)$:

$$v = \frac{h}{m_p\lambda} = \frac{6.63 \times 10^{-34}\,\text{J} \cdot \text{s}}{(1.675 \times 10^{-27}\,\text{kg})(0.100 \times 10^{-12}\,\text{m})} = 3.96 \times 10^6\,\text{m/s}.$$

(b) Let $eV = K = \frac{1}{2}m_p v^2$ and solve for V:

$$V = \frac{m_p v^2}{2e} = \frac{(1.67 \times 10^{-27}\,\text{kg})(3.96 \times 10^6\,\text{m/s})^2}{2(1.60 \times 10^{-19}\,\text{C})} = 8.18 \times 10^3\,\text{V}.$$

9P

(a)

$$\bar{\lambda} = \frac{h}{\bar{p}} = \frac{h}{\sqrt{2m\bar{K}}} = \frac{h}{\sqrt{2m(3kT/2)}} = \frac{hc}{\sqrt{3(mc^2)kT}}$$

$$= \frac{1240\,\text{eV} \cdot \text{nm}}{\sqrt{3(4)(938\,\text{MeV})(8.62 \times 10^{-5}\,\text{eV/K})(300\,\text{K})}} = 7.3 \times 10^{-11}\,\text{m} = 73\,\text{pm}.$$

$$\bar{d} = \frac{1}{\sqrt[3]{n}} = \frac{1}{\sqrt[3]{p/kT}} = \sqrt[3]{\frac{(1.38 \times 10^{-23}\,\text{J/K})(300\,\text{K})}{1.01 \times 10^5\,\text{Pa}}} = 3.4\,\text{nm}.$$

(b) Yes, since $\bar{\lambda} \ll \bar{d}$.

10P

(a) The momentum of the photon is given by $p = E/c$, where E is its energy. Its wavelength is

$$\lambda = \frac{h}{p} = \frac{hc}{E} = \frac{1240\,\text{eV} \cdot \text{nm}}{1.00\,\text{eV}} = 1240\,\text{nm}.$$

See Exercise 1 of Chapter 43. The momentum of the electron is given by $p = \sqrt{2mK}$, where K is its kinetic energy and m is its mass. Its wavelength is

$$\lambda = \frac{h}{p} = \frac{h}{\sqrt{2mK}}.$$

According to Exercise 2 if K is in electron volts this is

$$\lambda = \frac{1.226\,\text{nm}}{\sqrt{K}} = \frac{1.226\,\text{nm}}{\sqrt{1.00}} = 1.23\,\text{nm}.$$

(b) For the photon

$$\lambda = \frac{hc}{E} = \frac{1240\,\text{eV} \cdot \text{nm}}{1.00 \times 10^9\,\text{eV}} = 1.24 \times 10^{-6}\,\text{nm}.$$

Relativity theory must be used to calculate the wavelength for the electron. According to Eq. 42–40 the momentum p and kinetic energy K are related by $(pc)^2 = K^2 + 2Kmc^2$. Thus

$$pc = \sqrt{K^2 + 2Kmc^2} = \sqrt{(1.00 \times 10^9 \,\text{eV})^2 + 2(1.00 \times 10^9 \,\text{eV})(0.511 \times 10^6 \,\text{eV})}$$
$$= 1.00 \times 10^9 \,\text{eV}.$$

The wavelength is

$$\lambda = \frac{h}{p} = \frac{hc}{pc} = \frac{1240 \,\text{eV} \cdot \text{nm}}{1.00 \times 10^9 \,\text{eV}} = 1.24 \times 10^{-12} \,\text{nm}.$$

11P
(a) For the photon

$$E = \frac{hc}{\lambda} = \frac{1240 \,\text{nm} \cdot \text{eV}}{1.00 \,\text{nm}} = 1.24 \,\text{keV}$$

and for the electron

$$K = \frac{p^2}{2m_e} = \frac{(h/\lambda)^2}{2m_e} = \frac{(hc/\lambda)^2}{2m_e c^2}$$

$$= \frac{1}{2(0.511 \,\text{MeV})} \left(\frac{1240 \,\text{nm} \cdot \text{eV}}{1.00 \,\text{nm}} \right)^2 = 1.50 \,\text{eV}.$$

(b) Now for the photon

$$E = \frac{1240 \,\text{nm} \cdot \text{eV}}{1.00 \,\text{fm}} = 1.24 \,\text{GeV}$$

and for the electron

$$K = \sqrt{p^2 c^2 + (mc^2)^2} - mc^2 = \sqrt{(hc/\lambda)^2 + (mc^2)^2} - mc^2$$

$$= \sqrt{\left(\frac{1240 \,\text{fm} \cdot \text{MeV}}{1.00 \,\text{fm}} \right)^2 + (0.511 \,\text{MeV})^2} - 0.511 \,\text{MeV}$$

$$= 1.24 \times 10^3 \,\text{MeV} = 1.24 \,\text{GeV}.$$

Note that at short λ (large K), the kinetic energy of the electron (calculated with relativestic formula) is about the same as that of the photon. This is expected since now $K \approx E \approx pc$ for the electron, which is the same as $E = pc$ for the photon.

12P
(a) The kinetic energy acquired is $K = qV$, where q is the charge on an ion and V is the accelerating potential. Thus $K = (1.60 \times 10^{-19} \,\text{C})(300 \,\text{V}) = 4.80 \times 10^{-17} \,\text{J}$. The mass of a

single sodium atom is, from Appendix D, $m = (22.9898\,\text{g/mol})/(6.02 \times 10^{23}\,\text{atom/mol}) = 3.819 \times 10^{-23}\,\text{g} = 3.819 \times 10^{-26}\,\text{kg}$. Thus the momentum of an ion is

$$p = \sqrt{2mK} = \sqrt{2(3.819 \times 10^{-26}\,\text{kg})(4.80 \times 10^{-17}\,\text{J})} = 1.91 \times 10^{-21}\,\text{kg} \cdot \text{m/s}.$$

(b) The de Broglie wavelength is

$$\lambda = \frac{h}{p} = \frac{6.63 \times 10^{-34}\,\text{J} \cdot \text{s}}{1.91 \times 10^{-21}\,\text{kg} \cdot \text{m/s}} = 3.47 \times 10^{-13}\,\text{m}.$$

13P
We need to use the relativistic formula $p = \sqrt{(E/c)^2 - m^2 c^2} \approx E/c \approx K/c$ (since $E \gg mc^2$). So

$$\lambda = \frac{h}{p} \approx \frac{hc}{K} = \frac{1240\,\text{eV} \cdot \text{nm}}{20\,\text{GeV}} = 0.062\,\text{fm},$$

much less than the radius of an average nucleus.

14P
(a) Since $K = 7.5\,\text{MeV} \ll m_\alpha c^2 = 4(932\,\text{MeV})$, we may use the non-relativistic formula $p = \sqrt{2m_\alpha K}$. So

$$\lambda = \frac{h}{p} = \frac{hc}{\sqrt{2m_\alpha c^2 K}} = \frac{1240\,\text{nm} \cdot \text{eV}}{\sqrt{2(4)(932\,\text{MeV}(7.5\,\text{MeV})}} = 5.2\,\text{fm}.$$

(b) Since $\lambda = 5.2\,\text{fm} < 30\,\text{fm}$, to a fairly good approximation the wave nature of the α particle dose not need to be taken into consideration.

15P
The wavelength associated with the unknown particle is $\lambda_p = h/p_p = h/(m_p v_p)$, where p_p is its momentum, m_p is its mass, and v_p is its speed. The classical relationship $p_p = m_p v_p$ was used. Similarly, the wavelength associated with the electron is $\lambda_e = h/(m_e v_e)$, where m_e is its mass and v_e is its speed. The ratio of the wavelengths is $\lambda_p/\lambda_e = (m_e v_e)/(m_p v_p)$, so

$$m_p = \frac{v_e \lambda_e}{v_p \lambda_p} m_e = \frac{9.109 \times 10^{-31}\,\text{kg}}{3(1.813 \times 10^{-4})} = 1.675 \times 10^{-27}\,\text{kg}.$$

According to Appendix B this is the mass of a neutron.

16P

(a) Let $\lambda = h/p = h/\sqrt{(E/c)^2 - m^2c^2}$ and solve for $K = E - mc^2$:

$$K = \sqrt{(hc/\lambda)^2 + m^2c^4} - mc^2$$

$$= \sqrt{\left(\frac{1240\,\text{eV}\cdot\text{nm}}{10\times10^{-3}\,\text{nm}}\right)^2 + (0.511\,\text{MeV})^2} = 0.511\,\text{MeV}$$

$$= 0.015\,\text{MeV} = 15\,\text{keV}.$$

(b)

$$E = \frac{hc}{\lambda} = \frac{1240\,\text{eV}\cdot\text{nm}}{10\times10^{-3}\,\text{nm}} = 1.2\times10^5\,\text{eV} = 120\,\text{keV}.$$

(c) The electron microscope is more suitable, as the required energy of the electrons is much less than that of the photons.

17P

The same resolution requires the same wavelength and since the wavelength and particle momentum are related by $p = h/\lambda$, this means the same particle momentum. The momentum of a 100-keV photon is $p = E/c = (100\times10^3\,\text{eV})(1.60\times10^{-19}\,\text{J/eV})/(3.00\times10^8\,\text{m/s}) = 5.33\times10^{-23}\,\text{kg}\cdot\text{m/s}$. This is also the magnitude of the momentum of the electron. The kinetic energy of the electron is

$$K = \frac{p^2}{2m} = \frac{(5.33\times10^{-23}\,\text{kg}\cdot\text{m/s})^2}{2(9.11\times10^{-31}\,\text{kg})} = 1.56\times10^{-15}\,\text{J}.$$

The accelerating potential is

$$V = \frac{K}{e} = \frac{1.56\times10^{-15}\,\text{J}}{1.60\times10^{-19}\,\text{C}} = 9.76\times10^3\,\text{V}.$$

18P

(a) From $K = -E_1 = \frac{1}{2}mv^2$ we get

$$v = \sqrt{\frac{2|E|c^2}{mc^2}} = \sqrt{\frac{2(13.6\,\text{eV})(3.00\times10^8\,\text{m/s})^2}{0.511\,\text{MeV}}} = 2.19\times10^6\,\text{m/s}.$$

(b)

$$\lambda = \frac{h}{p} = \frac{h}{mv} = \frac{6.63\times10^{-34}\,\text{J}\cdot\text{s}}{(9.11\times10^{-31}\,\text{kg})(2.19\times10^6\,\text{m/s})} = 3.32\,\text{nm}.$$

(c) $\lambda/r = 3.32\,\text{nm}/0.529\,\text{nm} = 6.28 \simeq 2\pi$, or $\lambda = 2\pi r$.

19E

The angles ϕ satisfy $d\sin\phi = n\lambda$, where $d = 0.314\,\text{nm}$, $n = 0, 1, 2, \cdots$, and $\lambda = h/p = h/\sqrt{2mK}$. Thus

$$\sin\phi = \frac{nh}{d\sqrt{2mK}} = \frac{nhc}{d\sqrt{2mc^2K}} = \frac{n(1240\,\text{nm}\cdot\text{eV})}{0.314\,\text{nm}\sqrt{2(0.511\,\text{MeV})(380\,\text{eV})}} = 0.200n.$$

The value of ϕ are therfore $\phi_0 = 0$ (for $n = 0$), $\phi_1 = 11.5°$ (for $n = 1$), $\phi_2 = 23.6°$ (for $n = 3$), $\phi_3 - 36.9°$ (for $n = 4$), and $\phi_4 = 53.1°$ (for $n = 5$).

20P

(a) Use

$$\sin\phi_m = \frac{m\lambda}{d} = m\sin\phi_1 = m\sin 50° = 0.766\,\text{m}.$$

Since for $m \geq 2$ we have $0.766\,\text{m} > 1$, no solution exists for $\sin\phi_m = 0.766m$ for $m \geq 2$. So the beams corresponding to $m = 2$ and 3 are not present.

(b)

$$\sin\phi_1 = \frac{m\lambda}{d} = \frac{mh}{d\sqrt{2m_eK}} = \frac{mhc}{d\sqrt{2(m_ec^2)(e\Delta V)}}$$

$$= \frac{(1)(1240\,\text{eV}\cdot\text{nm})}{(0.34\,\text{nm})\sqrt{2(0.511\,\text{MeV})(60\,\text{eV})}} = 0.713.$$

The angle is $\phi_1 = 46°$.

21E

(a) Use Eq. 44-10:

$$E_{1P} = \frac{h^2}{8m_pL^2} = \frac{(hc)^2}{8(m_pc^2)L^2} = \frac{(1240\,\text{eV}\cdot\text{nm})^2}{8(938\,\text{MeV})(0.100\,\text{nm})^2} = 2.05 \times 10^{-2}\,\text{eV}.$$

(b) Now

$$E_{1e} = \frac{(hc)^2}{8(m_ec^2)L^2} = \frac{(1240\,\text{eV}\cdot\text{nm})^2}{8(0.511\,\text{MeV})(0.100\,\text{nm})^2} = 37.7\,\text{eV}.$$

22E

For $n = 3$, let $E_n = n^2h^2/(8mL^2) = 4.7\,\text{eV}$ and solve for L:

$$L = \frac{nh}{\sqrt{8mE_n}} = \frac{3(1240\,\text{eV}\cdot\text{nm})}{\sqrt{8(0.511\,\text{MeV})(4.7\,\text{eV})}} = 0.85\,\text{nm}.$$

23E

(a) Use Eq. 44–10, with $n = 1$ and L equal to the atomic diameter, to estimate the energy:

$$E = n^2 \frac{h^2}{8mL^2} = \frac{(6.63 \times 10^{-34}\,\text{J} \cdot \text{s})^2}{8(9.11 \times 10^{-31}\,\text{kg})(1.4 \times 10^{-14}\,\text{m})^2} = 3.07 \times 10^{-10}\,\text{J} = 1920\,\text{MeV}.$$

(b) The available binding energy is only a few MeV, so we cannot expect to find an electron bound inside a nucleus.

24E

Since $E_n \propto L^{-2}$, as L is doubled E_1 becomes $2.6\,\text{eV}(2)^{-2} = 0.65\,\text{eV}$.

25E

The energy to be absorbed is

$$\Delta E = E_4 - E_1 = \frac{(4^2 - 1^2)h^2}{8mL^2} = \frac{15(hc)^2}{8(mc^2)L^2}$$

$$= \frac{15(1240\,\text{eV} \cdot \text{nm})^2}{8(0.511\,\text{MeV})(0.250\,\text{nm})^2} = 90.4\,\text{eV}.$$

26P

(a) The allowed values of Mevy for a particle of mass m trapped in a box of length L are given by

$$E = n^2 \frac{h^2}{8mL^2},$$

where n is an integer. Since $(2)^2 - (1)^2 = 3$, the difference in energy of the two lowest energy states is

$$\Delta E = \frac{3h^2}{8mL^2}.$$

The mass of an argon atom is $m = (39.9\,\text{g/mol})/(6.02 \times 10^{23}\,\text{atoms/mol}) = 6.63 \times 10^{-23}\,\text{g} = 6.63 \times 10^{-26}\,\text{kg}$. Thus

$$\Delta E = \frac{3(6.63 \times 10^{-34}\,\text{J} \cdot \text{s})^2}{8(6.63 \times 10^{-26}\,\text{kg})(20 \times 10^{-2}\,\text{m})^2} = 6.2 \times 10^{-41}\,\text{J} = 3.9 \times 10^{-22}\,\text{eV}.$$

(b) The thermal energy (average kinetic energy) at absolute temperature T is given by $\overline{K} = \frac{3}{2}kT$, where k is the Boltzmann constant. Thus

$$\overline{K} = \frac{3}{2}(1.38 \times 10^{-23}\,\text{J/K})(300\,\text{K}) = 6.21 \times 10^{-21}\,\text{J} = 3.88 \times 10^{-2}\,\text{eV},$$

greater than the separation of the two lowest levels by a factor of about 10^{20}.

1093

(c) Set $\frac{3}{2}kT$ equal to ΔE and solve for T:

$$T = \frac{2\Delta E}{3k} = \frac{2(3.88 \times 10^{-22}\,\text{eV})(1.60 \times 10^{-19}\,\text{J/eV})}{3(1.38 \times 10^{-23}\,\text{J/K})} = 3.0 \times 10^{-18}\,\text{K} \,.$$

27P

$$E = \frac{h^2}{8L^2m}(n_1^2 + n_2^2 + n_3^2) = \frac{(1240\,\text{eV}\cdot\text{nm})^2}{8(250\,\text{nm})^2(0.511\,\text{MeV})}(n_1^2 + n_2^2 + n_3^2)$$
$$= (6.02\mu\,\text{eV})(n_1^2 + n_2^2 + n_3^2).$$

The energies of the lowest five distinct states are therefore
$E = (6.02\,\text{eV})(1^2 + 1^2 + 1^2) = 18.1\mu\,\text{eV}$ (for $n_1 = n_2 = n_3 = 1$),
$E = (6.02\,\text{eV})(2^2 + 1^2 + 1^2) = 36.2\mu\,\text{eV}$ (for $n_{1,2,3} = 2,\,1,\,1$ or $1,\,2,\,1$ or $1,\,1,\,2$),
$E = (6.02\,\text{eV})(2^2 + 2^2 + 1^2) = 54.2\mu\,\text{eV}$ (for $n_{1,2,3} = 2,\,2,\,1$ or $2,\,1,\,2$ or $1,\,2,\,2$),
$E = (6.02\,\text{eV})(1^2 + 1^2 + 3^2) = 66.3\mu\,\text{eV}$ (for $n_{1,2,3} = 1,\,1,\,3$ or $1,\,3,\,1$ or $3,\,1,\,1$),
$E = (6.02\,\text{eV})(2^2 + 2^2 + 2^2) = 72.3\mu\,\text{eV}$ (for $n_1 = n_2 = n_3 = 2$).

28P
First evaluate the integral

$$I = \int_0^L |\psi(x)|^2 \, dx = A^2 \int_0^L \sin^2(\pi x/L) \, dx \,.$$

Change the variable of integration to $u = \pi x/L$. Then $dx = (L/\pi)\,du$, the lower limit is $u = 0$, and the upper limit is $u = \pi L/L = \pi$. Since $\cos(2u) = \cos^2 u - \sin^2 u = 1 - 2\sin^2 u$, $\sin^2 u = \frac{1}{2}[1 - \cos(2u)]$, and the integral becomes

$$I = \frac{LA^2}{2\pi} \int_0^\pi [1 - \cos(2u)] \, du = \frac{LA^2}{2\pi}\left[u - \frac{1}{2}\sin(2u)\right]_0^\pi = \frac{LA^2}{2\pi}\pi = \frac{LA^2}{2} \,.$$

To normalize the wave function, set $I = 1$ and solve for A. The result is $A = \sqrt{2/L}$.

29P
(a)

$$P\,(0 < x < L/3) = \int_0^{L/3} \psi^2(x)\,dx = \frac{2}{L}\int_0^{L/3} \sin^2\left(\frac{\pi x}{L}\right) dx = 0.196.$$

(b)

$$P\,(L/3 < x < 2L/3) = \int_{L/3}^{2L/3} \psi^2(x)\,dx = \frac{2}{L}\int_{L/3}^{2L/3} \sin^2\left(\frac{\pi x}{L}\right) dx = 0.609.$$

(c)

$$P(2L/3 < x < L) = \int_{2L/3}^{L} \psi^2(x)\,dx = \frac{2}{L}\int_{2L/3}^{L} \sin^2\left(\frac{\pi x}{L}\right) dx = 0.196.$$

Note that by symmetry $P(0 < x < L/3) = P(2L/3 < x < L)$ and by normalization $P(0 < x < L/3) + P(L/3 < x < 2L/3) + P(2L/3 < x < L) = P(0 < x < L) = 1.$

30E
Use Eq. 44-18.
(a) At $r = 0$, $P(r) = (4R^2/rB^3)e^{-2r/r_B} = 0.$
(b) At $r = r_B$, $P(r) = (4r_B^2/r_B^3)e^{-2r/r_B} = (4/52.9\,\text{pm})e^{-2} = 0.010\,\text{pm}^{-1}.$
(c) At $r = 2r_B$, $P(r) = (16r_B^2/r_B^3)e^{-4r/r_B} = (16/52.9\,\text{pm})e^{-4} = 0.0055\,\text{pm}^{-1}.$
All the results above are in agreement with Fig. 44-12.

31E
According to Sample Problem 44–6 the probability the electron in the ground state of a hydrogen atom will be found inside a sphere of radius r is given by

$$p(r) = 1 - e^{-2x}\left(1 + 2x + 2x^2\right),$$

where $x = r/r_B$ and r_B is the Bohr radius. You want $r = r_B$, so $x = 1$ and

$$p(r_B) = 1 - e^{-2}\left(1 + 2 + 2\right) = 1 - 5e^{-2} = 0.323.$$

32E
(a) At $r = 0$

$$\psi^2(0) = \frac{1}{\pi r_B^3}e^{-2r/r_B} = \frac{1}{\pi(0.0529\,\text{nm})^3}e^{-0} = 2150\,\text{nm}^{-3}$$

and $P(r) = (4r^2/r_B^3)e^{-2r/r_B} = 0.$
(b) At $r = r_B$,

$$\psi^2(r_B) = \frac{e^{-2r_B/r_B}}{\pi(0.0529\,\text{nm}^3)} = 291\,\text{nm}^{-3}$$

and $P(r) = 0.0102\,\text{pm}^{-1} = 10.2\,\text{nm}^{-1}$ (see Exercise 30). $\psi^2(\mathbf{r})$ means the probability per unit volume of finding the electron in the vicinity of $\mathbf{r}$, while $P(r)dr$ is the probability of finding the electron between two concentric shells of radii r and $r + dr$.

33E

The probablity is

$$p\,(r_B < r < 2r_B) = p(2r_B) - p(r_B)$$
$$= 1 - e^{-2(2)}[1 + 2(2) + 2(2)^2] - (1 - e^{-2(1)}[1 + 2(1) + 2(1)^2])$$
$$= 5e^{-2} - 13e^{-4} = 0.439.$$

34P

$$\int \psi^2(r)\,dV = 4\pi \int_0^\infty \psi^2(r)r^2\,dr = 4\pi \int_0^\infty \frac{1}{\pi r_B^3} e^{-2r/r_B} r^2\,dr$$
$$= 4 \int_0^\infty e^{-2x} x^2\,dx = 1.$$

35P

$$p(r) = \int_0^r P(r)dr = \int_0^r \frac{4}{r_B^3} r^2 e^{-2r/r_B}\,dr = 4 \int_0^{r/r_B} y^2 e^{-2y}\,dy$$
$$= 4\left(-\frac{x^2}{2} e^{-2x} - \frac{x}{2} e^{-2x} - \frac{1}{4} e^{-2x} \right)\Bigg|_0^x$$
$$= 1 - e^{-2x}(1 + 2x + 2x^2),$$

where $x = r/r_B$.

36P

Use the equation given in Sample Problem 44–6: the probability an electron in the ground state of a hydrogen atom will be found inside a sphere of radius r is given by

$$p(r) = 1 - e^{-2x}\left(1 + 2x + 2x^2\right),$$

where $x = r/r_B$ and r_B is the Bohr radius. You want $r = 1.1 \times 10^{-15}$ m. Since $r_B = 5.292 \times 10^{-11}$ m, $x = (1.1 \times 10^{-15} \text{ m})/(5.292 \times 10^{-11} \text{ m}) = 2.08 \times 10^{-5}$. Since x is small and $p(r)$ is the difference between 1 and a number very close to 1, your calculator probably does not carry enough significant digits for you to obtain an accurate answer. It is better to use a power series expansion. The expansion of e^{-2x} for small x is $1 - 2x + 2x^2 - (4/3)x^3 + \ldots$, so

$$p(r) \approx 1 - \left(1 - 2x + 2x^2 - \frac{4}{3}x^3\right)\left(1 + 2x + 2x^3\right)$$
$$= 1 - \left(1 - \frac{4}{3}x^3\right) = \frac{4}{3}x^3 = \frac{4}{3}\left(2.08 \times 10^{-5}\right)^3 = 1.2 \times 10^{-14}.$$

When multiplying the quantities in parentheses, terms of the order x^3 and lower were retained; higher order terms were discarded.

37E

The probability T that a particle of mass m and energy E tunnels through a barrier of height U and width L is given by

$$T = e^{-2kL} ,$$

where

$$k = \sqrt{\frac{8\pi^2 m(U-E)}{h^2}} .$$

For the proton

$$k = \sqrt{\frac{8\pi^2(1.6726 \times 10^{-27}\,\text{kg})(10\,\text{Mev} - 3.0\,\text{Mev})(1.6022 \times 10^{-13}\,\text{J/MeV})}{(6.6261 \times 10^{-34}\,\text{J} \cdot \text{s})^2}}$$

$$= 5.8082 \times 10^{14}\,\text{m}^{-1} ,$$

$kL = (5.8082 \times 10^{14}\,\text{m}^{-1})(10 \times 10^{-15}\,\text{m}) = 5.8082$, and

$$T = e^{-2 \times 5.8082} = 9.02 \times 10^{-6} .$$

The value of k was computed to a greater number of significant digits than usual because an exponential is quite sensitive to the value of the exponent.

The mass of a deuteron is $2.0141\,\text{u} = 3.3454 \times 10^{-27}\,\text{kg}$, so

$$k = \sqrt{\frac{8\pi^2(3.3454 \times 10^{-27}\,\text{kg})(10\,\text{MeV} - 3.0\,\text{MeV})(1.6022 \times 10^{-13}\,\text{J/MeV})}{(6.6261 \times 10^{-34}\,\text{J} \cdot \text{s})^2}}$$

$$= 8.2143 \times 10^{14}\,\text{m}^{-1} ,$$

$kL = (8.2143 \times 10^{14}\,\text{m}^{-1})(10 \times 10^{-15}\,\text{m}) = 8.2143$, and

$$T = e^{-2 \times 8.2143} = 7.33 \times 10^{-8} .$$

38P

Let

$$T = \exp(-2kL) = \exp\left[-2L\sqrt{\frac{8\pi^2 m(U-E)}{h^2}}\right]$$

and solve for E:

$$E = U - \frac{1}{2m}\left(\frac{h \ln T}{4\pi L}\right)^2 = 6.0\,\text{eV} - \frac{1}{2(0.511\,\text{MeV})}\left[\frac{(1240\,\text{eV} \cdot \text{nm})(\ln 0.001)}{4\pi(0.70\,\text{nm})}\right]^2$$

$$= 5.1\,\text{eV}.$$

39P

The rate at which incident protons arrive at the barrier is $n = 1.0\,\text{kA}/1.60 \times 10^{-19}\,\text{c} = 6.25 \times 10^{23}/\text{s}$. Let $nTt = 1$ we find the waiting time t:

$$t = (nT)^{-1} = \frac{1}{n}\exp\left[2L\sqrt{\frac{8\pi^2 m(U-E)}{h^2}}\right]$$

$$= \frac{1}{6.25 \times 10^{23}/\text{s}}\exp\left[\frac{2\pi(0.70\,\text{nm})}{1240\,\text{eV} \cdot \text{nm}}\sqrt{8(938\,\text{MeV})(6.0\,\text{eV} - 5.0\,\text{eV})}\right]$$

$$= 3.37 \times 10^{111}\,\text{s} \approx 10^{104}\,\text{y}.$$

40P

(a) If m is the mass of the particle and E is its energy then the probability it will tunnel through a barrier of height U and width L is given by

$$T = e^{-2kL},$$

where

$$k = \sqrt{\frac{8\pi^2 m(U-E)}{h^2}}.$$

If the change ΔU in U is small (as it is) the change in the tunneling probability is given by

$$\Delta T = \frac{dT}{dU}\,\Delta U = -2LT\frac{dk}{dU}\,\Delta U.$$

Now

$$\frac{dk}{dU} = \frac{1}{2\sqrt{U-E}}\sqrt{\frac{8\pi^2 m}{h^2}} = \frac{1}{2(U-E)}\sqrt{\frac{8\pi^2 m(U-E)}{h^2}} = \frac{k}{2(U-E)}.$$

Thus

$$\Delta T = -LTk\frac{\Delta U}{U-E}.$$

For the data of Sample Problem 44–7, $2kL = 10.0$, so $kL = 5.0$ and

$$\frac{\Delta T}{T} = -kL\frac{\Delta U}{U-E} = -(5.0)\frac{(0.0100)(6.8\,\text{eV})}{6.8\,\text{eV} - 5.1\,\text{eV}} = -0.20.$$

There is a 20% decrease in the tunneling probability.

(b) The change in the tunneling probability is given by

$$\Delta T = \frac{dT}{dL}\,\Delta L = -2ke^{-2kL}\,\Delta L = -2kT\,\Delta L$$

and

$$\frac{\Delta T}{T} = -2k\,\Delta L = -2(6.67 \times 10^9\,\text{m}^{-1})(0.0100)(750 \times 10^{-12}\,\text{m}) = -0.10.$$

There is a 10% decrease in the tunneling probability.

(c) The change in the tunneling probability is given by

$$\Delta T = \frac{dT}{dE}\Delta E = -2Le^{-2kL}\frac{dk}{dE}\Delta E = -2LT\frac{dk}{dE}\Delta E \,.$$

Now $dk/dE = -dk/dU = -k/2(U - E)$, so

$$\frac{\Delta T}{T} = kL\frac{\Delta E}{U - E} = (5.0)\frac{(0.01000)(5.1\,\text{eV})}{6.8\,\text{eV} - 5.1\,\text{eV}} = 0.15 \,.$$

There is a 15% increase in the tunneling probability.

41E

$$\Delta P_{\text{min}} \approx h/\Delta x = 6.63 \times 10^{-34}\,\text{J} \cdot \text{s}/10\,\text{pm} = 7 \times 10^{-23}\,\text{kg} \cdot \text{m/s}.$$

42E

$$\Delta P \approx h/\Delta x = 6.63 \times 10^{-34}\,\text{J} \cdot \text{s}/50\,\text{pm} = 1.3 \times 10^{-23}\,\text{kg} \cdot \text{m/s}.$$

43E

$$\Delta x \approx \frac{\text{"}h\text{"}}{\Delta p} = \frac{\text{"}h\text{"}}{m\Delta v} = \frac{0.60\,\text{J} \cdot \text{s}}{(0.50\,\text{kg})(1.0\,\text{m/s})} = 1.2\,\text{m}.$$

It would indeed be hard to catch such a ball.

44E
(a)

$$E = \frac{n^2 h^2}{8mL^2} = \frac{(15)^2(1240\,\text{eV} \cdot \text{nm})^2}{8(0.511\,\text{MeV})(0.100\,\text{nm})^2} = 8.46\,\text{keV}.$$

(b) $\Delta p \approx h/\Delta x = (6.63 \times 10^{-34}\,\text{J} \cdot \text{s})/(100 \times 10^{-12}\,\text{m}) = 6.63 \times 10^{-24}\,\text{kg} \cdot \text{m/s}.$
(c) $\Delta x \approx 100\,\text{pm}.$

45E
The uncertainty in E_2 is

$$\Delta E_2 \approx \frac{h}{\Delta t} = \frac{(6.63 \times 10^{-34}\,\text{J} \cdot \text{s})}{(1.60 \times 10^{-19}\,\text{J/eV})(10^{-8}\,\text{s})} = 0.41\mu\,\text{eV},$$

and

$$\frac{\Delta E_2}{|E_2|} = \frac{0.41\mu\,\text{eV}}{13.6\,\text{eV}/2^2} = 1.2 \times 10^{-7}.$$

46P

If Δx is the uncertainty in the position and Δp is the uncertainty in the momentum of a particle, then the uncertainty principle tells us that $\Delta x \, \Delta p \geq h$, where h is the Planck constant. Now $p = mv$, where v is the velocity and m is the mass, so $\Delta p = m \, \Delta v$ and the uncertainty principle becomes $m \, \Delta x \, \Delta v \geq h$. Put $\Delta x = \lambda$, where λ is the de Broglie wavelength, and use $\lambda = h/p = h/mv$ to obtain $\Delta x = h/mv$. The uncertainty principle now becomes $m(h/mv)(\Delta v) \geq h$ or $\Delta v \geq v$. The minimum uncertainty in the velocity is the velocity itself.

47P

(a)

$$E = \frac{hc}{\lambda} = \frac{1240\,\text{nm} \cdot \text{eV}}{10.0 \times 10^{-3}\,\text{nm}} = 124\,\text{keV}.$$

(b)

$$\Delta E = \Delta\left(\frac{hc}{\lambda}\right) = hc\left(\frac{1}{\lambda} - \frac{1}{\lambda + \Delta\lambda}\right) = \left(\frac{hc}{\lambda}\right)\left(\frac{\Delta\lambda}{\lambda + \Delta\lambda}\right) = \frac{E}{1 + \lambda/\Delta\lambda}$$

$$= \frac{E}{1 + (\lambda/\lambda_C)(1 - \cos\phi)^{-1}} = \frac{124\,\text{keV}}{1 + (10.0\,\text{pm}/2.43\,\text{pm})(1 - \cos 180°)^{-1}}$$

$$= 40.5\,\text{keV}.$$

(c) It is impossible to "view" an atomic electron with such a high-energy photon, because with the energy imparted to the electron the photon will knock the electron out of its orbit.

48

From normalization

$$\int_L^0 |\psi|^2 \, dx = \int_0^L A^2 \, dx = A^2 L = 1$$

so $A = 1/\sqrt{L}$.

49

$$r_{\text{av}} = \int_0^\infty r P(r) \, dr = \int_0^\infty \left(\frac{4}{r_B^3} r^2 e^{-2r/r_B}\right) dr$$

$$= 4 r_B \int_0^\infty x^3 e^{-2x} \, dx = 1.5 r_B.$$

50

(a) Label the zero-potential region and the 100-V region with subscripts 1 and 2, respectively. Then

$$\frac{n_2}{n_1} = \frac{v_1}{v_2} = \frac{\sqrt{2mK_1}}{\sqrt{2mK_2}} = \sqrt{\frac{60\,\text{eV}}{60\,\text{eV} + 100\,\text{eV}}} = 0.61.$$

(b) $\sin \phi_2 = (\sin \phi_1)(n_2/n_1) = (\sin 50°)(0.61) = 28°.$

51

For $T = 1$ let $\sin^2(k_2 L) = 0$, i.e. $k_2 L = n\pi$ $(n = 0, \pm 1, \pm 2, \cdots)$. The corresponding energies are given by

$$E_n = \frac{h^2}{8\pi^2 m}\left(\frac{n\pi}{L}\right)^2 + U = \frac{h^2 n^2}{8mL^2} + U.$$

(a) Let $n = 0$, we get $E_{\min} = E_0 = U.$

(b) Let $n = \pm 1$, we get

$$E_1 = \frac{h^2}{8m}\left(\frac{1}{L}\right)^2 + U = \frac{h^2}{8mL^2} + U.$$

CHAPTER 45

1E

$$\hbar = \frac{h}{2\pi} = \frac{6.6260754 \times 10^{-34}\, \text{J} \cdot \text{s}}{2\pi} = 1.0546 \times 10^{-34}\, \text{J} \cdot \text{s}$$
$$= (1.0546 \times 10^{-34}\, \text{J} \cdot \text{s})/(1.60 \times 10^{-19}\, \text{C}) = 6.59 \times 10^{-16}\, \text{eV} \cdot \text{s}.$$

2E

$$\mu_B = \frac{eh}{4\pi m_e} = \frac{(1.60217738 \times 10^{-19}\, \text{C})(6.6260754 \times 10^{-34}\, \text{J} \cdot \text{s})}{4\pi(9.1093897 \times 10^{-31}\, \text{kg})}$$
$$= 9.274 \times 10^{-24}\, \text{J/T} = (9.274 \times 10^{-24}\, \text{J/T})(1.602 \times 10^{-19}\, \text{eV/J})$$
$$= 5.788 \times 10^{-5}\, \text{eV/T}.$$

3E
$$L = \sqrt{\ell(\ell+1)}\hbar = \sqrt{3(3+1)}(1.06 \times 10^{-34}\, \text{J} \cdot \text{s}) = 3.64 \times 10^{-34}\, \text{J} \cdot \text{s}.$$

4E
(a) For a given value of the principal quantum number n, the orbital quantum number ℓ ranges from 0 to $n-1$. For $n = 3$ there are 3 possible values: 0, 1, and 2.

(b) For a given value of ℓ, the magnetic quantum number m_ℓ ranges from $-\ell$ to $+\ell$. For $\ell = 1$, there are 3 possible values: -1, 0, and $+1$.

5E
The minimum angle $\phi_{\min}$ satisfies

$$\cos\phi_{\min} = \frac{L_{z,\,\max}}{L} = \frac{(m_\ell \hbar)_{\max}}{L} = \frac{\ell\hbar}{\sqrt{\ell(\ell+1)}\hbar} = \frac{5}{\sqrt{5(5+1)}} = \sqrt{\frac{5}{6}}.$$

The angle is $\phi_{\min} = \cos^{-1}(\sqrt{5/6}) = 24.1°$.

6E

$n = 4$; $\ell = 3$; $m_\ell = +3, +2, +1, 0, -1, -2, -3$; $m_s = \pm\frac{1}{2}.$

7E

The principal quantum number n must be greater than 3. The magnetic quantum number m_ℓ can have any of the values -3, -2, -1, 0, $+1$, $+2$, or $+3$. The spin quantum number can have either of the values $-\frac{1}{2}$ or $+\frac{1}{2}$.

8E

$\ell = (m_\ell)_{\max} = 4$; $n = \ell_{\max} + 1 \geq \ell + 1 = 5$; and $m_s = \pm\dfrac{1}{2}$.

9E

The total number of states is $N = 2n^2 = 2(5)^2 = 50$.

10P

(a) In the Bohr model of the hydrogen atom the electron travels in a circular orbit. Let r be the radius of the orbit and v be the speed of the electron. The magnitude of the magnetic dipole moment is given by $\mu = iA$, where i is the current and $A\ (=\pi r^2)$ is the area of the orbit. The current is $i = e/T$, where T is the period of the motion. Since $T = 2\pi r/v$, $i = ev/2\pi r$ and

$$\mu = \left(\frac{ev}{2\pi r}\right)\left(\pi r^2\right) = \frac{erv}{2}\,.$$

The orbital angular momentum of the electron is given by $L = mrv$, so $rv = L/m$ and

$$\mu = \frac{eL}{2m}\,.$$

Bohr assumed the angular momentum could have only the values $n\hbar$, where n is a positive integer and $\hbar$ is the Planck constant divided by 2π (see Chapter 43 of the text). This means

$$\mu = \frac{en\hbar}{2m} = n\mu_B\,,$$

where $\mu_B\ (=e\hbar/2m)$ is the Bohr magneton.

(b) The Bohr model predicts that the orbital angular momentum of the electron is a multiple of the Bohr magneton, which is correct, but it gives an incorrect relationship between the orbital angular momentum and the principal quantum number n. For most values of n the magnetic moment can have any of a number of values, not just one.

11P

Use $L_z = m_\ell \hbar$ to calculate the z component of the angular momentum, $\mu_z = -m_\ell \mu_B$ to calculate the z component of the magnetic dipole moment, and $\cos\theta = m_\ell/\sqrt{\ell(\ell+1)}$ to calculate the angle between the angular momentum vector and the z axis. Here $\hbar$ is the Planck constant divided by 2π ($\hbar = 1.055 \times 10^{-34}\,\text{J}\cdot\text{s}$) and μ_B is the Bohr magneton ($\mu_B = 9.274 \times 10^{-24}\,\text{J/T}$). Spin was ignored in computing the dipole moment. For $\ell = 3$ the magnetic quantum number m_ℓ can take on the values -3, -2, -1, 0, $+1$, $+2$, $+3$. Results are tabulated below.

m_ℓ	L_z (kg·m²/s)	μ_z (J/T)	θ (degrees)
-3	-3.16×10^{-34}	2.78×10^{-23}	$150.0°$
-2	-2.10×10^{-34}	1.85×10^{-23}	$125.3°$
-1	-1.05×10^{-34}	9.27×10^{-24}	$106.8°$
0	0	0	$90.0°$
1	1.05×10^{-34}	-9.27×10^{-24}	$73.2°$
2	2.10×10^{-34}	-1.85×10^{-23}	$54.7°$
3	3.16×10^{-34}	-2.78×10^{-23}	$30.0°$

The magnitude of **L** is $\sqrt{\ell(\ell+1)}\,\hbar = \sqrt{3 \times 4}\,(1.055 \times 10^{-34}\,\text{J·s}) = 3.655 \times 10^{-34}\,\text{kg·m}^2/\text{s}$. The magnitude of the dipole moment is $\mu_B\sqrt{\ell(\ell+1)} = (9.274 \times 10^{-24}\,\text{J/T})\sqrt{3 \times 4} = 3.21 \times 10^{-23}\,\text{J/T}$.

12P
(a) The value of ℓ satisfies $\sqrt{\ell(\ell+1)}\hbar \approx \sqrt{\ell^2}\hbar = \ell\hbar = L$, so $\ell \simeq L/\hbar \simeq 3 \times 10^{74}$. The calculation is the same as Exercise 75 in Chapter 43.
(b) The number is $2\ell + 1 \approx 2(3 \times 10^{74}) = 6 \times 10^{74}$.
(c) Since

$$\cos\theta_{\min} = \frac{m_{\ell\,\max}\hbar}{\sqrt{\ell(\ell+1)}\hbar} = \frac{\ell}{\sqrt{\ell(\ell+1)}} \approx 1 - \frac{1}{2\ell} = 1 - \frac{1}{2(3 \times 10^{74})}$$

or $\cos\theta_{\min} \simeq 1 - \theta_{\min}^2/2 \approx 1 - 10^{-74}/6$. So $\theta_{\min} \simeq \sqrt{10^{-74}/3} = 6 \times 10^{-38}$ rad. The correspondance principle requires that all the quantum effectes vanish as $\hbar \to 0$. In this case $\hbar/L$ is extremely small so the quantization effects are barely existent, with $\theta_{\min} \simeq 10^{-38}$ rad $\simeq 0$.

13P
$$\Delta L_z \cdot \Delta\phi = \left(\frac{\Delta L_z}{4}\right)(r\Delta\phi) = \frac{\Delta(mvr)}{r} \cdot (r\Delta\phi) = \Delta(mv) \cdot \Delta(\phi r) = \Delta p \cdot \Delta x = h.$$

14P

(a) Expanding both sides of the equation $\cos\theta_m = (1 + 1/\ell)^{-1/2}$ up to the first two terms:

$$\cos\theta_{\min} \approx 1 - \frac{\theta_{\min}^2}{2} \approx \left(1 + \frac{1}{\ell}\right)^{-1/2} \approx 1 - \frac{1}{2\ell},$$

we get $\theta_{\min}^2/2 \approx 1/2\ell$, or $\theta_{\min} \approx 1/\sqrt{\ell}$.

(b) For $\ell = 1$, $\theta_{\min} \simeq (1/\sqrt{1})\,\mathrm{rad} \simeq 57°$ (a substantial difference with $45°$, sine ℓ is not really large compared with 1). For $\ell = 10^2$, $\theta_{\min} \simeq (1/\sqrt{10^2})\,\mathrm{rad} = 5.7°$; for $\ell = 10^3$, $\theta_{\min} \approx 1/\sqrt{10^3} = 1.8°$; for $\ell = 10^4$, $\theta_{\min} \simeq (1/\sqrt{10^4})\,\mathrm{rad} = 0.57°$; and for $\ell = 10^9$, $\theta_{\min} \simeq (1/\sqrt{10^9})\,\mathrm{rad} = 0.0018°$. All in agreement with the results of sample problem 45-1.

(c) For $\ell = 10^5$, $\theta_{\min} \simeq (1/\sqrt{10^5})\,\mathrm{rad} = 0.18°$; for $\ell = 10^6$, $\theta_{\min} \simeq (1/\sqrt{10^6})\,\mathrm{rad} = 0.057°$; and for $\ell = 10^7$, $\theta_{\min} \simeq (1/\sqrt{10^7})\,\mathrm{rad} = 0.018°$.

(d) Since $\ell \gg 1$, $1/\ell \ll 1$. Suppose that $\ell = 10^9$ then $1 + 1/\ell = 1.000000009$. If you calculator can only display nine digits, you are out of luck. (And what if $\ell = 10^{100}$?)

15P

Since $L^2 = L_x^2 + L_y^2 + L_z^2$, $\sqrt{L_x^2 + L_y^2} = \sqrt{L^2 - L_z^2}$. Replace L^2 with $\ell(\ell+1)\hbar^2$ and L_z with $m_\ell\hbar$ to obtain

$$\sqrt{L_x^2 + L_y^2} = \hbar\sqrt{\ell(\ell+1) - m_\ell^2}.$$

For a given value of ℓ, the greatest that m_ℓ can be is ℓ, so the smallest that $\sqrt{L_x^2 + L_y^2}$ can be is $\hbar\sqrt{\ell(\ell+1) - \ell^2} = \hbar\sqrt{\ell}$. The smallest possible magnitude of m_ℓ is zero, so the largest $\sqrt{L_x^2 + L_y^2}$ can be is $\hbar\sqrt{\ell(\ell+1)}$. Thus

$$\hbar\sqrt{\ell} \le \sqrt{L_x^2 + L_y^2} \le \hbar\sqrt{\ell(\ell+1)}.$$

16P*

Let the mass of the iron cylinder be M and its radius be r. Then its angular momentum L is given by $L = I\omega = \frac{1}{2}MR^2\omega$, where ω is its angular speed of rotation. On the other hand $L = N\hbar$, where $N = M/m_{\mathrm{iron}}$ is the total number of iron atoms in the cylinder. So $L = \frac{1}{2}Mr^2\omega = N\hbar = M\hbar/m_{\mathrm{iron}}$. Thus

$$\begin{aligned}
T &= \frac{2\pi}{\omega} = \frac{\pi m_{\mathrm{iron}}r^2}{\hbar} \\
&= \frac{\pi(55.847\,\mathrm{u})(1.66\times10^{-27}\,\mathrm{kg/u})(5.0\times10^{-3}\,\mathrm{m})^2}{6.626\times10^{-34}\,\mathrm{J\cdot s}/2\pi} \\
&= 19\,\mathrm{h}.
\end{aligned}$$

17E
From Eq. 44-18

$$P(r) = \frac{4}{r_B^3} r^2 e^{-2r/r_B} \Big|_{r=2r_B} = \frac{4}{r_B^3}(2r_B)^2 e^{-2(2r_B)/r_B} = \frac{16}{r_B} e^{-4}$$

$$= \frac{16e^{-4}}{0.0529\,\text{nm}} = 5.54\,\text{nm}^{-1}.$$

18E
At $r = r_B$ we have

$$\psi^2(r_B) = \frac{1}{\pi r_B^3} e^{-2r/r_B}\bigg|_{r=r_B} = \frac{e^{-2}}{\pi r_B^3},$$

so the probability is

$$P \approx \frac{4\pi(0.10r_B)^3}{3}\psi^2(r_B) = \frac{4\pi(0.10r_B)^3}{3\pi r_B^3 e^2} = 1.8 \times 10^{-4}.$$

19E
The radial probability density for the ground state of hydrogen is given by Eq. 45–13:

$$P(r) = \left(\frac{4r^2}{r_B^3}\right) e^{-2r/r_B},$$

where r_B is the Bohr radius. The probability that the electron is in a spherical shell with inner radius r_1 and outer radius r_2 is

$$p = \int_{r_1}^{r_2} P(r)\,dr = \frac{4}{r_B^3}\int_{r_1}^{r_2} r^2\, e^{-2r/r_B}\, dr.$$

The indefinite integral $\int x^2\, e^{-ar}\, dx$ is given in Appendix G as $-(1/a^3)(a^2x^2 + 2ax + 2)e^{-ax}$. Let $x = r$ and $a = 2/r_B$ to obtain

$$p = -\frac{4}{r_B^3}\frac{r_B^3}{8}\left[\frac{4r^2}{r_B^2} + \frac{4r}{r_B} + 2\right] e^{-2r/r_B}\bigg|_{r_1}^{r_2}$$

$$= \frac{1}{2}\left[\frac{4r_1^2}{r_B^2} + \frac{4r_1}{r_B} + 2\right] e^{-2r_1/r_B} - \frac{1}{2}\left[\frac{4r_2^2}{r_B^2} + \frac{4r_2}{r_B} + 2\right] e^{-2r_2/r_B}.$$

Let $r_1 = 1.00r_B$ and $r_2 = 1.01r_B$. Then

$$p = \frac{1}{2}\left[4(1.00)^2 + 4(1.00) + 2\right] e^{-2\times1.00} - \frac{1}{2}\left[4(1.01)^2 + 4(1.00) + 2\right] e^{-2\times1.01}$$

$$= 0.00541.$$

20E
Since $P(r) = 4\pi r^2 \psi^2(r)$, we get

$$\psi(r) = \sqrt{\frac{P(r)}{4\pi r^2}} = \sqrt{\left(\frac{1}{4\pi r^2}\right)\left(\frac{r^2}{8r_B^3}\right)\left(2 - \frac{r}{r_B}\right)^2 e^{-r/r_B}}$$

$$= \frac{1}{\sqrt{32\pi r_B^3}}\left(2 - \frac{r}{r_B}\right)e^{-r/2r_B}.$$

21E
(a)

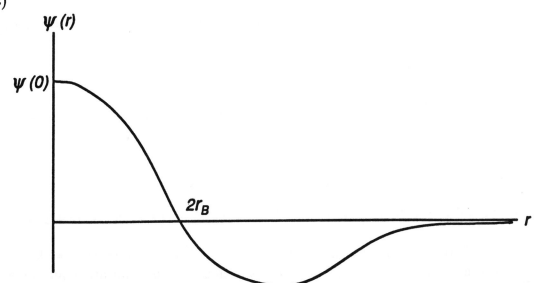

(b)

$$\psi(0) = \frac{1}{\sqrt{32\pi r_B^3}}\left(2 - \frac{0}{r_B}\right)e^{-0/2r_B} = \frac{2}{\sqrt{32\pi(0.0529\,\text{nm})^3}} = 16.4\,\text{nm}^{-3/2}.$$

22E
(a)

$$\psi(r = 5.00r_B) = \frac{1}{\sqrt{32\pi r_B^3}}\left(2 - \frac{r}{r_B}\right)e^{-r/2r_B}\bigg|_{r=5.00r_B}$$

$$= \frac{1}{\sqrt{32\pi r_B^3}}\left(2 - \frac{5.00r_B}{r_B}\right)e^{-5.00r_B/2r_B} = -\frac{3.00e^{-2.50}}{\sqrt{32\pi(0.0529\,\text{nm})^3}}$$

$$= -2.02\,\text{nm}^{-3/2}.$$

(b) $\psi^2(r = 5.00r_B) = (-2.02\,\text{nm}^{-3/2})^2 = 4.07\,\text{nm}^{-3}.$
(c) $P(r = 5.00r_B) = 4\pi r^2 \psi^2(r)|_{r=5.00r_B} = 4\pi[5(0.0529\,\text{nm})]^2(4.07\,\text{nm}^{-3}) = 3.58\,\text{nm}^{-1}.$

$$\int_0^\infty P(r)\,dr = \int_0^\infty \left(\frac{r^2}{8r_B^3}\right)\left(2 - \frac{r}{r_B}\right)^2 e^{-r/r_B}\,dr$$

$$= \frac{1}{8}\int_0^\infty x^2(2-x)^2 e^{-x}\,dx = \frac{1}{8}(-x^4 - 4x^2 - 8x - 8)e^{-x}\Big|_0^\infty$$

$$= \frac{1}{8}[0-(-8)] = 1.$$

Here the substitution $x = r/r_B$ was used.

24P

The radial probability density for the $n = 2$, $\ell = 0$, $m_\ell = 0$ state of hydrogen is given by Eq. 45-14:

$$P(r) = \left(\frac{r^2}{8r_B^3}\right)\left(2 - \frac{r}{r_B}\right)^2 e^{-r/r_B},$$

where r_B is the Bohr radius. Replace r/r_B with x to obtain

$$8r_B P = x^2\,(2-x)^2\,e^{-x}.$$

Differentiate with respect to x:

$$8r_B\frac{dP}{dx} = 2x(2-x)^2 e^{-x} - 2x^2(2-x)e^{-x} - x^2(2-x)^2 e^{-x} = x(2-x)(4-6x+x^2)e^{-x}.$$

There are 5 zeros. Three occur at $x = 0$, $x = 2$, and $x = \infty$. For each of these $P = 0$. They are minima. For the maxima, $4 - 6x + x^2 = 0$. The solutions to this quadratic equation are $x = 3 - \sqrt{5} = 0.7639$ and $x = 3 + \sqrt{5} = 5.236$. Thus the maxima of the radial distribution function occur at $r = 0.7639 r_B$ and $r = 5.236 r_B$.

25P

Define $x = r/r_B$, we rewrite $P(r)$ as

$$P(x) = \frac{1}{8r_B}x^2(2-x)^2 e^{-x}.$$

Set $dP(x)/dx = 0$ to find the maxima for $P(x)$:

$$8r_B\left[\frac{dP(x)}{dx}\right] = \frac{d}{dx}[x^2(2-x)^2 e^{-x}] = x(2-x)(x^2 - 6x + 4)e^{-x} = 0,$$

The solutions are: $x_1 = 0$, $x_2 = 2$, $x_3 = 3 - \sqrt{5}$ and $x_4 = 3 + \sqrt{5}$. It turns out (you can check this by taking the second derivative) that only x_3 and x_4 correspond to P_{max}:

$$P(x_3) = \frac{1}{8r_B}x^2(2-x)^2 e^{-x}\Big|_{x=3-\sqrt{5}} = \frac{0.0519}{r_B} = \frac{0.0519}{0.0529\,\text{nm}} = 0.918\,\text{nm}^{-1},$$

and

$$P(x_4) = \frac{1}{8r_B} x^2 (2-x)^2 e^{-x} \bigg|_{3+\sqrt{5}} = \frac{0.191}{r_B} = \frac{0.191}{0.0529\,\text{nm}} = 3.61\,\text{nm}^{-1}.$$

26P

Since $r_P = 1.1\,\text{fm} \ll r_B$ we may use the approximation

$$P(r) = \frac{r^2}{8r_B^3} \left(2 - \frac{r}{r_B}\right)^2 e^{-r/r_B} \approx \frac{r^2}{8r_B^3} (2)^2 e^{-0} = \frac{r^2}{2r_B^3}.$$

Thus the probability is

$$P(0 < r < r_P) \approx \int_0^{r_P} P(r)\, dr \approx \int_0^{r_P} \frac{r^2}{2r_B^3}\, dr = \frac{r_P^3}{6r_B^3}$$

$$= \frac{1}{6} \left(\frac{1.1 \times 10^{-6}\,\text{nm}}{0.0529\,\text{nm}}\right)^3 = 1.5 \times 10^{-15}.$$

27P

Let $r_1 = 5.00r_B$ and $r_2 = 5.01r_B$. Since $|r_2 - r_1|/r_B \ll 1$,

$$P(r_1 < r < r_2) \approx P(r_1)|r_2 - r_1| = \frac{r_1^2}{8r_B^3} \left(2 - \frac{r_1}{r_B}\right)^2 e^{-r_1/r_B} (r_1 - r_2)$$

$$= \frac{(5.01r_B)^2}{8r_B^3} \left(2 - \frac{5.00r_B}{r_B}\right)^2 e^{-5.00r_B/r_B} (5.01r_B - 5.00r_B)$$

$$= 0.0019.$$

28P

Since $0 < r < 2r_B$ (see Problem 25) we have

$$P(0 < r < 2r_B) = \int_0^{2r_B} P(r)\, dr = \int_0^{2r_B} \left(\frac{r^2}{8r_B^3}\right) \left(2 - \frac{r}{r_B}\right)^2 e^{-r/r_B}\, dr$$

$$= \frac{1}{8} \int_0^2 x^2 (2-x)^2 e^{-x}\, dx = \frac{1}{8}(-x^4 - 4x^2 - 8x - 8)e^{-x} \bigg|_0^2$$

$$= \frac{1}{8}[-56e^{-2} - (-8)] = 0.053.$$

29E

The magnitude of the spin angular momentum is $S = \sqrt{s(s+1)}\,\hbar = (\sqrt{3}/2)\hbar$, where $s = \frac{1}{2}$ was used. The z component is either $S_z = \hbar/2$ or $-\hbar/2$. If $S_z = +\hbar/2$ the angle θ between the spin angular momentum vector and the positive z axis is

$$\theta = \cos^{-1}\left(\frac{S_z}{S}\right) = \cos^{-1}\left(\frac{1}{\sqrt{3}}\right) = 54.7°.$$

If $S_z = -\hbar/2$ the angle is $\theta = 180° - 54.7° = 125.3°$.

30E

The acceleration is

$$a = \frac{F}{M} = \frac{(\mu \cos\theta)(dB/dz)}{M},$$

where M is the mass of a silver atom, μ is its magnetic dipole moment, B is the magnetic field, and θ is the angle between the dipole moment and the magnetic field. Take the moment and the field to be parallel ($\cos\theta = 1$) and use the data given in Sample Problem 45–3 to obtain

$$a = \frac{(9.27 \times 10^{-24}\,\text{J/T})(1.4 \times 10^3\,\text{T/m})}{1.8 \times 10^{-25}\,\text{kg}} = 7.21 \times 10^4\,\text{m/s}^2.$$

31E

(a) $\Delta E = 2\mu_B B = 2(9.27 \times 10^{-24}\,\text{J/T})(0.50\,\text{T}) = 9.27 \times 10^{-24}\,\text{J} = (9.27 \times 10^{-24}\,\text{J})/(1.60 \times 10^{-19}\,\text{J/eV}) = 58\,\mu\,\text{eV}$.

(b) From $\Delta E = hf$ we get $f = \Delta E/h = (9.27 \times 10^{-24}\,\text{J})/(6.63 \times 10^{-34}\,\text{J}\cdot\text{s}) = 1.4 \times 10^{10}\,\text{Hz} = 14\,\text{GHz}$.

(c) $\lambda = c/f = (3.00 \times 10^8\,\text{m/s})(1.4 \times 10^{10}\,\text{Hz}) = 2.1\,\text{cm}$. This is in the short radio wave region.

32E

(a) $F = \mu_B|\partial B/\partial z| = (9.27 \times 10^{-24}\,\text{J/T})(1.6 \times 10^2\,\text{T/m}) = 1.5 \times 10^{-21}\,\text{N}$.

(b) The vertical displacement is

$$\Delta x = \frac{1}{2}at^2 = \frac{1}{2}\left(\frac{F}{m}\right)\left(\frac{\ell}{v}\right)^2 = \frac{1}{2}\left(\frac{1.5 \times 10^{-21}\,\text{N}}{1.67 \times 10^{-27}\,\text{kg}}\right)\left(\frac{0.80\,\text{m}}{1.2 \times 10^5\,\text{m/s}}\right)^2$$
$$= 2.0 \times 10^{-5}\,\text{m}.$$

33E

Let

$$E_{\text{photon}} = hf = \frac{hc}{\lambda} = 2\mu_B B\Delta m_s$$

and find λ:

$$\lambda = \frac{hc}{2\mu_B B \Delta m_s} = \frac{1240\,\text{nm}\cdot\text{eV}}{2(5.788\times10^{-5}\,\text{eV/T})(0.200\,\text{T})(1)} = 5.35\,\text{cm}.$$

34E
Let $\Delta E = 2\mu_B B_{\text{eff}}$, we find

$$B_{\text{eff}} = \frac{\Delta E}{2\mu_B} = \frac{hc}{2\lambda\mu_B} = \frac{1240\,\text{nm}\cdot\text{eV}}{2(21\times10^{-7}\,\text{nm})(5.788\times10^{-5}\,\text{eV/T})} = 51\,\text{mT}.$$

35E
The total magnetic field, $B = B_{\text{local}} + B_{\text{ext}}$, satisfies $\Delta E = hf = 2\mu B$. So

$$B_{\text{local}} = \frac{hf}{2\mu} - B_{\text{ext}} = \frac{(6.63\times10^{-34}\,\text{J}\cdot\text{s})(34\times10^6\,\text{Hz})}{2(1.41\times10^{-26}\,\text{J/T})} - 0.78\,\text{T}$$

$$= 0.019\,\text{T} = 19\,\text{mT}.$$

36E
(a)

$$\Delta E = hc\left(\frac{1}{\lambda_1} - \frac{1}{\lambda_2}\right) = (1240\,\text{eV}\cdot\text{nm})\left(\frac{1}{588.995\,\text{nm}} - \frac{1}{589.592\,\text{nm}}\right)$$

$$= 2.13\,\text{meV}.$$

(b) From $\Delta E = 2\mu_B B$ we get

$$B = \frac{\Delta E}{2\mu_B} = \frac{2.13\times10^{-3}\,\text{eV}}{2(5.788\times10^{-5}\,\text{eV/T})} = 18\,\text{T}.$$

37E
(a) True. In fact the $n = 1$ and $n = 1$ one cannot exit, because $\ell_{\text{max}} = n - 1$.
(b) True. The number is $2\ell + 1$.
(c) True. The number of different ℓ's is 4.
(d) True, since $n = \ell_{\text{max}} + 1 \geq \ell + 1$, or $n_{\text{min}} = \ell + 1$.
(e) True, since m_ℓ ranges from $-\ell = 0$ to $+\ell = 0$.
(f) True. The number of different ℓ's is n.

38E

$n = 1$, $\ell = 0$, $m_\ell = 0$, and $m_s = \pm\dfrac{1}{2}$.

39E

(a) All states with principal quantum number $n = 1$ are filled. The next lowest states have $n = 2$. The orbital quantum number can have the values $\ell = 0$ or 1 and of these the $\ell = 0$ states have the lowest energy. The magnetic quantum number must be $m_\ell = 0$ since this is the only possibility if $\ell = 0$. The spin quantum number can have either of the values $m_s = -\frac{1}{2}$ or $+\frac{1}{2}$. Since there is no external magnetic field the energies of these two states are the same. Thus in the ground state the quantum numbers of the third electron are either $n = 2$, $\ell = 0$, $m_\ell = 0$, $m_s = -\frac{1}{2}$ or $n = 2$, $\ell = 0$, $m_\ell = 0$, $m_s = +\frac{1}{2}$.

(b) The next lowest state in energy is an $n = 2$, $\ell = 1$ state. All $n = 3$ states are higher in energy. The magnetic quantum number can be $m_\ell = -1$, 0, or $+1$; the spin quantum number can be $m_s = -\frac{1}{2}$ or $+\frac{1}{2}$. If both external and internal magnetic fields can be neglected, all these states have the same energy.

40P

(a) The number of different m_ℓ's is $2\ell + 1 = 3$ and the number of different m_s's is 2. Thus the number of combinations is $N = (3 \times 2)^2/2 = 18$.

(b) There are six states disallowed by the exclustion principle, in which both electrons share the quantum numbers $(n, \ell, m_\ell, m_s) = (2, 1, 1, \frac{1}{2})$, $(2, 1, 1, -\frac{1}{2})$, $(2, 1, 0, \frac{1}{2})$, $(2, 1, 0, -\frac{1}{2})$, $(2, 1, -1, \frac{1}{2})$, $(2, 1, -1, -\frac{1}{2})$.

41P

For a given value of the principal quantum number n there are n possible values of the orbital quantum number ℓ, ranging from 0 to $n - 1$. For any value of ℓ there are $2\ell + 1$ possible values of the magnetic quantum number m_ℓ, ranging from $-\ell$ to $+\ell$. Finally, for each set of values of ℓ and m_ℓ there are two states, one corresponding to the spin quantum number $m_s = -\frac{1}{2}$ and the other corresponding to $m_s = +\frac{1}{2}$. Hence the total number of states with principal quantum number n is

$$N = 2\sum_0^{n-1}(2\ell + 1).$$

Now

$$\sum_0^{n-1}2\ell = 2\sum_0^{n-1}\ell = 2\frac{n}{2}(n - 1) = n(n - 1),$$

since there are n terms in the sum and the average term is $(n-1)/2$. Furthermore,

$$\sum_{0}^{n-1} 1 = n.$$

Thus

$$N = 2\left[n(n-1) + n\right] = 2n^2.$$

42P
The periodic table would be affected. The number of electrons allowed per orbital would now be one instead of two so, for example, Helium would no longer be a noble gas, with one electron in the 1s state and another one in the 2s state, forming no closed shell. In fact the only element which would remain noble gas would be Argon, whose electronic structure would now be such that it has 1 electron in the $n = 1$ state, $2^2 = 4$ in the $n = 2$ states, $3^2 = 9$ in the $n = 3$ states.

43E
Let $eV = hc/\lambda_{\min}$, we get

$$\lambda_{\min} = \frac{hc}{eV} = \frac{1240\,\text{pm} \cdot \text{keV}}{eV} = \frac{1240\,\text{pm}}{V}.$$

44E
Use $eV = hc/\lambda_{\min}$:

$$h = \frac{eV\lambda_{\min}}{c} = \frac{(1.60 \times 10^{-19}\,\text{C})(40.0 \times 10^3\,\text{eV})(31.1 \times 10^{-12}\,\text{m})}{3.00 \times 10^8\,\text{m/s}} = 6.63 \times 10^{-34}\,\text{J} \cdot \text{s}.$$

45E
The kinetic energy of the electron is eV, where V is the accelerating potential. A photon with the minimum wavelength is produced when all of the electron's kinetic energy goes to a single photon in a bremsstrahlung event. Thus

$$eV = \frac{hc}{\lambda_{\min}} = \frac{1240\,\text{eV} \cdot \text{nm}}{0.10\,\text{nm}} = 1.24 \times 10^4\,\text{eV},$$

where the result of Exercise 1 of Chapter 43 was used. The accelerating potential is $V = 1.24 \times 10^4\,\text{V} = 12.4\,\text{kV}$.

(a) and (b) Let the wavelength of the two photons be λ_1 and $\lambda_2 = \lambda_1 + \Delta\lambda$, then

$$eV = \frac{hc}{\lambda_1} + \frac{hc}{\lambda_1 + \Delta\lambda},$$

or

$$\lambda_1 = \frac{-(\Delta\lambda/\lambda_0 - 2) \pm \sqrt{(\Delta\lambda/\lambda_0)^2 + 4}}{2/\Delta\lambda}.$$

Here $\Delta\lambda = 130\,\text{pm}$ and $\lambda_0 = hc/eV = 1240\,\text{keV} \cdot \text{pm}/20\,\text{keV} = 62\,\text{pm}$. Choose the plus sign in the expression for λ_1 (since $\lambda_1 > 0$) to obtain

$$\lambda_1 = \frac{-(130\,\text{pm}/62\,\text{pm} - 2) + \sqrt{(130\,\text{pm}/62\,\text{pm})^2 + 4}}{2/62\,\text{pm}} = 87\,\text{pm}$$

and

$$\lambda_2 = \lambda_1 + \Delta\lambda = 87\,\text{pm} + 130\,\text{pm} = 2.2 \times 10^2\,\text{pm}.$$

The energy of the electron after its first deceleration is

$$K = K_i - \frac{hc}{\lambda_1} = 20\,\text{keV} - \frac{1240\,\text{keV} \cdot \text{pm}}{87\,\text{pm}} = 5.7\,\text{keV}.$$

The energies of the two photons are

$$E_1 = \frac{hc}{\lambda_1} = \frac{1240\,\text{keV} \cdot \text{pm}}{87\,\text{pm}} = 14\,\text{keV}$$

and

$$E_2 = \frac{hc}{\lambda_2} = \frac{1240\,\text{keV} \cdot \text{pm}}{130\,\text{pm}} = 5.7\,\text{keV}$$

47P

The initial kinetic energy of the electron is $50.0\,\text{keV}$. After the first collision the kinetic energy is $25\,\text{keV}$, after the second it is $12.5\,\text{keV}$, and after the third it is zero. The energy of the photon produced in the first collision is $50.0\,\text{keV} - 25.0\,\text{keV} = 25.0\,\text{keV}$. The wavelength associated with the photon is

$$\lambda = \frac{1240\,\text{eV} \cdot \text{nm}}{25.0 \times 10^3\,\text{eV}} = 4.96 \times 10^{-2}\,\text{nm} = 49.6\,\text{pm},$$

where the result of Exercise 1 of Chapter 43 was used. The energies of the photons produced in the second and third collisions are each $12.5\,\text{keV}$ and their wavelengths are

$$\lambda = \frac{1240\,\text{eV} \cdot \text{nm}}{12.5 \times 10^3\,\text{eV}} = 9.92 \times 10^{-2}\,\text{nm} = 99.2\,\text{pm}.$$

48P

Suppose an electron with total energy E and momentum $\mathbf{p}$ spontaneously changes into a photon. If energy is conserved, the energy of the photon is E and its momentum has magnitude E/c. Now the energy and momentum of the electron are related by $E^2 = (pc)^2 + (mc^2)^2$, so $pc = \sqrt{E^2 - (mc^2)^2}$. Since the electron has non-zero mass E/c and p cannot have the same value. Hence momentum cannot be conserved. A third particle must participate in the interaction, primarily to conserve momentum. It does, however, carry off some energy.

49E

(a)

$$\lambda_{min} = \frac{hc}{eV} = \frac{1240\,\mathrm{keV \cdot pm}}{50.0\,\mathrm{keV}} = 24.8\,\mathrm{pm}.$$

(b) and (c) The values of λ for the K_α and K_β lines do not depend on extenal potential and are therefore unchanged.

50E

(a) The cut-off wavelength λ_{min} is characteristic of the incident electrons, not of the target material. This wavelength is the wavelength of a photon with energy equal to the kinetic energy of an incident electron. According to the result of Exercise 1 of Chapter 43,

$$\lambda_{min} = \frac{1240\,\mathrm{eV \cdot nm}}{35 \times 10^3\,\mathrm{eV}} = 3.54 \times 10^{-2}\,\mathrm{nm} = 35.4\,\mathrm{pm}.$$

(b) A K_α photon results when an electron in a target atom jumps from the L-shell to the K-shell. The energy of this photon is $25.51\,\mathrm{keV} - 3.56\,\mathrm{keV} = 21.95\,\mathrm{keV}$ and its wavelength is $\lambda_{K\alpha} = (1240\,\mathrm{eV \cdot nm})/(21.95 \times 10^3\,\mathrm{eV}) = 5.65 \times 10^{-2}\,\mathrm{nm} = 56.5\,\mathrm{pm}$.

(c) A K_β photon results when an electron in a target atom jumps from the M-shell to the K-shell. The energy of this photon is $25.51\,\mathrm{keV} - 0.53\,\mathrm{keV} = 24.98\,\mathrm{keV}$ and its wavelength is $\lambda_{K\beta} = (1240\,\mathrm{eV \cdot nm})/(24.98 \times 10^3\,\mathrm{eV}) = 4.96 \times 10^{-2}\,\mathrm{nm} = 49.6\,\mathrm{pm}$.

51E

For the K_α line from iron

$$\Delta E = \frac{hc}{\lambda} = \frac{1240\,\mathrm{pm \cdot keV}}{193\,\mathrm{pm}} = 6.42\,\mathrm{keV}.$$

For the hydrogen atom the corresponding energy difference is

$$\Delta E_{12} = -(13.6\,\mathrm{eV})\left(\frac{1}{2^2} - \frac{1}{1^1}\right) = 10.2\,\mathrm{eV}.$$

The difference is much greater in iron because its atomic nucleus contains 26 protons, exerting a much greater force on the K- and L- shell electrons than the single-proton nucleus of hydrogen.

52E

The energy difference $E_L - E_M$ for the x-ray atomic energy levels of molybdenum is

$$\Delta E = E_L - E_M = \frac{hc}{\lambda_L} - \frac{hc}{\lambda_M} = \frac{1240\,\mathrm{pm} \cdot \mathrm{keV}}{63.0\,\mathrm{pm}} - \frac{1240\,\mathrm{pm} \cdot \mathrm{keV}}{71.0\,\mathrm{pm}}$$
$$= 19.7\,\mathrm{keV} - 17.5\,\mathrm{keV} = 2.2\,\mathrm{keV}.$$

53E

As shown in Sample Problem 45–7, the ratio of the wavelength λ_{Nb} for the K_α line of niobium to the wavelength λ_{Ga} for the K_α line of gallium is given by

$$\frac{\lambda_{\mathrm{Nb}}}{\lambda_{\mathrm{Ga}}} = \left[\frac{Z_{\mathrm{Ga}} - 1}{Z_{\mathrm{Nb}} - 1}\right]^2,$$

where Z_{Nb} is the atomic number of niobium (41) and the Z_{Ga} is the atomic number of gallium (31). Thus

$$\frac{\lambda_{\mathrm{Nb}}}{\lambda_{\mathrm{Ga}}} = \left[\frac{30}{40}\right]^2 = \frac{9}{16}.$$

54P

The Moseley plot is given is Fig. 45-18. The slope is

$$a = \frac{(1.95 - 0.50)10^9\,\mathrm{Hz}^{-1/2}}{40 - 11} = 5.0 \times 10^7\,\mathrm{Hz}^{-1/2},$$

in agreement with Sample Problem 45-8.

55P

(a) An electron must be removed from the K-shell, so that an electron from a higher energy shell can drop. This requires an energy of 69.5 keV. The accelerating potential must be at least 69.5 kV.

(b) After it is accelerated the kinetic energy of the bombarding electron is 69.5 keV. The energy of a photon associated with the minimum wavelength is 69.5 keV, so its wavelength is

$$\lambda_{min} = \frac{1240\,\text{eV} \cdot \text{nm}}{69.5 \times 10^3\,\text{eV}} = 1.78 \times 10^{-2}\,\text{nm} = 17.8\,\text{pm}.$$

(c) The energy of a photon associated with the K_α line is 69.5 keV $-$ 11.3 keV $=$ 58.2 keV and its wavelength is $\lambda_{K\alpha} = (1240\,\text{eV} \cdot \text{nm})/(58.2 \times 10^3\,\text{eV}) = 2.13 \times 10^{-2}\,\text{nm} = 21.3\,\text{pm}$. The energy of a photon associated with the K_β line is 69.5 keV $-$ 2.30 keV $=$ 67.2 keV and its wavelength is $\lambda_{K\beta} = (1240\,\text{eV} \cdot \text{nm})/(67.2 \times 10^3\,\text{eV}) = 1.85 \times 10^{-2}\,\text{nm} = 18.5\,\text{pm}$.

56P
(a) From Fig. 45-15 we find that the wave lengths corresponding to K_α and K_β lines are $\lambda_\alpha = 70.0\,\text{pm}$ and $\lambda_\beta = 6.30\,\text{pm}$, respectively. So $E_\alpha = hc/\lambda_\alpha = (1240\,\text{keV} \cdot \text{pm})/(70.0\,\text{pm})$ $= 17.7\,\text{keV}$ and $E_\beta = (1240\,\text{keV} \cdot \text{nm})/(63.0\,\text{pm}) = 19.7\,\text{keV}$.
(b) Both Z_r or N_b can be used, since $E_\alpha < 18.00\,\text{eV} < E_\beta$ and $E_\alpha < 18.99\,\text{eV} < E_\beta$. See the hint given in the probelm statement Z_r is the better choice.

57P
From Eq. 41-29, let $2d\sin\theta = m\lambda = mhc/\Delta E$, where $\theta = 90° - 74.1° = 15.9°$, we get

$$d = \frac{mhc}{2\Delta E \sin\theta} = \frac{(1)(1240\,\text{keV} \cdot \text{nm})}{2(8.979 - 0.951)\,\text{keV}(\sin 15.9°)} = 282\,\text{pm}.$$

58P
(a) From Eqs. 45-20 and 45-21, $f \propto (Z - 1)^2$ so

$$\frac{f}{f'} = \left(\frac{Z - 1}{Z' - 1}\right)^2.$$

(b)

$$\frac{E}{E'} = \frac{f}{f'} = \left(\frac{Z - 1}{Z' - 1}\right)^2 = \left(\frac{92 - 1}{13 - 1}\right)^2 = 57.5 \quad (\text{Uranium vs aluminum});$$

$$\frac{E}{E'} = \left(\frac{92 - 1}{13 - 1}\right)^2 = 2070 \qquad (\text{Uranium vs lithium}).$$

59P
(a) and (b) The theoretical values for the energy of the K_α x rays is given by

$$E = \frac{me^4(Z - 1)^2}{8\epsilon_0^2 h^2}\left(\frac{1}{1^2} - \frac{1}{2^2}\right) = (10.2\,\text{eV})(Z - 1)^2.$$

The theoretical vs measured values of E are listed as follows:

element	Z	E_{theory} (eV)	$E_{measured}$ (eV)	Percentage deviation (%)
Li	3	40.8	54.3	25
Be	4	91.8	108.5	15
B	5	163.2	183.3	11
C	6	255	277	7.9
N	7	367.2	392.4	6.4
O	8	499.8	524.9	4.8
F	9	653.0	676.8	3.5
Ne	10	826.0	848.6	2.7
Na	11	1020	1041	2.0
Mg	12	1234	1254	1.6

(c)

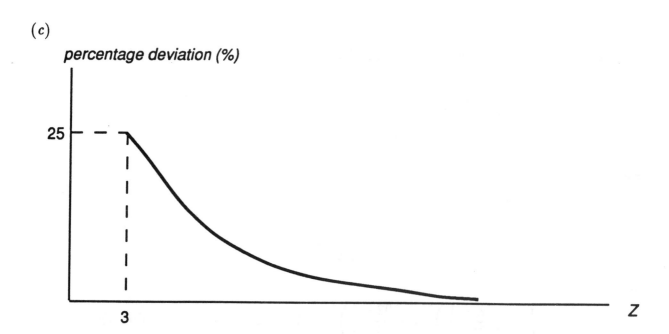

The percentage deviation decreases as Z increases. The theory is more precise at large Z's.

60E

The number of atoms in a state with energy E is proportional to $e^{-E/kT}$, where T is the temperature on the Kelvin scale and k is the Boltzmann constant. Thus the ratio of the number of atoms in the thirteenth excited state to the number in the eleventh excited state is

$$\frac{n_{13}}{n_{11}} = e^{-\Delta E/kT},$$

1118

where ΔE is the difference in the energies: $\Delta E = E_{13} - E_{11} = 2(1.2\,\text{eV}) = 2.4\,\text{eV}$. For the given temperature $kT = (8.62 \times 10^{-2}\,\text{eV/K})(2000\,\text{K}) = 0.1724\,\text{eV}$. Hence

$$\frac{n_{13}}{n_{11}} = e^{-2.4/0.1724} = 9.0 \times 10^{-7}.$$

61E
Use Eq. 45-24: $n_2/n_1 = e^{-(E_2-E_1)/kT}$. Solve for T:

$$T = \frac{E_2 - E_1}{k\ln(n_1/n_2)} = \frac{3.2\,\text{eV}}{(1.38 \times 10^{-23}\,\text{J/K})\ln(2.5 \times 10^{15}/6.1 \times 10^{13})} = 10,000\,\text{K}.$$

62E
Consider two levels, 1 and 2, with $E_2 > E_1$. Since $T > 0$,

$$\frac{n_2}{n_1} = e^{-(E_2-E_1)/kT} = e^{-|E_2-E_1|/(-k|T|)} = e^{|E_2-E_1|/(-k|T|)} > 1,$$

i.e. $n_2 > n_1$. This is population inversion. Solve for T:

$$T = -|T| = -\frac{E_2 - E_1}{k\ln(n_2/n_1)} = -\frac{2.26\,\text{eV}}{(8.62 \times 10^{-5}\,\text{eV/K})\ln(1 + 10.0\%)}$$
$$= -2.75 \times 10^5\,\text{K}.$$

63E
The number of photons emitted is

$$N = \frac{Pt}{E_{\text{photon}}} = \frac{(2.3 \times 10^{-3}\,\text{W})(60\,\text{s})}{(1240\,\text{eV} \cdot \text{nm}/632.8\,\text{nm})(1.60 \times 10^{-19}\,\text{J/eV})} = 4.4 \times 10^{17}.$$

64E
(a) If t is the time interval over which the pulse is emitted, the length of the pulse is $L = ct = (3.00 \times 10^8\,\text{m/s})(1.20 \times 10^{-11}\,\text{s}) = 3.60 \times 10^{-3}\,\text{m}$.

(b) If E_p is the energy of the pulse, E is the energy of a single photon in the pulse, and N is the number of photons in the pulse, then $E_p = NE$. The energy of the pulse is $E_p = (0.150\,\text{J})/(1.602 \times 10^{-19}\,\text{J/eV}) = 9.36 \times 10^{17}\,\text{eV}$ and the energy of a single photon is $E = (1240\,\text{eV} \cdot \text{nm})/694.4\,\text{nm} = 1.786\,\text{eV}$. Hence

$$N = \frac{E_p}{E} = \frac{9.36 \times 10^{17}\,\text{eV}}{1.786\,\text{eV}} = 5.24 \times 10^{17}\,\text{photons}.$$

65E

The rate is

$$\frac{dN}{dt} = \frac{P}{E_{\text{photon}}} = \frac{P}{hc/\lambda} = \frac{(5.0 \times 10^{-3}\,\text{W})(0.80 \times 10^3\,\text{nm})}{(1240\,\text{eV}\cdot\text{nm})(1.60 \times 10^{-19}\,\text{J/eV})} = 2.0 \times 10^{16}\,\text{s}^{-1}.$$

66E

The number of channels that could be accomodated is

$$N = \frac{\Delta f}{10\,\text{Hz}} = \frac{(3.00 \times 10^8\,\text{m/s})[(450\,\text{nm})^{-1} - (650\,\text{nm})^{-1}]}{10\,\text{MHz}} = 2.1 \times 10^7.$$

The higher frequencies of the visible light would allow for much more channels to be carried compared with using the microwave.

67E

The diameter of the spot on the moon is

$$D = 2R\tan\theta + d \approx 2R\tan\theta \approx 2R\theta$$
$$= 2R\left(\frac{1.22\lambda}{d}\right) = \frac{2(3.8 \times 10^8\,\text{m})(1.22)(600 \times 10^{-9}\,\text{m})}{0.12\,\text{m}}$$
$$= 4.6 \times 10^3\,\text{m} = 4.6\,\text{km}.$$

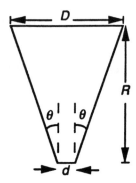

68P

(a) If both mirrors are perfectly reflecting there is a node at each end of the crystal. With one end partially silvered there is a node very close to that end. Assume nodes at both ends, so there are an integer number of half-wavelengths in the length of the crystal. The wavelength in the crystal is $\lambda_c = \lambda/n$, where λ is the wavelength in vacuum and n is the index of refraction of ruby. Thus $N(\lambda/2n) = L$, where N is the number of standing wave nodes, so

$$N = \frac{2nL}{\lambda} = \frac{2(1.75)(0.0600\,\text{m})}{694 \times 10^{-9}\,\text{m}} = 3.03 \times 10^5.$$

(b) Since $\lambda = c/f$, where f is the frequency, $N = 2nLf/c$ and $\Delta N = (2nL/c)\,\Delta f$. Hence

$$\Delta f = \frac{c\,\Delta N}{2nL} = \frac{(3.00 \times 10^8\,\text{m/s})(1)}{2(1.75)(0.0600\,\text{m})} = 1.43 \times 10^9\,\text{Hz}.$$

The speed of light in the crystal is c/n and the round-trip distance is $2L$, so the round-trip travel time is $2nL/c$. This is the same as the reciprocal of the change in frequency.

1120

(c) The frequency is $f = c/\lambda = (3.00 \times 10^8 \text{ m/s})/(694 \times 10^{-9} \text{ m}) = 4.32 \times 10^{14} \text{ Hz}$ and the fractional change in the frequency is $\Delta f / f = (1.43 \times 10^9 \text{ Hz})/(4.32 \times 10^{14} \text{ Hz}) = 3.31 \times 10^{-6}$.

69P

For the nth harmonic of the standing wave of wavelength λ in the cavity of width L we have $n\lambda = 2L$, so $n\Delta\lambda + \lambda\Delta n = 0$. Let $\Delta n = \pm 1$ and note that $\lambda = 2L/n$, we get

$$|\Delta\lambda| = \frac{\lambda|\Delta n|}{n} = \frac{\lambda}{n} = \lambda\left(\frac{\lambda}{2L}\right) = \frac{\lambda^2}{2L} = \frac{(533 \text{ nm})^2}{2(8.0 \times 10^7 \text{ nm})} = 1.8 \times 10^{-12} \text{ m} = 1.8 \text{ pm}.$$

70P

(a) Denote the upper level as level 1 and the lower one as level 2. From $n_1/n_2 = e^{-(E_1 - E_2)/kT}$ we get

$$n_1 = n_2 e^{-(E_1 - E_2)/kT} = n_2 e^{-hc/\lambda kT}$$
$$= (4.0 \times 10^{20}) e^{-(1240 \text{ eV} \cdot \text{nm})/[(580 \text{ nm})(8.62 \times 10^{-5} \text{ eV/K})(300 \text{ K})]}$$
$$= 5.0 \times 10^{-16} \ll 1,$$

i.e. practically no electron occupies the upper level.
(b) The energy released is

$$E = n_1 E_{\text{photon}} = \frac{n_1 hc}{\lambda} = \frac{(7.0 \times 10^{20})(1240 \text{ eV} \cdot \text{nm})(1.6 \times 10^{-19} \text{ J/eV})}{580 \text{ nm}} = 240 \text{ J}.$$

71P

(a)
$$R = \frac{1.22 f \lambda}{d} = \frac{(1.22)(3.50 \text{ cm})(515 \text{ nm})}{3.00 \text{ mm}} = 7.33 \mu\text{ m}.$$

(b) The average power flux density in the incident beam is

$$\frac{P}{\pi d^4/4} = \frac{4(5.00 \text{ W})}{\pi(3.00 \text{ mm})^2} = 707 \text{ kW/m}^2;$$

and the average power flux density in the central disk is

$$\frac{(84\%)P}{\pi R^2} = \frac{(84\%)(5.00 \text{ W})}{\pi(7.33 \mu\text{ m})^2} = 24.9 \text{ GW/m}^2.$$

72P

(a) The intensity at the target is given by $I = P/A$, where P is the power output of the source and A is the area of the beam at the target. You want to compute I and compare the result with $10^8 \text{ W}/m^2$.

The beam spreads because diffraction occurs at the aperture of the laser. Consider the part of the beam that is within the central diffraction maximum. The angular position of the edge is given by $\sin\theta = 1.22\lambda/d$, where λ is the wavelength and d is the diameter of the aperture (see Exercise 67). At the target, a distance D away, the radius of the beam is $r = D\tan\theta$. Since θ is small we may approximate both $\sin\theta$ and $\tan\theta$ by θ, in radians. Then $r = D\theta = 1.22D\lambda/d$ and

$$I = \frac{P}{\pi r^2} = \frac{Pd^2}{\pi(1.22D\lambda)^2} = \frac{(5.0 \times 10^6 \text{ W})(4.0\,\text{m})^2}{\pi\left[(1.22(3000 \times 10^3 \text{ m})(3.0 \times 10^{-6} \text{ m})\right]^2}$$
$$= 2.1 \times 10^5 \text{ W/m}^2 ,$$

not great enough to destroy the missile.

(b) Solve for the wavelength in terms of the intensity and substitute $I = 1.0 \times 10^8 \text{ W/m}^2$:

$$\lambda = \frac{d}{1.22D}\sqrt{\frac{P}{\pi I}} = \frac{4.0\,\text{m}}{1.22(3000 \times 10^3 \text{ m})}\sqrt{\frac{5.0 \times 10^6 \text{ W}}{\pi(1.0 \times 10^8 \text{ W/m}^2)}}$$
$$= 1.4 \times 10^{-7} \text{ m} = 140\,\text{nm} .$$

CHAPTER 46

1E

Solve p from $p = nkT$:

$$p = nkT = (8.43 \times 10^{28}\,\text{m}^{-3})(1.38 \times 10^{-23}\,\text{J/K})(300\,\text{K}) = 3.49 \times 10^8\,\text{Pa} = 3490\,\text{atm}.$$

2E

The number of atoms per unit volume is given by $n = d/M$, where d is the mass density of gold and M is the mass of a single gold atom. Since each atom contributes one conduction electron, n is also the number of conduction electrons per unit volume. Since the molar mass of gold is $A = 197\,\text{g/mol}$, $M = A/N_A = (197\,\text{g/mol})/(6.022 \times 10^{23}\,\text{mol}^{-1}) = 3.271 \times 10^{-22}\,\text{g}$. Thus

$$n = \frac{19.3\,\text{g/cm}^3}{3.271 \times 10^{-22}\,\text{g}} = 5.90 \times 10^{22}\,\text{cm}^{-3}.$$

3P

(a) Solve n from $p = nkT$:

$$n = \frac{p}{kT} = \frac{(1.0\,\text{atm})(1.0 \times 10^5\,\text{Pa/atm})}{(1.38 \times 10^{-23}\,\text{J/K})(273\,\text{K})} = 2.7 \times 10^{25}\,\text{m}^{-3}.$$

(b)

$$n = \frac{\rho_{\text{Cu}}}{m_{\text{Cu}}} = \frac{8.96 \times 10^3\,\text{kg/m}^3}{(63.54)(1.67 \times 10^{-27}\,\text{kg})} = 8.43 \times 10^{28}\,\text{m}^{-3}.$$

(c) The ratio is $(8.43 \times 10^{28}\,\text{m}^{-3})/(2.7 \times 10^{25}\,\text{m}^{-3}) = 3.1 \times 10^3$.

(d) Use $d_{\text{av}} = n^{-1/3}$. For case (a), $d_{\text{av}} = (2.7 \times 10^{25}\,\text{m}^{-3})^{-1/3} = 3.3\,\text{nm}$; and for case ($b$) $d_{\text{av}} = (8.43 \times 10^{28}\,\text{m}^{-3})^{-1/3} = 0.228\,\text{nm}$.

4P

(a) The volume per cubic meter of soium occupied by the sodium ions is

$$V_s = \frac{(971\,\text{kg})(6.022 \times 10^{23}/\,\text{mol})(4\pi/3)(98 \times 10^{-12}\,\text{m})^3}{(23\,\text{g/mol})} = 0.100\,\text{m}^3,$$

so the fraction available for conduction electron is $1 - (V_s/1.00\,\text{m}^3) = 1 - 0.100 = 0.900$.

(b) For copper

$$V_{\text{Cu}} = \frac{(8960\,\text{kg})(6.022 \times 10^{23}/\,\text{mol})(4\pi/3)(135 \times 10^{-12}\,\text{m})^3}{63.5\,\text{g/mol}} = 0.876\,\text{m}^{-3}$$

so the fraction is $1 - (V_{\text{Cu}}/1.00\,\text{m}^3) = 1 - 0.876 = 0.124$.

(c) Sodium, because the electrons occupy a greater portion of the space available.

5E

From Eq. 46-6

$$E_F = \frac{0.121h^2}{m}n^{2/3} = \frac{0.121(1240\,\text{eV}\cdot\text{nm})^2}{0.511\,\text{MeV}}(8.43\times10^{28}\,\text{m}^{-3})^{2/3} = 7.0\,\text{eV}.$$

6E

(a) Eq. 46–3 gives

$$n(E) = \frac{8\sqrt{2}\pi m^{3/2}}{h^3}E^{1/2}$$

for the density of states associated with the conduction electrons of a metal. This can be written

$$n(E) = CE^{1/2},$$

where

$$C = \frac{8\sqrt{2}\pi m^{3/2}}{h^3} = \frac{8\sqrt{2}\pi(9.109\times10^{-31}\,\text{kg})^{3/2}}{(6.626\times10^{-34}\,\text{J}\cdot\text{s})^3} = 1.062\times10^{56}\,\text{kg}^{3/2}/\text{J}^3\cdot\text{s}^3.$$

Now $1\,\text{J} = 1\,\text{kg}\cdot\text{m}^2/\text{s}^2$ (think of the equation for kinetic energy $K = \frac{1}{2}mv^2$), so $1\,\text{kg} = 1\,\text{J}\cdot\text{s}^2\cdot\text{m}^{-2}$. Thus the units of C can be written $(\text{J}\cdot\text{s}^2)^{3/2}\cdot(\text{m}^{-2})^{3/2}\cdot\text{J}^{-3}\cdot\text{s}^{-3} = \text{J}^{-3/2}\cdot\text{m}^{-3}$. This means

$$C = (1.062\times10^{56}\,\text{J}^{-3/2}\cdot\text{m}^{-3})(1.602\times10^{-19}\,\text{J}/eV)^{3/2} = 6.81\times10^{27}\,\text{m}^{-3}\cdot\text{eV}^{-3/2}.$$

(b) If $E = 5.00\,\text{eV}$ then

$$n(E) = (6.81\times10^{27}\,\text{m}^{-3}\cdot\text{eV}^{-3/2})(5.00\,\text{eV})^{1/2} = 1.52\times10^{28}\,\text{eV}^{-1}\cdot\text{m}^{-3}.$$

7E

Use the result of Exercise 6:

$$n(E) = CE^{1/2} = (6.78\times10^{27}\,\text{m}^{-3}\cdot\text{eV}^{-2/3})(8.0\,\text{eV})^{1/2} = 1.9\times10^{28}\,\text{m}^{-3}\cdot\text{eV}^{-1}.$$

This is consistent with Fig. 46-6(a).

8E

(a) At absolute temperature $T = 0$, the probability is zero that any state with energy above the Fermi energy is occupied.

(b) The probability that a state with energy E is occupied at temperature T is given by

$$p(E) = \frac{1}{e^{(E-E_F)/kT} + 1},$$

where k is the Boltzmann constant and E_F is the Fermi energy. Now $E - E_F = 0.062\,\text{eV}$ and $(E - E_F)/kT = (0.062\,\text{eV})/(8.62 \times 10^{-5}\,\text{eV}/K)(320\,\text{K}) = 2.248$, so

$$p(E) = \frac{1}{e^{2.248} + 1} = 0.0956.$$

See Sample Problem 46–4 for the value of k.

9E
Solve E from Eq. 46-7:

$$E = E_F + kT\ln(p^{-1} - 1) = 7.0\,\text{eV} + (8.62 \times 10^{-5}\,\text{eV}/K)(1000\,\text{K})\ln\left(\frac{1}{0.90} - 1\right)$$

$$= 6.8\,\text{eV}.$$

(b) $n(E) = CE^{1/2} = (6.78 \times 10^{27}\,\text{m}^{-3} \cdot \text{eV}^{-3/2})(6.8\,\text{eV})^{1/2} = 1.77 \times 10^{28}\,\text{m}^{-3} \cdot \text{eV}^{-1}$.
(c) $n_o(E) = p(E)n(E) = (0.90)(1.77 \times 10^{28}\,\text{m}^{-3} \cdot \text{eV}^{-1}) = 1.6 \times 10^{28}\,\text{m}^{-3} \cdot \text{eV}^{-1}$.

10E
According to Eq. 46–6 the Fermi energy is given by

$$E_F = \left(\frac{3}{16\sqrt{2\pi}}\right)^{2/3} \frac{h^2}{m} n^{2/3},$$

where n is the number of conduction electrons per unit volume, m is the mass of an electron, and h is the Planck constant. This can be written $E_F = An^{2/3}$, where

$$A = \left(\frac{3}{16\sqrt{2\pi}}\right)^{2/3} \frac{h^2}{m} = \left(\frac{3}{16\sqrt{2\pi}}\right)^{2/3} \frac{(6.626 \times 10^{-34}\,\text{J} \cdot \text{s})^2}{9.109 \times 10^{-31}\,\text{kg}} = 5.842 \times 10^{-38}\,\text{J}^2 \cdot \text{s}^2/\text{kg}.$$

Since $1\,\text{J} = 1\,\text{kg·m}^2/s^2$, the units of A can be taken to be $\text{m}^2 \cdot \text{J}$. Divide by $1.602 \times 10^{-19}\,\text{J}/\text{eV}$ to obtain $A = 3.65 \times 10^{-19}\,\text{m}^2 \cdot \text{eV}$.

11E
The number density of conduction electrons in gold is

$$n = \frac{(19.3\,\text{g}/\text{cm}^3)(6.022 \times 10^{23}/\text{mol})}{(197\,\text{g}/\text{mol})} = 5.90 \times 10^{22}\,\text{cm}^{-3}.$$

Thus

$$E_F = \frac{0.121h^2}{m}n^{2/3} = \frac{0.121(1240\,\text{eV} \cdot \text{nm})^2}{0.511\,\text{MeV}}(5.90 \times 10^{22}\,\text{cm}^{-3})^{2/3} = 5.52\,\text{eV}.$$

12E

Use $n_o = n(E)p(E) = CE^{1/2}[e^{(E-E_F)/kT} + 1]^{-1}$. At $E = 4.00\,\text{eV}$

$$n_o = \frac{(6.78 \times 10^{27}\,\text{m}^{-3} \cdot \text{eV}^{-3/2})(4.00\,\text{eV})^{1/2}}{e^{(4.00\,\text{eV} - 7.00\,\text{eV})/[8.62 \times 10^{-5}\,\text{eV/K})(1000\,\text{k})]} + 1}$$
$$= 1.36 \times 10^{28}\,\text{m}^{-3} \cdot \text{eV}^{-1}.$$

at $E = 6.75\,\text{eV}$

$$n_o = \frac{(6.78 \times 10^{27}\,\text{m}^{-3} \cdot \text{eV}^{-3/2})(6.75\,\text{eV})^{1/2}}{e^{(6.75\,\text{eV} - 7.00\,\text{eV})/[8.62 \times 10^{-5}\,\text{eV/K})(1000\,\text{k})]} + 1}$$
$$= 1.67 \times 10^{28}\,\text{m}^{-3} \cdot \text{eV}^{-1}.$$

Similarly at $E = 7.00$, 7.25 and $9.00\,\text{eV}$, the corresponding values of $n_o(E)$ are 0.90, 0.10 and $0.00 \times 10^{28}\,\text{m}^{-3} \cdot \text{eV}^{-1}$.

13E

Let $kT \gg E_F$ or

$$T \gg \frac{E_F}{k} = \frac{7.0\,\text{eV}}{8.62 \times 10^{-5}\,\text{eV/K}} = 80,000\,\text{k} \sim 10^5\,\text{K}.$$

This is the condition for the conduction electrons in copper to behave like an idea gas of the ordinary kind. In the case of Fig. 46-6(a), however, we have

$$p(E) \simeq \begin{cases} 1 & E < E_F \\ 0 & E < E_F. \end{cases}$$

This is possible only for $E_F/kT \gg 1$. In fact if $E_F/kT \gg 1$ then if $E - E_F > 0$ we have $p(E) \simeq [e^\infty + 1]^{-1} \to 0$ and if $E - E_F < 0$ we have $p(E) \simeq [e^{-\infty} + 1]^{-1} \to 1$, in agreement with Fig. 46-6(b).

14E

(a) Use $p(E) = [e^{(E-E_F)/kT} + 1]^{-1}$. So for $E = 4.4\,\text{eV}$

$$p(E) = \frac{1}{e^{(4.4\,\text{eV} - 5.5\,\text{eV})/[(8.62 \times 10^{-5}\,\text{eV/K})(273\,\text{k})]} + 1} = 1.0,$$

for $E = 5.4\,\text{eV}$

$$p(E) = \frac{1}{e^{(5.4\,\text{eV}-5.5\,\text{eV})/[(8.62\times10^{-5}\,\text{eV/K})(273\,\text{k})]} + 1} = 0.99,$$

for $E = 5.5\,\text{eV}$

$$p(E) = \frac{1}{e^{(5.5\,\text{eV}-5.5\,\text{eV})/kT} + 1} = 0.50;$$

for $E = 5.6\,\text{eV}$

$$p(E) = \frac{1}{e^{(5.6\,\text{eV}-5.5\,\text{eV})/[(8.62\times10^{-5}\,\text{eV/K})(273\,\text{k})]} + 1} = 0.014,$$

for $E = 6.4\,\text{eV}$

$$p(E) = \frac{1}{e^{(6.4\,\text{eV}-5.5\,\text{eV})/[(8.62\times10^{-5}\,\text{eV/K})(273\,\text{k})]} + 1} = 2.5 \times 10^{-17}.$$

Solve the expression for $p(E)$ for T:

$$T = \frac{E - E_F}{k \ln(p^{-1} - 1)} = \frac{5.6\,\text{eV} - 5.5\,\text{eV}}{(8.62 \times 10^{-5}\,\text{eV/K}) \ln(0.16^{-1} - 1)} = 7.0 \times 10^2\,\text{K}.$$

15E

Let N be the number of atoms per unit volume and n be the number of free electrons per unit volume. Then the number of free electrons per atom is n/N. Use the result of Exercise 10 to find n: $E_F = An^{2/3}$, where $A = 3.65 \times 10^{-19}\,\text{m}^2 \cdot \text{eV}$. Thus

$$n = \left(\frac{E_F}{A}\right)^{3/2} = \left(\frac{11.6\,\text{eV}}{3.65 \times 10^{-19}\,\text{m}^2 \cdot \text{eV}}\right)^{3/2} = 1.79 \times 10^{29}\,\text{m}^{-3}.$$

If M is the mass of a single aluminum atom and d is the mass density of aluminum then $N = d/M$. Now $M = (27.0\,\text{g/mol})/(6.022 \times 10^{23}\,\text{mol}^{-1}) = 4.48 \times 10^{-23}\,\text{g}$, so $N = (2.70\,\text{g/cm}^3)/(4.48 \times 10^{-23}\,\text{g}) = 6.03 \times 10^{22}\,\text{cm}^{-3} = 6.03 \times 10^{28}\,\text{m}^{-3}$. Thus the number of free electrons per atom is

$$\frac{n}{N} = \frac{1.79 \times 10^{29}\,\text{m}^{-3}}{6.03 \times 10^{28}\,\text{m}^{-3}} = 2.97.$$

16P

Consider two states, labeled 1 and 2, with $E_1 = E_F + \Delta E$ and $E_2 = E_F - \Delta E$. We have

$$p(E_1) + p(E_2) = \frac{1}{e^{(E_1 - E_F)/kT} + 1} + \frac{1}{e^{(E_2 - E_F)/kT} + 1}$$

$$= \frac{1}{e^{\Delta E/kT} + 1} + \frac{1}{e^{-\Delta E/kT} + 1}$$

$$= \frac{2 + e^{\Delta E/kT} + e^{-\Delta E/kT}}{(e^{\Delta E/kT} + 1)(e^{-\Delta E/kT} + 1)} = 1.$$

17P

The probability that a state is occupied by a hole is the same as the probability that state is unoccupied by an electron. Since the total probability that a state is either occupied or unoccupied by an electron is 1, we have $p_h + p = 1$. Thus

$$p_h = 1 - \frac{1}{e^{(E-E_F)/kT} + 1}$$

$$= \frac{e^{(E-E_F)/kT}}{1 + e^{(E-E_F)/kT}} = \frac{1}{e^{-(E-E_F)/kT} + 1}.$$

18P

(a)

$$n = \frac{2\rho_{Zn}}{m_{Zn}} = \frac{2(7.133\,\text{g/cm}^3)(6.022 \times 10^{22}/\,\text{mol})}{(65.37\,\text{g/mol})} = 1.31 \times 10^{29}\,\text{m}^{-3}.$$

(b)

$$E_F = \frac{0.121h^2}{m}n^{2/3} = \frac{0.121(6.63 \times 10^{-34}\,\text{J}\cdot\text{s})^2(1.31 \times 10^{29}\,\text{m}^{-3})^{2/3}}{(9.11 \times 10^{-31}\,\text{kg})(1.60 \times 10^{-19}\,\text{J/eV})}$$

$$= 9.43\,\text{eV}.$$

(c)

$$v_F = \sqrt{\frac{2E_Fc^2}{mc^2}} = \sqrt{\frac{2(9.43\,\text{eV})(3.00 \times 10^8\,\text{m/s})^2}{0.511\,\text{MeV}}} = 1.82 \times 10^6\,\text{m/s}.$$

(d)

$$\lambda = \frac{h}{p} = \frac{h}{mv_F} = \frac{6.63 \times 10^{-34}\,\text{J}\cdot\text{s}}{(9.11 \times 10^{-31}\,\text{kg})(1.82 \times 10^6\,\text{m/s})} = 0.40\,\text{nm}.$$

19P

(a)

$$n = \frac{\rho_{Ag}}{m_{Ag}} = \frac{(10.49\,\text{g/cm}^3)(6.022 \times 10^{22}/\,\text{mol})}{(107.87\,\text{g/mol})} = 5.86 \times 10^{28}\,\text{m}^{-3}.$$

(b)

$$E_F = \frac{0.121h^2}{m}n^{2/3} = \frac{0.121(6.63 \times 10^{-34}\,\text{J}\cdot\text{s})^2(5.86 \times 10^{28}\,\text{m}^{-3})^{2/3}}{(9.11 \times 10^{-31}\,\text{kg})(1.60 \times 10^{-19}\,\text{J/eV})}$$

$$= 5.52\,\text{eV}.$$

(c)

$$v_F = \sqrt{\frac{2E_Fc^2}{mc^2}} = \sqrt{\frac{2(5.52\,\text{eV})(3.00 \times 10^8\,\text{m/s})^2}{0.511\,\text{MeV}}} = 1.39 \times 10^6\,\text{m/s}.$$

(d)

$$\lambda = \frac{h}{p} = \frac{h}{mv_F} = \frac{6.63 \times 10^{-34}\,\text{J}\cdot\text{s}}{(9.11 \times 10^{-31}\,\text{kg})(1.39 \times 10^6\,\text{m/s})} = 0.522\,\text{nm}.$$

20P

Use the result of Exercise 10: at temperature $T = 0$ the Fermi energy is given by $E_F = An^{2/3}$, where n is the number of electrons per unit volume and $A = 3.65 \times 10^{-19}\,\text{m}^2\cdot\text{eV}$. If N is the number of atoms per unit volume and each atom contributes Z electrons, then $n = NZ$. If M_S is the mass of the star, R is its radius, and M is the mass of a single iron atom, then $N = (3M_S)/(4\pi R^3 M)$. Now $M_S = 1.99 \times 10^{30}\,\text{kg}$, $R = 6.37 \times 10^6\,\text{m}$, and $M = (55.847\,\text{g/mol})/(6.022 \times 10^{23}\,\text{mol}^{-1}) = 9.27 \times 10^{-23}\,\text{g} = 9.27 \times 10^{-26}\,\text{kg}$. The data used was found in appendices of the text. This means

$$N = \frac{3(1.99 \times 10^{30}\,\text{kg})}{4\pi(6.37 \times 10^6\,\text{m})^3(9.27 \times 10^{-26}\,\text{kg})} = 1.98 \times 10^{34}\,\text{m}^{-3}.$$

The atomic number of iron is 26, so $n = 26(1.98 \times 10^{34}\,\text{m}^{-3}) = 5.15 \times 10^{35}\,\text{m}^{-3}$. The Fermi energy is

$$E_F = \left(3.65 \times 10^{-19}\,\text{m}^2\cdot\text{eV}\right)\left(5.15 \times 10^{35}\,\text{m}^{-3}\right)^{2/3} = 2.35 \times 10^5\,\text{eV}.$$

21P

The number density of neutrons is

$$n = \frac{\rho}{m_n} = \frac{M}{Vm_n} = \frac{M}{(4\pi R^3/3)m_n}$$

$$= \frac{3(2.0)(1.99 \times 10^{30}\,\text{kg})}{4\pi(10 \times 10^3\,\text{m})^3(1.67 \times 10^{-27}\,\text{kg})} = 5.69 \times 10^{47}\,\text{m}^{-3}.$$

Thus

$$E_F = \frac{0.121h^2}{m_n}n^{2/3} = \frac{0.121(6.63 \times 10^{-34}\,\text{J}\cdot\text{s})^2(5.69 \times 10^{47}\,\text{m}^{-3})^{2/3}}{(1.67 \times 10^{-27}\,\text{kg})(1.60 \times 10^{-19}\,\text{J/eV})}$$

$$= 1.37 \times 10^8\,\text{eV} = 137\,\text{MeV}.$$

22P

Solve for h from Eq. 46-6:

$$h = \left(\frac{mE_F}{0.121}\right)^{1/2}n^{-1/3}.$$

Substituting this into Eq. 46-3:

$$n(E) = \frac{8\sqrt{2}\pi m^{3/2} E^{1/2}}{(mE_F/0.121)^{3/2} n^{-1}} = 8\sqrt{2}(0.121)^{3/2} n E_F^{-3/2} E^{1/2}$$

$$= 1.50 n E_F^{-3/2} E^{1/2}.$$

Since $E_F \propto n^{2/3}$ (Eq. 46-6), $n(E) \propto n E_F^{-3/2} \propto n(n^{2/3})^{-3/2} = 1$ is independent of the material.

23P
Using the result of Problem 22, we have

$$f = \frac{N}{m} \approx \frac{1}{n} \int_{E_F}^{E_F+4kT} n(E_F) \frac{1}{4} \, dE = \frac{1}{4n} \int_{E_F}^{E_F+4kT} \left(1.50 n E_F^{-3/2} E_F^{1/2}\right) dE$$

$$= \frac{1}{4n}(1.50 n E_F^{-3/2+1/2})(E_F + 4kT - E_F) = \frac{3kT/2}{E_F}.$$

The first integral above can only be expressed in terms of an infinite series if you do not wish to make any approximation.

24P
(a) At absolute zero $T = 0$ so $f \propto T = 0$.
(b) At $T = 300\,\text{K}$

$$f = \frac{3kT}{2E_F} = \frac{3(8.62 \times 10^{-5}\,\text{eV/K})(300\,\text{K})}{2(7.0\,\text{eV})} = 5.5 \times 10^{-3}.$$

(c) At $T = 1000\,\text{K}$

$$f = \frac{3kT}{2E_F} = \frac{3(8.62 \times 10^{-5}\,\text{eV/K})(1000\,\text{K})}{2(7.0\,\text{eV})} = 1.9 \times 10^{-2}.$$

25P
The fraction f of electrons with energies greater than the Fermi energy is given in Problem 23:

$$f = \frac{3kT/2}{E_F},$$

where T is the temperature on the Kelvin scale, k is the Boltzmann constant, and E_F is the Fermi energy. Solve for T:

$$T = \frac{2f E_F}{3k} = \frac{2(0.013)(4.7\,\text{eV}))}{3(8.62 \times 10^{-5}\,\text{eV/K})} = 473\,\text{K}.$$

26P

Use the result of Problem 23:

$$f = \frac{3kT}{2E_F} = \frac{3(8.62 \times 10^{-5} \, \text{eV/K})(1000 \, \text{K})}{2(5.5 \, \text{eV})} = 2.9 \times 10^{-2}.$$

27P

The average energy of the conduction electrons is given by

$$\overline{E} = \frac{1}{n} \int_0^\infty En(E)p(E) \, dE,$$

where n is the number of free electrons per unit volume, $n(E)$ is the density of states, and $p(E)$ is the probability function. The density of states is proportional to $E^{1/2}$, so we may write $n(E) = CE^{1/2}$, where C is a constant of proportionality. The probability function is unity for energies below the Fermi energy and 0 for energies above. Thus

$$\overline{E} = \frac{C}{n} \int_0^{E_F} E^{3/2} \, dE = \frac{2C}{5n} E_F^{5/2}.$$

Now

$$n = \int_0^\infty n(E)p(E) \, dE = C \int_0^{E_F} E^{1/2} \, dE = \frac{2C}{3} E_F^{3/2}.$$

Substitute this expression into the formula for $\overline{E}$ to obtain

$$\overline{E} = \left(\frac{2C}{5} \right) E_F^{5/2} \left(\frac{3}{2CE_F^{3/2}} \right) = \frac{3}{5} E_F.$$

28P

$$K_{\text{total}} = N\overline{E} = (8.43 \times 10^{28} \, \text{m}^{-3})(1.0 \times 10^{-6} \, \text{m}^3)\left(\frac{3}{5} \right)(7.0 \, \text{eV})(1.6 \times 10^{-19} \, \text{J/eV})$$

$$= 5.7 \times 10^4 \, \text{J} = 57 \, \text{kJ}.$$

29P

(a) The energy released would be

$$E = N\overline{E} = \frac{(3.1 \, \text{g})(6.02 \times 10^{23} / \, \text{mol})}{63.54 \, \text{g/mol}}\left(\frac{3}{5} \right)(7.0 \, \text{eV})(1.6 \times 10^{-19} \, \text{J/eV})$$

$$= 2.0 \times 10^4 \, \text{J} = 20 \, \text{kJ}.$$

(b) $t = E/P = 20\,\text{kJ}/100\,\text{W} = 200\,\text{s}$.

30E

(a) Now $E = 0.67\,\text{eV}$ and $E_F = 0.67\,\text{eV}/2 = 0.335\,\text{eV}$. So

$$p(E) = \frac{1}{e^{(E-E_F)/kT} + 1} = \frac{1}{e^{(0.67\,\text{eV}-0.335\,\text{eV})/[(8.62\times10^{-5}\,\text{eV/K})(300\,\text{K})]} + 1}$$
$$= 2.4 \times 10^{-6}.$$

(b) The probability is

$$1 - p(E) = 1 - \frac{1}{e^{(E-E_F)/kT} + 1} = \frac{1}{e^{-(E-E_F)/kT} + 1}$$
$$= \frac{1}{e^{-(0-0.335\,\text{eV})/[(8.62\times10^{-5}\,\text{eV/K})(300\,\text{K})]} + 1}$$
$$= 2.4 \times 10^{-6}.$$

31E

(a) n-type.
(b) The added charge carrier density is $n_p = 10^{-7} n_{\text{Si}} = 10^{-7}(5 \times 10^{28}\,\text{m}^{-3}) = 5 \times 10^{21}\,\text{m}^{-3}$.
(c) The ratio is $(5 \times 10^{21}\,\text{m}^{-3})/(2 \times 10^{16}\,\text{m}^{-3}) = 2.5 \times 10^{5}$.

32E

The number of phosphorus atoms needed is

$$N_p = \frac{(1.0\,\text{g})(10^{22}\,\text{m}^{-3})}{(2.33\,\text{g/cm}^3)} = 4.29 \times 10^{16},$$

so the mass of phosphorus is

$$M_p = N_p m_p = (4.29 \times 10^{16})(31)(1.67 \times 10^{-27}\,\text{kg}) = 0.22\mu\,\text{g}.$$

33P

(a) The probability that a state with energy E is occupied is given by

$$p(E) = \frac{1}{e^{(E-E_F)/kT} + 1},$$

where E_F is the Fermi energy, T is the temperature on the Kelvin scale, and k is the Boltzmann constant. If energies are measured from the top of the valence band, then the energy associated with a state at the bottom of the conduction band is $E = 1.11\,eV$. Furthermore, $kT = (8.62 \times 10^{-5}\,eV/K)(300\,K) = 0.02586\,eV$. For pure silicon $E_F = 0.555\,eV$ and $(E - E_F)/kT = (0.555\,eV)/(0.02586\,eV) = 21.46$. Thus

$$p(E) = \frac{1}{e^{21.46} + 1} = 4.79 \times 10^{-10}.$$

For the doped semiconductor $(E - E_F)/kT = (0.11\,eV)/(0.02586\,eV) = 4.254$ and

$$p(E) = \frac{1}{e^{4.254} + 1} = 1.40 \times 10^{-2}.$$

(b) The energy of the donor state, relative to the top of the valence band, is $1.11\,eV - 0.15\,eV = 0.96\,eV$. The Fermi energy is $1.11\,eV - 0.11\,eV = 1.00\,eV$. Hence $(E - E_F)/kT = (0.96\,eV - 1.00\,eV)/(0.2586\,eV) = -1.547$ and

$$p(E) = \frac{1}{e^{-1.547} + 1} = 0.824.$$

<u>34E</u>
(a) Measured from the top of the valence band, the energy of the donor state is $E = 1.11\,eV - 0.11\,eV = 1.0\,eV$. Solve E_F from Eq. 46-7:

$$E_F = E - kT\ln(p^{-1} - 1)$$
$$= 1.0\,eV - (8.62 \times 10^{-5}\,eV/K)(300\,K\ln[(5.00 \times 10^{-5})^{-1} - 1]$$
$$= 0.744\,eV.$$

(b) Now $E = 1.11\,eV$ so

$$p(E) = \frac{1}{e^{(E-E_F)/kT} + 1} = \frac{1}{e^{(1.11\,eV - 0.744\,eV)/[(8.62 \times 10^{-5}\,eV/K)(300\,K)]} + 1}$$
$$= 7.1 \times 10^{-7}.$$

<u>35P</u>
(a) The number of electrons in the valance band is

$$N_{ev} = N_v p(E_v) = \frac{N_v}{e^{(E_v - E_F)/kT} + 1}.$$

Since there are a total of N_v states in the valence band the number of holes in the valence band is

$$N_{hv} = N_v - N_{ev} = N_v\left[1 - \frac{1}{e^{(E_v - E_F)/kT} + 1}\right]$$
$$= \frac{N_v}{e^{-(E_v - E_F)/kT} + 1}.$$

Now, the number of electrons in the conduction band is

$$N_{ec} = N_c p(E_c) = \frac{N_c}{e^{(E_c - E_F)/kT} + 1},$$

so from $N_{ev} = N_{hc}$ we get

$$\frac{N_v}{e^{-(E_v - E_F)/kT} + 1} = \frac{N_c}{e^{(E_c - E_F)/kT} + 1}.$$

(b) In this case $e^{(E_c - E_F)/kT} \gg 1$ and $e^{-(E_v - E_F)/kT} \gg 1$ so from the result of part (a)

$$\frac{N_c}{e^{(E_c - E_F)/kT}} \approx \frac{N_v}{e^{-(E_v - E_F)/kT}},$$

or $e^{(E_v - E_c + 2E_F)/kT} \approx N_v/N_c$. Solve for E_F:

$$E_F \approx \frac{1}{2}(E_c + E_v) + \frac{1}{2}kT \ln\left(\frac{N_v}{N_c}\right).$$

36E
To find the maximum number of electrons that can be excited across the gap, assume that the energy received by each electron is exactly the difference in energy between the top of the conduction band and the bottom of the valence band (1.1 eV). Then the number that can be excited is

$$N = \frac{662 \times 10^3 \text{ eV}}{1.1 \text{ eV}} = 6.0 \times 10^5.$$

Since each electron that jumps the gap leaves a hole behind, this is also the maximum number of electron-hole pairs that can be created.

37P
(a)

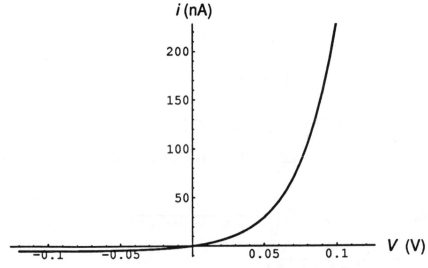

(*b*) The ratio is

$$\frac{i|_{v=+0.50\,\text{V}}}{i|_{v=-0.50\,\text{V}}} = \frac{i_0[e^{+0.50\,\text{eV}/[(8.62\times10^{-5}\,\text{eV/K})(300\,\text{K})]} - 1]}{i_0[e^{-0.50\,\text{eV}/[(8.62\times10^{-5}\,\text{eV/K})(300\,\text{K})]} - 1]} = 2.5 \times 10^8.$$

38E
(*a*) Let $E_{\text{photon}} = hc/\lambda_{\text{max}} = 7.0\,\text{eV}$, we get

$$\lambda_{\text{max}} = \frac{1240\,\text{nm} \cdot \text{eV}}{7.0\,\text{eV}} = 1.8 \times 10^2\,\text{nm}.$$

(*b*) Ultraviolet region.

39E
The valence band is essentially filled and the conduction band is essentially empty. If an electron in the valence band is to absorb a photon, the energy it receives must be sufficient to excite it across the band gap. Photons with energies less than the gap width are not absorbed and the semiconductor is transparent to this radiation. Photons with energies greater than the gap width are absorbed and the semiconductor is opaque to this radiation. Thus the width of the band gap is the same as the energy of a photon associated with a wavelength of 295 nm. Use the result of Exercise 1 of Chapter 43 to obtain

$$E_{\text{gap}} = \frac{1240\,\text{eV} \cdot \text{nm}}{\lambda} = \frac{1240\,\text{eV} \cdot \text{nm}}{295\,\text{nm}} = 4.20\,\text{eV}.$$

40E
Since

$$E_{\text{photon}} = \frac{hc}{\lambda} = \frac{1240\,\text{nm} \cdot \text{eV}}{140\,\text{nm}} = 8.86\,\text{eV} > 7.6\,\text{eV},$$

The light will be absorbed by the KCI crystal so the crystal is opaque to this light.

41P
(*a*)

(b) Check out n_i, the number of times each of the seven segments (labeled to the right) apperas in the ten displayed digits shown in part (a): $n_1 = 8$ [i.e. the numbr of no. 1 segments that appear in part (a) is 8], $n_2 = 9$, $n_3 = 7$, $n_4 = 4$, $n_5 = 6$, $n_6 = 8$, and $n_7 = 7$. The fraction that the ith segment appear is then $p_i = n_i/10$. The values of these probabilities, in the order of p_1 through p_7, are therefore 8/10, 9/10, 7/10, 4/10, 6/10, 8/10, and 7/10.

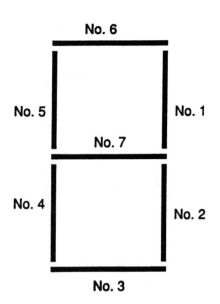

CHAPTER 47

1E

Let $K = 5.30\,\text{MeV} = U = (1/4\pi\epsilon_0)(q_\alpha q_{\text{Cu}}/r_{\text{mim}})$ and solve for the closest separation, r_{min}:

$$r_{\text{min}} = \frac{q_\alpha q_{\text{Cu}}}{4\pi\epsilon_0 K} = \frac{(2e)(29)(1.60 \times 10^{-19}\,\text{C})(8.99 \times 10^9\,\text{N} \cdot \text{m}^2/\text{C}^2)}{5.30 \times 10^6\,\text{eV}}$$

$$= 1.57 \times 10^{-14}\,\text{m} = 15.7\,\text{fm}.$$

2E

In order for the α particle to penetrate the gold nucleus the closest seqration between the centers of mass of the two particles must be no more than $r = r_{\text{Cu}} + r_\alpha = 6.23\,\text{fm} + 1.8\,\text{fm} = 8.03\,\text{fm}$. Thus the minimum energy K_α is given by

$$K_\alpha = U = \frac{1}{4\pi\epsilon_0}\frac{q_\alpha q_{\text{Au}}}{r}$$

$$= \frac{(8.99 \times 10^9\,\text{N} \cdot \text{m}^2/\text{C}^2)(2e)(79)(1.60 \times 10^{-19}\,\text{C})}{8.03 \times 10^{-15}\,\text{m}} = 28.3\,\text{MeV}.$$

3P

Apply the conservation of energy and linear momentum to the collision. The results are given in Chapter 10, Eqs. 10-18 and 10-19. The final speed of the α particle is

$$v_{\alpha f} = \frac{m_\alpha - m_{\text{Au}}}{m_\alpha + m_{\text{Au}}}v_{\alpha i}$$

and that of the recoiling gold nucleus is

$$v_{\text{Au}f} = \frac{2m_\alpha}{m_\alpha + m_{\text{Au}}}v_{\alpha i}.$$

(a)

$$E_{\text{Au},f} = \frac{1}{2}m_{\text{Au}}v_{\text{Au},f}^2 = \frac{1}{2}m_{\text{Au}}\left(\frac{2m_\alpha}{m_\alpha + m_{\text{Au}}}\right)^2 v_{\alpha i}^2 = E_{\alpha i}\frac{4m_{\text{Au}}m_\alpha}{(m_\alpha + m_{\text{Au}})^2}$$

$$= (5.00\,\text{MeV})\frac{4(197\,\text{u})(4.00\,\text{u})}{(4.00\,\text{u} + 197\,\text{u})^2} = 0.390\,\text{MeV}.$$

(b)

$$E_{\alpha f} = \frac{1}{2} m_\alpha v_{\alpha f}^2 = \frac{1}{2} m_\alpha \left(\frac{m_\alpha - m_{Au}}{m_\alpha + m_{Au}} \right)^2 v_{\alpha i}^2 = E_{\alpha i} \left(\frac{m_\alpha - m_{Au}}{m_\alpha + m_{Au}} \right)^2$$

$$= (5.00 \, \text{MeV}) \left(\frac{4.00 \, \text{u} - 197 \, \text{u}}{4.00 \, \text{u} + 197 \, \text{u}} \right)^2 = 4.61 \, \text{MeV}.$$

Note that $E_{\alpha f} + E_{Au,f} = E_{\alpha i}$ is indeed satisfied.

4E

Since $M = \rho V \propto \rho R^3$, we get $R \propto (M/\rho)^{1/3}$ so the new radius would be

$$R = R_s \left(\frac{\rho_s}{\rho} \right)^{1/3} = (6.96 \times 10^8 \, \text{m}) \left(\frac{1410 \, \text{kg/m}^3}{2 \times 10^{17} \, \text{kg/m}^3} \right)^{1/3} = 13 \, \text{km}.$$

so the diameter is $2R = 7.2 \, \text{km}$.

5E

(a) 6 protons (since $Z = 6$ for carbon).
(b) 8 neutrons (since $A - Z = 14 - 6 = 8$).

6E

Solve for A from Eq. 47-3:

$$A = \left(\frac{R}{R_0} \right)^3 = \left(\frac{3.6 \, \text{fm}}{1.2 \, \text{fm}} \right)^3 = 27.$$

7E

Locate a nuclide by finding the coordinates (N, Z) of the corresponding point in Fig. 47-4. You will easily find that all the nuclides listed in Table 47-1 are stable except the last two, ^{227}Ac and ^{239}Pu.

8E

(a) ^{142}Nd, ^{143}Nd, ^{146}Nd, ^{148}Nd, ^{150}Nd.
(b) ^{97}Rb, ^{98}Sr, ^{99}Y, ^{100}Sr, ^{101}Nd, ^{102}Mo, ^{103}Tc, ^{105}Rh. ^{109}In, ^{110}Sn, ^{111}Sb, ^{112}Te.
(c) ^{60}Zn, ^{60}Cu, ^{60}Ni, ^{60}Co, ^{60}Fe.

9E

(a) For ^{239}Pu $Q = 94e$ and $R = 6.64\,\mathrm{fm}$ so

$$U = \frac{3Q^2}{20\pi\epsilon_0 R} = \frac{3[94(1.60 \times 10^{-19}\,\mathrm{C})]^2(8.99 \times 10^9\,\mathrm{N \cdot m^2/C^2})}{5(6.64 \times 10^{-15}\,\mathrm{m})(1.60 \times 10^{-19}\,\mathrm{J/eV})}$$

$$= 1.15 \times 10^9\,\mathrm{eV} = 1.15\,\mathrm{GeV}.$$

(b) Since $Z = 94$ and $A = 239$, the electrostatic potential per nucleon is $1.15\,\mathrm{GeV}/239$ nucleons $= 4.81\,\mathrm{MeV/nucleon}$ and that per proton is $1.15\,\mathrm{GeV}/94 = 12.2\,\mathrm{MeV/proton}$. These are of the same order of magnitude as the binding energy per nucleon.

(c) The binding energy is significantly reduced by the electrostatic repulsion among the protons.

10E

From Fig. 47-4 we find that the neutron numbers of the two daughter nuclei are 40 and 74, respectively. The two nuclei are ^{89}Y and ^{127}I. The number of neutrons left over is $235 - 127 - 89 = 19$.

11E

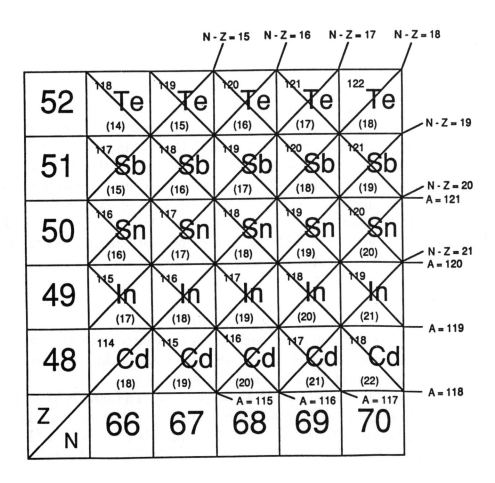

12E

(a) For ^{55}Mn

$$\rho_m = \frac{M}{V} = \frac{0.055 \, \text{kg/mol}}{(4\pi/3)[1.2 \, \text{fm}(55)^{1/3}]^3 (6.02 \times 10^{23}/\text{mol})} = 2.3 \times 10^{17} \, \text{kg/m}^3;$$

and for ^{209}Bi

$$\rho_m = \frac{M}{V} = \frac{0.209 \, \text{kg/mol}}{(4\pi/3)[1.2 \, \text{fm}(209)^{1/3}]^3 (6.02 \times 10^{23}/\text{mol})} = 2.3 \times 10^{17} \, \text{kg/m}^3;$$

(b) For ^{55}Mn

$$\rho_q = \frac{Ze}{V} = \frac{(25)(1.6 \times 10^{-19} \, \text{C})}{(4\pi/3)[1.2 \, \text{fm}(55)^{1/3}]^3} = 1.0 \times 10^{25} \, \text{C/m}^3;$$

and for ^{209}Bi

$$\rho_q = \frac{Ze}{V} = \frac{(83)(1.6 \times 10^{-19} \, \text{C})}{(4\pi/3)[1.2 \, \text{fm}(209)^{1/3}]^3} = 8.7 \times 10^{24} \, \text{C/m}^3;$$

(c) Since $V \propto R^3 = (R_0 A^{1/3})^3 \propto A$, we expect $\rho_m \propto A/V \propto A/A \approx$ const. for all nuclides, while $\rho_q \propto Z/V \propto Z/A$ should gradually decrease as $A \gtrsim 2Z$ for large nuclides.

13E

The binding energy is given by $E = [Z m_H + (A - Z)m_n - M_{\text{Pu}}]c^2$, where Z is the atomic number (number of protons), A is the mass number (number of nucleons), m_H is the mass of a hydrogen atom, m_n is the mass of a neutron, and M_{Pu} is the mass of a $^{239}_{94}$Pu atom. In principal, nuclear masses should have been used, but the mass of the Z electrons included in $Z M_H$ is canceled by the mass of the Z electrons included in M_{Pu}, so the result is the same. First calculate the mass difference in atomic mass units: $\Delta m = (94)(1.00783 \, \text{u}) + (239 - 94)(1.00867 \, \text{u}) - (239.05216 \, \text{u}) = 1.94101 \, \text{u}$. Since $1 \, \text{u}$ is equivalent to $931.5 \, \text{MeV}$, $E = (1.94101 \, \text{u})(931.5 \, \text{MeV/u}) = 1808 \, \text{MeV}$. Since there are 239 nucleons, the binding energy per nucleon is $E_n = (1808 \, \text{MeV})/(239) = 7.56 \, \text{MeV}$.

14E

(a) The mass number A is the number of nucleons in an atomic nucleus. Since $m_p \approx m_n$ the mass of the nucleus is approximately $A m_p$. Also, the mass of the electrons is neglegible since it is much less than that of the nucleus. So $M \approx A m_p$.

(b) For ^{1}H the approximate formula gives $M \approx A m_p = (1)(1.007276 \, \text{u}) = 1.007276 \, \text{u}$. The actual mass is (see Table 47-1) $1.007825 \, \text{u}$. The percent error committed is then $\delta = (1.007825 \, \text{u} - 1.007276 \, \text{u})/1.007825 \, \text{u} = 0.054\%$. Similarly $\delta = 5.0\%$ for ^{7}Li, 0.81% for ^{31}P, 0.83% for ^{81}Br, 0.81% for ^{120}Sn, 0.78% for ^{157}Gd, 0.74% for ^{197}Au, 0.72% for ^{227}Ac, and 0.71% for ^{239}Pu.

(c) No. In a typical nucleus the binding energy per nucleon is several MeV, which is a bit less than 1% of the nucleon mass times c^2. This is comparable with the percent error calculated in (b) so we need to use a more accurate method to calculate the nuclear mass.

15E

$$t = \frac{d}{v} = \frac{d}{\sqrt{2E/m_n}} = R\sqrt{\frac{2m_n}{E}}$$

$$\simeq (1.2 \times 10^{-15}\,\text{m})(100)^{1/3}\sqrt{\frac{2(938\,\text{MeV})}{(5\,\text{MeV})(3.0 \times 10^3\,\text{m/s})^2}}$$

$$= 4 \times 10^{-22}\,\text{s}.$$

16E

(a) The de Broglie wavelength is given by $\lambda = h/p$, where p is the magnitude of the momentum. The kinetic energy K and momentum are related by Eq. 42–40, which yields

$$pc = \sqrt{K^2 + 2Kmc^2} = \sqrt{(200\,\text{MeV})^2 + 2(200\,\text{MeV})(0.511\,\text{MeV})} = 200.5\,\text{MeV}.$$

Thus

$$\lambda = \frac{hc}{pc} = \frac{1240\,\text{eV} \cdot \text{nm}}{200.5 \times 10^6\,\text{eV}} = 6.18 \times 10^{-6}\,\text{nm} = 6.18\,\text{fm}.$$

(b) The diameter of a copper nucleus, for example, is about 8.6 fm, just a little larger than the de Broglie wavelength of a 200-MeV electron. To resolve detail the wavelength should be smaller than the target, ideally a tenth of the diameter or less. 200-MeV electrons are perhaps at the lower limit in energy for useful probes.

17E

Let $p \sim \Delta p \simeq h/\Delta x \simeq h/R$, we get

$$E = \frac{p^2}{2m} \simeq \frac{h^2}{2mR^2} = \frac{(1240\,\text{MeV} \cdot \text{fm})^2}{2(938\,\text{MeV})[1.2\,\text{fm}(100)^{1/3}]^2} \simeq 30\,\text{MeV}.$$

18E

(a) In terms of the original value of u, the newly defined u is greater by a factor of 1.007825. So the mass of ^{1}H would be 1.000000 u, the mass of ^{12}C would be $(12.000000/1.007825)\,\text{u} = 11.90683\,\text{u}$, and the mass of ^{238}U would be $(238.050785/1.007825)\,\text{u} = 236.2025\,\text{u}$.
(b) Defining the mass of ^{1}H to be exactly 1 does not result in any overall simplification.

19P

(a) Since the nuclear force has a short range, any nucleon interacts only with its nearest neighbors, not with more distant nucleons in the nucleus. Let N be the number of neighbors that interact with any nucleon. It is independent of the number A of nucleons in the nucleus. The number of interactions in a nucleus is approximately NA, so the energy associated with the strong nuclear force is proportional to NA and therefore proportional to A itself.

(b) Each proton in a nucleus interacts electrically with every other proton. The number of pairs of protons is $Z(Z-1)/2$, where Z is the number of protons. The Coulomb energy is therefore proportional to $Z(Z-1)$.

(c) As A increases, Z increases at a slightly slower rate but Z^2 increases at a faster rate than A and the energy associated with Coulomb interactions increases faster than the energy associated with strong nuclear interactions.

20P

Let f_{24} be the abundance of ^{24}Mg, let f_{25} be the abundance of ^{25}Mg, and let f_{26} be the abundance of ^{26}Mg. Then the entry in the periodic table for Mg is $24.312 = 23.98504 f_{24} + 24.98584 f_{25} + 25.98259 f_{26}$. Since there are only three isotopes, $f_{24} + f_{25} + f_{26} = 1$. Solve for f_{25} and f_{26}. The second equation gives $f_{26} = 1 - f_{24} - f_{25}$. Substitute this expression and $f_{24} = 0.7899$ into the first equation to obtain $24.312 = (23.98504)(0.7899) + 24.98584 f_{25} + 25.98259 - (25.98259)(0.7899) - 25.98259 f_{25}$. The solution is $f_{25} = 0.09303$. Then $f_{26} = 1 - 0.7899 - 0.09303 = 0.1171$. 78.99% of naturally occurring magnesium is ^{24}Mg, 9.30% is ^{25}Mg, and 11.71% is ^{26}Mg.

21P

(a) The first step: $^4\text{H} - p \rightarrow {}^3\text{H}$. The work needed is $\Delta E_1 = (m_{^3\text{H}} + m_p - m_{^4\text{He}})c^2 = (3.01605\,\text{u} + 1.00783\,\text{u} - 4.00260\,\text{u})(932\,\text{MeV/u}) = 19.8\,\text{MeV}$.
The second step: $^3\text{He} - n \rightarrow {}^2\text{H}$. The work needed is $\Delta E_2 = (m_{^2\text{H}} + m_n - m_{^3\text{He}})c^2 = 2.01410\,\text{u} + 1.00867\,\text{u} - 3.01605\,\text{u})(932\,\text{MeV/u}) = 6.26\,\text{MeV}$.
The third step: $^2\text{H} - p \rightarrow {}^1\text{H}$. The work needed is $\Delta E_3 = (m_p + m_p - m_{^2\text{H}}c^2 = (1.00783\,\text{u} + 1.00783\,\text{u} - 2.01410\,\text{u})(932\,\text{MeV/u}) = 2.22\,\text{MeV}$.
(b) The total binding energy is $E = \Delta E_1 + \Delta E_2 + \Delta E_3 = 19.8\,\text{MeV} + 6.26\,\text{MeV} + 2.22\,\text{MeV} = 28.3\,\text{MeV}$.
(c) $E/A = 28.3\,\text{MeV}/4 = 7.07\,\text{MeV}$.

22P

The nuclear reation in quesion is written as $n + p \rightarrow {}^2\text{H} + \gamma$. Conservation of energy gives $m_n c^2 + m_p c^2 = m_{^2\text{H}} c^2 + E_\gamma$, or

$$
\begin{aligned}
m_n &= m_{^2\text{H}} - m_p + E_\gamma/c^2 \\
&= 2.01410\,\text{u} - 1.00783\,\text{u} + (2.2233\,\text{MeV})/(938\,\text{MeV/u}) \\
&= 1.0087\,\text{u}.
\end{aligned}
$$

1142

23P

The nuclear energy released per copper nucleus is $\Delta E = (29m_p + 34m_n - m_{Cu})c^2$. The number of ^{63}Cu nuclei in a penny is $N = M/m_{Cu}$. So the total energy required is

$$\Delta E_{\text{total}} = N\Delta E = \frac{M}{m_{Cu}}(29m_p + 34m_n - m_{Cu})c^2$$

$$= \frac{3.0\,\text{g}[(29)(1.00783\,\text{u}) + 34(1.00867\,\text{u}) - 62.9260\,\text{u}](932\,\text{MeV/u})}{(62.9260\,\text{u})(1.661 \times 10^{-27}\,\text{kg/u})}$$

$$= 1.6 \times 10^{25}\,\text{MeV}.$$

24P

(a) For ^{1}H, $\Delta = (1.00783\,\text{u} - 1.00000\,\text{u})(932\,\text{MeV}/c^2) = 7.30\,\text{MeV}$.

(b) For the neutron, $\Delta = (1.00867\,\text{u} - 1.00000\,\text{u})(932\,\text{MeV}/c^2) = 8.08\,\text{MeV}$.

(c) For ^{120}Sn, $\Delta = (119.9022\,\text{u} - 120.0000\,\text{u})(932\,\text{MeV}/c^2) = -91.1\,\text{MeV}$.

25P

If a nucleus contains Z protons and N neutrons, its binding energy is $E = (Zm_H + Nm_n - m)c^2$, where m_H is the mass of a hydrogen atom, m_n is the mass of a neutron, and m is the mass of the atom containing the nucleus of interest. If the masses are given in atomic mass units then mass excesses are defined by $\Delta_H = (m_H - 1)c^2$, $\Delta_n = (m_n - 1)c^2$, and $\Delta = (m - A)c^2$. This means $m_H c^2 = \Delta_H + c^2$, $m_n c^2 = \Delta_n + c^2$, and $mc^2 = \Delta + Ac^2$. Thus $E = (Z\Delta_H + N\Delta_n - \Delta) + (Z + N - A)c^2 = Z\Delta_H + N\Delta_n - \Delta$, where $A = Z + N$ was used.

For $^{197}_{79}$Au, $Z = 79$ and $N = 197 - 79 = 118$. Hence

$$E = (79)(7.29\,\text{MeV}) + (118)(8.07\,\text{MeV}) - (-31.2\,\text{MeV}) = 1560\,\text{MeV}.$$

This means the binding energy per nucleon is $E_n = (1560\,\text{MeV})/(197) = 7.92\,\text{MeV}$.

26E

The number of atoms remaining is

$$N = N_0 e^{-\lambda t} = N_0 e^{-(t\ln 2)/\tau} = (48 \times 10^{19})e^{-(26\,\text{h})(\ln 2)/6.5\,\text{h}} = 3.0 \times 10^{19}.$$

27E

Let $N = N_0 e^{-\lambda t} = N_0 e^{-(t\ln 2)/\tau} = N_0/4$ and solve for t: $t = 2\tau = 2(140\,\text{d}) = 280\,\text{d}$.

28E

(a) Since $60\,\text{y} = 2(30\,\text{y}) = 2\tau$ the fraction left is $2^{-2} = 1/4$.

1143

(b) Since $90\,\text{y} = 3(30\,\text{y}) = 3\tau$ the fraction left is $2^{-3} = 1/8$.

29E

(a) The decay rate is given by $R = \lambda N$, where λ is the disintegration constant and N is the number of undecayed nuclei. Initially $R = R_0 = \lambda N_0$, where N_0 is the number of undecayed nuclei at that time. You must find values for both N_0 and λ. The disintegration constant is related to the half-life τ by $\lambda = (\ln 2)/\tau = (\ln 2)/(78\,\text{h}) = 8.89 \times 10^{-3}\,\text{h}^{-1}$. If M is the mass of the sample and m is the mass of a single atom of gallium, then $N_0 = M/m$. Now $m = (67\,\text{u})(1.661 \times 10^{-24}\,\text{g/u}) = 1.113 \times 10^{-22}\,\text{g}$ and $N_0 = (3.4\,\text{g})/(1.113 \times 10^{-22}\,\text{g}) = 3.05 \times 10^{22}$. Thus $R_0 = (8.89 \times 10^{-3}\,\text{h}^{-1})(3.05 \times 10^{22}) = 2.71 \times 10^{20}\,\text{h}^{-1} = 7.53 \times 10^{16}\,\text{s}^{-1}$.

(b) The decay rate at any time t is given by

$$R = R_0\, e^{-\lambda t}.$$

where R_0 is the decay rate at $t = 0$. At $t = 48\,\text{h}$, $\lambda t = (8.89 \times 10^{-3}\,\text{h}^{-1})(48\,\text{h}) = 0.427$ and

$$R = (7.53 \times 10^{16}\,\text{s}^{-1})\, e^{-0.427} = 4.91 \times 10^{16}\,\text{s}^{-1}.$$

30E

(a) The half-life τ and the disintegration constant are related by $\tau = (\ln 2)/\lambda$, so $\tau = (\ln 2)/(0.0108\,\text{h}^{-1}) = 64.2\,\text{h}$.

(b) At time t the number of undecayed nuclei remaining is given by

$$N = N_0\, e^{-\lambda t} = N_0\, e^{-(\ln 2)t/\tau}.$$

Substitute $t = 3\tau$ to obtain

$$\frac{N}{N_0} = e^{-3\ln 2} = 0.125.$$

In each half-life the number of undecayed nuclei is reduced by half. At the end of one half-life $N = N_0/2$, at the end of two half-lives $N = N_0/4$, and at the end of three half-lives $N = N_0/8 = 0.125 N_0$.

(c) Use

$$N = N_0\, e^{-\lambda t}.$$

$10.0\,d$ is $240\,\text{h}$, so $\lambda t = (0.0108\,\text{h}^{-1})(240\,\text{h}) = 2.592$ and

$$\frac{N}{N_0} = e^{-2.592} = 0.0749.$$

31E

(a) For ^{238}U we have $R_0 = 12/s = \lambda N_0$ so $\lambda = R_0/N_0 = (12\,s^{-1})/(2.5 \times 10^{18}) = 4.8 \times 10^{-18}\,s^{-1}$.

(b) $\tau = (\ln 2)/\lambda = (\ln 2)/(4.8 \times 10^{-18}\,s^{-1}) = 1.4 \times 10^{17}\,s \simeq 4.6 \times 10^9\,y$.

32E

(a) The number of nuclei is

$$N = \frac{M}{m_{Pu}} = \frac{2 \times 10^{-6}\,kg}{(239\,u)(1.66 \times 10^{-27}\,kg/u)} = 5.04 \times 10^{18}.$$

(b)

$$R = \lambda N = \frac{N \ln 2}{\tau} = \frac{(5.04 \times 10^{18})(\ln 2)}{(2.41 \times 10^4\,y)(3.15 \times 10^7/y)} = 4.60 \times 10^6\,s^{-1}.$$

33E

The rate of decay is given by $R = \lambda N$, where λ is the disintegration constant and N is the number of undecayed nuclei. In terms of the half-life τ the disintegration constant is $\lambda = (\ln 2)/\tau$, so

$$N = \frac{R}{\lambda} = \frac{R\tau}{\ln 2} = \frac{(6000\,Ci)(3.7 \times 10^{10}\,s^{-1}/Ci)(5.27\,y)(3.16 \times 10^7\,s/y)}{\ln 2}$$
$$= 5.33 \times 10^{22}\,nuclei.$$

34P

(a) Assume that the chlorine in the sample had the naturally occurring isotopic mixture, so the average mass number was 35.453, as given in Appendix D. Then the mass of ^{226}Ra was

$$m = \frac{226}{226 + 2(35.453)}(0.10\,g) = 76.1 \times 10^{-3}\,g.$$

The mass of a ^{226}Ra nucleus is $(226\,u)(1.661 \times 10^{-24}\,g/u) = 3.75 \times 10^{-22}\,g$, so the number of ^{226}Ra nuclei present was $N = (76.1 \times 10^{-3}\,g)/(3.75 \times 10^{-22}\,g) = 2.03 \times 10^{20}$.

(b) The decay rate is given by $R = N\lambda = (N \ln 2)/\tau$, where λ is the disintegration constant, τ is the half-life, and N is the number of nuclei. The relationship $\lambda = (\ln 2)/\tau$ was used. Thus

$$R = \frac{(2.03 \times 10^{20}) \ln 2}{(1600\,y)(3.156 \times 10^7\,s/y)} = 2.79 \times 10^9\,s^{-1}.$$

35P

The amount decayed is

$$\Delta m = m|_{t_f = 16.0\,\text{h}} - m|_{t_i = 14.0\,\text{h}} = m_0(1 - e^{-t_i \ln 2/\tau}) - m_0(1 - e^{-t_f \ln 2/\tau})$$

$$= m_0(e^{-t_f \ln 2/\tau} - e^{-t_i \ln 2/\tau}) = (5.50\,\text{g})[e^{-(16.0\,\text{h}/12.7\,\text{h})\ln 2} - e^{-(14.0\,\text{h}/12.7\,\text{h})\ln 2}]$$

$$= 0.256\,\text{g}.$$

36P

(a) Use $R = R_0 e^{-\lambda t}$ and find t:

$$t = \frac{1}{\lambda} \ln \frac{R_0}{R} = \frac{\tau}{\ln 2} \ln \frac{R_0}{R} = \frac{14.28\,\text{d}}{\ln 2} \ln \frac{3050}{170} = 59.5\,\text{d}.$$

(b) The factor is

$$\frac{R_0}{R} = e^{\lambda t} = e^{t \ln 2/\tau} = e^{(3.48\,\text{d}/14.28\,\text{d})\ln 2} = 1.18.$$

37P

Label the two isotopes with subscripts 1 (for ^{32}P) and 2 (for ^{33}P). Initially $R_{01} = \lambda_1 N_{01} = (1/9.00)R_{02} = \lambda_2 N_{02}/9.00$. At time t we have $R_1 = R_{01}e^{-\lambda_1 t}$ and $R_2 = R_{02}e^{-\lambda_2 t}$. Let $R_1/R_2 = 9.00$, we have $(R_{01}/R_{02})e^{-(\lambda_1 - \lambda_2)t} = 9.00$. Solve for t:

$$t = \frac{1}{\lambda_1 - \lambda_2} \ln\left(\frac{R_{01}}{9.00 R_{02}}\right) = \frac{\ln(R_{01}/9.00 R_{02})}{\ln 2/\tau_1 - \ln 2/\tau_2}$$

$$= \frac{\ln[(1/9.00)^2]}{\ln 2[(14.3\,\text{d})^{-1} - (25.3\,\text{d})^{-1}]} = 209\,\text{d}.$$

38P

The number N of undecayed nuclei present at any time and the rate of decay R at that time are related by $R = \lambda N$, where λ is the disintegration constant. The disintegration constant is related to the half-life τ by $\lambda = (\ln 2)/\tau$, so $R = (N \ln 2)/\tau$ and $\tau = (N \ln 2)/R$. Since 15.0% by mass of the sample is ^{147}Sm, the number of ^{147}Sm nuclei present in the sample is

$$N = \frac{(0.150)(1.00\,\text{g})}{(147\,\text{u})(1.661 \times 10^{-24}\,\text{g/u})} = 6.143 \times 10^{20}.$$

Thus

$$\tau = \frac{(6.143 \times 10^{20})\ln 2}{120\,\text{s}^{-1}} = 3.55 \times 10^{18}\,\text{s} = 1.12 \times 10^{11}\,\text{y}.$$

39P

The amount of ^{239}Pu that has decayed is

$$\Delta m_{\text{Pu}} = m(1 - e^{-t\ln 2/\tau})$$
$$= (12.0\,\text{g})[1 - e^{-(20,000\,\text{y}/24,100\,\text{y})\ln 2}] = 5.25\,\text{g}.$$

Thus the amount of helium produced is

$$m_{\text{He}} = \left(\frac{4.00\,\text{u}}{239\,\text{u}}\right) 5.25\,\text{g} = 0.0878\,\text{g}.$$

40P

Solve for m from $R_0 = N_0\lambda = (m/m_K)(\ln 2)/\tau$:

$$m = \frac{m_K R_0 \tau}{\ln 2}$$
$$= \frac{(40\,\text{u})(1.661 \times 10^{-27}\,\text{kg/u})(1.70 \times 10^5\,\text{disintegrations/s})(1.28 \times 10^9\,\text{y})}{(\ln 2)(1\,\text{y}/3.15 \times 10^7\,\text{s})}$$
$$= 6.6 \times 10^{-4}\,\text{kg} = 0.66\,\text{g}.$$

41P

The number of ^{90}Sr atoms needed to produce the decay rate of $R = 74,000/\text{s}$ is given by $R = \lambda N = \lambda(M/m)(a/A)$, with $M = 400\,\text{g}$, m the mass of the ^{90}Sr nucleus, $A = 2000\,\text{km}^2$, and a the area in question. Solve for a:

$$a = A\left(\frac{m}{M}\right)\left(\frac{R}{\lambda}\right) = \frac{AmR\tau}{M\ln 2}$$
$$= \frac{(2000 \times 10^6\,\text{m}^2)(90\,\text{g/mol})(29\,\text{y})(3.15 \times 10^7\,\text{s/y})(74,000/\text{s})}{(400\,\text{g})(6.02 \times 10^{23}/\text{mol})(\ln 2)}$$
$$= 7.3 \times 10^{-2}\,\text{m}^2 = 730\,\text{cm}^2.$$

42P

The following are $\ln R$ vs t plots for both ^{108}Ag and ^{110}Ag. The half-life of each of the isotopes can be obtained from the slope of the respective plot, similar to Sample Problem 47-4. The combined decay rate is $R = R_{108} + R_{110} = R_{0,\,108}e^{-\lambda_{108}t} + R_{0,\,110}e^{-\lambda_{110}t}$. You can see that taking the natural log of both sides will not produce an equation for a straight line in the $\ln R$ vs t plot.

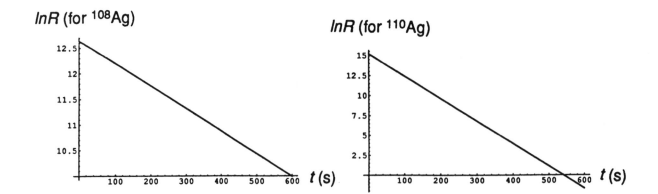

InR (for ^{108}Ag)

InR (for ^{110}Ag)

43P

If N is the number of undecayed nuclei present at time t, then

$$\frac{dN}{dt} = R - \lambda N,$$

where R is the rate of production by the cyclotron and λ is the disintegration constant. The second term gives the rate of decay. Rearrange the equation slightly and integrate:

$$\int_{N_0}^{N} \frac{dN}{R - \lambda N} = \int_{0}^{t} dt,$$

where N_0 is the number of undecayed nuclei present at time $t = 0$. This yields

$$-\frac{1}{\lambda} \ln \frac{R - \lambda N}{R - \lambda N_0} = t.$$

Solve for N:

$$N = \frac{R}{\lambda} + \left(N_0 - \frac{R}{\lambda} \right) e^{-\lambda t}.$$

After many half-lives the exponential is small and the second term can be neglected. Then $N = R/\lambda$, regardless of the initial value N_0. At times that are long compared to the half-life the rate of production equals the rate of decay and N is a constant.

44P

(a) The sample is in secular equilibrium with the source and the decay rate equals the production rate. Let R be the rate of production of ^{56}Mn and let λ be the disintegration constant. According the result of Problem 43, $R = \lambda N$ after a long time has passed. Now $\lambda N = 8.88 \times 10^{10}$ s^{-1}, so $R = 8.88 \times 10^{10}$ s^{-1}.

(b) They decay at the same rate as they are produced, 8.88×10^{10} s^{-1}.

(c) Use $N = R/\lambda$. If τ is the half-life, then the disintegration constant is $\lambda = (\ln 2)/\tau = (\ln 2)/(2.58\,\text{h}) = 0.269\,\text{h}^{-1} = 7.46 \times 10^{-5}\,\text{s}^{-1}$, so $N = (8.88 \times 10^{10}\,\text{s}^{-1})/(7.46 \times 10^{-5}\,\text{s}^{-1}) = 1.19 \times 10^{15}$.

(d) The mass of a ^{56}Mn nucleus is $(56\,\text{u})(1.661 \times 10^{-24}\,\text{g/u}) = 9.30 \times 10^{-23}\,\text{g}$ and the total mass of ^{56}Mn in the sample at the end of the bombardment is $Nm = (1.19 \times 10^{15})(9.30 \times 10^{-23}\,\text{g}) = 1.11 \times 10^{-7}\,\text{g}$.

45P
(a)

$$R = \lambda N = \left(\frac{\ln 2}{\tau}\right)\left(\frac{M}{m}\right) = \frac{(\ln 2)(1.00\,\text{mg})(6.02 \times 10^{23}/\text{mol})}{(1600\,\text{y})(3.15 \times 10^7\,\text{s/y})(226\,\text{g/mol})}$$
$$= 3.66 \times 10^7\,\text{s}^{-1}.$$

(b) Since $1600\,\text{y} \gg 3.82\,\text{d}$ the time required is $t \gg 3.82\,\text{d}$.

(c) It is decaying at the same rate as it is produced, or $R = 3.66 \times 10^7\,\text{s}^{-1}$.

(d) From $R_{R_a} = R_{R_n}$ and note that $R = \lambda N = (\ln 2/\tau)(M/m)$, we get

$$M_{R_n} = \left(\frac{\tau_{R_n}}{\tau_{R_a}}\right)\left(\frac{m_{R_n}}{m_{R_a}}\right)M_{R_a} = \frac{(3.82\,\text{d})(1.00 \times 10^{-3}\,\text{g})(222\,\text{u})}{(1600\,\text{y})(365\,\text{d/y})(226\,\text{u})} = 6.42 \times 10^{-9}\,\text{g}.$$

46E
The electrostatic potential is given by

$$U(r) = \frac{1}{4\pi\epsilon_0}\frac{q_\alpha q_{\text{Th}}}{r} = \frac{(8.99 \times 10^9\,\text{N}\cdot\text{m}^2\,\text{C}^2)(2)(90)(1.60 \times 10^{-19}\,\text{C})e}{r}$$
$$= \frac{259\,\text{MeV}}{r},$$

where r is in fm. The plot is as follows.

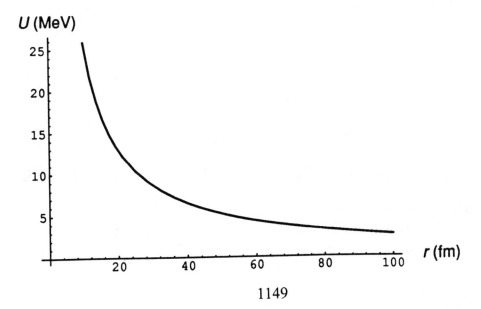

47E

The fraction of undecayed nuclei remaining after time t is given by

$$\frac{N}{N_0} = e^{-\lambda t} = e^{-(\ln 2)t/\tau},$$

where λ is the disintegration constant and $\tau \ (= (\ln 2)/\lambda)$ is the half-life. The time for half the original ^{238}U nuclei to decay is 4.5×10^9 y. For ^{244}Pu at that time

$$\frac{(\ln 2)t}{\tau} = \frac{(\ln 2)(4.5 \times 10^9 \,\text{y})}{8.2 \times 10^7 \,\text{y}} = 38.0$$

and

$$\frac{N}{N_0} = e^{-38.0} = 3.1 \times 10^{-17}.$$

For ^{248}Cm at that time

$$\frac{(\ln 2)t}{\tau} = \frac{(\ln 2)(4.5 \times 10^9 \,\text{y})}{3.4 \times 10^5 \,\text{y}} = 9170$$

and

$$\frac{N}{N_0} = e^{-9170} = 3.31 \times 10^{-3983}.$$

For any reasonably sized sample this is less than 1 nucleus and may be taken to be zero. Your calculator probably cannot evaluate e^{-9170} directly. Treat it as $(e^{-91.70})^{100}$.

48P

Energy and momentum are conserved. Assume the residual thorium nucleus is in its ground state. Let K_α be the kinetic energy of the alpha particle and K_{Th} be the kinetic energy of the thorium nucleus. Then $Q = K_\alpha + K_{\text{Th}}$. Assume the uranium nucleus is initially at rest. Then conservation of momentum yields $0 = p_\alpha + p_{\text{Th}}$, where p_α is the momentum of the alpha particle and p_{Th} is the momentum of the thorium nucleus.

Both particles travel slowly enough that the classical relationship between momentum and energy can be used. Thus $K_{\text{Th}} = p_{\text{Th}}^2/2m_{\text{Th}}$, where m_{Th} is the mass of the thorium nucleus. Substitute $p_{\text{Th}} = -p_\alpha$ and use $K_\alpha = p_\alpha^2/2m_\alpha$ to obtain $K_{\text{Th}} = (m_\alpha/m_{\text{Th}})K_\alpha$. Thus

$$Q = K_\alpha + \frac{m_\alpha}{m_{\text{Th}}}K_\alpha = \left(1 + \frac{m_\alpha}{m_{\text{Th}}}\right)K_\alpha = \left(1 + \frac{4.00\,\text{u}}{234\,\text{u}}\right)(4.196\,\text{MeV}) = 4.27\,\text{MeV}.$$

49P

(a) The nuclear reaction is written as ^{238}U $\rightarrow$ ^{234}Th $+$ ^{4}He. The energy released is

$$\Delta E_1 = (m_{\text{U}} - m_{\text{He}} - m_{\text{Th}})c^2$$
$$= (238.05079\,\text{u} - 4.00260\,\text{u} - 234.04363\,\text{u})(932\,\text{MeV/u})$$
$$= 4.25\,\text{MeV}.$$

(b) The reaction series is now $^{238}\text{U} \rightarrow {}^{237}\text{U} + n$, $^{237}\text{U} \rightarrow {}^{236}\text{Pa} + p$, $^{236}\text{Pa} \rightarrow {}^{235}\text{Pa} + n$, $^{235}\text{Pa} \rightarrow {}^{234}\text{Th} + p$. The net energy released is then

$$
\begin{aligned}
\Delta E_2 &= (m_{238_{\text{U}}} - m_{237_{\text{U}}} - m_n)c^2 + (m_{237_{\text{U}}} - m_{236_{\text{Pa}}} - m_p)c^2 \\
&\quad + (m_{236_{\text{Pa}}} - m_{235_{\text{Pa}}} - m_n)c^2 + (m_{235_{\text{Pa}}} - m_{234_{\text{Th}}} - m_p)c^2 \\
&= (m_{238_{\text{U}}} - 2m_n - 2m_p - m_{234_{\text{Th}}}) \\
&= [238.05079\,\text{u} - 2(1.00867\,\text{u}) - 2(1.00783\,\text{u}) - 234.04363\,\text{u}](932\,\text{MeV}/c^2) \\
&= -24.1\,\text{MeV}.
\end{aligned}
$$

(c) The binding energy of the α particle is $E_\alpha = (2m_n + 2m_p - m_{\text{He}})c^2 = |-24.1\,\text{MeV} - 4.25\,\text{MeV}| = 28.3\,\text{MeV}$.

50P
(a) For the first reaction

$$
\begin{aligned}
Q_1 &= (m_{\text{Ra}} - m_{\text{Pb}} - m_{\text{C}})c^2 \\
&= (223.01850\,\text{u} - 208.98107\,\text{u} - 14.00324\,\text{u})(932\,\text{MeV}/c^2) \\
&= 31.8\,\text{MeV}
\end{aligned}
$$

and for the second one

$$
\begin{aligned}
Q_2 &= (m_{\text{Ra}} - m_{\text{Rn}} - m_{\text{He}})c^2 \\
&= (223.01850\,\text{u} - 219.01008\,\text{u} - 4.00260\,\text{u})(932\,\text{MeV}/c^2) \\
&= 5.42\,\text{MeV}.
\end{aligned}
$$

(b) From $U \propto q_1 q_2 / r$ we get

$$
U_1 \approx U_2 \left(\frac{q_{\text{Pb}} q_{\text{C}}}{q_{\text{Rn}} q_{\text{He}}} \right) = (30.0\,\text{MeV}) \frac{(82e)(6.0e)}{(86e)(2.0e)} = 86\,\text{MeV}.
$$

51P
The disintegration energies are:

$$
\begin{aligned}
Q_3 &= (m_{235_{\text{U}}} - m_{232_{\text{Th}}} - m_{3_{\text{He}}})c^2 \\
&= (235.0439\,\text{u} - 232.0381\,\text{u} - 3.0160\,\text{u})(932\,\text{MeV}/c^2) \\
&= -9.51\,\text{MeV},
\end{aligned}
$$

$$
\begin{aligned}
Q_4 &= (m_{235_{\text{U}}} - m_{231_{\text{Th}}} - m_{4_{\text{He}}})c^2 \\
&= (235.0439\,\text{u} - 231.0363\,\text{u} - 4.0026\,\text{u})(932\,\text{MeV}/c^2) \\
&= 4.66\,\text{MeV},
\end{aligned}
$$

and

$$Q_5 = (m_{235\text{U}} - m_{230\text{Th}} - m_{5\text{He}})c^2$$
$$= (235.0439\,\text{u} - 230.0331\,\text{u} - 5.0122\,\text{u})(932\,\text{MeV/c}^2)$$
$$= -1.30\,\text{MeV},$$

Only the second decay process (the α decay) is spontaneous, as it releases energy .

52E

Let $_Z^A X$ represent the unknown nuclide. The reaction equation is

$$_Z^A X + _0^1\text{n} \rightarrow _{-1}^0\text{e} + 2\,_2^4\text{He}.$$

Conservation of charge yields $Z + 0 = -1 + 4$ or $Z = 3$. Conservation of mass number yields $A + 1 = 0 + 8$ or $A = 7$. According to the periodic table in Appendix E, lithium has atomic number 3, so the nuclide must be $_3^7\text{Li}$.

53E

Let M_{Cs} be the mass of one atom of $_{55}^{137}\text{Cs}$ and M_{Ba} be the mass of one atom of $_{56}^{137}\text{Ba}$. To obtain the nuclear masses we must subtract the mass of 55 electrons from M_{Cs} and the mass of 56 electrons from M_{Ba}. The energy released is $Q = [(M_{\text{Cs}} - 55m) - (M_{\text{Ba}} - 56m) - m]\,c^2$, where m is the mass of an electron. Once cancellations have been made, $Q = (M_{\text{Cs}} - M_{\text{Ba}})c^2$ is obtained. Thus

$$Q = [136.9073\,\text{u} - 136.9058\,\text{u}]\,c^2 = (0.0015\,\text{u})c^2 = (0.0015\,\text{u})(932\,\text{MeV/u}) = 1.40\,\text{MeV}.$$

54E

(a) The mass number A of a radionuclide changes by 4 in an α decay and is unchanged in a β decay. If the mass numbers of two radionuclides are given by $4n + k$ and $4n' + k$ ($k = 0, 1, 2, 3$) then the heavier one can decay into the lighter one by a series of α (and β) decays, as their mass numbers differ by only an integer times 4. If $A = 4n + k$, then after α-decaying for m times, its mass number becomes $A = 4n + k - 4m = 4(n - m) + k$, still in the same chain.
(b) $235 = 58 \times 4 + 3 = 4n_1 + 3$, $236 = 59 \times 4 = 4n_2$, $238 = 59 \times 4 + 2 = 4n_2 + 2$, $239 = 59 \times 4 + 3 = 4n_2 + 3$, $240 = 60 \times 4 = 4n_3$, $245 = 61 \times 4 + 1 = 4n_4 + 1$, $246 = 61 \times 4 + 2 = 4n_4 + 2$, $249 = 62 \times 4 + 1 = 4n_5 + 1$, $253 = 63 \times 4 + 1 = 4n_6 + 1$.

55E

The decay scheme is $\text{n} \rightarrow \text{p} + \text{e}^- + \nu$. The electron kinetic energy is a maximum if no neutrino is emitted. Then $K_{\text{max}} = (m_n - m_p - m_e)c^2$, where m_n is the mass of a neutron,

m_p is the mass of a proton, and m_e is the mass of an electron. Since $m_p + m_e = m_H$, where m_H is the mass of a hydrogen atom, this can be written $K_{\max} = (m_n - m_H)c^2$. Hence $K_{\max} = (840 \times 10^{-6}\,\text{u})c^2 = (840 \times 10^{-6}\,\text{u})(932\,\text{MeV/u}) = 0.783\,\text{MeV}$.

56E
(a)

$$\lambda = \frac{h}{p} = \frac{hc}{\sqrt{E^2 - (mc^2)^2}} = \frac{hc}{\sqrt{(mc^2 + K)^2 - mc^2}}$$
$$= \frac{1240\,\text{fm} \cdot \text{MeV}}{\sqrt{(0.511\,\text{MeV} + 1.0\,\text{MeV})^2 - (0.511\,\text{MeV})^2}} = 9.0 \times 10^2\,\text{fm}.$$

(b) $R = R_0 A^{1/3} = (1.2\,\text{fm})(150)^{1/3} = 6.4\,\text{fm}$.
(c) Since $\lambda \gg R$ the electron cannot be confined in the nuclide.
(d) Yes. See part (c) above.

57P
The energy of the particles before and after the decay is $E_i = \mathbf{m_v} c^2 + m_e c^2 - E_K$ and $E_f = \mathbf{m_{Ti}} c^2$. Thus $Q = E_i - E_f = \mathbf{m_v} - \mathbf{m_{Ti}} + m_e)c^2 - E_K$. Note that $\mathbf{m_v} = m_v - 23 m_e$ and $\mathbf{m_{Ti}} = m_{Ti} - 22 m_e$ so $\mathbf{m_v} - \mathbf{m_{Ti}} + m_e = (m_v - 23 m_e) - (m_{Ti} - 22 m_e) + m_e = m_v - m_{Ti}$. Thus $Q = (m_v - m_{Ti})c^2 - E_K$.

58P

$$Q = (m_v - m_{Ti})c^2 - E_K$$
$$= (48.94852\,\text{u} - 48.94787\,\text{u})(932\,\text{MeV}/c^2) - 5.47\,\text{keV}$$
$$= 600\,\text{keV}.$$

59P
(a) Use the result obtained in Problem 59, with the modification that no electron is at the initial stage of the process and one positron is present at the final stage. This means that there is an additional term $-m_e c^2 - m_e c^2 = -2 m_e c^2$ in the expression for $Q = E_i - E_f$. So $Q = (m_C - m_{Ti})c^2 - 2 m_e c^2 = (m_c - m_{Ti} - 2 m_e)c^2$.
(b) $Q = [11.011434\,\text{u} - 11.009305\,\text{u} - 2(0.0005486\,\text{u})](932\,\text{MeV/u}) = 0.961\,\text{MeV}$.
This compares favourably with the maximum energy of the positron of 0.960 MeV.

60P

(*a*) The rate of heat production is

$$\frac{dE}{dt} = \sum_{i=1}^{3} R_i Q_i = \sum_{i=1}^{3} \lambda_1 N_i Q_i = \sum_{i=1}^{3} \left(\frac{\ln 2}{\tau_i}\right) \frac{(1.00\,\text{kg}) f_i}{m_i} Q_i$$

$$= \frac{(1.00\,\text{kg})(\ln 2)(1.60 \times 10^{-13}\,\text{J/MeV})}{(3.15 \times 10^7\,\text{s/y})(1.661 \times 10^{-27}\,\text{kg/u})} \left[\frac{(4 \times 10^{-6})(51.7\,\text{MeV})}{(238\,\text{u})(4.47 \times 10^9\,\text{y})}\right.$$

$$\left. + \frac{(13 \times 10^{-6})(42.7\,\text{MeV})}{(208\,\text{u})(1.41 \times 10^{10}\,\text{y})} + \frac{(4 \times 10^{-6})(1.31\,\text{MeV})}{(40\,\text{u})(1.25 \times 10^9\,\text{y})}\right]$$

$$= 9.8 \times 10^{-10}\,\text{W}.$$

(*b*) $P = (2.7 \times 10^{22}\,\text{kg})(9.8 \times 10^{-10}\,\text{W/kg}) = 2.6 \times 10^{13}\,\text{W}.$

61P*

Since the electron has the maximum possible kinetic energy, no neutrino is emitted. Since momentum is conserved, the momentum of the electron and the momentum of the residual sulfur nucleus are equal in magnitude and opposite in direction. If p_e is the momentum of the electron and p_S is the momentum of the sulfur nucleus, then $p_S = -p_e$. The kinetic energy K_S of the sulfur nucleus is $K_S = p_S^2/2M_S = p_e^2/2M_S$, where M_S is the mass of the sulfur nucleus. Now the electron's kinetic energy K_e is related to its momentum by the relativistic equation $(p_e c)^2 = K_e^2 + 2K_e mc^2$, where m is the mass of an electron. See Eq. 42–40. Thus

$$K_S = \frac{(p_e c)^2}{2M_S c^2} = \frac{K_e^2 + 2K_e mc^2}{2M_S c^2} = \frac{(1.71\,\text{MeV})^2 + 2(1.71\,\text{MeV})(0.511\,\text{MeV})}{2(32\,\text{u})(931.5\,\text{MeV/u})}$$

$$= 7.83 \times 10^{-5}\,\text{MeV} = 78.3\,\text{eV},$$

where $mc^2 = 0.511\,\text{MeV}$ was used.

62E

(*a*) The mass of a ^{238}U atom is $(238\,\text{u})(1.661 \times 10^{-24}\,\text{g/u}) = 3.95 \times 10^{-22}\,\text{g}$, so the number of uranium atoms in the rock is $N_U = (4.20 \times 10^{-3}\,\text{g})/(3.95 \times 10^{-22}\,\text{g}) = 1.06 \times 10^{19}$. The mass of a ^{206}Pb atom is $(206\,\text{u})(1.661 \times 10^{-24}\,\text{g}) = 3.42 \times 10^{-22}\,\text{g}$, so the number of lead atoms in the rock is $N_{\text{Pb}} = (2.135 \times 10^{-3}\,\text{g})/(3.42 \times 10^{-22}\,\text{g}) = 6.24 \times 10^{18}$.

(*b*) If no lead was lost there was originally one uranium atom for each lead atom formed by decay, in addition to the uranium atoms that did not yet decay. Thus the original number of uranium atoms was $N_{U0} = N_U + N_{\text{Pb}} = 1.06 \times 10^{19} + 6.24 \times 10^{18} = 1.68 \times 10^{19}$.

(*c*) Use

$$N_U = N_{U0}\, e^{-\lambda t},$$

1154

where λ is the disintegration constant for the decay. It is related to the half-life τ by $\lambda = (\ln 2)/\tau$. Thus

$$t = -\frac{1}{\lambda} \ln\left(\frac{N_U}{N_{U0}}\right) = -\frac{\tau}{\ln 2} \ln\left(\frac{N_U}{N_{U0}}\right) = -\frac{4.47 \times 10^9 \, \text{y}}{\ln 2} \ln\left(\frac{1.06 \times 10^{19}}{1.68 \times 10^{19}}\right) = 2.97 \times 10^9 \, \text{y}.$$

63P

Solve for t from $R = R_0 e^{-\lambda t}$:

$$t = \frac{1}{\lambda} \ln \frac{R_0}{R} = \left(\frac{5730 \, \text{y}}{\ln 2}\right) \ln\left[\left(\frac{15.3}{63.0}\right)\left(\frac{5.00}{1.00}\right)\right] = 1.61 \times 10^3 \, \text{y}.$$

64P

The original amount of ^{238}U the rock contains is given by $m_0 = m e^{\lambda t} = (3.70 \, \text{mg})$ $e^{(\ln 2)(260 \times 10^6 \, \text{y})(4.47 \times 10^9 \, \text{y})} = 3.85 \, \text{mg}$. Thus the amount of lead produced is

$$m' = (m_0 - m)\left(\frac{m_{206}}{m_{238}}\right) = (3.85 \, \text{mg} - 3.70 \, \text{mg})\left(\frac{206}{238}\right) = 0.132 \, \text{mg}.$$

65P

We can find the age t of the rock from the masses of ^{238}U and ^{206}Pb. The initial mass of ^{238}U is

$$m_U(0) = m_U + \frac{238}{206} m_{Pb}$$

so $m_U = m_U(0) e^{-\lambda_U t} = (m_U +^{238} m_{Pb}/206)e^{-(t \ln 2)/\tau_U}$. Solve for t:

$$t = \frac{\tau_U}{\ln 2} \ln \frac{m_U + (238/206)m_{Pb}}{m_U}$$
$$= \frac{4.47 \times 10^9 \, \text{y}}{\ln 2} \ln\left[1 + \left(\frac{238}{206}\right)\left(\frac{0.15 \, \text{mg}}{0.86 \, \text{mg}}\right)\right]$$
$$= 1.18 \times 10^9 \, \text{y}.$$

Now, for the β decay of ^{40}K, the initial mass of ^{40}K is

$$m_K(0) = m_K + (40/40)m_{Ar} = m_K + m_{Ar}$$

so

$$m_K = m_K(0)e^{-\lambda_K t} = (m_K + m_{Ar})e^{-\lambda_K t}.$$

Solve for m_K:

$$m_K = \frac{m_{Ar}e^{-\lambda_K t}}{1 - e^{-\lambda_K t}} = \frac{m_{Ar}}{e^{\lambda_K t} - 1}$$

$$= \frac{1.6\,\text{mg}}{e^{(\ln 2)(1.18\times 10^9\,\text{y})/(1.25\times 10^9\,\text{y})} - 1} = 1.7\,\text{mg}.$$

66P

$$R = \frac{(8700\,\text{disintegrations/min})}{(3.7\times 10^{10}\,\text{disintegrations/s})/\,\text{C}_i} = 3.92\times 10^{-9}\,\text{C}_i.$$

67E

The decay rate R is related to the number of nuclei N by $R = \lambda N$, where λ is the disintegration constant. The disintegration constant is related to the half-life τ by $\lambda = (\ln 2)/\tau$, so $N = R/\lambda = R\tau/\ln 2$. Since $1\,\text{Ci} = 3.7\times 10^{10}$ disintegrations/s,

$$N = \frac{(250\,\text{Ci})(3.7\times 10^{10}\,\text{s}^{-1}/Ci)(2.7\,\text{d})(8.64\times 10^4\,\text{s/d})}{\ln 2} = 3.11\times 10^{18}.$$

The mass of a ^{198}Au atom is $M = (198\,\text{u})(1.661\times 10^{-24}\,\text{g/u}) = 3.29\times 10^{-22}$ g so the mass required is $NM = (3.11\times 10^{18})(3.29\times 10^{-22}\,\text{g}) = 1.02\times 10^{-3}\,\text{g} = 1.02\,\text{mg}$.

68E

The annual does is $(20\,\text{h})(52\,\text{week/y})(0.70\,\text{mrem/h}) = 730\,\text{mrem} = 0.73\,\text{rem}$.

69E

(a) The energy absorbed is

$$E = DM = (24\times 10^{-3}\,\text{rad})(10\,\text{mJ/kg})(75\,\text{kg}) = 18\,\text{mJ}.$$

(b) The equivalent does in rem is $D \cdot \text{RBE} = (0.024)(12) = 0.29\,\text{rem}$.

70P

The dose equivalent is the product of the absorbed dose and the RBE factor, so the absorbed dose is (dose equivalent)/(RBE) $= (25\times 10^{-3}\,\text{rem})/(0.85) = 2.94\times 10^{-2}$ rad. But $1\,\text{rad} = 10\,\text{mJ/kg}$, so the absorbed dose is $(2.94\times 10^{-2})(10\times 10^{-3}\,\text{J/kg}) = 2.94\times 10^{-4}\,\text{J/kg}$. To obtain the total energy received, multiply this by the mass receiving the energy: $E = (2.94\times 10^{-4}\,\text{J/kg})(44\,\text{kg}) = 1.29\times 10^{-2}\,\text{J}$.

71P

(a)

$$N_0 = \frac{(2.5 \times 10^{-3}\,\text{g})(6.02 \times 10^{23}/\,\text{mol})}{239\,\text{g/mol}} = 6.3 \times 10^{18}.$$

(b)

$$\begin{aligned}
\Delta N &= N_0(1 - e^{-t\ln 2/\tau}) \\
&= (6.3 \times 10^{18})[1 - e^{-(12\,\text{h})\ln 2/(24{,}100\,\text{y})(8760\,\text{h/y})]} \\
&= 2.5 \times 10^{11}.
\end{aligned}$$

(c) $\Delta E = (95\%)E_\alpha \Delta N = (95\%)(5.2\,\text{MeV})(2.5 \times 10^{11})(1.6 \times 10^{-13}\,\text{J/MeV}) = 0.20\,\text{J}.$

(d) $D = E/u = 200\,\text{mJ}/85\,\text{kg} = 0.24 \times 10\,\text{mJ/kg} = 0.24\,\text{rad}.$

(e) $D_{\text{bio}} = D \cdot \text{RBE} = (0.24)(13) = 3.1\,\text{rem}.$

72E

(a)

$$\Delta E \simeq \frac{h}{\Delta t} = \frac{4.14 \times 10^{-15}\,\text{eV} \cdot \text{s}}{10^{-22}\,\text{s}} \simeq 40\,\text{MeV}.$$

(b) No, since $\Delta t \ll 10^{-14}\,\text{s}$ (see Sample Problem 47-10).

73E

From Eq. 21-16

$$T = \frac{2\bar{K}}{3k} = \frac{2(5.00\,\text{MeV})}{3(8.62 \times 10^{-5}\,\text{eV/K})} = 3.87 \times 10^{10}\,\text{K}.$$

74E

Compare both the proton and neutron numbers of the nuclides given with the magic nucleon numbers.

(a) ^{18}O, ^{60}Ni, ^{92}Mo, ^{144}Sm, ^{207}Pb.

(b) ^{40}K, ^{91}Zr, ^{121}Sb, ^{143}Nd.

(c) ^{13}C, ^{40}K, ^{49}Ti, ^{205}Tl, ^{207}Pb.

75P

A generalized formation reaction can be written $X + x \to Y$, where X is the target nucleus, x is the incident light particle, and Y is the excited compound nucleus (^{20}Ne). Assume X is initially at rest. Then conservation of energy yields

$$m_X c^2 + m_x c^2 + K_x = m_Y c^2 + K_Y + E_Y,$$

1157

where m_X, m_x, and M_Y are masses, K_x and K_Y are kinetic energies, and E_Y is the excitation energy of Y. Conservation of momentum yields

$$p_x = p_Y .$$

Now $K_Y = p_Y^2/2m_Y = p_x^2/2m_Y = (m_x/m_Y)K_x$, so

$$m_X c^2 + m_x c^2 + K_x = m_Y c^2 + (m_x/m_Y)K_x + E_Y$$

and

$$K_x = \frac{m_Y}{m_Y - m_x}\left[(m_Y - m_X - m_x)c^2 + E_Y\right] .$$

(a) Let x represent the alpha particle and X represent the ^{16}O nucleus. Then $(m_Y - m_X - m_x)c^2 = (19.99244\,\text{u} - 15.99491\,\text{u} - 4.00260\,\text{u})(931.5\,\text{MeV/u}) = -4.722\,\text{MeV}$ and

$$K_\alpha = \frac{19.99244\,\text{u}}{19.99244\,\text{u} - 4.00260\,\text{u}}(-4.722\,\text{MeV} + 25.0\,\text{MeV}) = 25.35\,\text{MeV} .$$

(b) Let x represent the proton and X represent the ^{19}F nucleus. Then $(m_Y - m_X - m_x)c^2 = (19.99244\,\text{u} - 18.99841\,\text{u} - 1.00783\,\text{u})(931.5\,MeV/u) = -12.85\,\text{MeV}$ and

$$K_\alpha = \frac{19.99244\,\text{u}}{19.99244\,\text{u} - 1.00783\,\text{u}}(-12.85\,\text{MeV} + 25.0\,\text{MeV}) = 12.80\,\text{MeV} .$$

(c) Let x represent the photon and X represent the ^{20}Ne nucleus. Since the mass of the photon is zero we must rewrite the conservation of energy equation: if E_γ is the energy of the photon, then $E_\gamma + m_X c^2 = m_Y c^2 + K_Y + E_Y$. Since $m_X = m_Y$, this equation becomes $E_\gamma = K_Y + E_Y$. Since the momentum and energy of a photon are related by $p_\gamma = E_\gamma/c$, the conservation of momentum equation becomes $E_\gamma/c = p_Y$. The kinetic energy of the compound nucleus is $K_Y = p_Y^2/2m_Y = E_\gamma^2/2m_Y c^2$. Substitute this result into the conservation of energy equation to obtain

$$E_\gamma = \frac{E_\gamma^2}{2m_Y c^2} + E_Y .$$

This quadratic equation has the solutions

$$E_\gamma = m_Y c^2 \pm \sqrt{(m_Y c^2)^2 - 2m_Y c^2 E_Y} .$$

If the problem is solved using the relativistic relationship between the energy and momentum of the compound nucleus only one solution would be obtained, the one corresponding to the negative sign above. Since $M_Y c^2 = (19.99244\,\text{u})(931.5\,\text{MeV/u}) = 1.862 \times 10^4\,\text{MeV}$,

$$E_\gamma = (1.862 \times 10^4\,\text{MeV}) - \sqrt{(1.862 \times 10^4\,\text{MeV})^2 - 2(1.862 \times 10^4\,\text{MeV})(25.0\,\text{MeV})}$$
$$= 25.0\,\text{MeV} .$$

The kinetic energy of the compound nucleus is very small; essentially all of the photon energy goes to excite the nucleus.

76P

For each of the three decay processes, label the ^{20}Ne with subscript 0, and the larger and smaller nuclides resulting from the decay process with sbuscripts 1 and 2. Then the conservation of energy gives $Q = K_1 + K_2 = E_0 - E_1 - E_2 = (m_0 - m_1 - m_2)c^2$ and conservation of linear momentum gives $|p_1| = |p_2|$, which, upon noting that $p_{1,2}^2 = (K_{1,2} + E_{1,2})^2 - E_{1,2}^2$, can be rewritten as $K_1^2 + 2K_1E_1 = K_2^2 + 2K_2E_2$. Solve for K_1:

$$K_1 = \frac{Q^2 + 2E_2Q}{2E_0}.$$

(a) Now $Q = (m_0 - m_1 - m_2)c^2 = (19.99244\,\text{u} - 18.00094\,\text{u} - 2.01410\,\text{u})(932\,\text{MeV/u}) + 25.0\,\text{MeV} = 3.9368\,\text{MeV}$ so

$$K_d = K_1 = \frac{Q^2 + 2E_2Q}{2E_0}$$
$$= \frac{(3.9368\,\text{MeV})^2 + 2(18.00094\,\text{u})(932\,\text{MeV/u})(3.9368\,\text{MeV})}{2(19.99244\,\text{u})(932\,\text{MeV/u})}$$
$$= 3.55\,\text{MeV}.$$

(b) Now $Q = (m_0 - m_1 - m_2)c^2 = (19.99244\,\text{u} - 19.00188\,\text{u} - 1.00867\,\text{u})(932\,\text{MeV/u}) + 25.0\,\text{MeV} = 8.1215\,\text{MeV}$ so

$$K_n = K_1 = \frac{Q^2 + 2E_2Q}{2E_0}$$
$$= \frac{(8.1215\,\text{MeV})^2 + 2(19.00188\,\text{u})(932\,\text{MeV/u})(8.1215\,\text{MeV})}{2(19.99244\,\text{u})(932\,\text{MeV/u})}$$
$$= 7.72\,\text{MeV}.$$

(c) Now $Q = (m_0 - m_1 - m_2)c^2 = (19.99244\,\text{u} - 16.99913\,\text{u} - 3.01603\,\text{u})(932\,\text{MeV/u}) + 25.0\,\text{MeV} = 3.8250\,\text{MeV}$ so

$$K_{\text{He}} = K_1 = \frac{Q^2 + 2E_2Q}{2E_0}$$
$$= \frac{(3.8250\,\text{MeV})^2 + 2(16.99913\,\text{u})(932\,\text{MeV/u})(3.8250\,\text{MeV})}{2(16.99913\,\text{u})(932\,\text{MeV/u})}$$
$$= 3.25\,\text{MeV}.$$

77P

(a) Consider the process $^{209}\text{Bi} \rightarrow {}^{208}\text{Pb} + p$. The energy required for the process is $\Delta E_1 = (m_{\text{Pb}} + m_p - m_{\text{Bi}})c^2 = (207.9767\,\text{u} + 1.00783\,\text{u} - 208.9804\,\text{u})(932\,\text{MeV}/c^2) = 3.85\,\text{MeV}$. To remove a proton form the filled shell of ^{208}Pb: $^{208}\text{Pb} \rightarrow {}^{207}\text{Tl} + p$, we need $\Delta E_1' = (m_{\text{Tl}} + m_p - m_{\text{Pb}})c^2 = (206.9774\,\text{u} + 1.00783\,\text{u} - 207.9767\,\text{u})(932\,\text{MeV}/\text{u}) = 7.95\,\text{MeV} > \Delta E_1 = 3.85\,\text{MeV}$.

(b) Now the process is $^{209}\text{Pb} \rightarrow {}^{208}\text{Pb} + n$. The energy required is $\Delta E_2 = (207.9767\,\text{u} + 1.00807\,\text{u} - 208.9811\,\text{u})(932\,\text{MeV}/\text{u}) = 3.98\,\text{MeV}$. To remove a neutron from the filled shell of ^{208}Pb: $^{208}\text{Pb} \rightarrow {}^{207}\text{Pb} + n$, we need $\Delta E_2' = (206.9759\,\text{u} + 1.00867\,\text{u} - 207.9767\,\text{u})(932\,\text{MeV}/\text{u}) = 7.34\,\text{MeV} > \Delta E_2 = 3.98\,\text{MeV}$.

Both results are ($\Delta E_1' > \Delta E_1$ and $\Delta E_2' > \Delta E_2$) are expected.

78P

(a) The binding energy is $\Delta E_1 = (m_{90} + m_n - m_{91})c^2 = (89.90471\,\text{u} + 1.00867\,\text{u} - 90.90564\,\text{u})(932\,\text{MeV}/\text{u}) = 7.21\,\text{MeV}$.

(b) The binding energy for the next neutron is $\Delta E_2 = (m_{89} + m_n - m_{90})c^2 = (88.90890\,\text{u} + 1.00867\,\text{u} - 89.90471\,\text{u})(932\,\text{MeV}/\text{u}) = 12.0\,\text{MeV}$.

(c) The binding energy per nucleon is $\Delta E_3 = (40m_p + 51m_n - m_{91})c^2/A = [(40(1.00783\,\text{u}) + 51(1.00867\,\text{u}) - 90.90564\,\text{u})(932\,\text{MeV}/\text{u})/91 = 8.69\,\text{MeV}$. From the calculation above we see that $\Delta E_1 < \Delta E_3 < \Delta E_2$. This is expected. The extra neutron outside the filled shell is relatively easy to remove, so ΔE_1 is less than the average binding energy per nucleon (ΔE_2). To remove a neutron from a filled shell, however, is more difficult, which is why $\Delta E_3 < \Delta E_2$.

79P

(a) Consider the process $^{121}\text{Sb} \rightarrow {}^{120}\text{Sn} + p$. The energy needed is $\Delta E_1 = (m_{\text{Sn}} + m_p - m_{\text{Sb}})c^2 = (119.9022\,\text{u} + 1.00783\,\text{u} - 120.9038\,\text{u})(932\,\text{MeV}/\text{u}) = 5.81\,\text{MeV}$.

(b) Consider the process $^{120}\text{Sn} \rightarrow {}^{119}\text{In} + p$. The energy needed is $\Delta E_2 = (m_{\text{In}} + m_p - m_{\text{Sn}})c^2 = (118.9058\,\text{u} + 1.00783\,\text{u} - 119.9022\,\text{u})(932\,\text{MeV}/\text{u}) = 10.7\,\text{MeV}$.

80

The linear momentum of each recoiling nucleus is, by the conservation of momentum, $p \approx E/c$. Thus the kinetic energy of each recoiling nucleus is about $K \approx p^2/2m \approx E^2/2mc^2$. So $\Delta E \simeq 2K \approx E^2/mc^2$. So from $\Delta E \Delta t \approx h$

$$\Delta t \approx \frac{h}{\Delta E} \approx \frac{h}{E^2/mc^2} = \frac{hmc^2}{E^2}.$$

81

(a) Since $K_{\max}/mc^2 \sim 1$ we need to use the relativistic formula $p = \sqrt{(E/c)^2 - m^2c^2} = \sqrt{(mc + K/c)^2 - m^2c^2} = \sqrt{(K/c)^2 + 2mK}$. The de Broglie wavelength is then

$$
\begin{aligned}
\lambda = \frac{h}{p} &= \frac{hc}{\sqrt{K^2 + 2mc^2K}} \\
&= \frac{1240 \, \text{pm} \cdot \text{keV}}{\sqrt{(310 \, \text{keV})^2 + 2(511 \, \text{keV})(310 \, \text{keV})}} = 1.93 \, \text{pm}.
\end{aligned}
$$

(b) $R \simeq R_0 A^{1/3} = (1.2 \, \text{fm})(60)^{1/3} = 4.7 \, \text{fm}$.

(c) Since $\lambda \gg R$ the electron cannot exist in the nucleus prior to the emissilon.

CHAPTER 48

1E

(a) The mass of a single atom of ^{235}U is $(235\,\text{u})(1.661 \times 10^{-27}\,\text{kg/u}) = 3.90 \times 10^{-25}\,\text{kg}$, so the number of atoms in $1.0\,\text{kg}$ is $(1.0\,kg)/(3.90 \times 10^{-25}\,\text{kg}) = 2.56 \times 10^{24}$.

(b) The energy released by N fission events is given by $E = NQ$, where Q is the energy released in each event. For $1.0\,\text{kg}$ of ^{235}U, $E = (2.56 \times 10^{24})(200 \times 10^6\,\text{eV})(1.60 \times 10^{-19}\,\text{J/eV}) = 8.19 \times 10^{13}\,\text{J}$.

(c) If P is the power requirement of the lamp, then $t = E/P = (8.19 \times 10^{13}\,\text{J})/(100\,\text{W}) = 8.19 \times 10^{11}\,\text{s} = 26,000\,\text{y}$. The conversion factor $3.156 \times 10^7\,\text{s/y}$ was used to obtain the last result.

2E

The energy released is

$$E = \frac{(1.00\,\text{kg})(180\,\text{MeV})}{(239\,\text{u})(1.66 \times 10^{-27}\,\text{kg/u})} = 4.54 \times 10^{26}\,\text{MeV}.$$

3E

If R is the fission rate, then the power output is $P = RQ$, where Q is the energy released in each fission event. Hence $R = P/Q = (1.0\,\text{W})/(200 \times 10^6\,\text{eV})(1.60 \times 10^{-19}\,\text{J/eV}) = 3.12 \times 10^{10}\,fissions/s$.

4E

Use the conservation of A, N and Z. The missing entries are (by rows): ^{95}Sr, ^{95}Y, ^{134}Te, and 3.

5E

At $T = 300\,\text{K}$ the average kinetic energy of the neutrons is

$$\bar{K} = \frac{3kT}{2} = \frac{3}{2}(8.62 \times 10^{-5}\,\text{eV/K})(300\,\text{K}) \approx 0.04\,\text{eV}.$$

6E

If M_{Cr} is the mass of a ^{52}Cr nucleus and M_{Mg} is the mass of a ^{26}Mg nucleus, then the disintegration energy is $Q = (M_{Cr} - 2M_{Mg})\,c^2 = [51.94051\,\text{u} - 2(25.98259\,\text{u})]\,(931.5\,\text{MeV/u}) = -23.0\,\text{MeV}$.

7E

Consider the process $^{98}\text{Mo} \rightarrow {}^{49}\text{Sc} + {}^{49}\text{Sc}$. We have $Q = (m_{\text{Mo}} - 2m_{\text{Sc}})c^2 = [97.90541\,\text{u} - 2(48.95002\,\text{u})](932\,\text{MeV/u}) = 5.00\,\text{MeV}$.

8E

The energy released is

$$
\begin{aligned}
Q &= (m_{\text{U}} + m_{\text{n}} - m_{\text{Cs}} - m_{\text{Rb}} - 2m_{\text{n}})c^2 \\
&= (235.04392\,\text{u} - 1.00867\,\text{u} - 140.91963\,\text{u} - 92.92157\,\text{u}](932\,\text{MeV/u}) \\
&= 181\,\text{MeV}.
\end{aligned}
$$

9E

(a)

$$
\begin{aligned}
R_{\text{fiss}} &= \lambda_{\text{fiss}} N = \frac{N \ln 2}{\tau_{\text{fiss}}} = \frac{M \ln 2}{m_{\text{U}} \tau_{\text{fiss}}} \\
&= \frac{(1.0\,\text{g})(6.02 \times 10^{23}\,\text{g/mol}) \ln 2}{(235\,\text{g/mol})(3.0 \times 10^{17}\,\text{y})(365\,\text{d/y})} = 16\,\text{fissions/day}.
\end{aligned}
$$

(b) The ratio is

$$
\frac{R_\alpha}{R_{\text{fiss}}} = \frac{\tau_{\text{fiss}}}{\tau_\alpha} = \frac{3.0 \times 10^{17}\,\text{y}}{7.0 \times 10^8\,\text{y}} = 4.3 \times 10^8.
$$

10P

The mass of ^{235}U in $M = 1.0\,\text{kg}$ of UO_2 is

$$
\begin{aligned}
M_{235} &= \frac{3.0\% M (97\% m_{238} + 3.0\% m_{235})}{97\% m_{238} + 3.0\% m_{235} + 2m_{16}} \\
&= \frac{(3.0\%)(1.0\,\text{kg})[0.97(238) + 0.030(235)]}{0.97(238) + 0.030(235) + 2(16.0)} = 0.02644\,\text{kg}.
\end{aligned}
$$

The total energy released is then

$$
E = \frac{(0.02644\,\text{kg})(6.02 \times 10^{23}/\text{mol})(200\,\text{MeV})}{(0.235\,\text{kg/mol})(1.00\,\text{eV}/1.60 \times 10^{-19}\,\text{J})} = 2.17 \times 10^{12}\,\text{J}.
$$

The time this much energy can keep a 100-W lamp burnign is then

$$
t = \frac{E}{P} = \frac{2.17 \times 10^{12}\,\text{J}}{(100\,\text{W})(3.15 \times 10^7\,\text{s/y})} = 690\,\text{y}.
$$

11P

(a) Consider the process $^{238}\text{U} + n \rightarrow\,^{140}\text{Ce} +^{99}\text{Ru} + \text{Ne}$. We have $N = Z_f - Z_i = Z_{\text{Ce}} + Z_{\text{Ru}} - Z_{\text{U}} = 58 + 44 - 92 = 10$. So the number of beta-decay events is 10.

(b)

$$\begin{aligned}
Q &= (m_{\text{U}} + m_{\text{n}} - m_{\text{Ce}} - m_{\text{Ru}} - 10m_{\text{e}})c^2 \\
&= [238.05079\,\text{u} + 1.00867\,\text{u} - 139.90543\,\text{u} - 98.90594\,\text{u} - 10(0.511\,\text{MeV})](932\,\text{MeV/u}) \\
&= 226\,\text{MeV}.
\end{aligned}$$

12P

(a) If X represents the unknown fragment, then the reaction can be written

$$^{235}_{92}\text{U} +\,^{1}_{0}\text{n} \rightarrow\,^{83}_{32}\text{Ge} +\,^{A}_{Z}X \,,$$

where A is the mass number and Z is the atomic number of the fragment. Conservation of charge yields $92 + 0 = 32 + Z$, so $Z = 60$. Conservation of mass number yields $235 + 1 = 83 + A$, so $A = 153$. Look in Appendix D or E for nuclides with $Z = 60$. You should find that the unknown fragment is $^{153}_{60}\text{Nd}$.

(b) Ignore the small kinetic energy and momentum carried by the neutron that triggers the fission event. Then $Q = K_{\text{Ge}} + K_{\text{Nd}}$, where K_{Ge} is the kinetic energy of the germanium nucleus and K_{Nd} is the kinetic energy of the neodymium nucleus. Conservation of momentum yields $p_{\text{Ge}} + p_{\text{Nd}} = 0$, where p_{Ge} is the momentum of the germanium nucleus and p_{Nd} is the momentum of the neodymium nucleus. Since $p_{\text{Nd}} = -p_{\text{Ge}}$, the kinetic energy of the neodymium nucleus is

$$K_{\text{Nd}} = \frac{p_{\text{Nd}}^2}{2M_{\text{Nd}}} = \frac{p_{\text{Ge}}^2}{2M_{\text{Nd}}} = \frac{M_{\text{Ge}}}{M_{\text{Nd}}} K_{\text{Ge}} \,.$$

Thus the energy equation becomes

$$Q = K_{\text{Ge}} + \frac{M_{\text{Ge}}}{M_{\text{Nd}}} K_{\text{Ge}} = \frac{M_{\text{Nd}} + M_{\text{Ge}}}{M_{\text{Nd}}} K_{\text{Ge}}$$

and

$$K_{\text{Ge}} = \frac{M_{\text{Nd}}}{M_{\text{Nd}} + M_{\text{Ge}}} Q = \frac{153\,\text{u}}{153\,\text{u} + 83\,\text{u}}(170\,\text{MeV}) = 110\,MeV \,.$$

Similarly,

$$K_{\text{Nd}} = \frac{M_{\text{Ge}}}{M_{\text{Nd}} + M_{\text{Ge}}} Q = \frac{83\,\text{u}}{153\,\text{u} + 83\,\text{u}}(170\,\text{MeV}) = 60\,\text{MeV} \,.$$

(c) The initial speed of the germanium nucleus is

$$v_{\text{Ge}} = \sqrt{\frac{2K_{\text{Ge}}}{M_{\text{Ge}}}} = \sqrt{\frac{2(110 \times 10^6\,\text{eV})(1.60 \times 10^{-19}\,\text{J/eV})}{(83\,\text{u})(1.661 \times 10^{-27}\,kg/\text{u})}} = 1.60 \times 10^7\,\text{m/s} \,.$$

The initial speed of the neodymium nucleus is

$$v_{Nd} = \sqrt{\frac{2K_{Nd}}{M_{Nd}}} = \sqrt{\frac{2(60 \times 10^6 \text{ eV})(1.60 \times 10^{-19} \text{ J/eV})}{(153 \text{ u})(1.661 \times 10^{-27} \text{ kg/u})}} = 8.69 \times 10^6 \text{ m/s}.$$

13P

(a) The electrostatic potential energy is given by

$$U = \frac{1}{4\pi\epsilon_0} \frac{Z_{Xe}Z_{Sr}e^2}{R_{Xe} + R_{Sr}},$$

where Z_{Xe} is the atomic number of xenon, Z_{Sr} is the atomic number of strontium, R_{Xe} is the radius of a xenon nucleus, and R_{Sr} is the radius of a strontium nucleus. Atomic numbers can be found in Appendix D. The radii are given by $R = (1.2 fm)A^{1/3}$, where A is the mass number, also found in Appendix D. Thus $R_{Xe} = (1.2 fm)(140)^{1/3} = 6.23 fm = 6.23 \times 10^{-15}$ m and $R_{Sr} = (1.2 fm)(96)^{1/3} = 5.49 fm = 5.46 \times 10^{-15}$ m. Hence the potential energy is

$$U = (8.99 \times 10^9 \text{ m/F}) \frac{(54)(38)(1.60 \times 10^{-19} \text{ C})^2}{6.23 \times 10^{-15} \text{ m} + 5.49 \times 10^{-15} \text{ m}} = 4.08 \times 10^{-11} \text{ J}.$$

This is 251 MeV.

(b) The energy released in a typical fission event is about 200 MeV, roughly the same as the electrostatic potential energy when the fragments are touching. The energy appears as kinetic energy of the fragments and neutrons produced by fission.

14P

(a) The surface area a of a nucleus is given by $a \simeq 4\pi R^2 \simeq 4\pi[R_0 A^{1/3}]^2 \propto A^{2/3}$. Thus the percentage change in surface area is

$$\frac{\Delta a}{a_i} = \frac{a_f - a_i}{a_i} = \frac{(140)^{3/2} + (96)^{2/3}}{(236)^{2/3}} - 1 = 25\%.$$

(b) Since $V \propto R^3 \propto (A^{1/3})^3 = A$, we have

$$\frac{\Delta V}{V} = \frac{V_f}{V_i} - 1 = \frac{140 + 96}{236} - 1 = 0.$$

(c)

$$\frac{\Delta U}{U} = \frac{U_f}{U_i} - 1 = \frac{Q_{Xe}^2/R_{Xe} + Q_{Sr}^2/R_{Sr}}{Q_U^2/R_U} - 1$$

$$= \frac{(54)^2(140)^{-1/3} + (38)^2(96)^{-1/3}}{(92)^2(236)^{-1/3}} - 1 = -36\%.$$

15E

If P is the power output, then the energy E produced in the time interval Δt $(= 3\,\text{y})$ is $E = P\,\Delta t = (200 \times 10^6\,\text{W})(3\,\text{y})(3.156 \times 10^7\,\text{s/y}) = 1.89 \times 10^{16}\,\text{J}$, or $(1.89 \times 10^{16}\,\text{J})/(1.60 \times 10^{-19}\,\text{J/eV}) = 1.18 \times 10^{35}\,\text{eV} = 1.18 \times 10^{29}\,\text{MeV}$. At $200\,\text{MeV}$ per event, this means $(1.18 \times 10^{29})/(200\,\text{MeV}) = 5.92 \times 10^{26}$ fission events occurred. This must be half the number of fissionable nuclei originally available. Thus there were $2(5.92 \times 10^{26}) = 1.18 \times 10^{27}$ nuclei. The mass of a ^{235}U nucleus is $(235\,\text{u})(1.661 \times 10^{-27}\,\text{kg/u}) = 3.90 \times 10^{-25}\,\text{kg}$, so the total mass of ^{235}U originally present was $(1.18 \times 10^{27})(3.90 \times 10^{-25}\,\text{kg}) = 462\,\text{kg}$.

16E

From Fig. 48-4 we see that about 330 per $1,330$ neutrons produced by ^{235}U do not result in fission. So the mass of ^{235}U should be (see Exercise 15) $(1330/1000)(463\,\text{kg}) = 617\,\text{kg}$.

17E

When a neutron is captured by ^{237}Np it gains $5.0\,\text{MeV}$, more than enough to offset the $4.2\,\text{MeV}$ required for ^{238}Np to fissilon. So yes, ^{237}Np is fissionable by thermal neutrons.

18P

If R is the decay rate then the power output is $P = RQ$, where Q is the energy produced by each alpha decay. Now $R = \lambda N = N \ln 2/\tau$, where λ is the disintegration constant and τ is the half-life. The relationship $\lambda = (\ln 2)/\tau$ was used. If M is the total mass of material and m is the mass of a single ^{238}Pu nucleus, then

$$N = \frac{M}{m} = \frac{1.00\,\text{kg}}{(238\,\text{u})(1.661 \times 10^{-27}\,\text{kg/u})} = 2.53 \times 10^{24}\,.$$

Thus

$$P = \frac{NQ \ln 2}{\tau} = \frac{(2.53 \times 10^{24})(5.50 \times 10^6\,\text{eV})(1.60 \times 10^{-19}\,\text{J/eV})(\ln 2)}{(87.7\,\text{y})(3.156 \times 10^7\,\text{s/y})} = 558\,\text{W}\,.$$

19P

(a) Solve Q_{eff} from $P = RQ_{\text{eff}}$:

$$\begin{aligned}
Q_{\text{eff}} &= \frac{P}{R} = \frac{P}{N\lambda} = \frac{mP\tau}{M \ln 2} \\
&= \frac{(90.0\,\text{u})(1.66 \times 10^{-27}\,\text{kg/u})(0.93\,\text{W})(29\,\text{y})(3.15 \times 10^7\,\text{s/y})}{(1.00 \times 10^{-3}\,\text{g})(\ln 2)(1.60 \times 10^{-13}\,\text{J/MeV})} \\
&= 1.2\,\text{MeV}\,.
\end{aligned}$$

(b) The amount of ^{90}Sr needed is

$$M = \frac{150\,\text{W}}{(5.0\%)(0.93\,\text{W/g})} = 3.2\,\text{kg}.$$

20P
The reaction series is as follows: $^{238}\text{U} + n \rightarrow {}^{239}\text{U} \rightarrow {}^{239}\text{Np} + e$, $^{239}\text{Np} \rightarrow {}^{239}\text{Pu} + e$.

21P
(a) The TNT equivalent is

$$\frac{(2.50\,\text{kg})(4.54 \times 10^{26}\,\text{MeV/kg})}{2.6 \times 10^{28}\,\text{MeV}/10^6\,\text{tons}} = 4.4 \times 10^4\,\text{tons} = 44\,\text{kton}.$$

(b) The total mass of Plutomium in the bomb must exceed the critical mass to start the chain reaction.

22P
(a) The energy yield of the bomb is $E = (66 \times 10^{-3}\,M ton)(2.6 \times 10^{28}\,MeV/M ton) = 1.72 \times 10^{27}\,\text{MeV}$. At 200 MeV per fission event, $(1.72 \times 10^{27}\,\text{MeV})/(200\,\text{MeV}) = 8.58 \times 10^{24}$ fission events take place. Since only 4.0% of the ^{235}U nuclei originally present undergo fission, there must have been $(8.58 \times 10^{24})/(0.040) = 2.14 \times 10^{26}$ nuclei originally present. The mass of ^{235}U originally present was $(2.14 \times 10^{26})(235\,\text{u})(1.661 \times 10^{-27}\,\text{kg/u}) = 83.7\,\text{kg}$.

(b) Two fragments are produced in each fission event so the total number of fragments is $2(8.58 \times 10^{24}) = 1.72 \times 10^{25}$.

(c) One neutron produced in a fission event is used to trigger the next fission event, so the average number of neutrons released to the environment in each event is 1.5. The total number released is $(8.58 \times 10^{24})(1.5) = 1.29 \times 10^{25}$.

23P
After each time interval t_{gen} the number of nuclides in the chain reaction gets multiplied by k. The number of such time intervals that has gone by at time t is t/t_{gen}. Thus the numbr of nuclides engaged in the chain reaction at time t is $N(t) = N_0 k^{t/t_{\text{gen}}}$. Since $P \propto N$ we have $P(t) = P_0 k^{t/t_{\text{gen}}}$.

24P
Let P_0 be the initial power output, P be the final power output, k be the multiplication factor, t be the time for the power reduction, and t_{gen} be the neutron generation time. Then, according to the result of Problem 23,

$$P = P_0\, k^{t/t_{\text{gen}}}.$$

Divide by P_0, then take the natural logarithm of both sides of the equation and solve for $\ln k$. You should obtain

$$\ln k = \frac{t_{\text{gen}}}{t} \ln \frac{P}{P_0}.$$

Hence

$$k = e^{\alpha},$$

where

$$\alpha = \frac{t_{\text{gen}}}{t} \ln \frac{P}{P_0} = \frac{1.3 \times 10^{-3}\,\text{s}}{2.6\,\text{s}} \ln \frac{350\,\text{MW}}{1200\,\text{MW}} = -6.161 \times 10^{-4}.$$

This yields $k = .99938$.

25P
Form $E = Pt_{\text{gen}} = NQ$ we get the number of free neutrons:

$$N = \frac{Pt_{\text{gen}}}{Q} = \frac{(500 \times 10^6\,\text{W})(1.0 \times 10^{-3}\,\text{s})}{(181\,\text{MeV})(1.60 \times 10^{-13}\,\text{J/MeV})} = 1.7 \times 10^{16}.$$

26P
Use the formula from Problem 23:

$$\begin{aligned}
P(t) &= P_0 k^{t/t_{\text{gen}}} \\
&= (400\,\text{MW})(1.0003)^{(5.00\,\text{min})(60\,\text{s/min})/(30.0\,\text{ms})} \\
&= 8.03 \times 10^3\,\text{MW}.
\end{aligned}$$

27
(a)

befroe collision   after collision

Apply the conservation of energy and momentum:

$$\begin{cases} m_n v_{\text{ni}} = m_n v_{\text{nf}} + mu \\ \dfrac{1}{2} m_n v_{\text{ni}}^2 = \dfrac{1}{2} m_n v_{\text{nf}}^2 + \dfrac{1}{2} mu^2. \end{cases}$$

The solution to u is (see Eq. 10-19) $u = 2m_n v_{ni}/(m_n + m)$. Thus the fractional loss in neutron kinetic energy is

$$\frac{\Delta K_n}{K_n} = \frac{\frac{1}{2}mu^2}{\frac{1}{2}m_n v_{ni}^2} = \left(\frac{m}{m_n}\right)\left(\frac{u}{v_{ni}}\right)^2 = \left(\frac{m}{m_n}\right)\left(\frac{2m_n}{m_n + m}\right)^2$$

$$= \frac{4mm_n}{(m_n + m)^2}.$$

(b) For hydrogen:

$$\frac{\Delta K_n}{K_n} = \frac{4(1.0\,u)(1.0\,u)}{(1.0\,u + 1.0\,u)^2} = 1.0;$$

for deuterium:

$$\frac{\Delta K_n}{K_n} = \frac{4(2.0\,u)(1.0\,u)}{(1.0\,u + 2.0\,u)^2} = 0.89;$$

for carbon:

$$\frac{\Delta K_n}{K_n} = \frac{4(12\,u)(1.0\,u)}{(1.0\,u + 12\,u)^2} = 0.28;$$

and for lead:

$$\frac{\Delta K_n}{K_n} = \frac{4(207\,u)(1.0\,u)}{(1.0\,u + 207\,u)^2} = 0.019.$$

(c) The number of collisions, n, must satisfy $K = K_0(1 - \Delta K_n/K_n)^n$. Solve for n:

$$n = \frac{\ln(K/K_0)}{\ln(1 - \Delta K_n/K_n)} = \frac{\ln(0.025\,\text{eV}/1.00\,\text{MeV})}{\ln(1 - 0.89)} \approx 8.$$

28E
See Sample Problem 48-3. We have

$$\frac{N_5(t)}{N_8(t)} = \frac{N_5(0)}{N_8(0)} e^{-(\lambda_5 - \lambda_8)t}$$

or

$$t = \frac{1}{\lambda_8 - \lambda_5} \ln\left[\left(\frac{N_5(t)}{N_8(t)}\right)\left(\frac{N_8(0)}{N_5(0)}\right)\right]$$

$$= \frac{1}{(1.55 - 9.85)10^{-10}\,\text{y}^{-1}} \ln[(0.0072)(0.15)^{-1}] = 3.6 \times 10^9\,\text{y}.$$

29E

(a) $P_{av} = (15 \times 10^9 \, \text{W} \cdot \text{y})/(200,000 \, \text{y}) = 7.5 \times 10^4 \, \text{W} = 75 \, \text{kW}$.

(b)

$$M = \frac{m_U E_{total}}{Q} = \frac{(235 \, \text{u})(1.66 \times 10^{-27} \, \text{kg/u})(15 \times 10^9 \, \text{W} \cdot \text{y})(3.15 \times 10^7 \, \text{s/y})}{(200 \, \text{MeV})(1.6 \times 10^{-13} \, \text{J/MeV})}$$

$$= 5.8 \times 10^3 \, \text{kg}.$$

30P

Let t be the present time and $t = 0$ be the time when the ratio of ^{235}U to ^{238}U was 3.0%. Let N_{235} be the number of ^{235}U nuclei present in a sample now and $N_{235,\,0}$ be the number present at $t = 0$. Let N_{238} be the number of ^{238}U nuclei present in the sample now and $N_{238,\,0}$ be the number present at $t = 0$. The law of radioactive decay holds for each specie, so

$$N_{235} = N_{235,\,0} \, e^{-\lambda_{235} t}$$

and

$$N_{238} = N_{238,\,0} \, e^{-\lambda_{238} t}.$$

Divide the first equation by the second to obtain

$$r = r_0 \, e^{-(\lambda_{235} - \lambda_{238})t},$$

where $r = N_{235}/N_{238} \, (= 0.0072)$ and $r_0 = N_{235,\,0}/N_{238,\,0} \, (= 0.030)$. Solve for t:

$$t = -\frac{1}{\lambda_{235} - \lambda_{238}} \, \ln \frac{r}{r_0}.$$

Now use $\lambda_{235} = (\ln 2)/\tau_{235}$ and $\lambda_{238} = (\ln 2)/\tau_{238}$, where τ_{235} and τ_{238} are the half-lives, to obtain

$$t = -\frac{\tau_{235}\tau_{238}}{(\tau_{238} - \tau_{235}) \ln 2} \, \ln \frac{r}{r_0} = -\frac{(7.0 \times 10^8 \, \text{y})(4.5 \times 10^9 \, \text{y})}{(4.5 \times 10^9 \, \text{y} - 7.0 \times 10^8 \, \text{y}) \ln 2} \, \ln \frac{0.0072}{0.030} = 1.71 \times 10^9 \, \text{y}.$$

31P

The nuclei of ^{238}U can capture neutrons and beta-decay. With large amount of neutrons available due to the fission of ^{235}U the probability for this process is substantially increased, resulting in a much higher decay rate for ^{238}U, causing the depletion of ^{238}U and relative enrichment of ^{235}U.

1170

32E

The height of the Coulomb barrier is taken to be the value of the kinetic energy K each nucleus must initially have if they are to come to rest when their surfaces touch (see Sample Problem 48–4). If R is the radius of a nucleus, conservation of energy yields

$$2K = \frac{1}{4\pi\epsilon_0}\frac{e^2}{2R},$$

so

$$K = \frac{1}{4\pi\epsilon_0}\frac{e^2}{4R} = (8.99 \times 10^9 \text{ m/F})\frac{(1.60 \times 10^{-19}\text{ C})^2}{4(0.80 \times 10^{-15}\text{ m})} = 7.19 \times 10^{-14}\text{ J}.$$

This is 0.450 MeV.

33E

(a) 30 MeV.
(b) 6 MeV.
(c) 170 keV.
All of the answers above can be found in the text.

34E

The total energy released in the fusion of $M = 1.0$ kg of deuterium is

$$E = \frac{MQ}{2m_d} = \frac{(1.0\text{ kg})(3.27\text{ MeV})}{2(2.0\text{ u})(1.66 \times 10^{-27}\text{ kg/u})} = 4.92 \times 10^{26}\text{ MeV}.$$

Thus the time t in quesions is

$$t = \frac{E}{P} = \frac{(4.92 \times 10^{26}\text{ MeV})(1.60 \times 10^{-13}\text{ MeV/J})}{(100\text{ W})(3.15 \times 10^7\text{ s/y})} = 2.5 \times 10^4\text{ y}.$$

35E

(a) The voltage V required satisfies $2eV = U = 170$ keV, or $V = 170$ kV.
(b) No, it is not difficult to achieve.
(c) Only a very small amount of deuterons may be accelerated in a beam. The amount of energy generated would not be enough for a power plant.

36P

From the expression for $n(K)$ given we may write $n(K) \propto K^{1/2} e^{-K/kT}$. Thus

$$
\frac{n(K)}{n(\bar{K})} = \left(\frac{K}{\bar{K}} \right)^{1/2} e^{-(K-\bar{K})/kT}
$$

$$
= \left(\frac{5.00\,\text{keV}}{1.94\,\text{keV}} \right)^{1/2} e^{-(5.00\,\text{keV} - 1.94\,\text{keV})/[(8.62 \times 10^{-5}\,\text{eV/K})(1.50 \times 10^7\,\text{K})]}
$$

$$
= 0.151.
$$

37P

The radius of each lithium nucleus is $R = R_0 A^{1/3}$. Thus the minimum kinetic energy each nucleus must have to overcome the Coulomb barrier is

$$
K = \frac{1}{2} U = \frac{1}{2} \frac{1}{4\pi\epsilon_0} \frac{(Ze)^2}{2R} = \frac{1}{4\pi\epsilon_0} \frac{(Ze)^2}{4R_0 A^{1/3}}
$$

$$
= \frac{[3(1.60 \times 10^{-19}\,\text{C})]^2 (8.99 \times 10^9\,\text{N} \cdot \text{m}^2/\text{C}^2)}{4(1.2 \times 10^{-15}\,\text{m})(7)^{1/3}(1.60 \times 10^{-13}\,\text{J/MeV})}
$$

$$
= 1.41\,\text{MeV}.
$$

38P

(a) The energy distribution is given in the expression for $n(K)$ in Problem 36. Set $dn(K)/dK = 0$ for K_p:

$$
\left. \frac{dn(K)}{dK} \right|_{K=K_p} = \frac{1.13n}{(kT)^{3/2}} \left(\frac{1}{2K^{1/2}} - \frac{K^{3/2}}{kT} \right) e^{-K/kT} \bigg|_{K=K_p} = 0,
$$

which gives $K_p = \frac{1}{2} kT$. Numerically for $T = 1.5 \times 10^7$ K we find

$$
K_p = \frac{1}{2} kT = \frac{1}{2}(8.62 \times 10^{-5}\,\text{eV/K})(1.5 \times 10^7\,\text{K}) = 0.65\,\text{keV},
$$

in good agreement with Fig. 48-9.
(b) From Eq. 21-25 in Chapter 25

$$
v_p = \sqrt{\frac{2RT}{M}} = \sqrt{\frac{2RT}{mN_A}} = \sqrt{\frac{2kT}{m}},
$$

where $k = R/N_A$ was used. At $T = 1.5 \times 10^7$ K

$$
v_p = \sqrt{\frac{2(1.38 \times 10^{-23}\,\text{J/K})(1.5 \times 10^7\,\text{K})}{1.67 \times 10^{-27}\,\text{kg}}} = 5.0 \times 10^5\,\text{m/s}.
$$

(c)

$$K_{v,p} = \frac{1}{2}mv_p^2 = \frac{1}{2}m\left(\sqrt{\frac{2kT}{m}}\right)^2 = kT.$$

39E
In Fig. 48-10, let $Q_1 = 0.42\,\text{MeV}$, $Q_2 = 1.02\,\text{MeV}$, $Q_3 = 5.49\,\text{MeV}$, and $Q_4 = 12.86\,\text{MeV}$, then for the overall proton-proton cycle

$$Q = 2Q_1 + 2Q_2 + 2Q_3 + Q_4$$
$$= 2(0.42\,\text{MeV} + 1.02\,\text{MeV} + 5.49\,\text{MeV}) + 12.86\,\text{MeV} = 26.7\,\text{MeV}.$$

40E
If M_{He} is the mass of an atom of helium and M_C is the mass of an atom of carbon, then the energy released in a single fusion event is

$$Q = [3M_{\text{He}} - M_C]\,c^2 = [3(4.0026\,\text{u}) - (12.0000\,\text{u})]\,(931.5\,\text{MeV/u}) = 7.27\,\text{MeV}.$$

Note that $3M_{\text{He}}$ contains the mass of 6 electrons and so does M_C. The electron masses cancel and the mass difference calculated is the same as the mass difference of the nuclei.

41E
(a) From $\rho_H = 35\%\rho = n_p m_p$ we get the proton density n_p:

$$n_p = \frac{35\%\rho}{m_p} = \frac{(35\%)(1.5 \times 10^5\,\text{kg/m}^3)}{1.67 \times 10^{-27}\,\text{kg}} = 3.1 \times 10^{31}\,\text{m}^{-3}.$$

(b) From Sample Problem 21-7 in Chapter 21 you know that $n = 2.44 \times 10^{25}\,\text{m}^{-3}$. Thus

$$\frac{n_p}{n} = \frac{3.14 \times 10^{31}\,\text{m}^{-3}}{2.44 \times 10^{25}\,\text{m}^{-3}} = 1.3 \times 10^6.$$

42P

$$Q_1 = (2\mathbf{m}_p - \mathbf{m}_2 - m_e)c^2 = [2(m_1 - m_e) - (m_2 - m_e) - m_e]c^2$$
$$= [2(1.007825\,\text{u}) - 2.014102\,\text{u} - 2(0.0005486\,\text{u})](932\,\text{MeV/u})$$
$$= 0.42\,\text{MeV};$$

$$Q_2 = (\mathbf{m_2} + m_p - \mathbf{m_3})c^2 = (m_2 + m_p - m_3)c^2$$
$$= (2.014102\,\mathrm{u} + 1.007825\,\mathrm{u} - 3.016029\,\mathrm{u})(932\,\mathrm{MeV/u})$$
$$= 5.49\,\mathrm{MeV};$$

$$Q_3 = (2\mathbf{m_3} + \mathbf{m_4} - 2m_p)c^2 = (2m_3 - m_4 - 2m_p)c^2$$
$$= [2(3.016029\,\mathrm{u}) - 4.002603\,\mathrm{u} - 2(1.007825\,\mathrm{u})](932\,\mathrm{MeV/u})$$
$$= 12.86\,\mathrm{MeV}.$$

43P
(a)
$$E_1 = \frac{M_1 Q_1}{4m_p} = \frac{(1.0\,\mathrm{kg})(26.7\,\mathrm{MeV})}{4(1.67 \times 10^{-27}\,\mathrm{kg})} = 4.0 \times 10^{27}\,\mathrm{MeV}.$$

(b)
$$E_2 = \frac{M_2 Q_2}{m_\mathrm{U}} = \frac{(1.0\,\mathrm{kg})(200\,\mathrm{MeV})}{(235\,\mathrm{u})(1.66 \times 10^{-27}\,\mathrm{kg/u})} = 5.1 \times 10^{26}\,\mathrm{MeV}.$$

You see that $E_1/E_2 \simeq 8$.

44P
(a) Let M be the mass of the sun at time t and E be the energy radiated to that time. Then the power output is $P = dE/dt = (dM/dt)c^2$, where $E = Mc^2$ was used. At the present time
$$\frac{dM}{dt} = \frac{P}{c^2} = \frac{3.9 \times 10^{26}\,\mathrm{W}}{(3.00 \times 10^8\,\mathrm{m/s})^2} = 4.33 \times 10^9\,\mathrm{kg/s}.$$

(b) Assume the rate of mass loss remained constant. Then the total mass loss is $\Delta M = (dM/dt)\Delta t = (4.33 \times 10^9\,\mathrm{kg/s})(4.5 \times 10^9\,\mathrm{y})(3.156 \times 10^7\,\mathrm{s/y}) = 6.15 \times 10^{26}\,\mathrm{kg}$. The fraction lost is
$$\frac{\Delta M}{M + \Delta M} = \frac{6.15 \times 10^{26}\,\mathrm{kg}}{2.0 \times 10^{30}\,\mathrm{kg} + 6.15 \times 10^{26}\,\mathrm{kg}} = 3.07 \times 10^{-4}.$$

45P
(a) Since two neutrinos are produced per proton-proton cycle, the rate of neutrino production R_ν satisfies
$$R_\nu = \frac{2P}{Q} = \frac{2(3.9 \times 10^{26}\,\mathrm{W})}{(26.7\,\mathrm{MeV})(1.6 \times 10^{-13}\,\mathrm{J/MeV})} = 1.8 \times 10^{38}\,\mathrm{s}^{-1}.$$

(b)

$$R_{\nu, \text{Earth}} = R_\nu \left(\frac{\pi R_E^2}{4\pi r_{ES}^2} \right) = \frac{(1.8 \times 10^{38} \, \text{s}^{-1})}{4} \left(\frac{6.4 \times 10^6 \, \text{m}}{1.5 \times 10^{11} \, \text{m}} \right)^2$$

$$= 8.2 \times 10^{28} \, \text{s}^{-1}.$$

46P

(a) The mass of a carbon atom is $(12.0 \, \text{u})(1.661 \times 10^{-27} \, \text{kg/u}) = 1.99 \times 10^{-26}$ kg, so the number of carbon atoms in 1.00 kg of carbon is $(1.00 \, \text{kg})/(1.99 \times 10^{-26} \, \text{kg}) = 5.02 \times 10^{25}$. The heat of combustion per atom is $(3.3 \times 10^7 \, \text{J/kg})/(5.02 \times 10^{25} \, \text{atom/kg}) = 6.58 \times 10^{-19}$ J/atom. This is 4.11 eV/atom.

(b) In each combustion event two oxygen atoms combine with one carbon atom, so the total mass involved is $2(16.0 \, \text{u}) + (12.0 \, \text{u}) = 44 \, \text{u}$. This is $(44 \, \text{u})(1.661 \times 10^{-27} \, \text{kg/u}) = 7.31 \times 10^{-26}$ kg. Each combustion event produces 6.58×10^{-19} J so the energy produced per unit mass of reactants is $(6.58 \times 10^{-19} \, \text{J})/(7.31 \times 10^{-26} \, \text{kg}) = 9.00 \times 10^6$ J/kg.

(c) If the sun were composed of the appropriate mixture of carbon and oxygen, the number of combustion events that could occur before the sun burns out would be $(2.0 \times 10^{30} \, \text{kg})/(7.31 \times 10^{-26} \, \text{kg}) = 2.74 \times 10^{55}$. The total energy released would be $E = (2.74 \times 10^{55})(6.58 \times 10^{-19} \, \text{J}) = 1.80 \times 10^{37}$ J. If P is the power output of the sun, the burn time would be $t = E/P = (1.80 \times 10^{37} \, \text{J})/(3.9 \times 10^{26} \, \text{W}) = 4.62 \times 10^{10}$ s. This is 1460 y.

47P

(a) The products of the carbon cycle are $2e^+ + 2\nu +{}^4$ He, the same as that of the proton-proton cycle.

(b) $Q_{\text{carbon}} = Q_1 + Q_2 + \cdots + Q_6 = (1.95 + 1.19 + 7.55 + 7.30 + 1.73 + 4.97) \, \text{MeV} = 24.7 \, \text{MeV}$, which is the same as that for the proton-proton cycle: $Q_{p-p} = 26.7 \, \text{MeV} - 2(1.02 \, \text{MeV}) = 24.7 \, \text{MeV}$.

48P

The mass of the hydrogen in the sun's core is $M_H = (35\%)(M_s/8)$. Thus the time it takes for the hydrogen to be entirely consumed is

$$t = \frac{M_H}{R} = \frac{(0.35)(2.0 \times 10^{30} \, \text{kg/8})}{(6.2 \times 10^{11} \, \text{kg/s})(3.15 \times 10^7 \, \text{s/y})} = 4.5 \times 10^9 \, \text{y}.$$

49P

(a) From $E = NQ = (M/4m_p)Q$ we get

$$\varepsilon = \frac{E}{M} = \frac{Q}{4m_p} = \frac{(26.2 \, \text{MeV})(1.60 \times 10^{-13} \, \text{J/MeV})}{4(1.67 \times 10^{-27} \, \text{kg})} = 6.3 \times 10^{14} \, \text{J/kg}.$$

(b) The rate is

$$R = \frac{P}{\varepsilon} = \frac{3.9 \times 10^{26}\,\mathrm{W}}{6.3 \times 10^{14}\,\mathrm{J/kg}} = 6.2 \times 10^{11}\,\mathrm{kg/s}.$$

(c) From $E_s = M_s c^2$ we get $P = dE_s/dt = c^2 dM_s/dt$, or

$$\frac{dM_s}{dt} = \frac{P}{c^2} = \frac{3.9 \times 10^{26}\,\mathrm{W}}{(3.0 \times 10^8\,\mathrm{m/s})^2} = 4.3 \times 10^9\,\mathrm{kg/s}.$$

The reason why $R > dM_s/dt$ is because as hydrogens are consumed their mass is mostly turned into that of heliums, which are still in the sun.

(d) The time it takes is

$$t = \frac{0.10\% M_s}{dM_s/dt} = \frac{(0.10\%)(2.0 \times 10^{30}\,\mathrm{kg})}{(4.3 \times 10^9\,\mathrm{kg/s})(3.15 \times 10^7\,\mathrm{y/s})} = 1.5 \times 10^{10}\,\mathrm{y}.$$

50P

Since the mass of a helium atom is $(4.00\,\mathrm{u})(1.661 \times 10^{-27}\,\mathrm{kg/u}) = 6.64 \times 10^{-27}\,\mathrm{kg}$, the number of helium nuclei originally in the star is $(4.6 \times 10^{32}\,\mathrm{kg})/(6.64 \times 10^{-27}\,\mathrm{kg}) = 6.92 \times 10^{58}$. Since each fusion event requires three helium nuclei, the number of fusion events that can take place is $N = 6.92 \times 10^{58}/3 = 2.31 \times 10^{58}$. If Q is the energy released in each event and t is the conversion time, then the power output is $P = NQ/t$ and

$$t = \frac{NQ}{P} = \frac{(2.31 \times 10^{58})(7.27 \times 10^6\,\mathrm{eV})(1.60 \times 10^{-19}\,\mathrm{J/eV})}{5.3 \times 10^{30}\,\mathrm{W}} = 5.07 \times 10^{15}\,\mathrm{s}.$$

This is 1.6×10^8 y.

51P

(a) $Q = (5m_{^2\mathrm{H}} - m_{^3\mathrm{He}} - m_{^4\mathrm{He}} - m_{^1\mathrm{H}} - 2m_n)c^2 = [5(2.014102\,\mathrm{u}) - 3.016029\,\mathrm{u} - 4.002603\,\mathrm{u} - 1.007825\,\mathrm{u} - 2(1.008665\,\mathrm{u})](938\,\mathrm{MeV/u}) = 24.9\,\mathrm{MeV}$.

(b) The total energy released from the fusion is

$$E = NQ = \left(\frac{30.0\% M}{5m_{^2\mathrm{H}}}\right)Q.$$

Thus the rating is

$$R = \frac{E}{2.6 \times 10^{28}\,\mathrm{MeV/megaton\ TNT}}$$

$$= \frac{(30.0\%)(500\,\mathrm{kg})(24.9\,\mathrm{MeV})}{5(2.0\,\mathrm{u})(1.66 \times 10^{-27}\,\mathrm{kg/u})(2.6 \times 10^{28}\,\mathrm{MeV/megaton\ TNT})}$$

$$= 8.65\,\mathrm{megaton\ TNT}.$$

52E
In Eq. 48-9

$$Q = (2m_{2H} - m_{3He} - m_n)c^2$$
$$= [2(2.014102\,u) - 3.016049\,u - 1.008665\,u](932\,MeV/u)$$
$$= 3.27\,MeV;$$

in Eq. 48-10

$$Q = (2m_{2H} - m_{3H} - m_{1H})c^2$$
$$= [2(2.014102\,u) - 3.016049\,u - 1.007825\,u](932\,MeV/u)$$
$$= 4.03\,MeV;$$

and in Eq. 48-11

$$Q = (m_{2H} + m_{3H} - m_{3He} - m_n)c^2$$
$$= (2.01402\,u + 3.016049\,u - 4.002603\,u - 1.008665\,u)(932\,MeV/u)$$
$$= 17.59\,MeV.$$

53P
Conservation of momentum gives $p_{He} + p_n = 0$, and conservation of energy gives $p_{He}^2/2m_{He} + p_n^2/2m_n = Q$. Solve for K_{He} and K_n:

$$K_{He} = \frac{p_{He}^2}{2m_{He}} = \frac{m_n Q}{m_n + m_{He}} = \frac{(1.0\,u)(17.59\,MeV)}{1.0\,u + 4.0\,u} = 3.5\,MeV,$$

$$K_n = \frac{p_n^2}{2m_n} = \frac{m_{He} Q}{m_n + m_{He}} = \frac{(4.0\,u)(17.59\,MeV)}{1.0\,u + 4.0\,u} = 14\,MeV,$$

54P
Since $1.00\,L$ of water has a mass of $1.00\,kg$, the mass of the heavy water in $1.00\,L$ is $0.0150 \times 10^{-2}\,kg = 1.50 \times 10^{-4}\,kg$. Since a heavy water molecule contains one oxygen atom, one hydrogen atom and one deuterium atom, its mass is $(16.0\,u + 1.00\,u + 2.00\,u) = 19.0\,u$ or $(19.0\,u)(1.661 \times 10^{-27}\,kg/u) = 3.16 \times 10^{-26}\,kg$. The number of heavy water molecules in a liter of water is $(1.50 \times 10^{-4}\,kg)/(3.16 \times 10^{-26}\,kg) = 4.75 \times 10^{21}$. Since each fusion event requires two deuterium nuclei, the number of fusion events that can occur is $N = 4.75 \times 10^{21}/2 = 2.38 \times 10^{21}$. Each event releases energy $Q = (3.27 \times 10^6\,eV)(1.60 \times 10^{-19}\,J/eV) = 5.23 \times 10^{-13}\,J$. Since all events take place in a day, the power output is

$$P = \frac{NQ}{t} = \frac{(2.38 \times 10^{21})(5.23 \times 10^{-13}\,J)}{8.64 \times 10^4\,s} = 1.44 \times 10^4\,W = 14.4\,kW.$$

55E

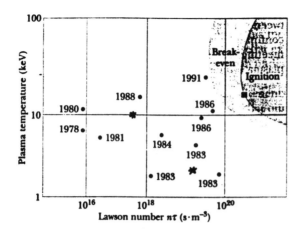

The two points in question are plotted on the figure using ∗ symbols.

56E

(a) The most probable speed is given by Eq. 21–25:

$$v_P = \sqrt{\frac{2RT}{M}},$$

where R is the universal gas constant $(8.31\,\text{J/mol}\cdot\text{K})$, T is the temperature on the Kelvin scale, and M is the molar mass $(2.0 \times 10^{-3}\,\text{kg/mol})$. Hence

$$v_P = \sqrt{\frac{2(8.31\,\text{J/mol}\cdot\text{K})(1.0 \times 10^8\,\text{K})}{2.0 \times 10^{-3}\,\text{kg}}} = 9.12 \times 10^5\,\text{m/s}.$$

(b) The confinement time for the conditions of Sample Problem 48–7 is $\tau = 1.0 \times 10^{-12}$ s. In this time a deuteron with speed v_P moves a distance $d = v_P\tau = (9.12 \times 10^5\,\text{m/s})(1.0 \times 10^{-12}\,\text{s}) = 9.12 \times 10^{-7}\,\text{m} = 912\,\text{nm}.$

57P

(a)

$$E = 10\% NQ = 10\%\left(\frac{rhoV}{m_{2\text{H}} + m_{3\text{H}}}\right)Q = 10\%\left[\frac{(4\pi/3)r^3\rho}{m_{2\text{H}} + m_{3\text{H}}}\right]Q$$

$$= \frac{(10\%)(4\pi/3)(200 \times 10^{-6}\,\text{m})^3(200\,\text{kg/m}^3)(17.59\,\text{MeV})(1.60 \times 10^{-13}\,\text{J/MeV})}{(2.0\,\text{u} + 3.0\,\text{u})(1.66 \times 10^{-27}\,\text{kg/u})}$$

$$= 2.3 \times 10^5\,\text{J}.$$

(b) The TNT equivalent is

$$\frac{2.3 \times 10^5\,\text{J}}{4.6\,\text{MJ/kg}} = 50\,\text{g}.$$

1178

(c) $P = E(100/\text{s}) = (2.3 \times 10^5 \text{ J})(100 \text{ s}^{-1}) = 2.3 \times 10^7 \text{ W}$.

58

From $P = 10\% R\bar{K}$, we get

$$\begin{aligned}
\bar{K} &= \frac{P}{10\% R} = \frac{P}{10\% N \lambda} = \frac{P\tau}{10\% N \ln 2} \\
&= \frac{(10 \text{ W})(88 \text{ d})(86{,}400 \text{ s/d})}{(10\%)(0.050 \text{ mol})(6.02 \times 10^{23} / \text{mol})(\ln 2)} \\
&= 3.6 \times 10^{-14} \text{ J}.
\end{aligned}$$

59

From Problem 14 we see that the Coulomb potential energy of charge Q distributed uniformly in a sphere of radius R is $U = (3/5)(Q^2/4\pi\epsilon_0 R)$. Initially there is a single charge $Q = Ze$ distributed over the radius $R = R_0 A^{1/3}$. Finally there are two charges, each with $Q' = Ze/2$ distributed over the radius $R' = R_0(A/2)^{1/3}$. Thus

$$\begin{aligned}
\Delta U = U_i - U_f &= \frac{3}{5}\left(\frac{Q^2}{4\pi\epsilon_0 R}\right) - 2\left(\frac{3}{5}\frac{Q'}{4\pi\epsilon_0 R'}\right) \\
&= \frac{3}{5}\left(\frac{1}{4\pi\epsilon_0}\right)\left[\frac{(Ze)^2}{R_0 A^{1/3}} - \frac{2(Ze/2)^2}{R_0(A/2)^{1/3}}\right] \\
&= (1 - 2^{-2/3})\frac{3}{5}\frac{Z^2 e^2}{4\pi\epsilon_0 R_0 A^{1/3}}.
\end{aligned}$$

60

The gravitationl potential energy of the sun is given by

$$U_G = -\frac{3GM_s^2}{5R_s} = -\frac{3GM_s^2}{5(3M_s/4\pi\rho)^{1/3}} = -\frac{3G(4\pi\rho)^{1/3}}{5(3)^{1/3}}M_s^{5/3}.$$

Thus

$$\begin{aligned}
\frac{dU_G}{dt} &= -\frac{3G}{5}\left(\frac{4\pi\rho}{3}\right)^{1/3}\frac{dM_s^{5/3}}{dt} = -G\left(\frac{4\pi\rho}{3}\right)^{1/3}M_s^{2/3}\frac{dM_s}{dt} \\
&= -G\left(\frac{4\pi R_s^3 \rho}{3}\right)^{1/3}\frac{M_s^{2/3}}{R_s}\frac{dM_s}{dt} = -\frac{GM_s}{R_s}\frac{dM_s}{dt} \\
&= -\frac{(6.67 \times 10^{-11} \text{ N} \cdot \text{m}^2/\text{kg}^2)(-6.2 \times 10^{11} \text{ kg/s})(2.0 \times 10^{30} \text{ kg})}{6.96 \times 10^8 \text{ m}} \\
&= 1.2 \times 10^{23} \text{ J/s}.
\end{aligned}$$

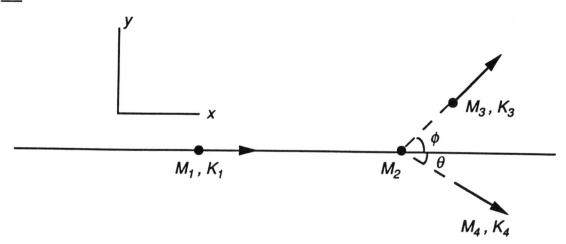

Write down conservation of momentum equations:

$$\begin{cases} p_{i_x} = p_1 p_{f_x} = p \cos\phi + p_4 \cos\theta \\ p_{i_y} = 0 = p_{f_y} = p_3 \sin\phi - p_4 \sin\theta. \end{cases}$$

Use the identity $\sin^2\theta + \cos^2\theta = 1$ to eliminate θ. The result is $p_4^2 = p_1^2 + p_2^2 - 2p_1 p_3 \cos\phi$. Thus

$$\begin{aligned} K_4 = \frac{p_4^2}{2M_4} &= \frac{p_1^2}{2M_4} + \frac{p_3^2}{2M_4} - \frac{p_1 p_3}{M_4}\cos\phi \\ &= \frac{M_1}{M_4}\left(\frac{p_1^2}{2M_1}\right) + \frac{M_3}{M_4}\left(\frac{p_3^2}{2M_3}\right) - \frac{2\sqrt{M_1 M_3}}{M_4}\left(\sqrt{\frac{p_1^2}{2M_1}}\sqrt{\frac{p_3^2}{2M_3}}\right)\cos\phi \\ &= \frac{M_1}{M_4}K_1 + \frac{M_3}{M_4}K_3 - \frac{2\sqrt{M_1 M_3}}{M_4}\sqrt{K_1 K_3}\cos\phi. \end{aligned}$$

Hence

$$Q = K_4 + K_3 - K_1 = K_3\left(1 + \frac{M_3}{M_4}\right) - K_1\left(1 - \frac{M_1}{M_4}\right) - \frac{2\sqrt{M_1 K_1 M_3 K_3}}{M_4}\cos\phi.$$

CHAPTER 49

1E

The difference in mass is

$$\Delta m = \frac{\Delta E}{c^2} = \frac{(33.9\,\text{Mev})(1.60 \times 10^{-13}\,\text{J/MeV})}{(3.00 \times 10^8\,\text{m/s})^2} = 6.03 \times 10^{-29}\,\text{kg}.$$

2E

Conservation of momentum requires that the gamma-ray particles move in opposite directions with momenta of the same magnitude. Since the magnitude p of the momentum of a gamma-ray particle is related to its energy by $p = E/c$, the particles have the same energy E. Conservation of energy yields $m_\pi c^2 = 2E$, where m_π is the mass of a neutral pion. According to Table 49-5 the rest energy of a neutral pion is $m_\pi c^2 = 135.0\,\text{MeV}$. Hence $E = (135.0\,\text{MeV})/2 = 67.5\,\text{MeV}$. Use the result of Exercise 1 of Chapter 43 to obtain the wavelength of the gamma-ray waves:

$$\lambda = \frac{1240\,\text{eV}\cdot\text{nm}}{67.5 \times 10^6\,\text{eV}} = 1.84 \times 10^{-5}\,\text{nm} = 18.4\,\text{fm}.$$

3E

$$\frac{F_{\text{grav}}}{F_{\text{ele}}} = \frac{Gm^2/r^2}{e^2/4\pi\epsilon_0 r^2} = \frac{4\pi\epsilon_0 Gm^2}{e^2}$$

$$= \frac{(6.67 \times 10^{-11}\,\text{N}\cdot\text{m}^2/\text{kg}^2)(9.11 \times 10^{-31}\,\text{kg})^2}{(9.0 \times 10^9\,\text{N}\cdot\text{m}^2/\text{C}^2)(1.60 \times 10^{-19}\,\text{C})^2}$$

$$= 2.4 \times 10^{-43}.$$

Since $F_{\text{grav}} \ll F_{\text{ele}}$ we can neglect the gravitational force acting between particles in a bubble chamber.

4E

Since the antiparticle of μ^+ is μ^- and that of ν is $\bar{\nu}$, the decay scheme of π^- is $\pi^- \rightarrow \mu^- + \bar{\nu}$.

5E

The energy released would be twice the rest energy of the Earth, or $E = 2mc^2 = 2(5.98 \times 10^{24}\,\text{kg})(3.00 \times 10^8\,\text{m/s})^2 = 1.08 \times 10^{42}\,\text{J}$.

6P

Since

$$\gamma = \left(1 - \frac{v^2}{c^2}\right)^{-1/2} = 1 + \frac{K}{mc^2} = 1 + \frac{80\,\text{MeV}}{135\,\text{MeV}} = 1.593,$$

we get $v = c\sqrt{1 - \gamma^{-2}} = \sqrt{1 - (1.593)^{-2}}(3.00 \times 10^8\,\text{m/s}) = 2.335 \times 10^8\,\text{m/s}$.
Thus

$$L_{\max} = v\tau = v\gamma\tau_0 = (2.335 \times 10^8\,\text{m/s})(1.593)(8.3 \times 10^{-17}\,\text{s})$$
$$= 3.1 \times 10^{-8}\,\text{m} = 31\,\text{nm}.$$

7P

Use $v = c\sqrt{1 - \gamma^{-2}}$ and $\gamma = 1 + K/mc^2$. We have

$$\Delta v = c - v = c\left[1 - \sqrt{1 - \left(1 + \frac{K}{mc^2}\right)^{-2}}\right]$$

$$= (3.00 \times 10^8\,\text{m/s})\left[1 - \sqrt{1 - \left(1 + \frac{1.5\,\text{MeV}}{2.0\,\text{eV}}\right)^{-2}}\right]$$

$$= 0.27\,\text{m/s}.$$

Note: since the quantity $x = (1 + 1.5\,\text{MeV}/20\,\text{eV})^{-2} \approx 1.78 \times 10^{-10} \ll 1$, your calculator may not give you the correct numerical answer to Δv due to errors in rounding off digits. Try use the approximation $\sqrt{1 - x} \approx 1 - \frac{1}{2}x$.

8P

The mass of the water in the pool is $m = \rho V = (1.00 \times 10^3\,\text{kg/m}^3)(114,000\,\text{gal})(231\,\text{in.}^3/\text{gal})$ $(1.639 \times 10^{-5}\,\text{m}^3/\text{in.}^3) = 4.316 \times 10^5\,\text{kg}$. The number of protons in this much water is

$$N = \frac{(4.316 \times 10^5\,\text{kg})(10/18)}{16.7\,\text{kg}} = 1.44 \times 10^{32}.$$

Thus the number of proton decay in one year is

$$n = Rt = \lambda Nt = \frac{Nt\ln 2}{\tau} = \frac{(1.44 \times 10^{32}\ln 2)(1.0\,\text{y})}{10^{32}\,\text{y}} \approx 1.$$

9P

(a) From $K = \gamma mc^2 - mc^2$ we get $\gamma = 1 + K/mc^2$. Also, $v = \sqrt{1 - \gamma^{-2}}\, c$. Thus

$$p = \gamma mv = mc\left(1 + \frac{K}{mc^2}\right)\sqrt{1 - \left(1 + \frac{K}{mc^2}\right)^{-2}}$$

$$= \frac{(1784\,\text{MeV})(1.60 \times 10^{-13}\,\text{J/MeV})}{3.00 \times 10^8\,\text{m/s}}\left(1 + \frac{2200}{1784}\right)\sqrt{1 - \left(1 + \frac{2200}{1784}\right)^{-2}}$$

$$= 1.90 \times 10^{-18}\,\text{kg} \cdot \text{m/s}.$$

(b)

$$R = \frac{\gamma mv}{qB} = \frac{p}{qB} = \frac{1.90 \times 10^{-18}\,\text{kg} \cdot \text{m/s}}{(1.60 \times 10^{-19}\,\text{C})(1.20\,\text{T})} = 9.90\,\text{m}.$$

10P

Table 49–5 gives the rest energy of each pion as 139.6 MeV. The magnitude of the momentum of each pion is $p_\pi = (358.3\,\text{MeV})/c$. Use the relativistic relationship between energy and momentum (Eq. 42–41) to find the total energy of each pion:

$$E_\pi = \sqrt{(p_\pi c)^2 + (m_\pi c^2)^2} = \sqrt{(358.3\,\text{MeV})^2 + (139.6\,\text{MeV})^2} = 384.5\,\text{MeV}.$$

Conservation of energy yields $m_\rho c^2 = 2E_\pi = 2(384.5\,\text{MeV}) = 769\,\text{MeV}.$

11P

Use the relativistic energy-momentum relationship for both particles 1 and 2: $(E_1 + K_1)^2 = p_1^2 c^2 + E_1^2$, $(E_2 + K_2)^2 = p_2^2 c^2 + E_2^2$. Note that $p_1^2 = p_2^2$ from momentum conservation. Eliminate p_1 and p_2 to obtain

$$(E_1 + K_1)^2 - (E_2 + K_2)^2 = E_1^2 - E_2^2.$$

Now write down the conservation of energy equation: $E_0 - E_1 - E_2 = K_1 + K_2$. Solve for K_2: $K_2 = E_0 - E_1 - E_2 - K_1$. Substitute this into the equation above:

$$(E_1 + K_1)^2 - (E_0 - E_1 - K_1)^2 = E_1^2 - E_2^2.$$

Some simple algebra then leads to

$$K_1 = \frac{1}{2E_0}[(E_0 - E_1)^2 - E_2^2].$$

12E

Consider the decay scheme $p \rightarrow e^+ + \gamma$.

(a) $Q_i = q_p = e = q_{e^+} = Q_f$.

(b) The conservation of energy equation $E_p = E_{e^+} + E_\gamma$ can be satisfied with the proper choice of E_γ, a continuous variable.

(c) Again, the conservation of linear momentum equation $p_p = p_{e^+} + p_\gamma$ may be satisfied with the proper choice of p_γ.

(d) The initial spin angular momentum is $\hbar/2$. If the angular momentum of e^+ and γ are antiparallel to each other then the magnitude of the final angular momentum is $|\hbar/2 - \hbar| = \hbar/2$, the same as the initial value.

13E

(a) The conservation laws considered so far are associated with energy, momentum, angular momentum, charge, and baryon number. The rest energy of the muon is 105.7 MeV, the rest energy of the electron is 0.511 MeV, and rest energy of the neutrino is zero. Thus the total rest energy before the decay is greater than the total rest energy after. The excess energy can be carried away as the kinetic energies of the decay products and energy can be conserved. Momentum is conserved if the electron and neutrino move away from the decay in opposite directions with equal magnitudes of momenta. Since the orbital angular momentum is zero, we consider only spin angular momentum. All the particles have spin $\hbar/2$. The total angular momentum after the decay must be either $\hbar$ (if the spins are aligned) or zero (if the spins are antialigned). Since the spin before the decay is $\hbar/2$, angular momentum cannot be conserved. The muon has charge $-e$, the electron has charge $-e$, and the neutrino has charge zero, so the total charge before the decay is $-e$ and the total charge after is $-e$. Charge is conserved. All particles have baryon number zero, so baryon number is conserved. The only conservation law not obeyed is the conservation of angular momentum.

(b) Analyze the decay in the same way. You should find that only charge is not conserved.

(c) Here you should find that energy and angular momentum cannot be conserved.

14P

(a) A positron (e^+).

(b) A_2^+ is a boson, since both ρ^0 and π^+ are bosons. It is also a meson, since $B_{A_2^+} = B_{\rho^0} + B_{\pi^+} = 2B_{\pi^+} + B_{\pi^-} = 0$.

15E

For purposes of deducing the properties of the antineutron, cancel a proton from each side of the reaction and write the equivalent reaction as

$$\pi^+ \rightarrow p + \bar{n}.$$

1184

Particle properties can be found in Tables 49–4 and 5. The pion and proton each have charge $+e$, so the antineutron must be neutral. The pion has baryon number zero (it is a meson) and the proton has baryon number $+1$, so the baryon number of the antineutron must be -1. The pion and the proton each have strangeness zero, so the strangeness of the antineutron must also be zero. In summary, $Q = 0$, $B = -1$, and $S = 0$ for the antineutron.

16E
Refer to Tables 49-4 and 49-5 for the strangeness of the particles involved.
(a) The strangeness of K^0 is $+1$, while it is zero for both π^+ and π^-. So the strangeness is not conserved here and therefore the decay $K^0 \rightarrow \pi^+ + \pi^-$ is not via strong interaction. Similarly:
(b) The strangeness of either sides is -1 so the decay is via strong interaction.
(c) The strangeness of Λ^0 is -1 while that of $p + \pi^-$ is zero so the decay is not via strong interaction.
(d) The strangeness of either side is -1 so the decay is via strong interaction.

17E
(a) See the solution to Exercise 13 for the quantities to be considered, but add strangeness to the list. The lambda has a rest energy of 1115.6 MeV, the proton has a rest energy of 938.3 MeV, and the kaon has a rest energy of 493.7 MeV. The rest energy before the decay is less than the total rest energy after, so energy cannot be conserved. Momentum can be conserved. The lambda and proton each have spin $\hbar/2$ and the kaon has spin zero, so angular momentum can be conserved. The lambda has charge zero, the proton has charge $+e$, and the kaon has charge $-e$, so charge is conserved. The lambda and proton each have baryon number $+1$ and the kaon has baryon number zero, so baryon number is conserved. The lambda and kaon each have strangeness -1 and the proton has strangeness zero, so strangeness is conserved. Only energy cannot be conserved.

(b) The omega has a rest energy of 1680 MeV, the sigma has a rest energy of 1197.3 MeV, and the pion has a rest energy of 135 MeV. The rest energy before the decay is greater than the total rest energy after, so energy can be conserved. Momentum can be conserved. The omega and sigma each have spin $\hbar/2$ and the pion has spin zero, so angular momentum can be conserved. The omega has charge $-e$, the sigma has charge $-e$, and the pion has charge zero, so charge is conserved. The omega and sigma have baryon number $+1$ and the pion has baryon number , so baryon number is conserved. The omega has strangeness -3, the sigma has strangeness -1, and the pion has strangeness zero, so strangeness is not conserved.

(c) The kaon and proton can bring kinetic energy to the reaction, so energy can be conserved even though the total rest energy after the collision is greater than the total rest energy before. Momentum can be conserved. The proton and lambda each have spin $\hbar/2$ and the kaon and pion each have spin zero, so angular momentum can be conserved. The kaon has charge $-e$, the proton has charge $+e$, the lambda has charge zero, and the pion has charge $+e$, so charge is not conserved. The proton and lambda each have baryon number $+1$ and the kaon and pion each have baryon number zero, so baryon number is conserved. The kaon has strangeness -1, the proton and pion each have strangeness zero, and the lambda has strangeness -1, so strangeness is conserved. Only charge is not conserved.

18E

(a)

$$\Delta E = \Delta mc^2 = (m_{\Sigma+} + m_{K+} - m_{\pi+} - m_p)c^2$$
$$= 1189.4\,\text{MeV} + 493.7\,\text{MeV} - 139.6\,\text{MeV} - 938.3\,\text{MeV}$$
$$= 605.2\,\text{MeV}.$$

(b)

$$\Delta E = \Delta mc^2 = (m_{\Lambda^0} + m_{\pi^0} - m_{K-} - m_p)c^2$$
$$= 1115.6\,\text{MeV} + 135.0\,\text{MeV} - 493.7\,\text{MeV} - 938.3\,\text{MeV}$$
$$= -181.4\,\text{MeV}.$$

19E

$$K_f = -\Delta mc^2 + K_i = (m_{\Sigma-} - m_{\pi-} - m_n)c^2 + K_i$$
$$= 1197.3\,\text{MeV} - 139.6\,\text{MeV} - 939.6\,\text{MeV} + 220\,\text{MeV}$$
$$= 338.1\,\text{MeV}.$$

20P

(a) As far as the conservation laws are concerned, we may cancel a proton from each side of the reaction equation and write the reaction as $p \rightarrow \Lambda^0 + x$. Since the proton and the lambda each have a spin angular momentum of $\hbar/2$, the spin angular momentum of x must be either zero or $\hbar$. Since the proton has charge $+e$ and the lambda is neutral, x must have charge $+e$. Since the proton and the lambda each have a baryon number of $+1$, the baryon number of x is zero. Since the strangeness of the proton is zero and the strangeness of the lambda is -1, the strangeness of x is $+1$. Take the unknown particle to be a spin zero meson with a charge of $+e$ and a strangeness of $+1$. Look at Table 49–5 to identify it as a K^+ particle.

(b) Similar analysis tells us that x is a spin-$\frac{1}{2}$ antibaryon $(B = -1)$ with charge and strangeness both zero. Inspection of Table 49–4 reveals it is an antineutron.

(c) Here x is a spin-0 (or spin-1) meson with charge zero and strangeness -1. According to Table 49–5 it could be a $\overline{K}^0$ particle.

21P

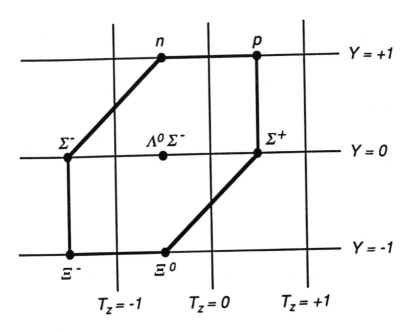

22P
(a)

$$\Delta E = (m_{\Lambda^0} - m_p - m_{\pi^-})c^2$$
$$= 1115.6\,\text{MeV} - 938.3\,\text{MeV} - 139.6\,\text{MeV} = 37.7\,\text{MeV}.$$

(b) Use the formula obtained in Problem 11:

$$K_p = K_1 = \frac{1}{2E_0}[(E_0 - E_1)^2 - E_2^2]$$
$$= \frac{(1115.6\,\text{MeV} - 938.3\,\text{MeV})^2 - (139.6\,\text{MeV})^2}{2(1115.6\,\text{MeV})} = 5.35\,\text{MeV}.$$

(c) $K_{\pi^-} = K_2 = E_0 - E_1 - E_2 - K_1 = 1115.6\,\text{MeV} - 938.3\,\text{MeV} - 139.6\,\text{MeV} - 5.35\,\text{MeV} = 32.4\,\text{MeV}.$

23E
(a) Since $p = uud$ we have $\bar{p} = \bar{u}\bar{u}\bar{d}$.
(b) Since $n = uud$ we have $\bar{n} = \bar{u}\bar{d}\bar{d}$.

24E

(a) The combination ddu has a total charge of $(-\frac{1}{3}-\frac{1}{3}+\frac{2}{3})=0$, and a total strangeness of zero. From Table 49-4 we find it to be a neutron (n).

(b) For the combination uus we have $Q=+\frac{2}{3}+\frac{2}{3}-\frac{1}{3}=1$ and $S=0+0-1=-1$. This is a Σ^{+}.

(c) For the combination ssd we have $Q=-\frac{1}{3}-\frac{1}{3}-\frac{1}{3}=-1$ and $S=-1-1+0=-2$. This is a Ξ^{-}.

25E

(a) and (b) From Tables 49-4 and 49-6 you can easily check that the combinations sud and uss give the correct Q and S quantum numbers of Λ^{0} and Ξ^{0}, respectively.

26E

(a) Look at the first three lines of Table 49–6. Since the particle is a baryon it must consist of 3 quarks. To obtain a strangeness of -2, two of them must be s quarks. Each of these has a charge of $-e/3$, so the sum of their charges is $-2e/3$. To obtain a total charge of e, the charge on the third quark must be $5e/3$. There is no quark with this charge, so the particle cannot be constructed. In fact, such a particle has never been observed.

(b) Again the particle consists of three quarks (and no antiquarks). To obtain a strangeness of zero, none of them may be s quarks. We must find a combination of three u and d quarks with a total charge of $2e$. The only such combination consists of three u quarks.

27E

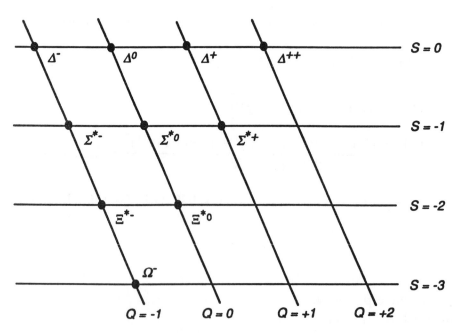

We see that an inverted equilateral triangle is formed.

28P

Since only the strange quark (s) has non-zero strangeness, in order to obtain $S = -1$ we need to combine s with another quark in Table 49-6. But none of the quarks listed in the Talbe has $Q = +\frac{3}{4}$, which is what would be needed to get the total charge of -1 (note that $Q_s = -\frac{1}{3}$). So a meson with $S = -1$ and $Q = +1$ cannot be formed with the quarks in Table 49-6. Similarly you can show that since no quark has $Q = -\frac{4}{3}$ there cannot be a meson with $S = +1$ and $Q = -1$.

29P

From $\gamma = 1 + K/mc^2$ and $v = \beta c = c\sqrt{1 - \gamma^{-2}}$, we get

$$v = c\sqrt{1 - \left(1 + \frac{K}{mc^2}\right)^{-2}}.$$

So for Σ^{*0}

$$v = (3.00 \times 10^8 \, \text{m/s})\sqrt{1 - \left(1 + \frac{1000 \, \text{MeV}}{1385 \, \text{MeV}}\right)^{-2}} = 2.442 \times 10^8 \, \text{m/s},$$

and for Σ^0

$$v' = (3.00 \times 10^8 \, \text{m/s})\sqrt{1 - \left(1 + \frac{1000 \, \text{MeV}}{1192.5 \, \text{Me}}\right)^{-2}} = 2.517 \times 10^8 \, \text{m/s}.$$

Thus Σ^0 moves faster than Σ^{*0} by $\Delta v = v' - v = (2.517 - 2.442)10^8 \, \text{m/s} = 7.54 \times 10^6 \, \text{m/s}$.

30E

Let $v = Hr = c$ to obtain

$$r = \frac{c}{H} = \frac{3.00 \times 10^8 \, \text{m/s}}{17 \times 10^{-3} \, \text{m/(s} \cdot \text{ly)}} = 1.8 \times 10^{10} \, \text{ly}.$$

31E

Apply Eq. 18–55 for the Doppler shift in wavelength:

$$\frac{\Delta\lambda}{\lambda} = \frac{v}{c},$$

where v is the recessional speed of the galaxy. (The speed is denoted by u in Eq. 18-55.) Use Hubble's law to find the recessional speed: $v = Hr$, where H is the Hubble constant and r

is the distance to the galaxy. Thus $v = [17 \times 10^{-3} \, \text{m}/(\text{s} \cdot \text{ly})](2.40 \times 10^8 \, \text{ly}) = 4.08 \times 10^6 \, \text{m/s}$ and

$$\Delta\lambda = \frac{v}{c}\lambda = \left(\frac{4.08 \times 10^6 \, \text{m/s}}{3.00 \times 10^8 \, \text{m/s}}\right)(656.3 \, \text{nm}) = 8.9 \, \text{nm}.$$

Since the galaxy is receding the observed wavelength is longer than the wavelength in the rest frame of the galaxy. Its value is $656.3 \, \text{nm} + 8.9 \, \text{nm} = 665.2 \, \text{nm}$.

32E

First, find the speed of the receding galaxy from Eq. 42-27: $\beta = f_0/f - 1 = \lambda/\lambda_0 - 1$. Then from Eq. 49-14

$$r = \frac{v}{H} = \frac{\beta c}{H} = \frac{(\lambda/\lambda_0 - 1)c}{H}$$
$$= \frac{(602.0 \, \text{nm}/590.0 \, \text{nm} - 1)(3.00 \times 10^8 \, \text{m/s})}{17 \times 10^{-3} \, \text{m}/(\text{s} \cdot \text{ly})} = 3.59 \times 10^8 \, \text{ly}.$$

33P

(a) From $f = c/\lambda$ and Eq. 42-26 we get

$$\lambda_0 = \lambda\sqrt{\frac{1-\beta}{1+\beta}} = (\lambda_0 + \Delta\lambda)\sqrt{\frac{1-\beta}{1+\beta}}.$$

Divide both sides by λ_0 to obtain

$$1 = (1+z)\sqrt{\frac{1-\beta}{1+\beta}}.$$

Solve for β:

$$\beta = \frac{(1+z)^2 - 1}{(1+z)^2 + 1} = \frac{z^2 + 2z}{z^2 + 2z + 2}.$$

(b) Now $z = 4.43$ so

$$\beta = \frac{(4.43)^2 + 2(4.43)}{(4.43)^2 + 2(4.43) + 2} = 0.934.$$

(c)

$$r = \frac{v}{H} = \frac{\beta c}{H} = \frac{(0.943)(3.00 \times 10^8 \, \text{m/s})}{17 \times 10^{-3} \, \text{m}/(\text{s} \cdot \text{ly})} = 1.65 \times 10^{10} \, \text{ly}.$$

34P

(a) Let $v(r) = Hr \leq v_e = \sqrt{2GM/r}$, we get $M/r^3 \geq H^2/2G$.